CARNEGIE INSTITUTION OF WASHINGTON

PUBLICATION NO. 376

1931

INTRODUCTION
TO THE
HISTORY OF SCIENCE

VOLUME II

FROM RABBI BEN EZRA TO ROGER BACON

BY
GEORGE SARTON
Associate in the History of Science
Carnegie Institution of Washington

IN TWO PARTS

PUBLISHED FOR THE
CARNEGIE INSTITUTION OF WASHINGTON
BY
THE WILLIAMS & WILKINS COMPANY
BALTIMORE

Reprinted 1950, 1953

PREFACE

During the slow gestation of this volume I could not help thinking now and then of the more general problems raised by my inquiries, but did not allow my mind to dwell too long upon them. I used to jot down these thoughts on slips of paper and put them in a box with a view of examining them when the time of writing my prolegomena would come. And so the weeks passed, and the months, yea, the years, and the slips accumulated. When the time finally came—that was last September (1930)—I was staggered and almost unnerved by their mass. I sifted and classified them, and made a plan, but it soon dawned upon me that any attempt to work them out would lead to the writing not of an introductory chapter but of another book. Now this could not be done without delaying considerably the appearance of the present volume. I then decided to store my materials away for ulterior and independent publication, and to write now an entirely different introduction.

At first it seemed very hard to forsake the pleasure of writing those prolegomena, around which my thoughts had so often played, and which were to be the reward of endless drudgery, but "partie remise n'est pas perdue," and I was reconciled to the postponement when I realized that however abundant my notes they were still utterly insufficient.

Indeed the main problem which I had planned to discuss was the relationship of the three cultures—Jewish, Christian, and Muslim—whose imperfect fusion had gradually created our own European civilization. Now this could not be done intelligently and thoroughly without a deep examination of these cultures not simply as they existed in the twelfth and thirteenth centuries but as each of them had originated and developed. It was necessary to find out their background, visible and hidden, and to investigate their changes, their ramifications, and their several interactions. This was not simply a large task, but one—I now keenly realize—which I was not yet qualified to undertake. During the last few years I have devoted much time and energy to the study of Arabic and Hebrew, of Islām and Israel, but my knowledge of these languages is passive, hence superficial, and my knowledge of the two civilizations is too literary, too purely "bookish" to be truly valuable. With regard to language, as I have put it before,[1] "a reading knowledge is really but half a knowledge, for one cannot know accurately a language which one does not write, nor fluently, one which one does not speak." In that sense, my knowledge of Arabic, and even more so of Hebrew, is very imperfect, for the best that I can do is to read them haltingly. My knowledge of the two cultures can hardly be better than that of the languages; it is if anything poorer because I have enjoyed no living contact with either. For my analytical investigations perhaps this did not matter so much; I could determine the main facts of a man's life or the contents of a scientific treatise without a deep understanding of the civilizations of which both—the man and the treatise—were the fruits; but for a synthetic judgment such as the one I intended to publish in my prolegomena a more penetrating knowledge, at once older and fresher, was absolutely requisite.

[1] The History of Science and the New Humanism (Colver lectures in Brown University, 148, New York 1931).

Thanks to the enlightened generosity of the Carnegie Institution, I shall be able to spend the academic year 1931–1932 in Egypt, Syria and Palestine for the purpose of obtaining a more fluent knowledge of both languages (chiefly of Arabic) and of studying more intimately the living cultures of which these languages are the vehicles. To be sure a year is but a short time and I cannot be expected to work miracles. Yet it will make a difference. Of course it is not as if I were going to the East without preparation; I have prepared myself for that journey for a great many years, and it is not so much positive knowledge which I go to seek, but intuition, sympathy, understanding. Learning which is too remote from life is false, dangerous, and wicked; it stinks to heaven like a rotting corpse. The pusillanimity of so many scholars is largely due to such remoteness and second-handedness, which are truly unforgivable, whenever they could have been remedied. Now Hebrew and Arabic are living languages to this day, and it is as such that they should be known if at all; Israel and Islām are living faiths and living cultures, and how could anybody be satisfied with books when there are living men and women to answer his questions and solve his doubts? I may be allowed to register biographical facts, to analyze scientific treatises, but it is clear enough I have no business to speak of the Jewish and Muslim minds as long as I have not had sufficiently intimate and frequent contacts with them, nor of Jewish and Muslim souls as long as I have not been able to catch them so to say on the wing, in their true reality, alive and quivering.

To return to the present work, in spite of the fact that its original prolegomena had to be postponed, it is nevertheless more than a mere accumulation of materials. The results of analytical investigations naturally form the core of it, but the extensive analysis was completed by a true synthetic effort, or rather by many. The introductory chapter, which replaces the missing prolegomena, is an attempt to survey the development of science during the twelfth and thirteenth centuries, each branch of science being considered in turn. A specialist—say a mathematician—may choose to read only the mathematical sections, but he should remember that he does so at his own peril. Moreover there are four other surveys—the first chapters of each of the four books—each of which purports to describe not only the development of science, but the whole intellectual background and "Weltanschauung" of each half century. The mathematician just mentioned should read at least the mathematical sections of each of these four chapters, and the mathematical chapters of each book, but by so doing many things would still escape his attention, and he should not complain of my book before having made full use of it. The discussions with which each first chapter ends will enable other specialists to determine the share of various civilizations or of various peoples in the creative undertaking of the whole race.

Thanks to the index, this volume may be used like a dictionary but that is certainly not the best way of using it. It is not a dictionary, or rather it is one only to the extent that the index makes it so. Nor is it merely a bibliography. To be sure it contains abundant bibliographical information, because I have been anxious to mention the sources of every statement and to make it easy for anyone to continue, complete, and correct my investigations. My purpose was not bibliographical but purely synthetic from the very beginning. I have tried to outline a map of the intellectual life of the Middle Ages, or—if I may change the metaphor—to draw the balance sheet of the scientific activity and the highest culture of each half century. The essential is the framework. I have taken endless pains to establish each fact as correctly and as clearly as possible, yet I have no interest in any of them: the thing that was uppermost in my mind from the beginning to the end was the interrelationship of these facts, their arrangement—not any single part but the whole.

This was an ambitious project, perhaps too ambitious, difficult and discouraging in many respects, yet soothing in another. No one can have spent as much time as I have in ascertaining numberless little facts, without being somewhat skeptical as to the possibility of reaching the truth with regard to each and every one. For example, I may state that Peter So-and-So was born in 1126 and wrote a treatise De natura rerum in 1159. How sure can one be of that, and that the treatise which has come down to us is really his as he wrote it? Our conclusions are always more or less uncertain: they cannot be absolutely certain. Such doubts would be almost unbearable if I had no interest outside of Peter and his De natura rerum, but as a matter of fact I do not care more for Peter than for many hundreds of his colleagues. Though I would not vouch for the absolute truth of any statement in my book, I can and do vouch for their average truth and for the general faithfulness of the whole.

The bibliography itself however large is not essential but incidental. It occupies less than one fifth of the work (by actual count 15.7%), and if it were entirely suppressed, the remainder would still be quite considerable. Critics who like to dispose of another man's work with a single label, should not call mine a dictionary or a bibliography but rather, if they please, a map—a scientific map with full indication of the sources. Such a comparison will help to appreciate its limitations. When the cartographer engaged in the compilation of a map discovers that the height of a mountain or the course of a river is uncertain, he cannot drop everything and start on a journey of exploration, or else his task would never be accomplished. The best that he can do is to state frankly the uncertainties he has come across; I have done that, but in many cases I have not been able to resist the temptation of indulging in little explorations of my own, and this may explain, if it does not justify, my increasing slowness.

My lack of predilection for any side of my work save its general structure and accuracy, is a guarantee that this survey of the twelfth and thirteenth century, whatever its faults, is tolerably well balanced. It made no difference to me whether a text was mathematical, medical or geographical, whether the author was a Spanish Jew, a Syrian Muslim, or a Japanese, whether the language was an European vernacular, Latin, Greek, Hebrew, Arabic or Chinese. To be sure the survey is very far from complete with regard to India, Central Asia, and the Far East; however this cannot be ascribed only to my own ignorance, but to that of the whole republic of letters. These gaps correspond to the "terrae incognitae" of the early maps. When the cartographer has clearly indicated them, with a few hints here and there to whet the reader's curiosity, he has done as much as could be expected from him.

The comparison with the map gives me an opportunity of answering a possible objection. I may be superficial or not (it is not for me to decide) but he who would judge this matter upon the simple consideration of the extraordinary scope of my studies would be very superficial indeed. It is as if one claimed that a cartographer who prepares a map of the Americas is more superficial than one compiling a map of his own village; he may be or not, it all depends upon his handling of the material and his own integrity. The point to remember is that these two mapmakers deal with different classes of facts; they are working on different levels but this cannot affect their scientific honesty and their thoroughness. The fact that I am interested in the history of mediaeval science as a whole rather than in any special incident proves that my vision is broad, but not that my mind is lax; one may assume that many details have escaped my attention or that I have deliberately neglected them, but one has no right to presume that I am not as conscientious and thorough as if I were engaged in microscopical investigations.

My ambition has been to provide a framework for the study of mediaeval science and mediaeval thought, and to enable scholars to know as exactly as possible the state of our present knowledge on each topic. This was another reason for giving abundant bibliographical references, and the more so that contributions to the history of science are scattered in an infinity of periodicals and in collections of every kind (scientific, historical, philosophical, philological, orientalist, economic, religious, etc.). If this survey had no result but to discourage futile and superfluous performances, it would already justify itself, but I trust it will also stimulate better efforts in the right direction. The sooner his framework is made obsolete by new researches, the happier the author will be.

Readers consulting only the synthetic parts of this work (the introductory chapter and the first chapters of each book) will please bear in mind that the statements contained in them are sometimes a little more dogmatic than is strictly warranted: one can hardly avoid losing in precision what one gains in generality. They will find the necessary qualifications in the analytical notes devoted to each topic.

The conciseness and neutrality of my notes are deliberate. How many a time have I not trimmed a sentence which had turned out to be more picturesque and suggestive than was safe and wise, or even replaced it altogether with another which was less colorful perhaps but more accurate, less striking but more perspicuous, less brilliant but more honest? Indeed I know well enough how easily a man can be driven by his own imagination and wit and his sense of style to indulge in statements which transcend his knowledge and which may become a source of deception to the unwary and a trap to the innocent. It has been my constant endeavor to tell the truth as plainly as possible, not to please or entertain anybody. In short I have done just the opposite of what popular writers do who try to color and spice their narrative to the utmost: the greater their literary talent the greater the danger of unconscious misstatements. My austerity does not necessarily imply a lack of spirit or of style; but it means that I love truth more than either.

Laconism offers a great scientific advantage in that each naked statement being more separate and more tangible, is easier to comprehend, to accept or to refute. If I say simply, without any flourish: "John was born in Montpellier in 1234" I am making two statements of facts, which, if they be erroneous, will be so, glaringly. If I add "He became the greatest mathematician of his time," I am stating an opinion but again so plainly, that it challenges immediate criticism, and that is all to the good. I believe that the use of laconism in historical science (as opposed to historical literature) is just as valuable as that of the Linnaean language in natural history. It may seem to be a disadvantage in that it multiplies considerably the number of statements and hence the possibilities of error in the same unit of space. In other words, while it dampens the historian's superficial prestige, it emphasizes his responsibility: a double gain.

The shortcomings of this work are many and it would scarce be possible to be more painfully conscious of them than I am. Indeed no day passes but that I have the opportunity of making some correction or addition here or there. I know by experience that there is not a page of this volume which I could not improve by a fresh study of it. Yet there must be an end to correcting, and a book cannot be kept on the stocks indefinitely. When it was completely typewritten I was sorely tempted to revise my manuscript a last time, but I was aware that the revision of so large a work would no sooner be finished than a new one would be necessary. I said to myself: "Granted, but each new revision is shorter than the preceding one," and the temptation continued. Then I bethought myself, just in time, of the interdiction expressed in Leviticus, chapter xix, 9–10, and chapter xxiii, 22, and resigned myself to my fate.

After having used every reasonable means of eschewing errors the author realizes that many must still remain. He craves the reader's indulgence for his sins of omission or commission. He thinks he deserves a modicum of it for three reasons.

Firstly, that he is doing pioneer duty. Indeed this is the first attempt to make a complete inventory of mediaeval science, East and West, not only on this scale but on any scale.

Secondly, that the scope of his investigations was inordinately and unavoidably large. He often suffered from this as it involved the constant necessity of jumping from one subject to another in order to be able to cover the whole ground within a reasonable time. Now it is clear that the probabilities of error increase with the area to be covered and faster than the area itself, say, like the square of it.

Thirdly, that he is not only ready but anxious to atone for his errors by giving full publicity to them. This has been done for volume I (1927): errata have been corrected in the Critical Bibliographies of Isis, beginning with the nineteenth (vol. 8 and following). Thus the scholar using vol. I must needs consult vol. 8 and following of Isis if he wishes to be on the safe side. This is no real burden for he would have to consult them in any case for the addenda, and he finds the errata at the same time without further effort. Indeed the Critical Bibliographies are so clearly arranged that a student of a certain time or of a certain personality can turn immediately to the place where additional information, if any, may be found.[2] The same policy will be pursued with regard to the present volume. The last Critical Bibliography to be so to say incorporated into it was the thirtieth published in vol. 15 of Isis. Errata and addenda will be published in the thirty-first Critical Bibliography and following. Thus vol. 16 of Isis will be the first volume to be consulted by students of the twelfth and thirteenth centuries.

On the other hand the bibliographical items quoted in the Introduction are frequently completed by a reference to a criticism published in Isis, and thus the amount of bibliographical information given is considerably larger than it seems.

The reader will please remember that the bibliography is not intended so much

[2] To illustrate, a student of Ibn Sīnā would begin by reading the note in vol. 1, 709–713, or preferably the whole chapter on the time of al-Bīrūnī (p. 693–737). Then he would take Isis and read the following pages: vol. 8, 738–739; vol. 9, 151, 501; vol. 10, 122; vol. 11, 168–169, 421; vol. 12, 354; vol. 13, 155–157, 418–419; vol. 14, 473–475; vol. 15, 206, 402–403; etc. Of course he might also consult the indices of Isis but that would not be so good, nor sufficient. Provided he had these volumes at his elbow, it would cost him hardly more than a quarter of an hour to collect all the needed information.

for bibliophiles as for men who actually read books and study their contents. I am not interested in the rarity of books but in their intrinsic value which is a very different matter. (It is indeed one of the blessings of our age that the most precious books, the immortal and priceless ones, are within the reach of all men, even of the poorest.) I am not interested in books as such but rather in the ideas of which they are the vehicles. In consequence my descriptions of books are very brief. Cumbersome titles are often abridged. I indicate the number of pages of each item to give an idea of its length, but I do this roughly (e.g., I write 320 p. instead of xxiii-295 p.). I do not disdain the precise descriptions in which bibliographers indulge—they are all right in their place—but this was not the place for them, nor was it possible for me to pay attention to bibliographical minutiae without sacrificing other matters of greater importance for my purpose.

I trust non-orientalists, that is, the great majority of the readers and users of this volume will appreciate the pains which have been taken to make its oriental elements as accessible to them as possible. I would have spared myself much trouble by quoting Arabic, Persian, and Hebrew words in their original script, for I would not have had to worry about their vocalization; it would have been much easier also to quote Chinese words in Chinese script. (I have not cited a single Chinese word without having identified it first.) This would have been more convenient and more pleasant to a very small number of scholars, but would have decreased the usefulness of the book for the majority in spite of a material increase in price. It is planned to compile eventually indices in Arabic, Hebrew, Sanskrit, and Chinese scripts. These indices would be published separately as each of them would interest a different category of scholars.

I do not like to speak of work still undone, yet I feel that the scholars using this Introduction have a right to be taken into the author's confidence and be told something of his projects. After my return from the East, in shā' allāh ta'ālā', my first task will be to write the prolegomena mentioned above and to try to explain to a larger public the particularities and meaning of mediaeval science and mediaeval thought. As soon as that is done, I shall prepare the publication of vols. 3 and 4 of this Introduction respectively devoted to the fourteenth and fifteenth centuries. A great part of the analytical groundwork is already completed; one of my assistants, Miss Mary Catherine Welborn is even now revising all the Latin notes, and I shall eventually recast the oriental ones. Finally another assistant, Dr. A. Pogo, is already collecting materials for vol. 5 relative to the first half of the sixteenth century.

The progress of this work is unfortunately bound to become slower and slower not only because the field extends and the author's methods improve, but also because the accumulation of materials lasts somewhat longer for each volume than for the preceding one. Indeed, the collection of these materials was begun for every volume in 1912. When I wrote volume 1 in 1927, I had hardly more than fifteen years of experience behind me; for the preparation of the present volume I had four years more; and so forth. It is already clear that I shall not be able to carry my investigations down to the twentieth century, but I hope that when the time of my release comes, my plans will be so well understood, and other scholars so well trained, that the work I began may safely be continued.

The Author Expresses his Gratitude

It gives me great pleasure to put on record the assistance I have received from various friends. More specific acknowledgments may be found in the body of this volume in their proper places. I hope I have forgotten no one, and if I have, the omission was unintentional and will be repaired at the earliest opportunity.

For *Arabic* and *Muslim* matters I am deeply indebted first of all to the Rev. Duncan B. Macdonald of the Hartford Theological Seminary, then to Dr. Max Meyerhof of Cairo, Don Miguel Asín y Palacios of Madrid, and the Rev. Shibly D. Malouf of Arlington.

For *Hebrew* and *Jewish* matters: to my Harvard colleague, Prof. Harry Austryn Wolfson, Dr. Alexander Marx of the Jewish Theological Seminary of America, Dr. Solomon Gandz of Yeshiva College, New York, Dr. Joshua Finkel, and Mr. Meyer H. Goldman.

For *Chinese:* to Mr. Arthur W. Hummel and Mr. B. A. Claytor of the Library of Congress, to Professor Yoshio Mikami of Tōkyō, Dr. Berthold Laufer of the Field Museum, Chicago, Prof. William Hung of Yenching University, Peiping, Dr. Yuen Ren Chao of Tsing Hua College, Peiping, Dr. Walter T. Swingle and Mr. Michael J. Hagerty of the U. S. Department of agriculture, Messrs. F. K. Kuang and Andrew S. Y. Ko, Dr. C. W. Ou.

My debt to the Library of Congress is especially great. Thanks to the kind collaboration of Mr. Hummel, Chief of its Division of Chinese Literature, I have been able to mention a good many Chinese editions of the works dealt with by me in this volume. Many of these editions would not be easy to find otherwise as they are not independent publications, but parts of collections or ts'ung shu (12039, 10024) of which the Chinese are particularly fond. The Library of Congress owns not fewer than 560 ts'ung shu, practically all of which have been completely analyzed and stroke-indexed, and contain 23,000 separate works.[3]

For *Japanese:* to Prof. Yoshio Mikami of Tōkyō.

For *Sanskrit:* to my Harvard colleagues, Prof. J. H. Woods and Prof. Walter E. Clark.

For *Icelandic* and other *Scandinavian* languages: to the late Dr. J. W. S. Johnsson[4] of Copenhagen, Dr. Sigfús Blöndal of the Royal Library of Denmark, Prof. Henning Larsen of the State University of Iowa, Prof. Halvdan Koht of the University of Oslo.

For *Russian:* to Dr. Alexander Pogo of the Carnegie Institution.

For *Armenian:* to Prof. Robert Pierpont Blake of Harvard University.

For *mediaeval science in the West:* to Prof. Charles Homer Haskins of Harvard University, Prof. Lynn Thorndike of Columbia University, Dr. John Kirtland Wright of the American Geographical Society, New York, the late Dr. Josef Drecker, of Dorsten in Westphalia.

For *incunabula:* to Miss Margaret Bingham Stillwell of the Annmary Brown Memorial in Providence, Rhode Island.

As the writing of this Introduction and the editing of Isis are two complementary undertakings, I owe thanks also to all the collaborators to Isis, above all to the managing editor, Mr. Léon Guinet, Director of the French Lycée in Brussels, and to the secretary of the History of Science Society, Mr. Frederick E. Brasch of the Smithsonian department of the Library of Congress; then to the associate editors,

[3] For additional information on the Chinese collections of the Library of Congress and their systematic investigation see Isis, passim, under Swingle and Hummel (chiefly vol. 5, 528; vol. 7, 260, 568; vol. 8, 791; vol. 10, 239; vol. 11, 509; vol. 13, 217; vol. 14, 525; etc.).

[4] 1868–1929. See obituary by Axel Hansen, with portrait and bibliography (Isis 13, 320–324, 1930).

contributors, reviewers, to the authors who are thoughtful enough to send copies of their works or reprints of their papers to the Editor of Isis as soon as they appear; finally to the scholars who have taken the trouble to review and discuss my Vol. 1, and to send me errata and addenda.[5]

To recall all the friends who have given me their help and sympathy during these many years of patient and obscure travail would be too long. Those mentioned in Vol. 1 (p. 45) have continued to support and encourage me.[6] The names of many other friends and wellwishers could be read in the list of the members of the International Committee of the History of Science. I owe a special debt of gratitude to Prof. David Eugene Smith of New York, Mme Hélène Metzger of Paris, Prof. Lynn Thorndike of New York, and above all to Mr. and Mrs. Carl Horber of Zurich.

The fact that my own offices are located within the Harvard Library has enabled me to do my work with greater ease, speed, accuracy, and completeness than would have been possible otherwise. Indeed it means not only that that exceedingly rich library is readily and entirely available to me, but that I can enjoy its resources without losing touch with my own apparatus. That apparatus may be thought insignificant as compared with the library, yet from my own point of view, it is the central thing, and the library but a gigantic annex to it. Every scholar will readily appreciate this, for does not his own carefully selected library contain the essential? My apparatus includes at present some 3100 books, some 4000 smaller books, pamphlets, reprints, etc., kept in 394 very large filing boxes, some 25,000 large size notes, some 41,000 bibliographic cards, many thousands of portraits and iconographic documents. With the exception of less than a hundred volumes, all of this is my own property but has been bequeathed to the Section of the History of Science of the Division of Historical Research of the Carnegie Institution. Thanks to Isis and to the Institution's assistance this apparatus is growing very fast, so fast indeed that before long the space allotted to it will be insufficient. It is hoped that some understanding will soon be reached by the Carnegie Institution and Harvard University to allow for the further development of this section and make it possible for myself, my assistants and apprentices to continue our several activities in the best manner.

My debt to the Carnegie Institution itself is immense: it is thanks to its generosity that I have been able to carry on my undertaking without undue anxiety and to see the results of it handsomely published. At times when I seemed to be working as if I had the whole of eternity before me (which I had not) it has been wonderfully patient with me and allowed me to go my own way. I am especially thankful to Dr. John C. Merriam, President of the Institution, and to Dr. Alfred Vincent Kidder, Chairman of the Division of Historical Research, for their keen interest in my work and the many marks of encouragement they have given me.

All of the proofs were read by Miss Mary Catherine Welborn, and some of them by Dr. Alexander Pogo. I am indebted to both for valuable corrections and suggestions. Miss Welborn compiled the table of contents.

Finally I would like to say how much I owe to my dearest friend and constant helpmate but I could hardly express my gratitude to her; it would be almost like expressing it to myself. It is hard for any man to be more disinterested than his

[5] The errata have been published in the Critical bibliographies of Isis (vol. 8 and following) as explained above; for the reviews of Vol. 1, see Isis (vol. 11, 234, 519; 12, 409; 13, 224, 534; 14, 540; etc.).

[6] One of them, the great chemist Theodore W. Richards, died in 1928.

wife: I am especially proud of mine because she has never expected me to avoid sacrifices and to follow an easier path; on the contrary, she has always rejoiced with me in the difficulties and hardships to overcome and has been to me a model of quiet abnegation.

George Sarton

Cambridge, Massachusetts
Harvard Library, Room 185
January 6, 1931

CONTENTS

PARTS I AND II

Prolegomena

PART I

The Twelfth Century

BOOK I

The Time of William of Conches, Abraham Ibn Ezra, and Ibn Zuhr (First Half of Twelfth Century)

Chapter I

Chapter II

Chapter III

Chapter IV

Chapter V

Chapter VI

CHAPTER VII

CHAPTER VIII

CHAPTER IX

CHAPTER X

CHAPTER XI

CHAPTER XII

CHAPTER XIII

BOOK II

The Time of Gerard of Cremona, Ibn Rushd, and Maimonides (Second Half of Twelfth Century)

CHAPTER XIV

Chapter XV

Chapter XVI

Chapter XVII

CHAPTER XVIII

CHAPTER XIX

CHAPTER XX

CHAPTER XXI

Chapter XXII

Chapter XXIII

Chapter XXIV

Chapter XXV

Chapter XXVI

Chapter XXVII

PART II

The Thirteenth Century

BOOK III

The Time of Robert Grosseteste, Ibn al-Baiṭār and Jacob Anaṭoli (First Half of Thirteenth Century)

Chapter XXVIII

..

CHAPTER XXIX

CHAPTER XXX

CHAPTER XXXI

CHAPTER XXXII

Chapter XXXIII

Chapter XXXIV

Chapter XXXV

Chapter XXXVI

Chapter XXXVII

Chapter XXXVIII

Chapter XXXIX

Chapter XL

Chapter XLI

BOOK IV

The Time of Roger Bacon, Jacob ben Maḥir ibn Tibbon, and Quṭb al-dīn al-Shīrāzī. (Second Half of Thirteenth Century)

Chapter XLII

CHAPTER XLV

Education... 862–866

CHAPTER XLVI

Philosophic and Cultural Background............................ 867–984

Chapter XLVII

Mathematics and Astronomy..................................... 985–1023

Chapter XLVIII

Physics, Technology and Music................................. 1024–1035

Chapter LIII

Chapter LIV

Chapter LV

Indices

INTRODUCTION TO THE HISTORY OF SCIENCE

Volume II

Pour un jour de synthèse il faut des années d'analyse.

—*Fustel de Coulanges*

(Histoire des institutions politiques de l'ancienne France, vol. 1, p. 4, Paris, 1875)

INTRODUCTORY CHAPTER

SURVEY OF SCIENTIFIC THOUGHT IN THE TWELFTH AND THIRTEENTH CENTURIES

The outstanding result of the investigations published in volume 1 was the establishment of the intellectual supremacy of the Muslim or Arabic peoples during a period extending from the middle of the eighth century to the end of the eleventh —more than three centuries. That hegemony had often been surmised, but my comparative studies gave the first irrefutable proof of its reality and illustrated it with an abundance of concrete details. Indeed how could it be proved otherwise? For instance how could a scholar knowing only the Latin, and maybe the Greek, aspects of the Middle Ages determine their relative importance, no matter how well he knew them? Or how could an Hebraist or an Arabist, who had never troubled to examine the Latin and vernacular writings appraise the relative value of his own Semitic texts? Moreover the Muslim superiority was not completely appreciated by the Muslims at the time of its climax, nor the Christian inferiority by the Christians at the time of its nadir. This would hardly have been possible. The Christians began to realize Muslim superiority only later when it was constantly decreasing, because on the one hand Muslims were less creative and more boastful, and on the other hand the Christians were growing in knowledge and in humility. This is a universal rule which applies to nations as well as to individuals. When people boast too much of their achievements it means either that they are still very young or that they are declining; it means that they are but just beginning to do things or that their days of glory are already over.

Volume 1 ended with a sort of Arabic apotheosis. Many readers must have wondered and asked themselves, what would happen next? If the Arabic writings were the main vehicles of progress in the eleventh century why and how did the situation change? The writer asked himself the same questions for many years and could not or would not answer them until he had completed his investigations, until all the pertinent facts had been collected, sifted, classified, and compared. It was essential in his judgment to postpone the synthesis until the eleventh hour in order to remain as unprejudiced as possible during the interminable analytical preparation.

The answer can now be given and it is expedient to tell the gist of it at once, not only to gratify the reader's curiosity but to indicate the contents of volume two. This volume—or more exactly these two volumes—will show that the twelfth century, and to a lesser extent the thirteenth century, was essentially a period of transition and compromise. Never were the exchanges between the three main civilizations of Europe and the Mediterranean world—the Jewish, the Christian, and the Muslim—more intense than in the twelfth century. For a long time the youngest of these remained supreme, yet its supremacy was constantly waning, while the others did not cease to absorb its strength and to transform it into their own substance. In the thirteenth century the symptoms of Christian vigor and originality were multiplying and by the end of it, when its respect for Muslim achievements was greatest, the genius of Western Christendom had already found itself. This is of very great importance because that genius has been ever since the main, almost the exclusive, creator of modern science.

The activity of the twelfth century was so intense that it has been possible to speak of "the Renaissance of the twelfth century" (C. H. Haskins), and the beginnings of European science and culture in the thirteenth century so striking that a Catholic enthusiast (J. J. Walsh) did not hesitate to call the thirteenth century "the greatest of centuries." The author will try to avoid such titles because of their highly subjective nature. Renaissance, like Middle Ages, is a relative term. I have shown in volume 1 that almost every age is a renascence in some respect, and so is every age a "middle age." Is it not the offspring of the preceding age and the begetter of the following? If one looks at it from the proper angle, each age is a compromise between the past and the future. However if the term Middle Ages had not already a definite meaning, or rather too many confusing meanings, it would be very tempting indeed to apply it to that period of one and a half centuries extending from about 1100 to about 1250. Indeed I can think of no other period during which the transitional elements were more conspicuous, and the compromise on a greater scale and more pregnant. It involved nothing less than a conflict between the three main civilizations of the Mediterranean world, itself a phasis—and the major one—in the immemorial conflict between East and West. We now know that the outcome was the triumph of the West, triumph which has never been reversed since but has increased as time went by—but this was far from obvious in the days of the Crusades.

However when we speak of a western triumph, we must not think of it as if eastern ideals had been then and there superseded by western ones. The western victory consisted rather in an assimilation of the East by the West. The treasures of Greco-Arabic science were feverishly poured out from Arabic vessels into Latin and Hebrew ones. The transfer of all these elements and their assimilation and elaboration took place in a number of ways, but toward the end of the thirteenth century most of them finally emerged under a Latin label. Thus the western victory did not imply for mankind a change of purpose or direction, but simply a change in leadership.

The twelfth century (or more generally the period 1100–1250) was a period of transition and compromise as defined above; it was also a period of absorption and fusion. It is then that the conflicting cultures were brought most closely together, especially the Christian and Muslim, and that their interpenetration constituted the solid core of the new Europe. From this point of view, the twelfth century might be called a Renaissance, and a tremendous Renaissance it was.

Needless to say the fusion remained incomplete. A man and a woman may easily imagine in the exaltation of their love that they have fulfilled the scriptural injunction and that they are "no more twain, but one flesh," yet however deep their love of one another, they remain separate: two bodies, two hearts, two minds, two souls. Even so—and much more so—when civilizations meet and coalesce, the fusion extends only to the parts which are assimilable, and these are far smaller than the others. Hence the conflict between East and West was not by any means solved in the twelfth century, but simply transformed.

The achievement was nevertheless immense. By the middle of the thirteenth century there was finally set up in Western Europe the core of a new civilization.

That core was essentially Greco-Arabic-Latin. The description of it presented in these volumes will prove this with considerable detail, and help us to realize at once its complexity and its identity. We shall realize that identity even better when we put it in contrast with the other contemporary cultures, which remained more completely separate. One may say that there were in the thirteenth century three independent civilizations: the Greco-Arabic-Latin, the Hindu, and the Sino-Japanese. These civilizations were not absolutely independent; sundry exchanges took place between them (examples may be found in these volumes), but these exchanges were too casual and too short to influence them deeply; there were or might be mutual stimulations, but never true anastomoses. The conflict between East and West continued to make itself felt within the Arabic-Latin culture, but it was far more obvious between that culture on the one hand, and the two others, the Hindu-Buddhist or Asiatic culture, on the other.

The consequences of this are twofold. First that a study of mediaeval thought must necessarily include the Arabic and Hebrew elements as well as the Latin under penalty of being not only incomplete but erroneous. Second that the study of the Hindu and Sino-Japanese elements, whatever their intrinsic importance, may be somewhat neglected without risk of falsifying the picture. This is very fortunate because it is still impossible to tell the history of Asiatic science with any completeness and any great accuracy. If our knowledge of Arabic science had not been on a much higher level, there would have been no point in attempting this synthesis, for it would have been too vague and shaky to have any value. Though I have spent considerable time gathering together all the information on Asiatic science available today in the European languages, the result is disappointingly meager. It must be added in justice to myself, that even specialists able to read the Asiatic languages easily, could not do much more within our time, because of the lack of datable texts properly edited, and of other preparatory investigations. With but few exceptions almost everything remains to be done from the bottom up. This is a gigantic task which will occupy many generations of scholars, but thus far a real start has not yet been made. When that task is finally accomplished, we shall have a far better knowledge of the history of mankind. It will not help us much to understand the development of European thought, but it will enable us to compare independent cultural streams, and thus to penetrate more deeply the essence of humanity.

In order to realize more clearly the cultural exchanges which took place in the twelfth and thirteenth centuries and the progress which was fulfilled under their stimulation in every part of the civilized world, we shall now attempt to summarize the work done in various fields. We shall consider only the main branches of science proper—from mathematics to medicine—but examine each of them apart, in its totality and also in its details. This is a synthesis of a new kind. It will enable the reader to measure not only the total advance of mankind and the gradual transformation of its Weltanschauung, but also its progress in each of the main directions, and the share of each type of culture and of each people in each department of science.

In such a summary as this statements are apt to be somewhat broad and dogmatic; yet they are probably correct—within their scale—for I have taken great pains for many years to obtain and digest all the pertinent information. To be sure new facts may oblige us at any time to modify our conclusions, and this will be done promptly in Isis whenever necessary. The conclusions expressed below may be considered a good approximation to the truth as far as it is now attainable. Moreover the reader who wishes to check up any statement and to find out to what extent it ought to be qualified on a larger scale can do so very easily by reference to the index. I will be grateful to him if he does not simply consult the article specifically devoted to the person or to the topic of special interest to him, but also takes the trouble to read the part of the survey relative to it, in order that he may see that person or topic in the background in which I have placed him (or it).

Let us begin with the most fundamental branch of science, Mathematics, and then consider every other in its turn.

MATHEMATICS

1. *Hindu numerals*—By the end of the eleventh century the Arabic speaking people were already well acquainted with the Hindu numerals, for their use had been repeatedly explained to them: the earliest Muslim exponent was al-Khwārizmī (first half of the ninth century) whose work remained the fountain head on the subject; one of the best expositions was made two centuries later by the great Persian encyclopaedist al-Bīrūnī. These numerals were as well known in the Maghrib as in the East, but those used by the Moors, ḥurūf al-ghubār, were somewhat different in shape from the Eastern ones. Gerbert may have known these ghubār numerals, but if so, his understanding of them was very imperfect.[1]

Though some knowledge of Hindu numerals filtered outside of the Muslim world as early as the second half of the tenth century it remained latent for a long time. We have to wait until the twelfth century for that knowledge to materialize in any way. The main introducer into the Latin world was in all probability Adelard of Bath, and at about the same time Abraham ibn Ezra explained to the Jews a Hebrew system of numeration which was obviously an adaptation of the Muslim one.

In spite of Adelard and Abraham's efforts the diffusion of Hindu numerals in non-Muslim Europe was incredibly slow. The twelfth century and even the thirteenth constitute in this respect a period of transition and compromise. To illustrate, Ralph of Laon and Ocreatus, the latter a pupil of Adelard, used at once Roman and Hindu numerals. Hence they were at once abacists and algorists. Ocreatus' numerals were an especially queer mixture of both systems. However little by little, very slowly indeed, the knowledge of the new numerals increased. An Arabic treatise on the subject, more elaborate than al-Khwārizmī's, was translated by John of Seville.

The progress of the new algorism was delayed by the fact that it did not stop the development of the older one. The use of the abacus became more popular and more systematic, East and West, at the very time when the Hindu numerals were introduced. Treatises on the abacus continued to be published; e.g., one of them was written by Adelard himself. The prevailing confusion of thought is reflected in the confusion of terms. In 1202 there was published a book which was the main landmark in the introduction of the new numerals and marked the beginning of European mathematics; that book was entitled curiously enough Liber abaci. It includes the first complete and systematic explanation of Hindu numerals by a Christian writer. The author, Fibonacci, had obtained his knowledge from Mus-

[1] New views on this subject will be found in Solomon Gandz: The origin of the ghubār numerals, or the Arabian abacus and the articuli (to appear in Isis, vol. 16 or 17).

lims during a stay on the Barbary Coast, but his account was original. Fibonacci's arithmetic was propagated by such writers as Villedieu and Sacrobosco. By the way the latter was the first to ascribe the invention of the Hindu numerals to Arabs, a mistake which was natural enough as the Latin writers had actually received those numerals from Muslim hands; a little later, when the Jewish transmission was becoming more obvious than the Muslim, these numerals were even called Jewish.

However much such a great work as the Liber abaci could do to promote the new arithmetic, it could not put an end to the older one. In fact a contemporary of Fibonacci, Jordanus Nemorarius, wrote arithmetical treatises which showed no trace of Arabic influence and continued quietly the tradition of Nicomachos and Boetius. One of Nemorarius' treatises was entitled Demonstratio de algorismo. Somewhat later there appeared another arithmetical treatise, the Algorismus demonstratus, which was strictly Boetian. Hence it is clear that the words abacus and algorismus were used somewhat promiscuously, and this was certainly caused by intellectual hesitancy and ambiguity, by the fact that the issue involved was not squarely faced. In the meanwhile more treatises were explaining the new numerals and the new system in Arabic, Latin, Greek, and French.

The delay in the acceptance of the Hindu numerals was largely due to material causes. In spite of their advantages they were not actually needed by business men because most computations were done by mechanical means (abacus, counters) only the results being written down. There was no social need for the new numerals. Nor was there for a long time any scientific need because hardly anybody realized the implications of the new symbolism. In spite of all the explanations it had not yet dawned upon them that this was not simply a matter of new symbols, but of a radically new arithmetic. How else could we explain for example the absence of Hindu numerals in the Alphonsine tables?[1a] The compilers of these tables were certainly familiar with those numerals: they used them when they wrote in Arabic, but used Roman numerals when they wrote in Latin or Castilian. The numerals of each kind were considered as peculiarities of the corresponding script, and were naturally dropped together with that script. Does this not clearly show that the Hindu system was not really understood?

There are signs that the Hindu numerals were actually used by practical people in northern Italy before the end of the thirteenth century; yet these numerals did not finally triumph until three centuries later. Deeper implications of their use were not perceived except after long intervals. For decimal fractions one had to wait until Stevin and Napier; for decimal weights and measures until the French Revolution, and a great part of the civilized world has not understood them yet.

I have dealt with the new numerals at some length because their vicissitudes were typical. A similar confusion obtained in many other fields: new ideas were slowly emerging out of a chaos of conflicting traditions. Moreover this very simple example may help us to realize the importance of symbols. The old types of numerals, Greek and Hebrew letters, Roman signs were equally inefficient; they made arith-

[1a] However Hindu numerals appear in other contemporary tables, e.g., in Grosseteste's Compotus, British Museum MSS. Further Add. 27589 and Harley 3735, two MSS. of the second half of the thirteenth century. Examples of Hindu numerals in Latin MSS. can be traced back to the end of the tenth century, but they remained rare and hardly known until the thirteenth century. G. F. Hill: On the early use of Arabic numerals in Europe (Archaeologia, vol. 62, 137–190, 1910; see p. 139).

metical progress along certain lines almost impossible, they blocked the way; on the contrary the Hindu-Arabic numerals opened it. The long drawn battle between the Roman and the Arabic symbols was not simply a matter of numerals; the whole future of arithmetic, nay of mathematics, was involved.

2. *The continuation of the Greco-Arabic traditions*—Section 1 was devoted to the consideration of a purely mediaeval tradition. That tradition did not supersede the ancient one except within its own limited field, but it was a magnificent addition to it. In the meanwhile the Greek tradition was continued. I have explained in volume 1 how the main bulk of Greek science was gradually translated into Arabic. At the beginning of the twelfth century, the treasures of Greek knowledge were available in Greek and Arabic. Strange to say, for a Latin scholar the Arabic translations were more accessible or, let us say, less remote, than the Greek originals. The Greek world was far more distant in time and space; the Greek originals were almost forgotten, in not a few cases they were actually lost. Arabic civilization was tangible enough in Sicily and in Spain, not only in the Moorish part of it, but in places like Toledo, which were again in Christian hands;[2] the Arabic speaking people encircled the Mediterranean Sea and dominated the Asiatic trade.

Hence when the West was sufficiently mature to feel the need of deeper knowledge, when it finally wanted to renew its contacts with ancient thought it turned its attention first of all, not to the Greek sources, but to the Arabic ones. The main intellectual task of the twelfth century and to a smaller extent of the thirteenth century, was one of translation. The best work of that kind was done in Spain, chiefly in Toledo. A large body of mathematical and astronomical literature was translated from the Arabic. The translators hailed from many parts of Europe: two of the earliest ones, Walcher of Malvern and Adelard of Bath were English (Walcher it is true was of Lotharingian origin), and two others, Robert of Chester and Michael Scot came from the same island; many of course were Spaniards: John of Seville, Hugh of Santalla, and those working under the patronage of King Alfonso; another, named Hermann, hailed from Dalmatia; two came from Flanders, Rudolf of Bruges and Henry Bate; many, from southern France: Armengaud son of Blaise, Jacob Anaṭoli, Moses ibn Tibbon, Jacob ben Maḥir; and from Italy: Plato of Tivoli, Gerard of Cremona, Aristippus of Catania, Salio of Padua, John of Brescia.

By far the most prominent of all these was Gerard of Cremona (d. 1187), one of the greatest translators of all times, whose prodigious activity was centered in Toledo. Many of the translators whom I have named were Jews. This is natural enough, for the Spanish Jews knew Arabic as well as if not better than Hebrew. Translations were often made by Christians and Jews working in collaboration.

During the twelfth century Arabic mathematical and astronomical texts were translated only into Latin; in the following century this movement was largely replaced by a new series of translations into Hebrew, by the Spanish versions made under King Alfonso's direction, and finally by the direct translations made by William of Moerbeke from Greek into Latin. It should be noted that the translations into Hebrew were generally later than those of the same works into Latin. This did not affect the Jews immediately, for almost as soon as they ceased to know Arabic

[2] For the anastomosis between the Christian and Muslim cultures which took place in Spain, and particularly in Toledo, see Angel González Palencia: Los Mozárabes de Toledo en los siglos XII y XIII (4 vols., Madrid, 1926–1930; Isis, 15, 183–187).

they began to know Latin, yet it reduced their intellectual importance and helped to prepare and later to sanction the Latin and Christian hegemony.

At the beginning of the twelfth century it was impossible to become a full-fledged mathematician and astronomer without a good knowledge of Arabic; by the end of the thirteenth century the situation was very different, for many classics of Greek science were already available in Latin and in Hebrew. The Christian and Jewish students, who knew no Arabic, had already a sufficient amount of Greek knowledge to go forward. All they needed now was genius, and genius "bloweth where it listeth." However they were not yet by any means on a footing of equality with the Arabic reading students: not only were many Greek mathematical works still untranslated and available only in Arabic (and in Greek, if extant), but there was also a valuable body of Arabic commentaries and of Arabic treatises. Moreover the Arabic texts of the Greek classics were gradually improved and the Latin and Hebrew translations were not always based upon the best Arabic editions. The process of emendation and explanation of the Arabic texts was still going on at the very end of the period we are dealing with, when most Latin translations were already completed. Indeed the mathematical school of Marāgha in Adharbāijān, led by Nāṣir al-dīn al-Ṭūsī, was even then preparing a new edition of the Kitāb al-mutawassiṭāt, a large collection of Greek and Arabic classics.

It so happened however that this was almost the end of the Arabic mathematical efforts—the end of their greatest and best efforts certainly—while the Christians could compensate their insufficient knowledge of past literature by a growing originality and enthusiasm. The Muslims had reached their climax; the Christians were preparing to take off.

3. *The birth of European mathematics*—The immense activity of the translators proved that there was a waxing demand in the West for mathematical knowledge and mathematical books. It did not prove by itself the existence of mathematical genius, though it could not fail to stimulate any genius that might exist, and that is the very thing that happened. In the twelfth century there were no mathematicians in the West; or rather there were two great ones in Spain, but one of them, Jābir ibn Aflaḥ, was a Moor, and the other, Abraham bar Ḥiyya, a Jew. In the following century, there were at least four Christians, Fibonacci, Nemorarius, Grosseteste, and Bacon. Only one of these, the first, was directly stimulated by Moorish contacts; Nemorarius was apparently unaffected by Arabic examples. Grosseteste was under Greek influence, moreover he and his pupil Bacon knew many Arabic writings in their Latin versions. These two were not creative mathematicians, but their prophetic understanding of mathematics amounted to genius.

Fibonacci and Nemorarius stand at the threshold of European mathematics. Not only was Fibonacci the first to explain Arabic arithmetic but his works, especially his later ones, contain many original ideas. His Liber abaci of 1202 may be called the first monument of European mathematics. Jordanus Nemorarius was less remarkable as a mathematician than as a physicist; he continued the Greco-Roman tradition rather than the Greco-Arabic one but he did so with much independence.

4. *Theory of numbers*—Progress in this direction was not very significant. Oriental science was mixed up with a good deal of superstition, hence it is not surprising that Muslim and Jewish mathematicians showed some interest in the occult properties of numbers, especially in the "magic" squares. These are dealt with, e.g., by al-Ghazzālī, Abraham ibn Ezra, and al-Būnī.

Some simple rules of combinatorial analysis are implied in the writings of Ibn Ezra, Nemorarius, and Bhāskara.[3]

Many small contributions to the theory of numbers may be found in the writings of Fibonacci and Nemorarius.

5. *Algebra*—Our history of algebra in vol. 1 ended gloriously with an account of Omar Khayyam's classification and partial solution of cubic equations. That achievement was one of the high peaks—perhaps the very highest—of mediaeval mathematics, but though it was not isolated and was in fact a normal development of earlier Arabic work it was so singular that we could hardly expect it to be repeated. We cannot quote anything comparable with it, certainly not in the Dār al-Islām, nor in the West, but please note that Omar Khayyam's algebraical work may belong to this period. I dealt with it in vol. 1, because his remarkable calendar was computed about 1079, but Omar lived until 1123–1124. For aught we know he may have done his algebraical investigations after 1100.

Muslim algebra was transmitted to the West through the Latin translations of Adelard of Bath, John of Seville, and Robert of Chester, and indirectly through Fibonacci's writings. It was also transmitted through the Hebrew treatise of Abraham bar Ḥiyya, itself retranslated into Latin by Plato of Tivoli. Plato's translation appeared in the same year, 1145, as Robert of Chester's translation of al-Khwārizmī's algebra. That year 1145 might well be counted as the birth year of European algebra; but if we mean to reserve that title for the publication of the first original treatise (as opposed to translations), then the birth year was 1202 when the Liber abaci appeared. The two dates tally very well; they are like two steps placed at the correct distance from one another in the long road leading to our own knowledge and beyond! By the middle of the twelfth century thanks to Plato of Tivoli and Robert of Chester, Latin mathematicians could become acquainted, if they were sufficiently eager to do so, with the main results of the Arabic algebra of the ninth and tenth centuries. It amounts to this that they could find the positive roots of quadratics and could solve imperfectly special cubics. Some sixty and eighty years—that is, two and three generations—later the first Christian algebraist added a few contributions of his own, first in the Liber abaci (1202), then in the Flos (1225). In the Flos we find many novelties, e.g., the negative root of a financial problem interpreted as a debt. Fibonacci did not simply know Arabic algebra, he was able to stand on his own feet and go further.

Though Fibonacci was the leading algebraist of Christendom, in one respect he was surpassed by Nemorarius. In at least one case Fibonacci used letters instead of numerals; on the other hand in Nemorarius' Arithmetica letters were constantly used instead of figures for the sake of generality.

The algebraic renaissance of Latindom had been preceded by another, even more remarkable, in central India.[4] Bhāskara, who flourished about the middle of the twelfth century, did not simply explain matters which had hardly been discussed before (e.g., meaning of division by zero) but his algebraic knowledge was better integrated. Unfortunately while the European renaissance was the dawn of a new age, the Hindu one was but a glorious twilight. Bhāskara was the last great mathematician of his race until almost our own days; Fibonacci on the contrary was the forerunner of a splendid and endless legion of western mathematicians.

[3] For the two last named, see Johannes Tropfke: Geschichte der Elementar-Mathematik (vol. 6, 2d ed., 64–65, Berlin 1924; Isis, 7, 314).

[4] In the ancient city of Ujjain (Gwalior state), mathematical and astronomical center of mediaeval India.

Even more extraordinary than Bhāskara's achievements were those of the Chinese mathematicians of the thirteenth and fourteenth centuries, Ch'in Chiu-shao, Li Yeh, Yang Hui, Chu Shih-chieh. They evolved an algebra of their own, the sources of which have not yet been penetrated. It enabled Ch'in Chiu-shao to solve numerical equations of any degree. Li Yeh treated a number of geometrical problems by means of a similar method. Yang Hui was more interested in arithmetic and algebra. Though the best work of Chu Shih-chieh belongs only to the fourteenth century he must be referred to because of his mathematical introduction (largely algebraical) which appeared in 1299. He was the main agent in the transmission of Chinese mathematics to Japan. Our knowledge of Chinese mathematics is still so imperfect that we are unable to explain its origin and development. We do not even know with any precision how much each Chinese mathematician was influenced by the others, and we cannot yet retrace the early history of the method of the "celestial element" (t'ien yüan shu). Chinese algebra was possibly influenced by Arabic and Sanskrit models, but we do not know to what extent, nor can we account for the transmission of such influences. On the other hand while Hindu mathematics ended in a cul-de-sac, the Chinese effort was continued in Japan: it was thus the beginning of a new tradition essentially independent from the western one. Chinese mathematics might almost be left out of a general account of mathematical history but it is highly interesting from another point of view—that of the logician and philosopher—for it enables us to compare two independent evolutions, two independent methods of approaching the same problems.

6. *Geometry*—With two brilliant exceptions noted below, the best geometrical work was done by Easterners: Muslims, Jews, and Hindus.

Let us first consider the Euclidean tradition, for one of the miracles of Greek genius was the creation at the beginning of the third century B. C. of a synthesis of elementary geometry which was so masterly that it dominated human thought almost to our own days—nay, it is still dominating it now.

"Euclid alone has looked on Beauty bare.
Let all who prate of Beauty hold their peace,
And lay them prone upon the earth and cease
To ponder on themselves, the while they stare
At nothing, intricately drawn nowhere
In shapes of shifting lineage; let geese
Gabble and hiss, but heroes seek release
From dusty bondage into luminous air."[5]

Euclid's name has remained a synonym for geometry, and the history of elementary geometry for the last twenty-two centuries is essentially a history of the Euclidean tradition. In our period a whole series of mathematicians, most of them Muslims, wrote commentaries on Euclid. For example, a commentary on Book X ascribed to Muḥammad ibn 'Abd al-Bāqī, who flourished at the beginning of the twelfth century, was very popular. Before the end of the century it was translated into Latin by Gerard of Cremona. Muẓaffar al-Asfuzārī, a collaborator of Omar Khayyam, wrote a summary of Books I to XIV. Fakhr al-dīn al-Rāzī discussed Euclid in Arabic and in Persian. Somewhat later the school of Marāgha devoted

[5] Edna St. Vincent Millay: The harp-weaver (XXII, New York 1923).

considerable attention to Greek geometry in general and to Euclid in particular. The great Syrian encyclopaedist Abū-l-Faraj lectured in Marāgha on Euclid in 1268. I have already referred to the edition of the Kitāb al-mutawassiṭāt undertaken in that city under the direction of Nāṣir al-dīn al-Ṭūsī and of Muḥyī al-dīn al-Maghribī. It is clear enough that the geometrical interest of these Muslim scholars was very far from superficial. Witness the discussions of the postulates by Omar Khayyam, Fakhr al-dīn, Qaiṣar ibn abī-l-Qāsim, and Nāṣir al-dīn. The latter's discussion was especially elaborate; it inspired Gerolamo Saccheri (1733) who was the forerunner of the nineteenth-century non-Euclidean geometry.

It would take too long to deal with every author included in the Kitāb al-mutawassiṭāt, but we may select two of them, Apollonios and Theodosios. Apollonian geometry appealed to the Muslims and they never neglected it very long. In the second half of the twelfth century 'Abd al-Malik al-Shīrāzī made a summary of Apollonios' Conics, and Muḥammad ibn al-Ḥusain, aided by Kamāl al-dīn ibn Yūnus wrote a treatise on the "perfect compass" by means of which every conic could be drawn. The Spherics of Theodosios of Bithynia were translated (from the Arabic) into Latin by Plato of Tivoli, then again by Gerard of Cremona.

The two most remarkable geometrical treatises of the twelfth century were written respectively in Hebrew and in Sanskrit. The Ḥibbur ha-meshiḥah, one of the most important Hebrew scientific works of the Middle Ages, was composed by Abraham bar Ḥiyya. It deals with practical geometry and with algebra; its algebraical importance has already been mentioned. It was translated by Plato of Tivoli in 1145 under the title Liber embadorum. The Siddhāntaśiromaṇi of Bhāskara, though far less influential and hence extrinsically less significant than the Ḥibbur ha-meshiḥah, was intrinsically more valuable. It includes a study of regular polygons having as many as 384 sides, leading to a remarkably accurate value of π, and one may find in it an anticipation of Kepler's method of integration.

In the thirteenth century the leading treatises were in Arabic and in Latin. The Arabic treatises of Nāṣir al-dīn al-Ṭūsī and his school have already been referred to; they were the fruit of a splendid but shortlived mathematical renaissance in Persia. In 1229, just a little before Nāṣir al-dīn's time of greatest activity an older contemporary of his, the Moor al-Ḥasan al-Marrākushī had produced an excellent treatise on gnomonics and trigonometry, to which we shall come back presently. Thus geometry was still flourishing in the Dār al-Islām from Persia to the Far West.

Latin geometry began very humbly. The first Latin translation of Euclid was made by the Englishman Adelard of Bath probably before 1142, naturally from the Arabic. By that time Muslim mathematicians had been studying Euclid for more than three centuries! The text of that translation being very uncertain, it is impossible to appreciate the value of Adelard's work. More than a century elapsed and then Adelard's version was revised with the help of other Arabic materials, by the Italian, Giovanni Campano. As opposed to Adelard's Campano's text is very well known, for it was actually printed, in 1482, this being the first (printed) edition of Euclid in any form and any language. One had to wait twenty-three years more to obtain a printed edition of a translation from the Greek (1505); and even then, four years later (1509) the Arabico-Latin text of Campano was reprinted! Observe the slowness of the Latin awakening.

That slowness can still be illustrated in another way. We have a text dating probably from the second half of the twelfth century, the Practica geometriae

Hugonis, which is almost completely innocent of Arabic knowledge. This unknown Hugh is somewhat superior to the schoolmen of a century earlier, like Ragimbold of Cologne and Radolf of Liége, in that he is vaguely aware of the existence of Euclidean geometry while they were not. He may be compared to elementary teachers of to-day who know that there is such a thing as synthetic geometry—but that is all they know of it.

And yet! And yet! While western mathematicians are slowly assimilating the Greco-Arabic traditions, there are already in the first half of the thirteenth century, that is, long before that assimilation is completed, unmistakable signs of a revival. Those signs are writ large in the geometrical works of Fibonacci and Nemorarius. The latter deals with problems on triangles, finds their center of gravity, etc., and in another book gives the first general demonstration of the fundamental property of stereographic projection (circles are projected as circles). Fibonacci's Practica geometriae of 1220 was based on the lost book of Euclid περὶ διαιρέσεων and on Heron's Metrica. It contained many novelties in substance and also in method: the application of algebra to the solution of geometrical problems.

By the end of the thirteenth century it cannot yet be said that the West has succeeded in completing its connection with the Greco-Arabic past, and yet it has already proved its own genius. The Arabic world is still ahead of the Latin one, but the latter is growing—not very fast—but growing: it makes me think of an ignorant youth whose intelligence is slowly but unmistakably showing through in spite of his uncouthness. Fibonacci and Nemorarius, humble as they were, represented something definitely new; something which was neither Greek, nor Arabic—they were the forefathers of Gauss and Galois.

7. *Trigonometry*—It is fitting to conclude this mathematical section with a brief account of trigonometry, this being the natural introduction to astronomy. In fact trigonometry was more a part of astronomy, than of pure mathematics, and it was only toward the end of this period that it began to be considered independently.

The construction of astronomical tables implied trigonometrical theories and computations which were generally explained in the introductory chapters to these tables. This was the case, for example, for the Toledan Tables computed by al-Zarqālī and others in the second half of the eleventh century. Al-Zarqālī gave an account of the trigonometrical knowledge of his time and of the means of constructing his tables. His work was translated into Latin by Gerard of Cremona, and was very popular for more than two centuries.

The next step was the trigonometrical introduction to the Iṣlāḥ al-majisṭī, the great astronomical treatise of another Spaniard, Jābir ibn Aflaḥ of Seville, who died about the middle of the twelfth century. In the meanwhile, Arabic trigonometry of an earlier time was being translated into Latin. The need of it revealed itself as vigorous as it was sudden. In the first half of the twelfth century no less than three or four scholars were engaged in that undertaking: Adelard of Bath, Hermann the Dalmatian (?), Robert of Chester, and Plato of Tivoli. The former translated in 1126 the tables of al-Khwārizmī as revised by Maslama ibn Aḥmad of Madrid (second half of the tenth century). Another translation of the same tables is ascribed to Hermann. Robert of Chester's work was less a translation than an adaptation of the tables of al-Battānī and al-Zarqālī for the coördinates of London, 1149. He also revised al-Khwārizmī's tables for the same position. He it was who introduced the Latin word sinus. Finally in 1145 Plato translated al-Battānī's astronomy. Thus by the middle of the twelfth century, the most up-to-date Latin mathematicians were acquainted with Arabic trigonometry if not in its very latest stage at least in the one it had reached before the end of the preceding century. If they had been as gifted for trigonometry as the Muslims proved to be, that would have been sufficient to start their own improvements; unfortunately they were not, they did not fully wake up to their opportunity until the fourteenth century, when Latin trigonometry made a new beginning at Merton College in Oxford.

During the thirteenth century trigonometrical progress was entirely due to the Muslim efforts. It is interesting to note that in the first half of the century the main effort was made in Morocco, and in the second half, far away east in Adharbāijān, beyond the Lake of Urmīyah. In 1229, Ḥasan al-Marrākushī completed a very elaborate treatise on practical astronomy wherein a large place was naturally given to trigonometry. It contained tables of sines for each half degree, also tables of versed sines, arc sines, and arc cotangents. Mathematical and astronomical work began in Marāgha in 1259 under Mongol patronage. I have already referred many times to the scientific leader of that group, Nāṣir al-dīn al-Ṭūsī. His most original contribution was his Kitāb shakl al-qaṭṭā', a treatise on geometry and trigonometry, the very first treatise wherein trigonometry was not considered simply as prolegomena to astronomy but for its own sake, the greatest work of its kind until the De triangulis of Regiomontanus two centuries later. Nāṣir al-dīn gave the fundamental rules for the solution of triangles, plane and spherical. In the case of the latter he indicated a method equivalent to the consideration of polar triangles, which were not explicitly defined until the end of the sixteenth century (Vieta, 1593).

Nor is this all, for Nāṣir al-dīn's investigations were improved upon by one of his assistants, Muḥyī al-dīn al-Maghribī, who wrote a new treatise bearing the same title, Shakl al-qaṭṭā'.

This outline of trigonometry in the twelfth and thirteenth centuries cannot but give the reader a very high idea of Muslim science. Indeed all the progressive work to the very end of this period was published in Arabic. Latin trigonometry was but a pale reflection of the Arabic, and it was already a little behind the times when it was new, for the Arabic efforts did not stop but continued with increased efficiency. It is highly probable that Chinese trigonometry, as used by Kuo Shouching in the second half of the thirteenth century and the beginning of the fourteenth, was also of Arabic origin. The transmission of Arabic trigonometry to the Far East would have been particularly easy at that time because the Muslim East and China were then integral parts of the same Mongol empire.

ASTRONOMY

8. *Instruments. Observations*—Inasmuch as we have just dealt with trigonometry, it would be natural to examine the tables which were generally inseparable from it. But before doing that, let us consider what progress was made in the experimental technique.

At the beginning of the twelfth century the best known instrument in the Arabic and Jewish circles of Spain was the improved astrolabe devised by al-Zarqālī, the saphaea Arzachelis. It had displaced the earlier kind of astrolabe such as was described in Latin by Hermann the Lame. Eventually it was very popular also in Latin circles, but strangely enough this did not occur until much later. Al-

Zarqālī's description of it was not translated into Latin until 1263, by Jacob ben Maḥir and John of Brescia. It is true a Spanish translation had been made in 1255, again in 1277, by order of Alfonso el Sabio, but that translation was almost a supererogation: were not the majority of Alfonso's astronomers Moors and Jews, who could read Arabic as easily as Spanish and were sufficiently familiar with the instrument itself? To be sure most of the observations upon which the Toledan tables were based were made with other—stabler—instruments, but the shape of these instruments had changed but little, witness the description of them in the Libros del saber.

Another instrument was probably invented in Spain a little later by Jābir ibn Aflaḥ—that is, if Regiomontanus' ascription is correct—the torquetum, a system of two graduated circles in two perpendicular planes.

Jābir's Christian contemporaries were naturally far less well trained in every respect than their Muslim colleagues. Many were content to translate Arabic texts; their ambition hardly went beyond that, and—as is usual with people of their kind—they did not take special pains to translate the latest texts; following the line of least resistance, they got hold of the treatises which were best known, that is, of older ones. Thus a tenth century treatise of Maslama ibn Aḥmad al-Majrīṭī was translated into Latin by John of Seville, then again by Rudolf of Bruges; another anonymous one, by Robert of Chester, in 1147; Ibn al-Ṣaffār's Treatise (first half of the eleventh century) by Plato of Tivoli. The Englishman Adelard of Bath showed a little more independence, for he wrote an "original" treatise on the astrolabe, c. 1144. Curiously enough the only Christian observer of this time was another Englishman, Walcher of Malvern. Walcher died only in 1135, but he had observed lunar eclipses in Italy with an astrolabe as early as 1091–1092. This Walcher may be called the first European[6] astronomer. He was of Lotharingian[7] origin and familiar with Arabic science. The interesting point about him however is that he made and recorded genuine observations.

Let us now proceed to the East—to Persia. The importance attached to instruments by Muslims is reflected in the extravagant praise lavished upon al-Badī' al-Aṣṭurlabī of Ispahan, though he was primarily an instrument maker. A century later Muẓaffar al-Ṭūsī wrote a treatise on the astrolabe, and invented a new instrument called after him al-Ṭūsī's staff, a graduated staff with strings attached to it to measure angles. The organization of the Marāgha observatory in 1259 was a great opportunity for practical astronomers and instrument makers. It was the most important establishment of its kind in the East from the time of Ibn Yūnus at the beginning of the eleventh century to that of Ulūgh Beg more than four centuries later. There was a large staff of astronomers some of whom hailed from distant countries. They had at their disposal a very rich library and a splendid collection of instruments, which were described by their constructor, the Syrian Mu'ayyad al-dīn al-'Urḍī al-Dimishqī. Unfortunately the observatory's existence was too short, it hardly survived its creator, or the latter's sons; hence the best results, those which can only be obtained by a long accumulation of observations, were necessarily forfeited.

[6] The word European, as I use it here and in other places, refers to Christians as opposed to Muslims and Jews, and to Latins (i. e., Latin writers and Roman Catholics), as opposed to Greeks and Slavs and other Orientals.

[7] On the share of Lotharingia in the introduction of Arabic science into Europe, see James Westfall Thompson: The introduction of Arabic science into Lorraine in the tenth century (Isis, 12, 184–193, 1929). Mary Catherine Welborn: Lotharingia as a center of Arabic and scientific influence in the eleventh century (to appear in Isis).

One of al-'Urḍī's sons, Muḥammad, was apparently also an instrument maker. At any rate a celestial globe bearing his name and the date 1279 (or 1289) is still preserved in the mathematical salon of Dresden. Some four or five Arabic globes anterior to the fourteenth century are still extant, and there may be more which have not yet been identified.

It is said that some Chinese scientists worked in Marāgha under Nāṣir al-dīn's direction, and that is quite plausible. If this fact were established it would help to explain the transmission of Arabic trigonometry to China, but we would still be a long way from understanding the strange development of Chinese mathematics in the thirteenth and fourteenth centuries. For example, Kuo Shou-ching's astronomy and his instruments had many particularities of their own. Certain it is that Kuo was himself a good observer.

We may now return to the West. In the last quarter of the thirteenth century the Muslim examples were beginning to produce valuable fruits. For instance the Montpellier astronomers were becoming restless. (Montpellier being one of the leading medical schools of Europe, was ipso facto, as will be explained later, a center of astronomical research.) They wanted to improve their instruments, and this is always one of the best signs of scientific revival, even if the want is not yet very strong nor entirely genuine. Two of these astronomers were Robert the Englishman and Jacob ben Maḥir ibn Tibbon. In or about 1276 Robert described a new quadrant and its uses. That quadrant was probably a very simple adaptation of an older Arabic one to Christian needs, even as to-day a new name is often given to an instrument which is but slightly different from a previous one. However Robert's treatise was very popular, being translated into many languages. For centuries good people of divers lands continued to wonder at Robert's ingenuity and learning. Not so however in Montpellier, for hardly fourteen years after the publication of Robert's treatise there appeared a new one—in Hebrew this time—by Jacob ben Maḥir, which described a new and better quadrant. From then on, the few who knew, called Robert's instrument, the old one (quadrans vetus) and Jacob's, the new one (quadrans novus). For the Middle Ages, when the rhythm of life was incomparably slower than it is now, this was rather a swift change. Without attaching too much importance to it, it certainly illustrates a keener interest in instruments, and hence in observations.

While this occurred in Languedoc, where scientific life was powerfully stimulated and catalyzed by rivalries between Jews and Christians, other events happening in Paris were even more encouraging. Under Baconian influence some Parisian astronomers, notably Bernard of Verdun and William of Saint Cloud, were finally beginning to shake off scholasticism and to take a more independent and experimental view of things. This is especially true of William of Saint Cloud who was an ingenious and careful observer. He inaugurated a new tradition which—we can see it now from a distance—was fated to become in the course of time the main stream of practical astronomy.

At the end of this period, very few people in the West were already able to appreciate the fundamental value of good observations, but these few cannot be praised too highly, for they were the harbingers of modern astronomy.

9. *Astronomical tables*—Now that we have some idea of the mathematical and experimental equipment of the astronomers of this period, the next step is to survey the tables in which their observations were summarized. The astronomical tables were of course inseparable from the trigonometrical ones, but we shall deal here only with their astronomical parts.

Dealing first with Arabic tables, the period begins with the Toledan ones of al-Zarqālī (c. 1080) and ends with the Īlkhānic ones of Nāṣir al-dīn (c. 1272). It begins in Spain and ends in Persia. To be sure other tables were published within these two centuries, but of less importance, e.g., the Tables of Marw, 1115, compiled by al-Khāzinī. It is not known whether the Zīj īlkhānī were first written in Persian or in Arabic, but there is no doubt about their popularity in the Muslim and Buddhist East.

A brief history of European tables is very analogous to that of the Arabic ones. It begins almost in the same way with al-Zarqālī, for the Toledan Tables found their way into Christian hands before the middle of the twelfth century, and curiously enough ends at about the same year, 1272, with the Alphonsine Tables. However the development of European tables was more complex. This is natural enough for they had to obtain their first inspiration and their guidance from Arabic documents, and these, as I have already pointed out, did not reach them except with some amount of lag and irregularity. It took about half a century for the Toledan Tables to supersede earlier Arabic ones in Christendom. Of course that is not very much—and might be used as an example of the increasing rapidity of diffusion of Arabic knowledge across the Pyrenees; yet during that half century other traditions were established which were bound to become confusing and must be taken into account.

First of all we have the tables of Pedro Alfonso and Walcher of Malvern, the Arabic sources of which are not clear to me. In 1126, Adelard of Bath, translated the tables of al-Khwārizmī as revised by Maslama ibn Aḥmad al-Majrīṭī. The same tables were translated or revised by Hermann the Dalmatian (?) c. 1140, and by Robert of Chester.

The first Christian to adapt the Toledan Tables to a new place and time was Raymond of Marseilles in his Marseilles Tables of c. 1140. Then in 1149, Robert of Chester compiled London Tables which were derived from al-Battānī as well as from al-Zarqālī. Almost a century later, in 1231, William the Englishman compiled new Marseilles Tables. William had a deep knowledge of Arzachelian astronomy, but he had also become familiar with the ideas of al-Farghānī. The astronomical works of al-Farghānī and al-Battānī exerted a deep influence upon European astronomy almost until Copernicus' time. But please observe in what irregular order these Arabic astronomers reached Latindom: al-Khwārizmī (first half of the ninth century), al-Zarqālī (second half of the eleventh century), al-Battānī (end of the ninth century), al-Farghānī (first half of the ninth century). The confusion was increased by the fact that few Latin readers were aware of the real chronological sequence of these writings.

The climax of these vicissitudes was the preparation of new Toledan Tables by Judah ben Moses and Isaac ibn Sid under the patronage of King Alfonso el Sabio. These tables were completed about 1272, that is, at the very time when the Īlkhānic Tables gave new chronological standards to the East. Being written in Spanish, not in Latin, they did not spread as rapidly as one might have expected: it took them twenty years to reach Paris. Their popularity did not begin before the second quarter of the fourteenth century but then it continued unabated until the astronomical renaissance of the sixteenth century.

For the period 1272 to 1300, I find only three sets of tables to mention, the Malines Tables of Henry Bate (c. 1281), the Parisian Tables of William of Saint Cloud (1292 etc.), the Montpellier Tables of Jacob ben Maḥir (1300). All of these tables including the latest were still essentially derived from those of al-Zarqālī. It is true a criticism of the Alphonsine Tables is ascribed to Henry Bate, but it is lost and in all probability posterior to his own tables. Bate's main source was Abraham ibn Ezra, and this led him back to the older Toledan Tables. The newer ones, the Alphonsine Tables, did not really begin to tell until the following century, and the story of their reception and revision will be outlined in the following volumes.

10. *Astronomical theories and treatises*—We may now pass on to the theories and to the dogmatic accounts of astronomical facts in treatises. In reality there is no methodical progression from observation and mathematical elaboration to tables and finally to theories; on the contrary all of these activities are of necessity simultaneous, though each be in a different stage of development. Theories should come in the end, but they are also needed in the beginning to give a direction to one's efforts. The whole progress of knowledge is based on such vicious circles, or rather on such apparent circles, for there are no circles of course, but only a kind of helicoidal curve which might be considered the best symbol of the fundamental method of science, the method of successive approximations.

To return to our subject, it will be expedient to explain the evolution firstly of Muslim and Jewish astronomy, and secondly of Latin astronomy, because the latter evolution was entirely dominated by the former.

As we have already noticed, in the twelfth century the main work was done in the Maghrib (West of Islām), while in the thirteenth century these western efforts came almost to a stop. The work was then continued in the Mashriq (East of Islām), and the Muslim scientists in the West were replaced by Jews and Christians.

The only eastern Muslim of the twelfth century was the Persian Muḥammad al-Kharaqī who wrote a treatise derived from Ibn al-Haitham wherein he revived the latter's extraordinary theory according to which the celestial orbs are not simply mechanical conceptions but solid spheres. This is not mentioned only as a curiosity; Ibn al-Haitham's theory was taken far more seriously and retained for a longer time than it deserved.

The most interesting development in the West was a growing discontent with Ptolemaic astronomy. This was initiated by the philosopher Ibn Bājja (Avempace), and considerably elaborated by Jābir ibn Aflaḥ, the greatest astronomer of the twelfth century. Jābir wrote a treatise, the Correction of the Almagest (Iṣlāḥ al-majisṭī), which exerted a deep influence upon mediaeval thought through its Latin and Hebrew translations. The Latin translation was made by Gerard of Cremona before 1187—that is, when the Iṣlāḥ was still a novelty in Muslim circles; the first Hebrew translation did not appear until a century later, but then Jews did not need translations from the Arabic as badly as did the Christians.

In the meanwhile the anti-Ptolemaic tendency of the Iṣlāḥ was aggravated by the philosopher Ibn Ṭufail and by his pupil al-Biṭrūjī. That tendency was largely reactionary. Of course they had no idea of the real defects of Ptolemaism and their criticism was necessarily superficial. Good observers could not help noticing increasing divergencies between their observations and the ephemerides. They concluded rightly that the latter must be at fault, and needed correction. But how to correct them? According to Ptolemy, the movements of planets were accounted for, "the phenomena were saved," by eccentrics and epicycles; under Aristotelian influence Ibn Ṭufail and al-Biṭrūjī proposed to return to the theory of homocentric spheres which the Almagest had superseded. After all the change was defensible;

the eccentrics and epicycles did not give satisfaction, why not try again, after having improved it, the method which had been used by the Master of all Knowledge? Remember that not only the people of the Middle Ages, but those of the Renaissance as well, were absolutely inhibited by the strangest prejudice: celestial motions must be circular. Hence elliptical trajectories were unconceivable and remained so until Kepler's time (1609). Without such trajectories one was reduced to makeshifts. The anti-Ptolemaic efforts of al-Biṭrūjī led to the replacement of one kind of makeshifts by another. In our judgment of them we must not forget that, except by removing the prejudice mentioned above, it was hardly possible to do much better. The Muslim astronomers failed to correct the Ptolemaic errors, but they deserve credit for having seen them and insisted upon the need of correction.

Before passing to the East, we must still say a few words of a Moroccan scientist who wrote a little later, in 1229, one of the greatest astronomical and mathematical textbooks of the Middle Ages, the Jāmi' al-mabādi' wal-ghāyāt fī 'ilm al-mīqāt (The uniter of beginnings and ends in the knowledge of time). The purpose of the Jāmi' was much humbler than that of the Iṣlāḥ al-majisṭī. It was a treatise of practical astronomy, explaining the construction and use of instruments, and the trigonometrical and graphical methods for the solution of astronomical problems.

Jābir's anti-Ptolemaic views were espoused by Maimonides who carried them with him to Egypt in 1165. Their transmission to Eastern Islām was largely due to him and to his disciple Joseph ben Judah ibn 'Aqnīn (needless to say both of them wrote in Arabic). In other words the most advanced astronomical views were diffused in the East by Jews. By a strange irony of fate, the western (Hebrew writing) Jews did not hear of these views, or did not assent to them until much later. For example consider the case of two Provençal philosophers who lived in the second half of the thirteenth century, Levi ben Abraham ben Ḥayyim and Gershon ben Solomon. In spite of the fact that Levi was a Maimonidean and the leader of liberal Judaism in southern France, his astronomy was on the same level as that of Abraham ibn Ezra. Gershon's knowledge was derived from al-Farghānī, Ibn Sīnā, and Ibn Rushd. Levi's astronomy, Sefer ha-tekunah, was completed in 1276, and Gershon's encyclopaedia, the Sha'ar ha-shamayim, probably a few years later. It should be noted that at that time the Iṣlāḥ al-majisṭī of Jābir and the Kitāb al-hai'a of al-Biṭrūjī were already available in Hebrew, for both were translated by another Provençal, Moses ibn Tibbon; the second in 1259, the first in 1274. However these dates are all in a cluster; it is possible that Levi and Gershon did not hear of these translations, or that they only heard of them much later, or that their minds were closed. I may still add that the Almagest itself had been translated into Hebrew only c. 1231, by Jacob Anaṭoli.

The Persian revival led by Nāṣir al-dīn al-Ṭūsī caused the publication of at least two important treatises. Nāṣir al-dīn himself wrote one, the Tadhkira fī 'ilm al-hai'a, a very condensed summary which was immensely popular. This was elaborated by his most distinguished pupil, Quṭb al-dīn of Shīrāz. It is strange to find in those two treatises, close to each other, some of the most advanced theories together with the fantastic views of Ibn al-Haitham and Muḥammad al-Kharaqī referred to at the beginning of this section. It is not clear to me whether Alpetragian astronomy had reached the Marāgha astronomers (the chances are it had) but they were not sparing in their criticism of Ptolemy. As in the case of their Spanish brethren, however sharp their criticism, it could not be truly constructive, because they were unable to propose a different theory which was better. Hence as far as theory goes, the Marāgha school had no superiority over the Moorish school of a century earlier.

To pass to Latindom. At the very time when the Moorish astronomers were engaged in trying to improve the Almagest, the Latin world was just beginning to read it! One could not find a better illustration of the out-of-phaseness of the Latin and Arabic scientists. At the very moment when the Muslims were beginning to demolish the Almagest, the Latins were discovering it! In spite of its being a little out of date, that discovery was so important that we may consider it one of the landmarks of European astronomy. It was made twice: the Almagest was translated directly from Greek into Latin, in Sicily, c. 1160; fifteen years later it was translated from Arabic into Latin by Gerard of Cremona in Toledo. As the first translation remained practically unnoticed, it is the second that counts. Thus we may say that the Almagest was introduced in 1175, and like the majority of other Greek classics, it reached us through Arabic channels. By that time Jābir ibn Aflaḥ and al-Biṭrūjī had done what they could to undermine the Almagest; in fact the same Gerard who translated the old classic, also translated its correction (the Iṣlāḥ), but al-Biṭrūjī's treatise was only translated in 1217, by Michael Scot.

Two Latin works of about the fourth decade of the thirteenth century are especially significant. The Astrologia of William the Englishman and the Sphaera mundi of John of Holywood (Sacrobosco). It is remarkable that both authors were Englishmen settled in France: John in Paris and William in Marseilles. Both works were original treatises, which simply means that they were not translations, but independent digests of Arabic materials. The Sphaera was a textbook almost slavishly derived from al-Farghānī and al-Battānī. In spite (or because) of its mediocrity, it was one of the most popular textbooks ever written; witness the number of MSS., printed editions, translations into many languages, elaborations and commentaries. Its popularity did not stop with the Middle Ages, nor even with the Renaissance, and editions of it continued to appear even after Kepler's time! The Astrologia, though if anything a little earlier, was far more scientific; its author was not a textbook writer but a practical astronomer who had made a deep study of al-Zarqālī. He was well acquainted also with the Greco-Arabic knowledge of al-Farghānī; his up-to-dateness is proved by references to al-Biṭrūjī.

The second half of the thirteenth century was a true philosophical renaissance in the Latin West, and naturally every self-respecting philosopher must reach his own conclusions with regard to the arrangement of the world. By this time the views of Jābir ibn Aflāḥ and al-Biṭrūjī were sufficiently known to the Latin writers (as opposed to the Hebrew ones, see above), and the issue which they raised could not be avoided. What was the truth, Ptolemaism or Alpetragianism? As usual the purely scientific question was confused by philosophical prejudices but an additional and more serious difficulty was caused by the wrong theory of the trepidation of the equinoxes which had been integrated into Alpetragianism. The best minds like Grosseteste and Bacon did not commit themselves, and in the end the leading philosophers concluded in favor of the Almagest, but neither blindly nor unreservedly. The Almagest, they realized, was far from perfect, but no better system had yet been devised. Similar conclusions had been arrived at in the East, and moreover Eastern astronomers had seriously considered the question whether the earth was at rest or not, and decided that the first alternative was the true one. Thus Ptolemaism was more secure at the end of the thirteenth century than a century before, but the crisis which it had weathered had not been in vain: it was an indirect preparation for the astronomical revolution of the sixteenth and seventeenth centuries.[8]

11. *Calendar*—The eleventh century approached its end with an astounding achievement: the Ta'rīkh Jalālī of Omar Khayyam (1079) which was probably more accurate than our Gregorian calendar. However this was of greater theoretical than practical importance, for there is no evidence that Omar's calendar was used to any considerable extent. It was probably patronized by the Saljūqian rulers who followed Jalāl al-dīn Malik Shāh but their dynasty did not last very long, the last Great Saljūq dying in 1157.[9] The Ta'rīkh Jalālī remained unsurpassed not only in the East but also in the West. No other Muslim calendar deserves to be mentioned. Of course calendrical tables would generally be appended to other astronomical ephemerides. For example the first book of the Zīj īlkhānī is devoted to chronology; I shall come back to it presently. For other tables, see section 9.

The Sefer ha 'ibbur (1122) of Abraham bar Ḥiyya was the earliest Hebrew treatise dealing exclusively with the calendar, unless the treatise by his contemporary Abraham ibn Ezra antedated it, which is unlikely.

In 1220, Yeh-lü Ch'u ts'ai proposed a reform of the Chinese calendar. Additional reforms were ordered by Kublai Khān, and accomplished by Cha-ma-li-ting in 1267, and by Kuo Shou-ching in 1276.

The emancipation of European countries from Latin tutelage is illustrated by the appearance of calendars written in the vernacular, for example, one in French by Philip of Thaon, c. 1116, and others in Icelandic. There are Icelandic Easter tables going back to the first half of the twelfth century, but the earliest compotus in that language was composed by Bjarni Bergþórsson (d. 1173). Needless to say these French and Icelandic treatises were derived from Latin ones of which there were quite a few, e.g., by Franco of Liége and Gerland of Besançon. A treatise written by Sacrobosco in or before 1244 was translated into Icelandic before the end of the century. The first compotus to appear in print (1483) was the Compotus manualis written in verse by the unknown Magister Anianus.

These elementary works are interesting from the point of view of the historian of civilization and popular education, but they hardly concern the historian of science. The Compotus of Robert Grosseteste (c. 1232) was far more important for it contained an elaborate discussion, which was the main source of ulterior writings on the subject from Roger Bacon to Peter of Ailly. We may say that Grosseteste's Compotus was the first great step toward the Gregorian Reform which was not realized until three and a half centuries later (1582).

The abundant contacts between peoples of different culture, the cosmopolitanism of the universities, the growing needs of travelers and merchants made it necessary to compare various types of calendars. Comparisons between the Jewish, Christian, and Muslim calendars may be found in the Sefer ha-'ibbur of Abraham bar Ḥiyya (1122–1123) and in a special treatise of Aaron ben Meshullam (1206). Grosseteste compares the Christian calendar with the Muslim, and Bacon compares it also with the Jewish.

[8] For a more elaborate discussion of astronomical thought in the second half of the thirteenth century, see p. 756–760.

[9] F. K. Ginzel: Handbuch der mathematischen und technischen Chronologie (vol. 1, 304, 1906).

Similar needs were felt in Persia. The Īlkhānic culture was even more cosmopolitan than that of any European center, for it brought together Muslims, Franks, Jews, Hindus, Mongols, and Chinese. Many different chronologies were involved; for example, the Persian was different from the Muslim. The first book of the Zīj īlkhānī, edited by Nāṣir al-dīn (c. 1272) was devoted to Chinese, Greek, Arabic and Persian chronology. Another Marāgha astronomer, Muḥyī al-dīn al-Maghribī, wrote a treatise explaining the Chinese and Uighūr calendars. Thus little by little did people become aware of their neighbors. The primitive impulse had been to ignore them altogether. Under the combined pressure of commercial, political, and scientific needs, people were gradually learning to do better—but this was only a beginning.

12. *Astrology*—It is impossible not to speak of astrology, not only because of the importance which was attached to it (remember that to understand mediaeval science we must look at it, partly, from a mediaeval point of view), but also because it was inseparable from astronomy. The two domains were interlocked in many ways. For example there were so many astronomical tables because they were needed for astrological purposes. Astronomical observations were carefully made, and instruments created, with the same unscientific end in view. Fortunately the wrong purpose did not invalidate the observations, nor jeopardize the efficiency of the instruments.

Every astronomer was also an astrologer. Every writer on astronomical subjects was bound to publish also some astrological treatises. Hence a complete account of astrology would involve a new review of the same procession. This would be tedious and futile. Instead of which let us select a few examples.

'Adnān al-'Ainzarbī, who hailed from the same town as Dioscorides (in ancient Cilicia, Little Armenia) wrote a treatise on the application of astronomy to medicine. This was typical of many other treatises of the same kind (see section 62). Astronomy, i.e., astrology, was then the nearest equivalent to our premedical sciences of to-day; it was just as necessary for a mediaeval physician to know astrology, as for a modern one to know physics and chemistry. The more astrology he knew, the more scientific he believed himself to be. When such knowledge and assurance were combined with stupidity the result was disastrous, but in many cases the ills of the system were unconsciously compensated by common sense. Astrological treatises were written in Persian and Arabic by the great polygraph Fakhr al-dīn al-Rāzī. The Jewish apostate Samū'il ibn 'Abbās, who was of western origin but moving eastward had finally settled in Marāgha, composed in 1165 a treatise wherein he denounced the errors of astrologers.

These three Muslims belonged to the twelfth century. The main astrologer of the West in the same century was Abraham ibn Ezra. He translated astrological treatises from Arabic into Hebrew, and he wrote in Hebrew new treatises which exerted a deep influence not only upon Jews, but also upon Christians, since they were promptly translated into Latin, French and Catalan.

The Greek world was naturally an easy prey to astrological fancies because of its deep ignorance. Astrological poems by Prodromos, Tzetzes, and Camateros are conspicuous among the few Greek "scientific" writings of the period.

In the first half of the twelfth century the Latin West was deluged with a flood of astrological literature translated from the Arabic. It is clear that this could not be due simply to the whims of translators. The West had finally heard of the treasures hidden in the Arabic writings, and the most precious ones were they not those astrological treatises which would give men the means of acting prudently in health or illness according to their stars? John of Seville was the main artisan in the transmission of that literature; others were Hermann the Dalmatian and Plato of Tivoli. John of Seville did not simply translate Arabic treatises, but compiled himself an astrological summary—naturally derived from Arabic models—the Epitome totius astrologiae (1142). There was of course very little originality in that; the main difference between a translation and an "original" treatise was that the former was based upon a single Arabic text and the latter upon many. There would be no point in trying to draw up a list of the Latin astrological treatises and it would not be at all easy, because the line between astronomy and astrology is so difficult to draw. The titles are very misleading, for the meanings of the words astrologia and astronomia were different from our own and almost interchanged (see my note on p. 760). It will suffice to mention a few treatises: Three composed by Michael Scot after 1228; a medical astrology by William the Englishman about the same time; the Compilatio de astrorum scientia of Leopold of Austria, containing an especially interesting section on (astrological) meteorology; the Liber astronomicus of Guido Bonatti, after 1261, perhaps the most elaborate and uncompromising explanation of the whole subject; the treatises of Henry Bate, c. 1281–1292, representing the Arabico-Hebrew tradition of Abraham ibn Ezra.

Very few people had enough intellectual acuteness to penetrate the fallacies of judicial astrology, and enough courage to denounce them. One of these few was the Italian Dominican John of Vicenza (d. after 1260). He was himself a visionary and unbalanced, but the astrological delusion was so widely spread and so deep that it took an unbalanced man or one so regarded by his neighbors, a man out of joint with his environment, to be aware of it and to think of exposing it. It was certainly no task for a "level-headed" philosopher. John was a freak. The special wisdom of the age was not represented by him, but by his adversary, Guido Bonatti, the most brilliant and successful astrologer and the foremost defender of the universal delusion. Bonatti's fame lasted a long time; an English translation of his Liber astronomicus appeared in London as late as 1676, ten years before Newton's Principia! Hence we must not blame too much his own contemporaries if they were not more critical. Would we have been under the same coalition of circumstances?

PHYSICS

13. *Mechanics*—Nowhere is the growing maturity of the West at the beginning of the thirteenth century more certain than in the field of pure mechanics. I say more certain, not more obvious—for this is not obvious at all, and not one mediaevalist out of a thousand would be able to recognize it by himself. In the course of the century we witness a true mechanical rebirth; under the combined pressure of philosophical and mathematical progress, the Greek tradition of Archimedes, Aristotle and later of Philoponos and Simplicios is taken up again, this time in Latindom. The torchbearers change but it is the same lampadephoria which goes on. The new torchbearers are Jordanus Nemorarius and perhaps one unknown disciple of his, "the forerunner of Leonardo," then Gerard of Brussels, Roger Bacon, Peter Olivi.

Jordanus introduced two important novelties: the notion of "gravitas secundum situm," and the axiom "that which can lift a certain weight up to a certain height, can also lift a weight k times heavier to a height k times smaller." Another treatise ascribed to him seems to be somewhat younger. If Jordanus was not himself the author of it, it was in all probability composed by a disciple who was strangely called (by Duhem) "the forerunner of Leonardo da Vinci." That treatise contains the notion of statical moment and its application to the study of the angular lever and of the inclined plane. We have here some of the fundamental ideas of dynamics and statics. We may even ascribe to the school of Nemorarius a vague recognition of the principle of virtual displacements which was not clearly enunciated until almost five hundred years later.

At an unknown time within this same century an unknown Fleming, Gerard of Brussels, began to wonder at the difficulties and paradoxes which were to be solved later by the distinction between linear and angular velocity and could not be solved otherwise. Of course he did not hit upon that distinction, but he was the first to be unconsciously aware of it.

Peter Olivi, a Franciscan of southern France, was apparently the first after Philoponos to discuss the notion of impetus, which was a crude anticipation of the concept of inertia.

Finally, Roger Bacon, under the combined inspiration of Nemorarius and Grosseteste, gave considerable thought to mechanical problems, e.g., the mathematical expression of force and the nature of action at distance. How are forces, light, astrological influences propagated? Of course he failed to solve these problems—but have we yet succeeded?

Villard de Honnecourt and Peter the Stranger were entertaining the idea of perpetual motion.

Put all this together as the effort of a single century, and the importance of that mechanical revival cannot be denied. During that century, Latin writers accomplished more than all the mechanicians of the past with the exception of Archimedes. This implied a deeper spiritual transformation, a real process of intellectual maturity. Their final coming of age is even clearer if one compares them with their Muslim contemporaries. At the very time when Nemorarius and Bacon were groping for the principles of mechanics, the Muslims were still living on the inferior mechanical knowledge which had been handed down to them from the Hellenistic age. Instead of being concerned with ideas, they had but a childish interest in automata and in mechanical toys and contrivances. Without further theoretical studies, their progress in that direction was naturally very limited. In fact they hardly improved upon the Hellenistic technique.

I must make an exception however in favor of the Persian astronomers who in the second half of the thirteenth century discussed the possibility of the rotation of the earth: 'Alī ibn 'Umar al-Kātibī and Quṭb al-dīn al-Shīrāzī. They both finally rejected that possibility on mechanical grounds: sublunar motions cannot be circular. It is very remarkable that they should have bothered to discuss the question; it implies that some other scientists had accepted the hypothesis of the earth's rotation or had at least entertained it. The rejection of that hypothesis under the influence of a prejudice which was not removed until more than three centuries later, was not discreditable.

14. *Optics and meteorology*—It may seem strange to consider together two subjects, optics and meteorology, which are now widely separated. To be sure modern meteorologists study a number of optical problems; but apart from these their own branch of science is as distinct from optics as, say, from chemistry. In the

thirteenth and following centuries however the distinction was hardly realized: optics, "perspective," meteorology was one vast subject. This was due to an old Greek tradition, that of Aristotle's Meteorologica, which became available to Latin and Hebrew readers (via Arabic channels) before the beginning of the thirteenth century; that book was even translated into French before the middle of the century. Now the miscellaneous contents of mediaeval meteorology were largely identical with those of the Meteorologica.[10]

Mediaeval optics not only in Christendom but also in Islām was still dominated by another great book, the Kitāb al-manāẓir of Ibn al-Haitham, i.e., the Opticae thesaurus of Alhazen. Alhazen was often called "auctor perspectivae," which confirms the interchangeability of the terms optics and perspective. The same confusion was still observable in the notebooks of Leonardo da Vinci and it continued at least until the middle of the seventeenth century. The Kitāb al-manāẓir was translated into Latin by Gerard of Cremona. Strange to say, at about the same time (or a little before) a Greek optical treatise, the one ascribed to Ptolemy, was translated from the Arabic into Latin by Eugene the Amīr. However the Kitāb al-manāẓir included the substance of Ptolemaic optics, plus many innovations, and Eugene's translation was entirely eclipsed by Gerard's.

As the Latin and Muslim opticians (or meteorologists) derived their knowledge from the selfsame book, it is not surprising to find that they had much in common. The first outstanding student of the subject in the West was Robert Grosseteste. Grosseteste was well aware of the magnifying properties of lenses, and he transmitted that information together with considerably more to Bacon. The latter made many optical experiments, had some understanding of spherical aberration and of its correction by means of paraboloidal and hyperboloidal surfaces, and he may have conceived vaguely of the compound microscope and the telescope. According to his wont Bacon did not restrict himself to experiments, but indulged in various speculations and tried vainly to penetrate the nature of light. Three other Latin opticians must still be named: the Pole Witelo, John Peckham, and Theodoric of Freiberg. Witelo's Optics was hardly superior to the Kitāb al-manāẓir, but much attention was paid to it, even as late as the beginning of the seventeenth century and by such a man as Kepler. Peckham's Perspectiva communis was not more original, but it shared the popularity of Witelo's work until the seventeenth century. The Saxon Theodoric of Freiberg is named here because the greatest part of his life was spent in the thirteenth century, but his main optical treatise appeared only in the first decade of the fourteenth.

The Arabic works contemporary with those of Witelo and Peckham though essentially alike were somewhat superior. Nāṣir al-dīn al-Ṭūṣī revised the Arabic text of Euclid's optics, and wrote a few optical tracts including original ideas. The astronomical works of Quṭb al-dīn al-Shīrāzī contain valuable discussions of optical topics, above all, the first satisfactory theory of the rainbow. It is true the same explanation—i.e., essentially the Cartesian one—was also given by Theodoric of Freiberg, but only in or after 1304. We do not know the date of the Nihāyat al-idrāk which contains Quṭb al-dīn's account of the rainbow; hence we cannot guarantee that it is anterior to Theodoric's treatise, but it probably is. Quṭb al-dīn and Theodoric died in the same year 1311, but the former was about fourteen years older, and it is very probable that the Nihāyat appeared within the thirteenth

[10] For an analysis of the latter, see Isis, 6, 138.

century. Quṭb al-dīn's most illustrious disciple was Kamāl al-dīn al-Fārisī, who wrote sometime during the first decade of the fourteenth century an elaborate commentary on Ibn al-Haitham's optics, the Tanqīḥ al-manāẓir wherein Quṭb al-dīn's explanation of the rainbow was repeated. This would confirm our assumption that that explanation must be a little anterior to the fourteenth century, without transforming it into a certitude.

In conclusion there is a very remarkable parallelism between Latin and Arabic optics of this period, the advantage remaining however with the Muslims. Not only were these the initiators, but they were all the time a little ahead of the Christians. For example Quṭb al-dīn was in all probability ahead of Theodoric. It is very strange that these two men should have made the same discovery at almost the same time at such a tremendous distance from one another, but after all they were drawing conclusions from the same premises and the same experimental data. The Arabic tradition of Ibn al-Haitham was gradually improved upon by a series of disciples: Nāṣir al-dīn al-Ṭūsī, Quṭb al-dīn al-Shīrāzī, Kamāl al-dīn al-Fārisī. There was no such gradation in the West, but instead Bacon's prophetic genius.

The earliest spectacles seem to date back to the end of the thirteenth century, but their diffusion and their improvement were equally slow, and it took many centuries before they obtained any practical importance.

15. *Magnetism*—We have seen in volume 1, that the attractive property of the magnet was discovered by the early Greeks (Thales?) and its directive property by the Chinese. The latter failed to apply their discovery to any rational purpose. According to their own testimony, foreigners (probably Muslims) were the first to apply the magnetic needle to navigation. That discovery seems to emerge toward the end of the eleventh century, but it may have been made a few centuries earlier and kept secret for commercial reasons. The earliest references to it are found not in Arabic or Persian texts but in Latin ones, those of Alexander Neckam (before 1217) and James of Vitry (c. 1219), and in the French "Bible" of Guiot of Provins (c. 1205); the earliest reference in a Muslim book, is that made by Muḥammad al-'Awfī in his Persian collection of anecdotes, the Jawāmi' al-ḥikāyāt (c. 1231).

Thus we may assume that by the middle of the thirteenth century the compass was beginning to be fairly well known among Christians and Muslims. Its actual use by sailors was naturally anterior to the literary references but how much anterior it was we cannot know.

In 1269 Peter the Stranger, a French soldier in the army which was then besieging Lucera dei Pagani, wrote a little treatise on the magnet which is one of the foremost monuments of experimental science in the Middle Ages. It contains an account of a whole series of experiments on magnetism. It also includes descriptions of improved types of compasses, which afford an additional proof if such were needed that the compass was then already a familiar instrument. Finally one may find in Peter's Epistola the earliest suggestions relative to terrestrial and cosmic magnetism, but its main value lies in its being a fine and rare exemplar of new scientific method.

Its appearance in 1269 is one of the main landmarks in the history of science, and the fact that it was a Latin and Christian production is a symbol of the intellectual awakening of Western Christendom.

16. *Music*—Of all the branches of knowledge which developed in the West under Muslim influences, music was probably the first, and this is not very surprising considering its nature, for it is preëminently an art and a very popular one. The

art would transmit itself in the simplest manner upon the wings of song, and its theoretical core would be carried with it empirically and more or less subconsciously. A more technical transmission of musical theory would follow by and by. Certain it is that Latin musical theory continued to shape itself throughout the eleventh century, and that its growth was largely stimulated by Muslim examples.[10a]

By the end of the eleventh century the West was already sufficiently aquainted with the mensural music invented by Muslims, to go its own way, but it continued to be submitted to Muslim influences especially in Spain. The Latin translation of an Arabic musical treatise is ascribed to Adelard of Bath, and the Hebrew translation of another to Abraham bar Ḥiyya. A third treatise by Abū-l-Ṣalt is lost in the original Arabic but preserved in Hebrew.

The time was now come for the publication of more original treatises in Latin and they began to appear, e.g., those of Magister Leoninus and of his disciple Perotinus, both organists and precentors at Notre Dame in Paris in the first half of the twelfth century, then a little later the two treatises Ars cantus mensurabilis and Compendium discantus ascribed to the elusive Franco of Cologne (or Paris), wherein mensural music was for the first time fully explained in Latin. The new musical notation aptly called the Franconian notation is not essentially different from our own, but its diffusion, which we shall not attempt to describe, was very slow. The second of these treatises which seems much younger than the first, may bring us already in the thirteenth century. A later treatise, ascribed to John of Garland, deals with ochetus, that is, rhythmic mode. By the way the term ochetus[11] is simply a transformation of the Arabic īqā'āt (plural of īqā', meaning rhythm). Many other musical terms are witnesses of the Arabic origin of European music, e.g., the names of instruments, lute, guitar, rebec, canon, eschaquiel or exaquir, etc.

So much for musical theory. In the meanwhile abundant examples of the sweet art were distributed all over western Europe by troubadours, trouvères and Minnesänger. One of the finest bodies of mediaeval melodies that have come down to us are the Galician songs composed by King Alfonso el Sabio. They bear the marks of Arabic influence but are nevertheless very much of their own kind. European music had proved its vitality even before Alfonso's time, witness many troubadour melodies; and above all—in that remote western island, England—there had blossomed out before 1240 that little masterpiece, the oldest known canon as well as the oldest known 6-part composition, Sumer is icumen in.

The Muslims themselves, East and West, continued to show considerable interest in music. Much importance was attached to it in Muslim education. For example, when the Egyptian Qaiṣar ibn abī-l-Qāsim went to Mūṣul to sit at the feet of Kamāl al-dīn Ibn Yūnus he was given a program of study beginning with music. This Kamāl al-dīn was considered one of the most learned and wisest men of his time, and questions asked by the emperor Frederick II were submitted to him. Another of the emperor's correspondents was the Moor Ibn Sab'īn to whom we owe a discussion of related musical modes.

Musical minded as many of the Muslims were they naturally associated music with religion. This occurred quite spontaneously in many cases, even as it has

[10a] Henry George Farmer: Historical facts for the Arabian musical influence (388 p., London 1930; Isis, 15, 370–372).

[11] Hocket in English. Some would relate it to the French hoquet, hiccough. The real origin of the word is more probably Arabic as indicated in the text.

done all over the earth, music being one of the best means of intensifying man's sensibility and emotion. The darwīsh taking part in a dhikr[12] needed music with the same intensity as the negro at his camp meeting. Theologians soon began to discuss these tendencies as far as they concerned religion and morality. For example, one of the very greatest Muslim philosophers, al-Ghazzālī (their St. Thomas Aquinas, almost two centuries anterior to ours), devoted a whole book of his "Revivification of theology" (Iḥyā 'ulūm al-dīn) to the questions involved. His final conclusion, sensible enough, was that music and the ecstasy induced by it might be good or bad according to the persons concerned. It must be remembered that the average darwīsh was intemperate and likely to carry his ecstasy to unwholesome extremes. Many theologians were less patient than al-Ghazzālī, and some were so puritanical that for them music was nothing but a source of sensual danger to be forbidden. Hence we have a number of Arabic treatises discussing whether it is lawful to listen to music, and if so, which instruments are allowable and which are not, etc. One such treatise was composed in 1221 by Muḥammad al-Shalāḥī of Seville. The same questions were agitated in Christendom but much later, and we hear an echo of them in one of Sir Thomas Browne's sallies "Whosoever is harmonically composed delights in harmony; which makes me much distrust the symmetry of those heads which declaim against all Church-Musick. For my own part not only from my obedience but my particular Genius, I do embrace it: for even that vulgar and Tavern-Musick, which makes one man merry, another mad, strikes in me a deep fit of devotion and a profound contemplation of the First Composer."[13]

Musical treatises were written by the leaders of the Marāgha school: Nāṣir al-dīn al-Ṭūsī and Quṭb al-dīn al-Shīrāzī, but the greatest musical theorist of that time (not simply in Islām but everywhere) was another Persian, Ṣafī al-dīn, one of the founders of the "systematist" scale said to be the most perfect ever devised.

17. *Hydrostatics and hydraulics*—The Muslims were much interested in Archimedean and Hellenistic mechanics. The application of the principle of Archimedes to the measurement of densities made a special appeal to them, partly, I assume, because it afforded a ready means of determining precious stones and metals. This subject was investigated by them at least from the middle of the ninth century on: Sanad ibn 'Alī, al-Rāzī, al-Bīrūnī, Ibn Sīnā, 'Umar al-Khayyāmī, Muẓaffar al-Asfuzārī, Samū'il ibn 'Abbās, each of these paid some attention to it, but the standard work was written by 'Abd al-Raḥmān al-Khāzinī. Indeed the Kitāb mīzān al-ḥikma completed by the latter in 1121 is one of the main physical treatises of the Middle Ages. It contains tables of specific gravities of liquids and solids and various physical facts and theories.

With regard to hydraulics, there is but little to report. We know that before proceeding to Marāgha (c. 1259) the Syrian architect al-'Urḍī did some hydraulic work in Damascus, but its nature is not clear.[14] On the other hand we also know

[12] Dhikr (meaning remembrance) is a ceremony inspired by the Qur'ān (33, 41), consisting essentially in the endless repetition of religious phrases and spiritual songs. The darwīsh (dervish) is the Muslim equivalent of the Christian friar. See articles by D. B. Macdonald in Encyclopaedia of Islām (vol. 1, 949–951, 958, 1912).

[13] Quoted by Duncan B. Macdonald in his Emotional religion in Islām as affected by music and singing. Being a translation of a book of the Iḥyā 'ulūm al-dīn, etc. (Journal Royal Asiatic Society, 195–252, 705–748, 1901; 1–28, 1902; see p. 196).

[14] He leveled the basin for the separation of water by means of an instrument called afaḍain? H. J. Seemann: Die Instrumente der Sternwarte zu Marāgha (112, Erlangen 1928; Isis, **13**, 111).

on archaeological and literary evidence that ingenious water-wheels were used in Syria. Some of them were constructed upon the Orontes by Qaiṣar ibn abī-l-Qāsim (d. 1251). The nawā'īr (pl. of nā'ūrah) or water-wheels of the Orontes in Antioch and even more so those of Ḥamā were famous. The Crusaders saw them and introduced them into Germany. In Abū-l-Fidā's time (he died in 1331) there were 32 nawā'īr in Ḥamā alone.[15] We have no idea how long they had been there. The invention might have been made or remade almost at any time: some kinds of water-wheels were already known to Philon of Byzantium, Lucretius, Strabon, Vitruvius, Pliny, etc. Hence the Muslims cannot be credited with the basic idea, but only with some improvement and with a very remarkable utilization of it.

The year 1269 is an important one in the history of mankind, for it was then that Peter the Stranger wrote his Epistola de magnete and that William of Moerbeke translated directly from the Greek the Archimedean treatise on floating bodies. It is a landmark at once in the history of magnetism and in the history of hydrostatics.

18. *Clocks and automata*—The making of clocks and other automata appealed to the Muslim imagination and to their technical ability, but there is no reason to believe that they went beyond the achievements of Hellenistic mechanicians in any essential point. Nowhere is the limitation of their genius more obvious. This interest began early with them, witness the waterclock presented in 807 by Hārūn al-Rashīd to Charlemagne. A little later, toward the middle of the same century we hear of various contrivances devised by Leon of Thessalonica, but neither the Muslims nor the Byzantines succeeded in inventing anything new and worthwhile. Yet the Muslims went on playing with automata. There are references to them in Firdawsī's Shāhnāma (c. 1010).

There was a famous clock in one of the gates of Damascus, which was called because of it, Bāb sā'a. It was placed there about the middle of the twelfth century and divers mediaeval travelers mentioned it. It was constructed and taken care of by one Muḥammad ibn 'Alī al-Khurasānī, and after Muḥammad's death it was repaired and kept in good order by his son, Riḍwān Ibn al-Sā'ātī. In 1203, the latter wrote a treatise explaining its construction and use.

The most elaborate treatise on mechanical contrivances (chiefly hydraulic ones) was written in 1205 at Āmid, on the upper Tigris, by Ismā'īl ibn al-Razzāz al-Jazarī. It is interesting but not truly important. The first part of that treatise (out of six) deals with various types of clepsydras indicating either equal or temporal hours. More information on Muslim clocks may be found in the Libros del saber translated from Arabic into Spanish by order of Alfonso el Sabio.

19. *Arts and crafts. Engineering. Varia*—The best account of various mechanical arts (e.g., bell-founding) in Latindom is the Diversarum artium schedula of the priest Theophilus which belongs to the very beginning of our period.

A history of mediaeval engineering remains to be written.[16] We know of but a few public works here and there, but there were in all probability many more. In the absence of preliminary studies, we can but select a few examples to illustrate the continuation of engineering. Of course the practical needs of life enforced that

[15] M. Sobernheim: Ḥamā (Encyclopaedia of Islām, vol. 2, 240, 1915).

[16] Some indications will be found in a book which appeared too late to be used by me. Franz M. Feldhaus: Die Technik der Antike und des Mittelalters (442 p., 15 pl., 452 ill., Potsdam 1931). Rich collection of historical facts and iconographic documents, but the twelfth and thirteenth centuries are but poorly represented (Isis, 16).

continuation. For example the growth of cities involved a number of engineering problems which had to be solved in one way or another. Milano was obliged to build the Naviglio grande (1179–1258), and Genoa to construct a gigantic mole to protect her harbor (c. 1276–1283), and an aqueduct to bring water to her growing population (1295). One of the greatest engineering works of the Middle Ages was the construction of the Grand Canal connecting the Mongol capital Khānbaliq with the old Sung capital, Hangchow; a total length of twelve hundred miles. The northern portion of it (some five hundred miles) was built under the rule of Kublai Khān (1260–1294); the southern part from Hangchow to the Yellow River was much older.

The main improvements in the art of war were due to Muslims. We have two Arabic treatises on the subject written by the Syrian al Ḥasan al-Rammāḥ. Other Muslims—Persians—were employed by the Mongols for the construction of ballistic engines.

Some empirical knowledge of surface tension is revealed in the writings of Bhāskara and al-Khāzinī.

The earliest Artesian well on record is the one dug at Lillers (Pas-de-Calais) in 1126, but such wells were certainly older. Al-Bīrūnī, who lived a century earlier, already referred to them and gave a correct explanation of them.

One of the incidental results of the Crusades was the introduction of hot baths (ḥammāmāt) of the Muslim type in western Europe. By the middle of the thirteenth century such baths were already available in the main cities.

Paper money was printed in Chinese and Arabic in 1294 at Tabrīz. The invention of block printing was then already old—the Chinese had completed it in the first half of the eighth century if not earlier still—but this is the earliest record of it in Islām, and though it is much later than the original invention, it is also much anterior to western printing. This is a very good illustration of the slowness of human progress. It is not always slow, but for some mysterious reasons the human mind seems to resist certain innovations as much as possible. Here was a practical invention of a very simple nature; its advantages—economy of labor and standardization—are obvious to us. How is it that it took more than six centuries for so simple and fruitful an idea to travel from China to western Europe? No explanation of that extraordinary delay can be given, except an utter lack of interest in the idea and instinctive resistance to it.

20. *Weights and measures*—There remains to be dealt with a subject which is related to physics at least in theory. The usual way of approaching it would be the archaeological: one would investigate all of the actual weights and measures which have come down to us from mediaeval times. However this would carry us too far beyond the scope of our own investigations, for we are not so much interested in the weights themselves as in the ideas concerning them.

The most curious literary source for this study in our period is a treatise written by the Egyptian 'Abd al-Raḥmān ibn Naṣr probably in Saladin's time. It is a handbook for the muḥtasib, i.e., the police officer in charge of markets. Valuable information is generally found in the treatises on materia medica and the medical encyclopaedias; for example, there are special chapters on weights and measures in the Kitāb al-irshād of Ibn Jamī' and in the Minhāj al-dukkān of al-Kūhīn al-'Aṭṭār, two admirable productions of the Judeo-Egyptian school of medicine.

Information of a different kind and far less valuable may be found in the writings of Joseph ibn 'Aqnīn (Maimonides' favorite disciple) and of the great translator

Moses ibn Tibbon. They both discuss the weights and measures mentioned in the Bible and the Talmud.

CHEMISTRY

21. *Gunpowder and pyrotechnics*—The invention of gunpowder was probably made in Western Europe or in Syria in the second half of the thirteenth century, i.e., toward the very end of this period. The recipe ascribed to Bacon is certainly apocryphal, but there are other reasons for believing that he had perhaps some knowledge of gunpowder and of its explosive properties. The Liber ignium of Marc the Greek, while mainly devoted to other pyrotechnic recipes of all kinds and times, refers to explosive substances, and contains a formula for gunpowder (of course the latter may be an interpolation). Finally one of the military treatises of al-Ḥasan al-Rammāḥ contains pyrotechnic recipes of the same type as those found in the Liber ignium, special attention being paid by him to saltpeter, its preparation and purification.

It is thus very probable that gunpowder was actually made, in divers places, before 1300. However that invention was not by any means as important as is generally thought. It remained of but little value as long as tolerably good firearms were not available. The first firearms appeared in the second quarter of the fourteenth century, but these were very crude. In contradistinction to common belief, the discovery of gunpowder, or even of firearms, was hardly revolutionary. It would have been revolutionary indeed, and highly so, if it had been made all at once, or completed very quickly. In fact it was rather slow, and the development of firearms was protracted for so many centuries, that the impact of the discovery was largely frittered away. A development which is as gradual as that is not a revolution, but simply an evolution.

22. *Distilled waters and alcohol*—The early history of distillation is very obscure, and will probably remain so unless datable Arabic texts are discovered and published which contain new data. On the basis of all the information at present available, the earliest mentions of alcohol—in a revised edition of the Mappae clavicula ascribed to Adelard of Bath and in a treatise of Magister Salernus—date only from the first half or the second third of the twelfth century. Of course other forms of distillation may have been practiced before that of alcohol. It is possible, e.g., that rose-water or other essences were distilled first, and if so, Muslim druggists were probably the initiators. A treatise on distilled waters ascribed to a fifteenth century German writer, Michael Puff, may be possibly traced back to Bartholomew of Salerno, i.e., to the first half of the twelfth century.

Mediaeval physicians were much interested in various kinds of waters credited with medicinal or magical virtues. There are quite a few Latin treatises on the subject which are anonymous or else bear the names of Theodoric Borgognoni, Peter of Spain, Albert the Great, Arnold of Villanova, or Ramon Lull. A comparative study of these texts might produce some interesting results though the chances are that their chemical contents are very meager. An Arabic book on the preparation of perfumes is ascribed to the Syrian historian 'Umar Ibn al 'Adīm.

Medicinal waters call to our mind other drugs. Chemistry has been much indebted for its early growth to the study of materia medica. In our period the main iatrochemical investigators were Hugh and Theodoric Borgognoni of the school of Bologna and the Hindu physician Śārṅgadhara. The date of the latter is uncertain, and his efforts were but the culmination of an immemorial Hindu tradition, the study of rasa (i.e., juices, quintessence, metallic preparations, mercury, etc.).[17]

23. *Chemical arts and crafts*—Another perennial source of chemical knowledge was the practice of the arts. I have already referred to Theophilus for the mechanical arts, but his work is more important from the chemical than from the physical point of view, as were all the collections of artistic recipes. Indeed they are mainly concerned with painting, gilding, limning, dyeing, etc. One interesting feature of Theophilus' Schedula is his description of the preparation and use of oil colors. His technique of oil painting was very imperfect it is true. It is thus not correct to ascribe the discovery of oil-painting to the brothers Van Eyck or to other painters of the Renaissance: what the latter discovered was some improvement—e.g., some better siccative or other ingredient, or a better mixture—in the use of oil, not the use itself.

There are many Latin treatises containing recipes for limners, scribes, painters, dyers, etc., notably one by Peter of Saint Omer. We may still mention a similar text written by one Abraham ben Judah ibn Ḥayyim in Portuguese language and Hebrew script.

The making of porcelain—i.e., of ceramic wares with high-fired feldspathic glazes as opposed to the soft lead silicate glazes—was invented by the Chinese before the middle of the ninth century but strangely enough these beautiful wares remained practically unknown outside of China until the end of the twelfth century. It is possible that the new manufacture remained for a long time but small and local. We know very little of T'ang porcelain but its existence is certain: some fragments of white glazed and celadon ware have been found in the ruins of Sāmarrā on the Tigris.[18] That city was the 'Abbāsid capital from 836 to 889, then abandoned; hence the Sāmarrā fragments are certainly anterior to 889. During the Sung dynasty (960–1279), the fabrication of porcelain increased considerably and we have many and magnificent examples of it, but these examples have been astoundingly slow in reaching the West. How is it that they were not exported along the great silk roads? Besides the specimens which found their way to Mesopotamia in the ninth century, the earliest recorded appearance of porcelain in the Near East was in 1171 (or 1188) when Ṣalāḥ al-dīn sent forty pieces of it as a present to the sulṭān of Damascus. Some knowledge of porcelain may have filtered into Europe after the Crusades, but on the whole our Middle Ages were unacquainted with it.

In the meanwhile the Chinese technique for the manufacture of faïence, i.e., a glazed earthenware rougher than true porcelain, was imported into Japan, in 1228, by Katō Shunkei. The making of porcelain was introduced only some three centuries later.

As opposed to porcelain which cannot be traced back beyond the T'ang dynasty in China, beyond the sixteenth century in Japan, beyond the very end of the seventeenth century in Europe, the making of glass goes back almost to the beginning of historic times in Egypt and Mesopotamia. The art was much cultivated in ancient times, and the Roman glass makers, especially those of Alexandria, were already very proficient. Glass making continued throughout the Middle Ages,

[17] The meaning of rasa is extremely fluid, which makes the discussion of it more difficult. See Sir Monier Monier-Williams: Sanskrit-English dictionary (new edition, 869, 1899).

[18] Friedrich Sarre: Die Kleinfunde von Samarra und ihre Ergebnisse für das islamische Kunstgewerbe des 9. Jahrhunderts (Der Islam, vol. 5, 180–195, 1914). Fragments reproduced on pls. 1–2. Specimens are on view in Metropolitan Museum.

in Christendom and in Islām. A good account of the mediaeval technique was given by Theophilus Presbyter about 1100. In the thirteenth century Venice was the main center of glass manufacture in the world; it kept that supremacy for at least four centuries and the phrase "Venetian glass" which became gradually generic—for Venetian glass was made in many places outside of Venice—has remained a symbol of it.

24. *Alchemy*—In section 21 to 23 we have dealt with some of the main sources of chemical experience: pyrotechnics, materia medica, and the decorative arts; other sources were mining and metallurgy and finally chemistry for its own sake, alchemy, the search for the transmutation of metals and for other operations of practical or philosophical interest. We shall refer to mining in another section (34). We may now turn to the purely alchemical investigations and to the books wherein the inchoate but growing experience of the craftsmen and of the potential chemists was gradually collected, summarized, analyzed, discussed, and systematized. It would be difficult to say whether the empirical sources of knowledge were richer in the East or in the West, but there is no doubt that the more conscious chemical efforts were first made in the Muslim world. This is equally true of the experimental and of the philosophical efforts: the Muslims were the true continuers of the Hellenistic tradition and the initiators of mediaeval alchemy.

We shall thus proceed in the following order: (A) Account of the Arabic alchemical efforts and writings; (B) Their introduction into Latindom; (C) Beginnings of European alchemy. However it is well to keep in mind that these three phases are not consecutive, but more or less simultaneous.

(A) *Arabic alchemy*—Arabic alchemy was built upon Hellenistic and Iranian foundations. Too few of the Arabic texts have been thus far investigated to make it possible to explain its development, but it would seem that the main principles and the main operations were already established long before the twelfth century. Even if the writings ascribed to Jābir are apocryphal, they can be traced back at least to the tenth century. Those bearing al-Rāzī's name have not yet been seriously challenged, and they take us back at least to the beginning of that same century. One of the most influential alchemical books East and West was the Kitāb al-shifā' composed by Ibn Sīnā c. 1022. That encyclopaedia included, among many other things, a sort of commentary on Aristotle's Meteorologica and a continuation of it. Ibn Sīnā's attitude was rather conservative, not to say skeptical. Thus before the twelfth century the Muslims had not only made many experiments and produced several alchemical writings, but they had begun to discuss and to doubt the most advanced alchemical theories. This proves that they had attained a relatively high level of alchemical thinking.

As far as I can make out, the twelfth and thirteenth centuries added nothing essential to their alchemical knowledge, but their work continued in various directions. For example the Persian poet al-Ṭughrā'ī wrote sundry alchemical treatises, one of which, the Ḥaqā'iq al-istishhād, was a refutation of Ibn Sīnā's skepticism. Then we have a number of alchemical poems, such as are collected in the Dīwān of the Moroccan, Ibn Arfa'ra'sahu. The skeptical tendencies reappear in the writings of 'Abd al-Laṭīf and al-Jawbarī. The latter wrote c. 1226 a most interesting book wherein he denounced all kinds of quacks, including "the people of al-kīmīyā' who know three hundred ways of making dupes." This seems to prove that there were then already a number of chemists who used their knowledge and their dexterity to fool their fellowmen. Nothing surprising in this: there have always been and there will always be dishonest and fraudulent people, and chemistry is their best arsenal. The chemical means of cheating people are (and were already then) more numerous and more successful than any other.

The worst thing with regard to alchemy and other secret sciences is that it is not always easy to distinguish between genuine knaves and self-deceived enthusiasts, between evil quacks and innocent ones. And one must bear in mind also that chemical experiments might produce important results irrespective of their purpose. Even as war has been indirectly a source of progress in spite of its utter wrongness, even so treachery and adulteration might lead incidentally to valuable discoveries. Thus the historian of science must be very patient and tolerant and be ready in turn to give men full credit for their intentions, or to disregard the latter altogether.

The main alchemical writer of the period was Abū-l-Qāsim Muḥammad al-'Irāqī who flourished in the second half of the thirteenth century and was at once an experimenter and a theorist. He was a radical alchemist, and his works represent the full development of the Arabic doctrine: later additions to it were of little, if any, intrinsic value; and their extrinsic importance was negligible because they ceased to influence western opinion and hence were not finally included in the main stream of chemical thought. For that matter Abū-l-Qāsim's own work remained practically unknown in the West, except that the bulk of it was simply a restatement of the Greco-Arabic tradition which reached Latin writers through other channels.

(B) *Introduction of Arabic alchemy into Latindom*—The two Latin treatises, bearing Artephius' name, are probably translated from the Arabic, but we cannot yet date them with any accuracy nor are the Arabic original texts identified. The earliest dated Latin translation is the Liber de compositione alchemiae completed by Robert of Chester in 1144. The famous Emerald Table was translated at about the same time by Hugh of Santalla, and a little later a version of al-Rāzī's treatise on alums (or vitriols) and salts was prepared by Gerard of Cremona. The Emerald Table was almost as worthless to the chemist as it was popular, but al-Rāzī's treatise was a very valuable contribution in the right direction; indeed it was a treatise on practical chemistry based on genuine experiments and describing the methods of preparation of many substances. The importance of al-Rāzī's treatise and of its impact upon Latin culture, e.g., through Vincent of Beauvais and Bacon, can hardly be exaggerated.

The next translation was that of the alchemical part of the Kitāb al-shifā' of Ibn Sīnā by Alfred of Sareshel about the turn of the twelfth century. That treatise exerted a deep and beneficial influence upon Latin writers. It helped to sustain their critical spirit in the face of chemical conceit or imposture.

Some of the treatises ascribed to other Latin writers were possibly translations, or hardly more original: the line between original works and others is sometimes very difficult to draw. We shall come back to these treatises presently.

At any rate we may take the date 1144 as the date of introduction of Arabic alchemy into western Europe. More Arabic treatises were translated or interpreted during the twelfth and thirteenth centuries, but on the whole the introduction of Arabic alchemy was rather slow, in great contrast with the introduction of Arabic astrology.

(C) *Beginnings of European alchemy*—Of course that same year 1144 might be called the birthyear of European alchemy, but would that not be attaching too much importance to a translation?

With the second half of the twelfth century more original treatises began to appear: the De rebus metallicis of Roger of Hereford; a little later Alfred of Sareshel's commentary on Aristotle's Meteorologica; in the first half of the thirteenth century two treatises credited to Michael Scot, and the Correctorium alchymiae ascribed to Richard of Wendover. The part played by Englishmen in the early history of Latin alchemy is remarkable: Robert of Chester, Roger of Hereford, Alfred of Sareshel, Michael Scot, Richard of Wendover—but we must not forget that one of the most valuable contributions was made by an Italian, Gerard of Cremona.

The attitude of the Latin encyclopaedists of the second half of the thirteenth century was hesitant and their hesitations were natural enough. The Arabic influences which had reached them were rather discordant: there was on one side the mystical and occult tendencies of Artephius and of the Emerald Table; on the other side, the philosophical spirit of the Kitāb al-shifā' of Ibn Sīnā; in between, pointing to the right direction, the more practical recipes of al-Rāzī. Unfortunately the full value of the latter could only be appreciated by those who were prepared to follow humbly in al-Rāzī's footsteps, and ready to make dirty and disgusting experiments. With but too few exceptions the Latin schoolmen were still more eager to discuss these matters in the abstract than to test the validity of the facts in the only possible way. That way—the experimental way—had hardly dawned upon them. Thus they hesitated and made subtle distinctions: e.g., transmutation was possible but transmuted gold was not quite the same as real gold! Or else, like Bacon, they divided alchemy into a practical kind, which might come very near to chemistry as we understand it, and a theoretical kind, for which the sky was the limit. Or else they spoke of good and bad alchemy. Among the very few who made concrete observations and experiments were Bacon and probably also Albert the Great. Their point of view was moderate: they felt that there was truth in alchemy but were not prepared to say how much.

The best Latin alchemical treatises of the period were those ascribed to Geber, especially the Summa perfectionis. This was an elaborate work, at once theoretical and practical, essentially derived from Arabic sources. The exact nature of the derivation is not yet determined. The Summa perfectionis probably dates from the end of the thirteenth century: it represents, so to say, the upper limit of alchemical knowledge at that time in Latindom. We may also consider it as the first monument of Latin chemistry. It is not a great achievement in point of originality, but it may be chosen to symbolize the beginning of a chemical awakening in the West.

GEOGRAPHY

25. *Pilgrims*—The primary kind of geographical knowledge is the one which any intelligent person could obtain by traveling. The opportunities for travel increased considerably during the twelfth and thirteenth centuries. Perhaps the foremost incentive to it was religious. The leading religions, Judaism, Buddhism, Christianity, Islām had this in common, that while they were universal in their scope, some places of the earth were especially sacred to them. It was one of the ambitions of the faithful to visit these places and thus to acquire forgiveness or merit.

There were many centers of pilgrimage in Christendom, above all to be sure

Jerusalem and Bethlehem, but only a few people could undertake the long journeys involved to reach the Holy Land. Most of the other centers were only of local or regional importance, but a few attracted pilgrims from many and distant countries. Such were, for example, Santiago de Compostela (especially dear to Englishmen), St. Martin of Tours, Our Lady of Chartres, Our Lady of Le Puy-en-Velay (Podium Sanctae Mariae), St. Thomas of Canterbury (after the murder of Thomas à Becket in 1170, and even more after the translation of his body in 1220), Aachen, Einsiedeln, and Assisi.[19] We must not forget Rome, which was second in importance only to the Holy Land, even before the organization of the Jubilee Year in 1300. The popularity of some international pilgrimages is proved by the early creation of hospices for the reception of the wayfarers in the Alpine and Pyrenaean Passes.[20] In the thirteenth century such hospices were already available in the Pyrenees at Roncesvalles, also in the Alps, at the Great St. Bernard, the Simplon, and the Septimer Passes (the last named goes back to the Carolingian age). The earliest of the orders of knighthood, the Order of St. John of Jerusalem (Hospitalers) had been founded as early as 1099 for the care and protection of pilgrims.

Christians were not normally obliged to go on pilgrimages, but they had many inducements to do so, either to obtain indulgences, of which one could never have too many for oneself or for others, or to atone for sins or crimes. Expiatory pilgrimages were often included in the sentences of ecclesiastical and civil courts. That custom was so well established that there were in many cities graduated lists of pilgrimages for various infractions, and that it was possible to redeem oneself from making any pilgrimage with a definite sum of money or the hiring of a substitute.[21] It is also very likely that many men set out on distant pilgrimages not so much for religious motives, as to gratify their own adventurous spirit, their Wanderlust, or to escape momentarily from their family, or from any kind of relationship which had become irksome. We are not concerned here with the motives of the pilgrims, but with the fact that so many of them were following the main roads of Europe in almost every direction: these pilgrims were not carrying only their staff and their gourd but many other things as well, material and immaterial. They could not be traveling so long, without learning and remembering something, and acquiring a different notion of the world. Like the insects or birds who are the unwitting carriers of pollen or seed, these pilgrims helped to convey all kinds of habits and ideas from one end of Europe to the other.

Unfortunately the pilgrim in search of miracles was by definition very gullible, and more apt to transmit extraordinary tales than plain facts. Hence the pilgrim literature has but very little scientific value; yet its mass is impressive, and an analysis of it gives us some precious information on the manner and culture of their age, the relationships between different groups and classes of people, etc. Most of the western itineraries to the Holy Land were written in Latin. The earliest one posterior to the First Crusade was written by an Englishman, Saewulf, c. 1103;

[19] An idea of the abundance of pilgrimages may be obtained in Louis de Sivry and J. B. J. Champagnac: Dictionnaire des pèlerinages anciens et modernes et des lieux de dévotion les plus célèbres de l'univers (2 vols., 2656 cols., Migne, Paris 1859).

[20] J. E. Tyler: The Alpine Passes in the Middle Ages, 962–1250 (190 p., Oxford 1930). A conscientious investigation which reached me too late for use in the present volume (Isis, 16).

[21] Etienne Van Cauwenbergh: Les pèlerinages expiatoires et judiciaires dans le droit communal de la Belgique au moyen âge (252 p., Louvain 1922). Excellent study but it deals mainly with the fourteenth and fifteenth centuries (Isis, 15, 448).

the second Latin one by the Italian, Belardo d'Ascoli, some ten years later. Two vernacular accounts belong to about the same time: the Russian one of Daniel of Kiev, c. 1106, and the Icelandic saga narrating the exploits of Sigurd of Norway who made an astounding journey to Palestine and back in 1107–1111. Later in the twelfth century we have the narratives of John of Würzburg, Theodoric of Hirschau, Burchard of Strassburg, Fetellus, Wolfger of Ellenbrechtskirchen, the gesta of Richard Lionheart, all of these in Latin; the accounts of John Phocas in Greek, of Nikulás Saemundarson in Icelandic, of Anthony of Novgorod in Russian.

The procession continues throughout the thirteenth century, the leading pilgrims being Wilbrand of Oldenburg and Burchard of Mount Sion. The latter's Descriptio Terrae Sanctae was one of the best works of its kind and exceedingly popular. There was also a narrative of St. Sabbas' pilgrimage in Slavonic, and of that of Ogmund of Spånheim in Icelandic. Most accounts were still written in Latin, but we have quite a few in French, the other languages being represented only by rare examples as indicated above.

To complete the picture of Christian travel (besides the great Asiatic and Atlantic adventures to be dealt with in section 26), we may recall that many religious orders had a central organization which required frequent intercourse between the mother community and her daughters, also that abbots and high ecclesiastics were often requested or inclined to present themselves ad limina apostolorum.

So much for Christendom. There were also Jewish pilgrims to the Holy Land but they were fewer and less heard of. Except Benjamin of Tudela, Petaḥiah of Ratisbon, Judah al-Ḥarizi, and Moses ben Naḥman, who were not pilgrims in the narrow sense, I can only name Samuel ben Samson and Jacob of Paris.

Passing to Islām the situation was very different. To begin with, for a Muslim the Pilgrimage to Mecca was not a matter of choice; it was his positive duty within the limits of possibility to undertake it. Mecca was the constant magnet of his thoughts for his every prayer was said in its direction, and the dream of going there was always with him. Thus there ran into Arabia a constant stream of visitors hailing from every part of the Dār al-islām. Some of them came all the way from Central Asia or beyond, others hailed from the western end of the world. All of them had many opportunities of meeting one another and countless other people in the sacred places or in other Muslim cities, or along the innumerable roads leading to their heart's desire. Needless to say the remarks made above about Christian pilgrims might be applied to the Muslim ones. Few pilgrims were so single minded that they thought only of their main purpose. The Pilgrimage was the accomplishment of a religious duty, but it was also a unique vacation, an initiation into the great world of Islām, and for scholars, the exact equivalent of our journeys for study abroad. The years spent on the way to and from Mecca were the "Wanderjahre" of Muslim students, young and old.

The Arabic narratives of Muslim pilgrims are far superior to the Christian ones and their scientific value is greater. For example, the Latin relations are truly childish as compared with the one wherein Ibn Jubair of Valencia described his first journey to the Near East in 1183–1185. We have also for the same period an elaborate guide book by the Persian 'Alī al-Harawī; then about a century later, the itineraries of another Valencian, Muḥammad al-'Abdarī and of the Moroccan, Muḥammad ibn Rushaid. These Muslim travelers were many-sided men who took pains to obtain information of various kinds and to meet famous scholars.

26. *Travelers*—Having disposed of the relatively large body of pilgrims, let us now consider the other travelers. To be sure the line between the two groups is not always easy to draw. Most travelers to the East visited the holy places on their way beyond. Should we count them as pilgrims or not? In most cases I have not counted them because their pilgrimages were incidental, but the reader is welcome to do otherwise if he pleases.

At any rate we can easily spare them for there was during those two centuries an abundance of travelers. This was truly a golden age in the history of exploration, and though men of many types distinguished themselves—Jews, Muslims, Chinese, Christians—the latter were easily the leaders.

Strangely enough, however, in the first half of that period—i.e., in the twelfth century—there were only two travelers of exceptional importance, not counting the pilgrims, and these two were Jews: Benjamin of Tudela and Petaḥiah of Ratisbon. This is the more remarkable because the number of distinguished Jewish travelers is rather small in spite of the Diaspora. Benjamin and Petaḥiah traveled extensively across Europe and in the Near East; both went beyond the Euphrates and wrote in Hebrew very valuable accounts of their experiences.

In the first quarter of the thirteenth century the main travelers were Scandinavians and Chinese. We shall come back to the latter presently. There were two outstanding Scandinavians: Rafn Sveinbjörnsson who was born in Iceland, traveled in western Europe as far south as Spain and then returned to his country, and Ogmund of Spånheim, who was the leader of an expedition to the White Sea, then crossed the whole of Russia to reach the Holy Land and finally returned to Norway. Ogmund is the representative of a number of other Scandinavian sailors, known or unknown, who explored the northern seas.

While these bold Norsemen affronted the peculiar dangers of their own climate, the southern navigators were more and more fascinated by the mysteries of the western Ocean. What would happen if one tried to navigate westward? Would one fall off the earth? Or if one followed the African coast southward, would it end anywhere and allow one to turn eastward? If we may trust Arabic traditions, such questions had already caused Muslim sailors to make adventurous journeys in the Atlantic. We are on somewhat safer ground with regard to the Genoese expeditions of the last quarter of the thirteenth century: Lanzarote Malocello discovered the northern Canaries, and tried to colonize them; the brothers Vivaldi set out on a navigation along the western coast of Africa, reached Cape Nun and then disappeared. Another aspect of African exploration is revealed incidentally in Ramon Lull's religious romance, Blanquerna, since he refers in it to the earliest European journey to the Sūdān.

We now come to some of the greatest achievements of the thirteenth century: the immense journeys across Asia. Any single journey of that size would have been remarkable enough; it would still be so to-day; but the astounding fact is that there were so many.

As far as western travelers are concerned the explanation is that Asia had fired their imaginations. (By Asia is meant not the Near East which was in many respects nearer to Europe, and an intrinsic part of the old Mediterranean world, but Central Asia, India, and the Far East; we might call it Buddhist Asia, for it was largely Buddhist or had been so.) The lure of Asia had grown considerably since the second half of the twelfth century under the influence of the wonderful stories relative to Prester John. At the beginning of the following century the organization of the Franciscan and Dominican orders caused a powerful revival of missionary zeal, and could a more attractive field ever have been found for it than the mysterious lands of the rising sun? Then again, the Crusades had been rather disappointing, the hated Saracens had proved to be much more powerful than was at first suspected, but perhaps it would be possible to defeat them with the help of Prester John or of other eastern allies: the Saracens would be caught between two fires? These circumstances and various others such as commercial enterprise and the love of adventure, upon which it is unnecessary to descant, created a strong eastward pressure.

The details of those great adventures are told in volume 2. It will almost suffice to call the roll of the main heroes: Giovanni Pian del Càrpine, who reached the Mongolian capital Qaraqorum, south of Lake Baikal; Ascelin the Lombard, who did not go beyond Armenia; Andrew of Longjumeau, who visited Kuyuk's Horde on the Imil; William of Rubruquis, who renewed Giovanni's performance and wrote a more elaborate account of it; Buscarello de' Ghizolfi, who became the Īl-khān's own ambassador to European courts; Geoffrey de Langele, English envoy to Persia; John of Montecorvino, founder of the first Catholic missions in India and China; Ricoldo di Monte Croce, who was long established in Baghdād; finally the Venetian brothers Niccolò and Maffeo Polo, and Niccolò's son, Marco—no need to say who they were and what they did, for they belong to that very small group of mediaeval personalities which are still alive to-day.

Note that of these eleven men, no less than eight, including all the greatest but one, were Italian. The single protagonist who was not Italian, was the Fleming William of Rubruquis. Note also that out of eleven, three were Dominicans, and three others Franciscans, that is, more than half were monks. This should not conceal the fact, that with two exceptions (Montecorvino and Monte Croce) the motives of these Asiatic journeys were primarily diplomatic and commercial, the religious motive being secondary. On the other hand the monks whom I have mentioned represent not only themselves but many others who were nothing but missionaries and evangelists and who sacrificed everything to their faith. Some of them suffered martyrdom for its sake.

The Latin Christians were the main explorers of Asia but not by any means the only ones. To give a tolerably complete outline of Asiatic travel in those days, to these eleven Latin names should be added at least eleven others: two Armenians, one Muslim, and eight Chinese, making a grand total of twenty-two illustrious Asiatic travelers—certainly a fine record for a single century.

The Armenians were King Hayton the Elder and his brother Sempad. Both traveled all the way from Cilicia to Mongolia and back. The Muslim al-Juwainī traveled twice to Mongolia and back but he did not have to go so far as did the Armenians for his own home was in Persia; later he became secretary to the Īl-Khān, Hūlāgū.

Finally, consider the splendid Chinese group: Yeh-lü Ch'u-ts'ai accompanied Chingiz Khān all the way to Persia; that expedition took place in 1219; soon afterwards Wu-ku-sun Chung-tuan was sent on an embassy to the north, meaning to the Mongol Court, but as Chingiz was still in Persia, the Chinese ambassador had to follow him there; thirdly Chingiz sent Ch'iu Ch'ang-ch'un to Persia and the Indian frontier and we have an elaborate report of the latter's journey. So much for the Chingiz period, that is, for the first quarter of the thirteenth century. In the third quarter, there were two distinguished travelers: Ch'ang Tê, who went from Qaraqorum to Baghdād, and Yeh-lü Hsi-liang who visited Central Asia. Toward the end of the century Chou Ta-kuan was sent on a mission to Cambodia, and he wrote an exceedingly valuable memoir on Cambodian customs; his description of Angkor Vat was the first and also the last until very recent times. The greatest of these Chinese travelers was the Nestorian Bar Sauma who was the first identified member of his race to reach western Europe (1287). Another Chinese Nestorian, Marcos Bainiel, had accompanied Bar Sauma as far as Baghdād and became eventually the patriarch of his people. Bar Sauma followed almost the same road as Marco Polo in the opposite direction. He returned the compliment of the European travelers who had been irresistibly attracted by his own country, mysterious Cathay.

Two more travelers should still be named, both Muslims and both of Spanish origin: Abū-l-'Abbās al-Nabātī of Seville and his pupil Ibn al-Baiṭār of Malaga. Both were physicians and botanists, and during the course of their journeys they devoted much attention to herbs and other plants. As compared with the immense trans-Asiatic journeys, their own were almost insignificant, though it was not by any means a small thing to cross the whole of North Africa as they did. However these journeys are extremely important because of their scientific purpose. In this respect Islām was again showing the way to the rest of the world. Abū-l-'Abbās and Ibn al-Baiṭār may be quoted as pioneers in a glorious line of botanical explorers.

It is impossible for us to deal with the economic development of Europe in the twelfth and the thirteenth centuries, nor is it necessary for this has been well done in a number of books which are easily available,[22] but we may recall that travel and commerce walked hand in hand. The greatest of the many great travelers mentioned above, the Poli, were primarily merchants. The eastward pressure across Asia, and also the southward pressure along the western coast of Africa, were largely commercial. Each geographical discovery created new commercial opportunities, and in its turn the commercial expansion and the trade rivalries which were implied created the need of new outlets; i.e., of new geographical discoveries. By the middle of the thirteenth century international commerce had already developed to such an extent that various means had been invented to organize business methods, credit facilities, insurance, and protection. The outstanding trade organization of the Middle Ages was the Hanseatic League, an association of German towns and merchants; it was not fully established until 1360, yet its earlier history can be traced back for more than a century. In the meanwhile the Mediterranean trade had been almost monopolized by Genoese and Venetian merchants, whose activity had been "boomed" by the Crusades.[23] As we have already said, Genoa had sent some of her bravest men to the Atlantic; the glory of Venice had been carried by some of her sons as far as the Pacific Ocean.

27. *Regional descriptions. Topography*—Another form of geographical work was the description of specific regions. This was done more or less elaborately, more or less scientifically, by a number of men for divers parts of the world.

A good example of such description had been given by Adam of Bremen (c. 1072) n the fourth part of his history of the church of Hamburg. Adam's account of the

[22] E.g., James Westfall Thompson: An economic and social history of the Middle Ages (New York 1928).

[23] G. I. Bratianu: Recherches sur le commerce génois dans la Mer Noire au XIIIe siècle (367 p., Paris 1929). Eugene H. Byrne: Genoese shipping in the twelfth and thirteenth centuries (169 p., Cambridge, Mass., 1930; Isis, 15, 445).

northern countries was completed in the thirteenth century by the Danish historian Saxo Grammaticus and in the Konungs skuggsjá, an encyclopaedic dialogue written in old Norwegian. These works are among the most original in the geographical literature of that period. The unknown author of the Konungs skuggsjá was especially well informed as to natural phenomena, and his scientific knowledge was remarkably sound.

Godfrey of Viterbo wrote a poem dealing with the Holy Roman Empire, Gerald the Welshman composed excellent descriptions of Ireland and Wales, and Gervase of Canterbury described England, Wales, and a part of Scotland under the strange title Mappa mundi.

Needless to say many of the publications referred to in the section on Pilgrims contain descriptions of the Holy Land. The best of these descriptions are probably those included in the Historia rerum in partibus transmarinis gestarum of William of Tyre, in Ernoul's French continuation to it, and in another French text, L'estat de la citez de Jherusalem, of unknown authorship.

Three Muslim accounts stand out: the earliest, by Ibn al-Balkhī, is a description of the province of Fārs (s. w. part of modern Persia) in Persian (c. 1110); the two others are in Arabic and deal with Egypt. The physician Ibn Jamī' described Alexandria and discussed its climate. 'Abd al-Laṭīf's description of Egypt is one of the most important topographical works of the Middle Ages.

A geography ascribed to Vardan the Great and probably composed by one of his disciples is our most valuable source for the study of Armenian topography.

In the case of topography as well as in that of exploration, the only people to compare with the Europeans in this period were the Chinese. We have descriptions of Korea by Hsü Ching; of the Su-chou region in Chiang-nan by Fan Ch'êng-ta (this being one of the earliest prefecture gazetteers); of Southern China by the same Fan Ch'êng-ta and by Wang Hsiang-chih; of Cambodia by Chou Ta-kuan. Wang's account of Southern China was especially remarkable, because of the many notes devoted to natural and historical curiosities. He has been called the Sung Pausanias.

28. *Maps and portolani*—The main cartographical achievement of the Middle Ages was the creation of portolani or sailing charts. However, in spite of the fact that there is a fragment of the text of a portolano in Adam of Bremen (d. c. 1076), one may say that these charts were not fully developed until the very end of the thirteenth century. Yet they belong to our period which might be appropriately called the period of gestation of the portolani. Their origin is very mysterious. Instead of postulating a single one, as most students of the subject have done, would it not be more natural to assume that they appeared independently in various places as soon as the need of them was felt strongly enough? The Arabic pilots guiding ships across the Indian Ocean and the East Indies must have felt that need quite as strongly as the Genoese ones sailing across the Mediterranean and the Black Sea. These men had no personal contacts, but must not the same simple needs acting upon brains of the same essential nature, produce similar results? We are aware of the existence of portolani East and West because of literary references to them. Moreover the reality of Arabic ones is rendered very probable because we know that there were already in the first half of the twelfth century (if not before) professional pilots (mu'allim, or musta'mil markab) and writers of nautical instructions, like the three "Lions of the sea," Sahl ibn Abān, Muḥammad ibn Shādhān, Laith ibn Kahlān. In the same way the chronicle of England of Roger of

Howden implies the existence of some kind of manuals of navigation relative to the Mediterranean coasts before the thirteenth century. We do not yet know any Arabic portolano anterior to the fourteenth century and the earliest Mediterranean one, the undated Carte pisane, dates only from the end of the thirteenth century, but this lack of documents is not at all surprising. Such maps were likely to be worn out or lost by the men using them, and furthermore we may assume that those anterior to the fourteenth century were never numerous. What we might call the industrial production of portolani, that is, the production of them in multiple copies, did not begin before the fourteenth century.

The value of portolani lies in the fact that they were derived from experience. That experience was crude enough, but the crudity of the data was somewhat compensated by their abundance, and the crudest experimentation is better than the deliberate neglect of it. Unfortunately the portolani were meant only for seafaring men; they did not bother about the inlands, and thus were of little interest to the great majority of the people, even of the learned ones.

What kind of maps did the latter use? Nowhere is the weakness of scholasticism more apparent than here, for schoolmen were apparently satisfied with mappae mundi which were not only schematic to the point of absurdity but also essentially wrong. It would not have been very difficult for them to verify the wrongness of these maps in particular instances, but they were not interested enough to try; above all they did not want to verify concrete instances (which is the only means of establishing the premises of a scientific argument), they preferred to dwell in the empyrean of abstract thought. Philosophy divorced from reality was bad enough; abstract geography was the limit. Needless to say such mappae mundi were necessarily unprogressive. This can be easily proved by examining the abundant specimens which have come down to us: about six hundred ranging in date from the eighth to the fifteenth century.[24] For our period we have a fine series of them associated with the names of Pedro Alfonso, Henry of Mayence, "Jerome," Lambert of Saint Omer, Matthew Paris, etc. We have also the famous Hereford and Ebstorf maps, both of the last quarter of the thirteenth century.

There was still another cartographic tradition, different at once from the portolani and from the mappae mundi, a sort of remnant of the Ptolemaic and Roman traditions, a compromise between experience and abstraction. This was represented by some of the English maps of Matthew Paris, by itineraries and other sketches which did or might accompany the guide books for pilgrims and the topographical studies, and probably also by the maps (now lost) which Roger Bacon sent to the Pope. That tradition however is very weak; it did not attain any importance in the West until the last quarter of the fifteenth century.

The outstanding example of Arabic cartography[25] was the work of the Sicilian, al-Idrīsī (d. 1166). This was entirely different from the Christian traditions, except for some common elements derived from the Ptolemaic school. Arabic cartography was also represented by the Syriac map of Abū-l-Faraj and by the Arabic or Persian ones of the Marāgha astronomers.

[24] These 600 examples (considerably more than were suspected to exist) have been collected by Michael C. Andrews: The study and classification of mediaeval mappae mundi (Archaeologia, vol. 75, 61–76, 2 pls., 1925; Isis, 14, 515). Unfortunately I heard of Andrew's memoir too late to make full use of it in my own investigations.

[25] For Arabic or Muslim cartography in general, see Konrad Miller: Mappae arabicae (Stuttgart, 1926, et sqq.) or my review of it (Isis, 9, 458–462). However this only scratches the surface; deeper investigations are badly needed.

The two oldest Chinese maps which have come down to us were engraved on both sides of a stone slab in 1137, but Chinese cartography can be traced to much earlier times, and the exemplar of one of the maps engraved in 1137 was almost a century older. It is a map of China and of a part of Korea; another map of China was compiled toward the end of the twelfth century and engraved in 1247.

To sum up, there were at least five cartographic traditions in the twelfth and thirteenth centuries: (1) the portolani (at least two independent lines, and probably more); (2) mappae mundi; (3) topographical maps of parts of Europe; itineraries to Jerusalem, etc.; (4) Arabic and Syriac maps; (5) Chinese maps.

29. *Dictionaries*—The compilation of geographical dictionaries was a purely Arabic or Muslim tradition at least in our period. This is natural enough, for the Arabic speaking people had always been deeply interested at once in geography and in lexicography. Two of the most important scientific works of the Middle Ages were the fruits of that special tradition, but before dealing with them, we may just mention an earlier work of the same kind, the Kitāb al-amkina wal-jibāl wal-miyā of the great Persian scholar, al-Zamakhsharī (d. 1144).

The two greater works were both composed in Arabic in the thirteenth century, the earlier one by Yāqūt, the later one by al-Qazwīnī. Yāqūt's Mu'jam al-buldān (1228) is an immense compilation of geographical facts listed in alphabetical order. It deals with geography in the broadest manner—astronomical, physical, historical, archaeological, human. Al-Qazwīnī's 'Ajā'ib al-buldān (1262) is smaller, and instead of being arranged in a single alphabetical sequence, it is divided into seven, one for each climate. It exerted a deep influence not only upon the people reading Arabic but also upon those reading Persian and Turkish.

30. *Scientific geography. General treatises*—We finally come to the climax of all geographical labor: the formulation of geographical theories and the compilation of treatises wherein an attempt was made to set forth the known facts and theories. These treatises were not necessarily on a very high intellectual level; then even as now, all kinds of treatises were written, and the really good ones, up to date and high minded, were rather scarce. Whatever their scientific value, these treatises are interesting documents. Together with the discoveries proper, which are far more individual and may even be accidental, they enable us to appreciate the scientific level of various countries.

The superiority of Islām over Christendom continued throughout the two centuries, and it was only toward the very end that Christian efforts contained the promise of greater achievements in the future.

As the Muslims were and remained in the vanguard, let us begin with them. The Spaniard Muḥammad ibn 'Alī al-Zuhrī wrote a general treatise sometime after 1140. A Moroccan, al-Idrīsī, who was established at the Norman court of Sicily, composed for Roger II the most elaborate description of the world of mediaeval times. Thanks to the fact that the author was patronized by a Christian king he did not confine himself like other Arabic geographers to the Dār al-Islām, but dealt as well with many Christian countries. Between 1154 and 1166 al-Idrīsī compiled another geographical encyclopaedia, even larger than the former, for William I, but that second one is lost. Other treatises were composed at about the same time by al-Māzinī of Granada, who had traveled extensively not only in the Near East and as far East as Khurāsān but also in the Volga region, and by Muḥammad ibn Maḥmūd al-Ṭūsī. The latter's work, a cosmography, was written in Persian.

The most important contribution to mathematical geography—not only in

Islām but anywhere—was the Jāmi' al-mabādi' wal-ghāyāt (1229) of al-Ḥasan al-Marrākushī. It has already been mentioned with the astronomical works, but its geographical importance was not inferior to its astronomical one. It includes among other things the coördinates of 135 places, the observation having been made by himself in 34 of them. No mediaeval writer has taken equal pains to explain scientific methods and instruments.

In the second half of the thirteenth century the geographical work was mainly done in the East. Ibn Sa'īd al-Maghribī wrote a very valuable treatise derived from al-Idrīsī but with many important additions, e.g., a list of coördinates (had he been guided in this by al-Ḥasan al-Marrākushī?). Ibn Sa'īd's work was much used by Abu-l-Fidā' in the following century. When Hūlāgū was in Armenia Ibn Sa'īd was his guest. This is a connecting link between the latter and the Marāgha institute which was patronized by the same Hūlāgū. The Marāgha astronomers were necessarily interested in geography, and not only in the mathematical part of it. The third chapter of the Tadhkira of Nāṣir al-dīn al-Ṭūsī deals with geodesy and ends with a description of the seas, sea-winds, etc. Nāṣir al-dīn also compiled lists of geographical coördinates. The Nihāyat al-idrāk of Quṭb al-dīn al-Shīrāzī, being an elaboration of the Tadhkira, is naturally largely devoted to the same questions, astronomical and geographical. Abundant geographical information will also be found in the cosmography of al-Qazwīnī (different from his dictionary) and in the smaller one of al-Waṭwāṭ.

It is interesting to note that this immense amount of geographical thought and work was almost equally shared between Easterners and Westerners. Up to the middle of the thirteenth century the main work was done in the West, later in the East. Of the six leading geographers, three were Moors: al-Idrīsī, al-Māzinī, and al-Ḥasan al-Marrākushī; three were Persians: Nāṣir al-dīn al-Ṭūsī, Quṭb al-dīn al-Shīrāzī, and al-Qazwīnī. It is true al-Māzinī was half an Easterner himself, for he migrated eastward in middle life and spent the rest of his life in the East (he died in Damascus). The same thing happened to Ibn Sa'īd al-Maghribī as we might guess from his name, for a man was not called al-Maghribī in the Maghrib anymore than an Englishman was called "the Englishman" in England. This constant drainage of genius from the West of Islām into the East was partly caused by the Pilgrimage. Of the Western scholars who accomplished it, and most of them did, many succumbed to the physical and spiritual attractions of the East. Moreover in the thirteenth century Moorish Spain was gradually reduced to the little kingdom of Granada, and it is understandable that the Moors who remembered the glories of the Omayyads of Cordova, of the Almoravides, and of the Almohades preferred to find themselves in countries where Islām was still supreme. A good Muslim of Spain could breathe more easily in Syria or in Egypt than in the dwindling kingdom of his fathers. To be sure he could also cross the straits to Africa, but the combined attractions of the East were greater than those of Morocco could possibly be, and there was always to pull him eastward that powerful magnet, the Pilgrimage. If he emigrated, Morocco was but a stopping place, and when he went eastward we may be sure that many Moroccans went with him.

To complete this picture of Muslim geography a few words should be said of Hebrew and Syriac writings which were the direct echoes of it. The great Provençal scholar Jacob Anaṭoli translated al-Farghānī's astronomy from Arabic into Hebrew, and added three new chapters one of which contains a list of geographical coördinates. Syriac geography was represented in the thirteenth century by the

Book of treasures of Jacob bar Shakkō and to a lesser extent by Abū-l-Faraj's chronicle.

Syriac geography was not original but it had the advantage of being very close to the Arabic sources. As compared with it Greek geography was contemptible. Eustathios of Thessalonica wrote a commentary on the geographical poem composed by Dionysios Periegetes more than a thousand years earlier, and a century later Nicephoros Blemmydes was still doing the same thing. It is true the latter also wrote a treatise in which he explained the spherical shape of the earth and discussed the seven climata. Geographical extracts are included in one of the three anthologies of Maximos Planudes.

Latin geography was on a much lower level than the Arabic but on a much higher than the Greek, at least in the thirteenth century. The twelfth century Latin writings were still rather childish. I am thinking of those of Henry of Mayence, Guido the Geographer, Lambert of Saint Omer, all of which are pre-Arabic and continue the Roman and the early mediaeval traditions. Geographical titbits may be found in the De essentiis of Hermann the Dalmatian and in the De mundi universitate of Bernard Silvester. The latter made curious remarks on how plants and animals are affected by the soil upon which they live. The most advanced Latin philosopher and cosmographer was William of Conches. These three, Hermann, Bernard and William had all been exposed to Arabic influences.

At the end of the first decade of the thirteenth century a mediocre hotchpotch, the Otia imperialia, was stewed for Otto IV by Gervase of Tilbury. Of the two Latin encyclopaedias of the first half of the thirteenth century, the De proprietatibus rerum or Bartholomew the Englishman is the most important from the geographical standpoint; two books of it out of nineteen are specifically devoted to physical and political geography. The De natura rerum of Thomas of Cantimpré has only one book, out of nineteen again, which may be called geographical, the thirteenth, dealing with fountains and rivers but needless to say, both encyclopaedias contain geographical data outside of these special chapters.

The average geographical knowledge of that time is well reflected in two French treatises, the Mappe-monde of Peter of Beauvais and the Image du monde of Gautier (or Gossuin) of Metz. Both authors knew the Imago mundi of Honorius Inclusus, but Peter's knowledge was essentially of a much earlier type, his main authority being still the late Roman writer Solinus. Gautier was a little more modern. Another vernacular treatise of much greater value than the French ones, was the Konungs skuggsjá, written in Norwegian. In spite of his remoteness the author was much better informed than his French colleagues, and he was also far more intelligent. His work is naturally of special interest with regard to the conditions obtaining in the Arctic (glaciers, icebergs, geysers, etc.). All in all this is by far the most important geographical work of Christendom in the first half of the thirteenth century.

With the exception of this Norwegian work, which contained many original observations and must be set apart from all others, and of Hermann the Dalmatian, Bernard Silvester, and William of Conches—all of the Latin and vernacular authors hitherto mentioned simply continued patristic and Latin traditions. By the middle of the thirteenth century there was a perceptible change in the situation: much Arabic knowledge was then available in western Europe; scholars were not simply aware of it but were beginning to feel the need of it. Partly under the stimulation of the new knowledge, the Latin genius was finally awakening. As compared with the encyclopaedists of the first half of the thirteenth century, Bartholomew the Englishman and Thomas of Cantimpré, those of the second half of the century, Vincent of Beauvais, Albert the Great and above all, Roger Bacon, were working on a much higher level. Vincent's Speculum naturale is an immense treasure of information on every subject then conceivable. Under Arabic influence Albert the Great was especially interested in meteorology and climatology. Roger Bacon was by far the best geographer of the three: Many of his data were relatively recent, e.g., those relative to William of Rubruquis. His synthetic mind made him realize the need of a new geographic survey of the world. So much of it had been recently discovered that the old view was becoming obsolete. Bacon was alone in his time to feel this. That was his greatness. Moreover he indicated the possibility of reaching India by a westerly navigation across the ocean; that suggestion of his reached Columbus indirectly and may have been the germ of the latter's heroic adventure.

One remarkable Chinese contribution dates from about the middle of the thirteenth century: Chao Ju-kua, commercial inspector in the port of Chüan Chou (Polo's Zayton), compiled what might be called a treatise on commercial geography, containing information on the countries with which China was then trading, and on the main products which were exchanged. In this case, the originality of China naturally induced by her independent growth was once more revealed, for there was no treatise like this one in Latin or any vernacular, and only one in Arabic which could be at all compared to it, namely, the Nihāyat al-rutbat al-ẓarīfat, written by the muḥtasib 'Abd al-Raḥmān Ibn Naṣr.

At the time when Arabic astronomy and geography were beginning to penetrate Latindom, they were also percolating into China. Indeed during the Yüan dynasty relations between Muslims and Chinese considerably multiplied. The Chinese astronomer Kuo Shou-ching had probably some knowledge of Muslim mathematics, and it was probably under Muslim influence that he ordered the determination of the coördinates of many points of the empire.

31. *The shape and movement of the earth*—The reader will certainly ask himself: what were the views of the scientists of that time and of educated men with regard to the shape of the earth? Did they know that it was spherical? Simple as this question may seem, it is not so easy to answer it. Or rather it is too easy to answer it both ways. Throughout the Middle Ages, from the earliest patristic age on,[26] one finds men who explain the sphericity of the earth side by side with others who do not speak of it. Upon closer examination one often discovers that those who explain it do not really understand it, nor genuinely believe in it.

During our period the same facts may be observed. There is never a complete lack of reference to the sphericity. Lambert of Saint Omer speaks of it in the first half of the twelfth century and moreover he had a correct (i.e., Eratosthenian) idea of the size of the earth. In the following century, the author of the Konungs skuggsjá explained it at the Norwegian court, and so did Nicephoros Blemmydes at the court of Nicaea. Needless to say all of the Arabic geographers believed in the sphericity of the earth; the Erastosthenian theory of climate so fully elaborated by them implied that belief.[27]

Closely connected with the question of sphericity was that of the antipodes.

[26] For the patristic age, see Isis, 8, 212–213.

[27] Ernst Honigmann: Die sieben Klimata und die πόλεις ἐπίσημοι (Heidelberg 1929; Isis, **14**, 270–276).

The author of the Konungs skuggsjá and Bacon did not hesitate to postulate the existence of inhabitants in the southern hemisphere, but they hardly deserve any praise for that. How could they know whether that hemisphere was inhabited or even habitable? It was on their part a mere guess, hardly more scientific than the discussions of the ancients on the size of the οἰκουμένη, or on the proportion of the earth's surface which was covered with water. See Bacon's long and unconvincing argument on the subject in the Opus majus.[28] Indeed such problems cannot be solved a priori.

Christian opinion on the antipodes had been very clearly expressed by St. Augustine many centuries before (c. 428). As this is a "locus classicus" it deserves to be quoted verbatim.

"Whether there bee any inhabitants of the earth, called the Antipodes. But whereas they fable of a people that inhabite that land where the sunne riseth, when it setteth with vs, and goe with their feete towards ours, it is incredible. They haue no authority for it, but onely coniecture that such a thing may bee, because the earth hangeth within the orbes of heauen, and each part of the world is aboue and below alike, and thence they gather that the other hemysphere cannot want inhabitants. Now they consider not that although that it bee globous as ours is, yet it may bee all couered with Sea: and if it bee bare, yet it followeth not, that it is inhabited, seeing that the Scripture (that prooueth all that it saith to be true, by the true euents that it presageth) neuer maketh mention of any such thing. And it were too absurd to say, that men might sayle ouer that huge Ocean, and goe inhabite there: that the progenie of the first man might people that part also."[29]

St. Augustine's conclusion was a very wise one and it was commonly accepted during the Middle Ages, except by a few bolder spirits, such as Bacon, or many centuries before Bacon, by Virgil of Salzburg (vol. 1, 516). Virgil was said to have suggested the possibility of another world and other men below the earth (alius mundus et alii homines sub terra). Pope Zachary wrote to St. Boniface on May 1, 748, ordering him to investigate the matter and if Virgil did not renounce that perverse teaching to excommunicate him. We do not know the end of that story, but in all probability Virgil recanted or succeeded in exculpating himself for he was consecrated archbishop of Salzburg in 767 and was eventually canonized. I

[28] Opus majus, edited by J. H. Bridges (vol. 1, 290–296, Oxford 1897). R. B. Burke's English translation (vol. 1, 310–316, Philadelphia 1928; Isis, 11, 138–141).

[29] Quoted from the quaint English translation of "Of the citie of God" made by John Healey on the Latin text of Io. Lod. Vives, and published posthumously in the year of his death, 1610. Book 16, chapter 9, p. 583. Here is the Latin text from the edition of B. Dombart (vol. 2, 138, Teubner, Leipzig 1905).

"An inferiorem partem terrae, quae nostrae habitationi contraria est, antipodas habere credendum sit.

"Quod vero et antipodas esse fabulantur, id est homines a contraria parte terrae, ubi sol oritur, quando occidit nobis, adversa pedibus nostris calcare vestigia: nulla ratione credendum est. Neque hoc ulla historica cognitione didicisse se adfirmant, sed quasi ratiocinando coniectant, eo quod intra convexa caeli terra suspensa sit, eundemque locum mundus habeat et infimum et medium; et ex hoc opinantur alteram terrae partem, quae infra est, habitatione hominum carere non posse. Nec adtendunt, etiamsi figura conglobata et rutunda mundus esse credatur sive aliqua ratione monstretur, non tamen esse consequens, ut etiam ex illa parte ab aquarum congerie nuda sit terra; deinde etiamsi nuda sit, neque hoc statim necesse esse, ut homines habeat. Quoniam nullo modo scriptura ista mentitur, quae narratis praeteritis facit fidem eo, quod eius praedicta conplentur, nimisque absurdum est, ut dicatur aliquos homines ex hac in illam partem, Oceani inmensitate traiecta, navigare ac pervenire potuisse, ut etiam illic ex uno illo primo homine genus institueretur humanum."

recall these facts because they help us to understand St. Augustine's opinion. The perversity of Virgil's thought was not in the belief of antipodal regions or even antipodal people, but in the suggestion that there might be "other" people, not our own kindred, but of an altogether different race. How could Adam's children ever have reached a region so remote and inaccessible?

This digression may be excused because it concerns a crucial point which has been the cause of many misunderstandings. The Church never had a serious hostility to the idea of sphericity, but it could not brook the suggestion of a polygenetic humanity; its objections were not geographical but anthropological.

Until the sixteenth century the existence of antipodal people remained highly hypothetical, somewhat like the ever recurring idea that other planets (the planets of other stars) might be inhabited. On the contrary the sphericity of the earth was not purely hypothetical, the curvature of its surface having been proved and measured. Unfortunately, it would seem that a good many people did not succeed in making that distinction between an unwarranted hypothesis on the one hand and an easily verifiable one on the other; they were equally frightened by both and refused to countenance either.

As far as I know the question whether the earth was at rest or not was not discussed in Europe: the earth was assumed to be at rest in the center of the world. On the other hand at least three Eastern astronomers discussed the question in the second half of the thirteenth century: two Muslims, 'Alī ibn 'Umar al-Kātibī and Quṭb al-dīn al-Shīrāzī, and a Syrian, Abū-l-Faraj. 'Alī considered the possibility of a daily rotation, but rejected it on a general principle: sublunar motions cannot be circular. Quṭb al-dīn and Abū-l-Faraj argued in a similar vein. It would seem that the latter also considered the possibility of a rectilinear motion but rejected it as well as the other. Hence these three wise men finally reached the same conclusion as their Latin colleagues, but their doubts were much to their credit. There is a great difference between taking something for granted, and accepting it only after investigation. The doubts expressed in these Arabic writings were not sterile. Together with the persistent criticism of Ptolemaic astronomy, dealt with in section 10, they helped prepare the Copernican reform of 1543.

At any rate within our period such views were not entertained in the West. The consideration of a spherical earth, with its startling implications, was already bold enough for them. As many of us have probably played with a terrestrial globe in our nurseries, and known that the earth was a ball even before we learned it in school—in fact we do not remember a time when we did not know it—it requires a real effort to imagine the opposite psychological conditions. The mediaeval man, if he was one of the very few who had heard of that theory, had heard of it relatively late in life, and in nine cases out of ten had not grown entirely accustomed to its strangeness. To return to our initial question, did he know that the earth was spherical? Yes and no. He was certainly not as sure of it as we are; it was really difficult for him to realize a spherical earth, it would be equally difficult for us to realize a flat one; at best his acquiescence was but of the mind and half hearted. The hypothesis remained somewhat paradoxical and fantastic to him, even as the theory of relativity to the elderly scientists of to-day.

NATURAL HISTORY

32. *Generalities*—Natural history is perhaps the most difficult subject to deal with in a survey of this kind. Every encyclopaedist, every philosopher, every scientist was necessarily obliged now and then to contemplate nature, even if he was not at all anxious to do so. Queries relative to stones, plants, and animals forced themselves upon his attention, and yet very few were naturalists in the proper sense of the term. The subject was not yet clearly defined. However in spite of the fact that there were so few specialists, knowledge of nature increased materially during the twelfth and thirteenth centuries as we shall show presently.

The simplest way of subdividing our subject is to examine separately the three kingdoms of nature, and we shall devote sections 33 and 34 to the minerals, sections 35 to 39 to the plants, and sections 40 to 44 to the animals, but before doing this we must consider a number of personalities and of books which cannot be assigned to this or that kingdom, but belong indistinctly to the three.

To illustrate, the world chronicle composed by Michael Glycas about the middle of the twelfth century includes an account of creation wherein the three kingdoms are reviewed. Information of interest to naturalists will be found in many Arabic writings such as the treatise on wares and their falsifications by Ja'far ibn 'Alī of Damascus, the manual for police officers in charge of markets by 'Abd al-Raḥmān Ibn Naṣr, the cosmographies of al Qazwīnī and al-Waṭwāṭ, the itineraries of Muḥammad ibn Rushaid, etc.; in Persian ones, such as the Four discourses of Niẓāmī-i-'Arūḍī, the cosmography of Muḥammad ibn Maḥmūd of Ṭūs, and the collection of anecdotes of Muḥammad al-'Awfī; in Chinese ones, such as the Description of barbarian peoples by Chao Ju-kua; in Hebrew ones, such as the Sha'ar ha-shamayim of Gershon ben Solomon.

A large number of Latin writings might be consulted and compared with the same purpose in view. The Western awakening is evidenced first of all by a renewed interest in the Naturalis historia of Pliny, which was for centuries the most popular encyclopaedia of its kind. There are traces of interest in Pliny throughout the Middle Ages. As early as the last third of the fourth century Symmachus was sending to Ausonius a part of the work. It is often quoted in mediaeval catalogues. We have many MSS. of it, some of them of the ninth century.[30] However for more tangible proofs of Plinian study we have to wait until the first half of the twelfth century when the English humanist, Robert of Cricklade, compiled an anthology of extracts from the Natural history and the French chronicler, Robert of Torigny, wrote a preface to another.[31]

The mediaeval encyclopaedias of the thirteenth century may have been partly inspired by the Natural history. We have a whole series of them, those of Bartholomew the Englishman, Arnold the Saxon, and Thomas of Cantimpré, and the Norwegian Konungs skuggsjá in the first half; the elaborate syntheses of Vincent of Beauvais, Albert the Great, and Roger Bacon in the latter half. Bacon was

[30] For the MSS. see J. E. Sandys: History of classical scholarship (vol. 1, 3d ed., 654, 1921). For the printed editions, which ran into the hundreds, see E. W. Gudger: Pliny's Historia naturalis (Isis, 6, 269–281, 1924).

[31] Extracts from the Natural history (Books 2 and 18) may also be found in a number of early MSS. of a mathematical compilation dating from the eighth century. Karl Rück: Auszüge aus der Naturgeschichte des C. Plinius Secundus in einem astronomisch-komputistischen Sammelwerke des achten Jahrhunderts (Gymn. Progr., 95 p., München 1888). The text of the extracts covers only 17 small pages.

the poorest naturalist of these three; he was too much of a Platonist to be a good one and he was more interested in mathematics and physics than in natural curiosities. If the first stimulus was provided by Pliny's work, a new, deeper and better one was due to the explorations, e.g., the Asiatic journeys of William of Rubruquis and others, but that influence was hardly felt until the following century. The discovery of new countries and of new faunas and floras has always stimulated naturalists more than anything else; we cannot yet verify this in our period but we realize that the stimulation is beginning to act toward its end.

33. *Lapidaries*—Few mediaeval writings enjoyed more popularity than the Liber lapidum, a poem composed by Marbode, bishop of Rennes, probably before the beginning of this period. It was read in Latin, in Hebrew, and in many vernaculars. It deals with the medical and magical properties of sixty precious stones, and is essentially pagan (vol. 1, 764–765). At the beginning of the twelfth century a very comprehensive lapidary, the so-called Alphabetical lapidary, was composed in Anglo-Norman. It deals with 78 stones. It is independent of Marbode, but represents also the magical and scientific traditions of the ancients. Its author is unknown; it may be Philip of Thaon who wrote at about the same time another and much shorter Anglo-Norman lapidary (15 stones). It is very curious that while the bestiaries were permeated with Christian influences, the lapidaries remained almost completely impervious to them until the appearance of the "Lapidaire chrétien" in the thirteenth century.[32]

The Hebrew translation of Marbode mentioned above was made in the thirteenth century by one Jacob ben Reuben, under the title Sefer ha-'osher (Book of richness). This is a rhymed version, but there is also an unidentified one in prose.[33] Another Hebrew lapidary (73 stones) is ascribed to Berakya ha-Naqdan, and still another was a translation of the one included in the popular encyclopaedia of Arnold the Saxon.

It would be unprofitable to discuss at greater length the lapidaries produced in many languages during these two centuries, for it is doubtful whether any valuable information can be extracted from them beyond bare enumerations of stones. To be sure a comparative study of them should be made, but this is neither the place nor the time.

The most elaborate Latin lapidaries of the thirteenth century were those forming part of the popular encyclopaedias which I have already quoted so often. Of the many written in various European vernaculars, the most remarkable ones are the Danish adaptation of Marbode by Henrik Harpestraeng and the one translated from the Arabic into Spanish by Judah ben Moses for King Alfonso (360 stones).

The eastern tradition was continued in Arabic by al-Tīfāshī and by Bailak al-Qabajaqī, and in Persian by Nāṣir al-dīn al-Ṭūsī.

34. *Geology*—The main sources of geological knowledge were Aristotle's Meteorologica, the pseudo-Aristotelian Liber de elementis (De causis et proprietatibus elementorum) and the Kitāb al-shifā' of Ibn Sīnā, the so-called Avicennae Mineralia (vol. 1, 133, 135, 711). The first of these works was Greek, the two others Arabic. The three were available in Latin before the beginning of the thirteenth century. I have already referred to the Meteorologica; the De elementis was translated from the Arabic by Gerard of Cremona, and the Mineralia, by Alfred

[32] Paul Studer and Joan Evans: Anglo-Norman lapidaries (424 p., Paris 1924; Isis, 9, 123–124).

[33] M. Steinschneider: Hebraeische Übersetzungen (957, Berlin 1893).

of Sareshel. The geological ideas of the great encyclopaedists, Vincent of Beauvais and Albert the Great, were essentially derived from these works, especially from the third. When they explain the movements of the sea, erosion, the generation of mountains, they are simply repeating the words of Ibn Sīnā or of the unknown author of the De elementis. It is true Albert had acquired some additional knowledge by his own observations and by his visits to laboratories and even to mines. He explained the presence of fossil shells in rocks by displacements of the sea, such as he had been able to observe near Bruges but in general he attached far more importance to eruptive forces than to hydraulic ones. Needless to say, both Albert and Vincent had also assimilated the earlier Latin encyclopaedias of Thomas of Cantimpré and Arnold the Saxon.

Albert's observations were more hopeful symptoms of progress than his learning. It is so often repeated that mediaeval scholars were constitutionally unable to make observations, that we cannot insist too much upon these. To be sure, such a statement is true but only as a first approximation. There were exceptions to the rule, and it is thanks to them that the Middle Ages did not stand still but moved on however slowly. Albert was one of these exceptions. His immense learning did not succeed in destroying the originality and the scientific bent of his mind. Two other exceptions, both anterior to himself, were Michael Scot and the author of the Konungs skuggsjá. Michael's Liber particularis includes descriptions of hot sulphur springs and of the volcanic phenomena of the Lipari islands. The originality of the Konungs skuggsjá has already been pointed out. Obviously the author was favored by the circumstance that many of the strange facts observed by him in the Arctic had never been witnessed by earlier writers. He could not help being original but he improved his opportunity. These facts—glaciers, icebergs, geysers, etc.—may be called geographical or geological according to one's point of view. Their knowledge would have necessarily affected what little geological thought there was, but unfortunately the Konungs skuggsjá remained practically unknown outside of Scandinavia until relatively modern times.

It is difficult to speak of mining in the twelfth and thirteenth centuries. Various forms of mining go back to very early—prehistorical—times, and the miner's craft continued to be practised in many localities throughout the ages. However we know very little about mediaeval mining; we are far better informed for example with regard to conditions in the fifth century B. C. (vol. 1, 104, 90). There are a good many monographs relative to mediaeval mining in some privileged districts of Germany and other countries but that knowledge has never been integrated and most of the available documents are posterior to our period.

35. *Herbals*—The subject of herbals cannot be dissociated from that materia medica. A disinterested botanical science was hardly conceivable in those days; we get only a few glimpses of it now and then. Plants were mainly collected for their medical properties. The herbals wherein these properties were discussed, together with various means of identification of each herb, contained also other drugs derived from the mineral and animal kingdoms, but the plants were so predominant that they gave the tone—as well as their name—to these collections. The complete history of these herbals is very difficult to extricate, because such works were naturally eclectic and invited interpolations. Thus a Latin herbal including Arabic elements, might influence another Arabic compilation, etc. Bearing these restrictions in mind it will be best to consider successively five herbalistic traditions: (a) Latin, (b) Greek, (c) Arabic, (d) Sanskrit, (e) Sino-

Japanese. The first three are only partially independent; one should imagine a whole series of links connecting them at different chronological levels.

(a) *The Latin tradition*—The Macer floridus, ascribed to Odo of Meung, was probably just anterior to our period. Even as Marbode's Liber lapidum for the lapidaries, it forms a convenient starting point for the Latin herbals. The botanical knowledge of the Salernitan school is best represented by three works, the Antidotarium parvum bearing the name of one master Nicholas, the Circa instans of Matthew Platearius, and the Regimen sanitatis. The second is in reality a commentary on the first (these three works belong already to the purely medical literature but the line is difficult to draw). The Salernitan antidotary was derived from ancient and early mediaeval sources, with Arabic and other accretions. A century later one hears an echo of the Salernitan teachings of the Antidotarium in the work of Henrik Harpestraeng, the earliest medical writer of Scandinavia. The most popular commentary on the Salernitan pharmacopoeia was composed at the end of our period by the Belgian physician, John of Saint Amand, who taught in Paris.

The earliest medical writer of Germany, that is, the earliest identified one, was a woman, Hildegard of Bingen, one of the most original personalities of mediaeval times. Her medical knowledge can be traced back to Roman sources through the unbroken Benedictine tradition; she also knew the popular remedies—mostly herbs—of her people. The folkloric origin of much of her learning is emphasized by the fact that she names about a thousand plants and animals in the German vernacular. Another independent link with ancient botany was forged by Alfred of Sareshel who translated from the Arabic the De plantis ascribed to Nicolaos Damascenos.

Albert the Great made full use of the De plantis as well as of other ancient writings but in spite of his ardent love of learning he could not be entirely restricted to a purely literary diet; he made observations of his own, outlined the first ideas of botanical geography, alluded to the relationship between galls and insects, studied seeds and recognized the embryo within. He was the greatest botanist of our period in Christendom.

Though no mediaeval herbarium has come down to us—which is not surprising for herbaria are very perishable objects unless extraordinary precautions are taken to protect them—it is possible that some of these botanists already collected dry plants. That assumption is fortified by a recipe to preserve the coloration of dried flowers in the album of Villard de Honnecourt (middle of the thirteenth century).

(b) *The Greek tradition*—The most important medico-botanical work of the Greek Middle Ages is the *Δυναμερόν* of Nicholas Myrepsos who flourished at the court of Nicaea about the middle of the thirteenth century. This work which enjoyed considerable popularity under various forms, was largely derived from the Salernitan antidotary and from Arabic sources. This is a good illustration of the extreme eclecticism of such books and of the continuous exchanges between them. Here we have a Greek work derived from Latin and Arabic writings themselves derived from Greek sources; furthermore this Greek work was translated into Latin in the first half of the fourteenth century and exerted a deep influence upon western medicine until the seventeenth century. And this is but a part of the story, dealing only with the main exchanges, but there were many others, and the recipes of a single antidotary were drawn from everywhere, far and near, high and low.

It must be added that the Δυναμερόν was even more strictly medical than the Latin treatises, yet we have no better source for the study of Byzantine botany of that period.

(c) *The Arabic tradition*—By far the most important herbalistic tradition in almost every respect was the Arabic or Muslim one. This was already the case at the beginning of our period and the initial superiority increased during the twelfth and thirteenth centuries. The Latin and Greek herbalists were influenced directly or indirectly by Arabic models, but these models were generally earlier ones. If one examines a chronological series of Latin antidotaries the number of Arabic accretions increases with their date, but these accretions did not originate from the contemporary Arabic traditions which remained steadily far ahead.

Our account may properly begin with the mysterious Ibn Sarābī or Serapion the Younger, who was probably an Arabic writing Christian. His treatise on simples exists only partly in Arabic, but there are Latin and Hebrew versions. It has been suggested that the Latin text was not a genuine translation, the Arabic origin being adduced only for the sake of prestige; in any case, the Latin text was by far the most popular and the most influential.

Outside of Ibn Sarābī's controversial book, the foremost Arabic antidotary of the first half of the twelfth century was written by Ibn al-Tilmīdh, a Christian who was then at the head of the medical profession in Baghdād. Christian physicians had distinguished themselves in the Dār al-Islām, that is, in the eastern part of it, from the earliest days. In the second half of the same century a very good treatise devoting considerable space to simple and compound medicines was the Irshād composed by an Egyptian Jew, Ibn Jamī'. The same author wrote papers on lemons and on rhubarb and their uses, which were eventually incorporated in Ibn al-Baiṭār's compilation. With the exception of Ibn Jamī' the best work of the second half of the twelfth century was done in the West and here we come across new tendencies as yet unheard of in Christendom: deliberate herborization. Al-Ghāfiqī of Cordova traveled far and wide in Spain and Africa to collect simples, and he described them with greater precision than had ever been done before. The famous geographer al-Idrīsī composed a herbal containing the description of 360 simples together with an elaborate botanical introduction in the Aristotelian manner: as opposed to many other herbals and antidotaries, al-Idrīsī's is far more important from the botanical than from the medical point of view or to put it otherwise, botanico-geographical considerations tended for al-Ghāfiqī and al-Idrīsī to supplant or to rival the purely medical ones.

These excellent tendencies, without equivalent in Christendom, were continued during the first half of the thirteenth century by an admirable group of four botanists, two Easterners, 'Abd al-Laṭīf of Baghdād, and his pupil, Ibn al-Ṣūrī of Damascus, and two Westerners, Abū-l-'Abbās al-Nabātī of Seville and Ibn al-Baiṭār of Malaga. 'Abd al-Laṭīf's account of Egypt contains valuable botanical facts. Ibn al-Ṣūrī herborized in the country surrounding Damascus and in the Lebanon mountains, and he took pains to observe plants at different stages of their growth. Abū-l-'Abbās, surnamed al-Nabātī (the botanist!), made botanical explorations in Spain and all along the African coast to Arabia; he observed a series of new plants along the shores of the Red Sea. I have explained above that the duty of the Pilgrimage could be conciliated with many other duties or pleasures; a born naturalist like Abū-l-'Abbās would naturally turn the Pilgrimage to the best botanical advantage! Finally Ibn al-Baiṭār compiled the most elaborate

Arabic book on the subject, in fact the most important for the whole period extending from Dioscorides down to the sixteenth century. It was a true encyclopaedia on the subject, incorporating the whole of Greek and Arabic experience, Dioscorides and Galen, al-Rāzī, Ibn Sīnā, al-Ghāfiqī, al-Idrīsī, etc. It may be that we have exaggerated Ibn al-Baiṭār's fame to the detriment of his Muslim contemporaries and predecessors; that his borrowings from al-Ghāfiqī and al-Idrīsī were large enough to be called by an uglier name; the matter is not yet fully investigated. In any case he was himself a famous physician and botanist; he had actually herborized together with his teacher Abū-l-'Abbās around Seville, and he had attained a marvelous grasp of his subject. His originality may have been smaller than was formerly believed but the synthetic power of his mind cannot be denied.

The most important Arabic pharmacopoeia of the second half of the thirteenth century was written by an Egyptian Jew, al-Kūhīn al-'Aṭṭār. This work, entitled Minhāj al-dukkān, has not yet outlived its popularity in the Arabic world of today.

(d) *The Sanskrit tradition*—Hindu knowledge of plants may be inferred from Hemacandra's botanical glossary and from the materia medica of Śārṅgadhara. However the originality of the latter seems to lie more in metallic and mercurial preparations than in the use of herbs.

(e) *The Sino-Japanese tradition*—The study of the innumerable editions of the Chinese herbals or pên-ts'ao is far more difficult than that of the Latin or Arabic ones, and has hardly been begun (Isis, 14, 262). Many editions of it have been quoted in my volume 1 (passim) and many more will be mentioned and briefly discussed in volumes 2 and 3. Even as our herbals, the pên-ts'ao deal with a variety of subjects beyond the herbs and roots themselves. Their contents are even more heterogeneous. For example, the Pên-ts'ao yen-i of 1115 contains a reference to the magnetic needle (vol. 1, 764).

The Chinese pên-ts'ao was naturally the foundation of Japanese materia medica. Its first adaptation to Japanese needs was made by Wake Hiroyo as early as the end of the eighth century (vol. 1, 539, 498). Various treatises derived from the pên-ts'ao were written by Henchiin Seiken in 1156. The Japanese materia medica was somewhat in the same relation to the Chinese, as the Latin to the Arabic: that is, it was always influenced not by the contemporary Chinese pên-ts'ao but by an earlier one. This was of course unavoidable. Wake's knowledge was derived from a pên-ts'ao of the seventh century; Henchiin's from one of the eleventh century; Koremune's, from one of the twelfth century; in each case, there was a delay of at least a century. In the second one the original Chinese text, the Tu-ching pên-ts'ao, is lost, and we know it only through the extracts quoted in other Chinese pên-ts'ao and in Henchiin's treatises. This shows that a complete study of the Chinese pên-ts'ao would involve the investigation of Japanese as well as of Chinese materials; it would probably involve also the examination of Korean, Annamese and other far-eastern herbals.

The Chêng lei pên-ts'ao of 1108 and the Shao hsing pên-ts'ao of 1159 are especially important from the Japanese point of view, because they were the main basis of their own materia medica: the first was introduced into Japan before the second half of the thirteenth century, for Koremune's index referred to it, and it remained the standard until the much belated introduction of the second in 1592. It is true the latter was very soon followed by the great Ming herbal, the Pên-ts'ao kang-mu.

The Sanskrit and Sino-Japanese traditions were independent of the three others.

As soon as they are better known it will be extremely interesting to compare the European and Near Eastern developments with the purely Asiatic ones. How were identical problems solved independently in distant parts of the world? How much did the independent solutions have in common? How can the resemblances and the dissemblances be accounted for? It will be the privilege of later historians of science to answer these and similar questions, and maybe their answers will throw a new light on the nature of scientific progress, and the relationship of East to West.

36. *Botanical dictionaries*—I have reserved for special consideration a group of books which may be called botanical dictionaries, though in general they were not essentially different from other herbals or other antidotaries. Indeed many antidotaries were arranged in alphabetical order and were to that extent dictionaries. Moreover the lexicographical point of view occupied always a large place in the minds and writings of the herbalists, even of those who were themselves good observers and had some subconscious understanding of experimental science. This was due in the first place to the fact that the transmission of knowledge involved many languages, and hence that it was necessary to establish lists of names corresponding to identical objects; in the second place, to the persistence of literary and scholastic methods. If we bear in mind that correct, clear, and unambiguous definitions of plants were hardly introduced before Linnaeus (middle of the eighteenth century), we must not be too impatient if these early botanists were somewhat clumsy in their descriptions and their nomenclature. Their main delusion, as far as I can make it out, was to believe that if you can name a thing you already know it, while this is only the first step to knowledge, and that the more names you can give to it, the better you know it. They did not take enough trouble to identify the names and the things, and to make sure that synonyms actually corresponded to identical objects.

The books to be dealt with in this section differ from other herbals in that the lexicographical point of view is more in the foreground. I thought it would be worthwhile to bring them together to evidence the universality of the need which called them into being.

One of the most remarkable works of that kind in the Middle Ages was compiled in Greek just before the beginning of our period by Symeon Seth (vol. 1, 771). It is of considerable value to help us trace the transmission of Hindu and Arabic knowledge to Eastern Europe. A century later, the greatest lexicographer of India, Hemacandra, published a Sanskrit botanical glossary. A little later still, about the middle of the thirteenth century, the Kashmirian physician Narahari compiled a dictionary of materia medica.

In the second half of the thirteenth century, three such books appeared in China, Japan, and Italy. The Chinese work, Ch'üan-fang pei-tsu, completed in 1256 by Ch'ên Ching-i, was an encyclopaedia dealing with all kinds of flowers, fruits, and plants, not only from the botanical, but also from the historical and literary point of view. The scientific description of each plant is followed by a poetical one: a delightful mixture of fact and fancy without equivalent in the West. In 1282, the Japanese scholar, Koremune Tomotoshi, compiled an index of plant names to the pên-ts'ao of 1108. Finally toward the end of the century, Simon of Genoa published his Synonyma medicinae or Clavis sanationis, a most elaborate medical and botanical dictionary, which was used considerably until the sixteenth century, and is still one of the best tools today for the study of mediaeval terminology.

37. *Botanical iconography*—Another means of exploring botanical knowledge is to examine the illustrations of plants. However we should realize at once that its scope is limited, for one may know plants without the ability or the wish of representing them, and one may represent them, even beautifully, without any scientific knowledge or interest.

Traditions of botanical iconography can be traced back at least to the first century B. C., but there are many solutions of continuity in our records. In spite of these it is possible to reconstruct the transmission of plant drawings throughout the Middle Ages down to the early printed herbals. The greatest obstacle to the transmission was not any interruption in artistic ability, nor any lack of interest in herbs, but the substitution of stylization for naturalism; that is, it was essentially a matter of artistic fashion which can be best elucidated or at least described by the historian of art. Under the influence maybe of scholastic philosophy, or other influences, naturalistic drawings were periodically replaced by schematic, symbolic, and magical ones. Yet there continued to occur from time to time a few artists, or artistically minded botanists, whose vision could not be entirely obscured by schemes or symbols and who could not help producing naturalistic drawings if they drew at all. One of these artists was an unknown monk who illustrated a herbal in Bury St. Edmunds about the beginning of the twelfth century. Some of his drawings are remarkably good. Other artists left witnesses of their untrammeled vision in the decoration of cathedrals, or the margins of prayer books. However, when everything is taken into account, the number of original drawings of the twelfth and thirteenth century is exceedingly small. The new iconographic tradition did not really begin in earnest before the fifteenth century.[34]

Similar remarks would apply to the Arabic tradition, though one should be even more cautious in doing so than in the case of western Christendom, because the study of the manuscripts and other documents is even less advanced. There are, e.g., illustrated Arabic MSS. of Dioscorides. What is more interesting, we are told apropos of the great botanist Ibn al-Ṣūrī that when he was herborizing in Syria he was accompanied by an artist who made colored drawings of plants as they were encountered in different stages of their growth. This is an indication of an iconographical purpose of the best kind without any equivalent in the West until a much later time.

Passing to the Far East we find a greater wealth of illustrations. This is natural enough for Chinese painters showed a deep interest in nature long before the European ones. The earliest realistic reproduction of a plant by an European painter is found in a fresco of Giotto's in Padua (c. 1300). By that time under the combined influence of Buddhism and Taoism, Chinese painters had already produced quantities of landscapes. They loved to paint mountain scenes at a time when Christendom was still recoiling from them with horror. However no scientific analysis of these paintings, from the purely iconographical point of view, has ever been undertaken.

To return to illustrations of a more scientific or didactic nature, we have first of all the "Illustrations of husbandry and weaving" published by Lou Shou about the middle of the twelfth century. This is a collection of 45 drawings of which 21 illustrate the cultivation of rice and the others, sericulture and the silk industry.

[34] C. Singer: The herbal in antiquity (Journal of Hellenic studies, vol. 47, 1927; Isis, 10, 519–521). Hermann Fischer: Mittelalterliche Pflanzenkunde (p. 114–126, Munich 1929; Isis, 15, 367).

Some at least of the pên-ts'ao were illustrated, and the figures used in one edition were often reproduced in another. For example, the Tu ch'ing pên-ts'ao of 1061 was illustrated; that particular pên-ts'ao is lost, but its figures are preserved in the Shao-hsing pên-ts'ao of 1159, and also in the Japanese treatises of Henchiin Seiken. Finally there is a treatise written in 1299 by Li K'an wherein are minutely explained the means of drawing sundry kinds of bamboo!

In 1267 a Japanese veterinary, Seia, secured the collaboration of an artist to publish faithful images of seventeen plants which were used to relieve horse complaints.

38. *Husbandry*—It is not possible to separate agriculture from the breeding of domestic animals and from sericulture, hence this section concerns the zoologist as well as the botanist.

The continuity and slow progress of European agriculture was largely due to the Benedictine monasteries. These monasteries included not only extensive fields, but kitchen and physic gardens. We know how some of these gardens were arranged; for example we can picture those of the famous Swiss abbey of Saint Gall as they were about the beginning of the ninth century. The agricultural services of the Benedictine order were still emphasized by the Cistercian Reform in the first half of the twelfth century. It has been said that the Cistercians changed the agricultural face of Europe. To be sure that agricultural reform implied no technical inventions,[35] it was economic rather than scientific; it was chiefly a matter of better organization of human and animal labor and of a longer vision with regard to works of reclamation and clearing. One of the greatest organizers of French husbandry was the abbot Suger of Saint Denis.

The task which was accomplished in France and in other parts of western Europe by great abbots was done in Portugal by King Dinis the Liberal. He improved the methods of cultivation of his people and planted pine forests upon the dunes of Leiria.

The transmission of ancient traditions was helped by Burgundio of Pisa who translated directly from Greek into Latin the part of the Geoponica dealing with vineyards.[36]

The earliest treatise on husbandry of Western Christendom was written in French by the Englishman Walter of Henley. It was soon translated into Latin and into English, and the English version remained the leading English treatise until the Renaissance. The second European treatise which can be assigned to a known author was composed in Latin by the Bolognese Peter of Crescenzi. This second treatise may be said to represent thirteenth-century thought on the subject, but as its author did not complete it until about 1305 in his old age, it really belongs

[35] With the exception of a better utilization of animal power for transportation. The strength of horses and oxen was considerably increased by better harnessing. As far as horses are concerned, ancient and new methods of draw-gear differ in three essential points: collar, nailed shoes, arrangement of animals in files. By the twelfth century these three improvements were sufficiently perfected and used in the West to revolutionize agricultural methods, e.g., to decrease materially the need of slaves. Commandant Lefebvre des Noëttes: La force motrice animale à travers les âges (146 p., 80 pls., Paris 1924); La force motrice animale et la question de l'esclavage (Anthropologie, 36, 297–308, 1926; Isis, 10, 278, 124). For similar questions in the Far East, see Paul Pelliot: T'oung pao (vol. 24, 256–268, 1926).

[36] On the development of viticulture in Europe, see H. Fischer: Mittelalterliche Pflanzenkunde (154–157, Munich 1929).

to the following period. It will be dealt with more thoroughly later. Meanwhile we may say that it was a combination of all the ancient Greco-Roman learning together with the fruits of mediaeval experience and of his own observations. Peter's work remained the standard European work until the end of the sixteenth century.

Walter's Hosebondrie and Peter's Liber ruralium commodorum were the main separate treatises on husbandry, but the subject was naturally dealt with in the encyclopaedias, for example in the Speculum doctrinale of Vincent of Beauvais, and in Albert the Great's botany.

The most important agricultural treatise of the period was written in Arabic by a Moor, Ibn al-'Awwām of Seville, about the end of the twelfth century. Ibn al-'Awwām was thus continuing one of the finest traditions of his race. A century before another Sevilian, Abū 'Umar ibn Ḥajjāj, had written another but less important treatise on the same subject. Ibn al-'Awwām's work deals with 585 plants and explains the cultivation of a great many fruit trees; it includes many valuable observations and rudiments of phytopathology. To be sure much of that was ancient lore derived from Greek and Arabic literature, but many additions were due to Ibn al-'Awwām himself or to the accumulated experience of his Moorish brethren. Horticultural improvements constituted the finest legacies of Islām, and the gardens of Spain proclaim to this day one of the noblest virtues of her Muslim conquerors.

The Chinese were also agriculturists of the first order who in this time had already accumulated many centuries or possibly millennia of experience. Their husbandry was entirely independent of the Greco-Latin-Arabic traditions which we have thus far considered. Agricultural subjects were treated by them in their encyclopaedias and dynastic histories, but the earliest treatises specifically devoted to husbandry in general do not go back beyond the first half of the twelfth century. In that time we have the Illustrations of husbandry and weaving of Lou Shou referred to in section 37, and the Nung shu of Ch'ên-fu. A more elaborate treatise, the Nung sang chi yao, was compiled by order of Kublai Khān in 1273, and revised editions of it were published from time to time during the Yüan dynasty.

Chinese books relative to special cultures will be considered in sections 39, but one of these—sericulture—was such an integral part of Chinese husbandry that we must deal with it at once. Indeed much space was devoted to sericulture in every Chinese treatise. In the title of the one published by order of Kublai Khān, the word nung means agriculture, and the word sang, mulberry tree. In our period the rearing of silkworms and the weaving of silk was still considerably more developed in China than anywhere else, but it had long ceased to be a monopoly and by the twelfth century the importation of Chinese silk into the West had already become insignificant. Silkworms had been introduced from Khotan into Constantinople under Justinian in 552, and their culture developed rapidly in the Peloponnesos (vol. 1, 439, 452). However the prosperity of Byzantine sericulture was jeopardized by excessive state control and by the vigorous Muslim (Persian and Syrian) competition. The Muslims were soon the masters of the silk industry and of the silk trade. Sericulture was introduced by them into Spain where it prospered exceedingly. It was introduced into Sicily by the Normans after 1147; by the second half of the twelfth century Sicilian silks were already driving out the Byzantine. The art spread gradually during the thirteenth and fourteenth centuries to other parts of Italy; it did not reach France, England and Germany until the fifteenth century.[37]

39. *Special cultures and monographs*—If the general treatises on agriculture—nung[2] (8408)—give us much respect for the Chinese husbandmen, that respect is still further enhanced by the examination of a number of treatises specifically devoted to the culture of definite plants. There was absolutely nothing in Latin or in other European languages, or even in Arabic, at all comparable to them. To be sure one may find details on some special type of cultivation in this or that book, e.g., on sugar-cane in Sicily in the chronicle of Hugh Falcandus, but the Chinese publications of which I am going to speak were deliberately and entirely devoted to such subjects.

Indeed this is not a novelty for the readers of this Introduction, for we had occasion to mention in volume 1 (p. 766, 777) a treatise on the litchi written by Ts'ai Hsiang in 1059 and two others of about the same time on the peony by Ou-yang Hsiu and by Wang Kuan. The Li-chich-p'u was the earliest monograph on any fruit tree published anywhere; a little more than a century later, in 1178, Han Ch'an-chich wrote a treatise on oranges which was the earliest monograph on citrous fruits in any literature. Han described about twenty-seven varieties of oranges and their cultivation. A contemporary of his who lived at the same time in the same province, Chehkiang, the geographer Fan Ch'êng-ta described thirty-five varieties of chrysanthemums cultivated by himself. In the thirteenth century we have still two extraordinary monographs, a treatise on mushrooms by another son of Chehkiang, Ch'ên Jên-yü, and a treatise on bamboo by Li K'an. This second treatise was meant for artists rather than for husbandmen; it was chiefly concerned with the means of drawing the particularities of different varieties of bamboo, but an artistic analysis of that kind came very close to scientific analysis. The strange mixture of both motives was typically Chinese.

As we might expect, these Chinese tendencies reappeared in Japan. In 1156, Henchiin Seiken wrote a treatise on cereals, and not much later, the monk Eisai, the founder of Zen Buddhism, introduced the cultivation of tea and wrote a book on the subject. It is rather puzzling that there was no Chinese treatise on tea, anterior to Eisai's (outside of encyclopaedias and general works on nung), for tea—ch'a[2] (208)—was known to them from time immemorial, witness their ascription of its discovery to Shên-nung, the second of the legendary Five Rulers who stand at the threshold of their history. Perhaps there was one, but I have not heard of it.

40. *Bestiaries*—As opposed to the lapidaries which remained essentially pagan until the thirteenth century, the western bestiaries being all of them influenced directly or indirectly by the Physiologos, were essentially Christian. I shall not try to give a complete account of them, as this would hardly be profitable for our

[37] For the study of sericulture and silk manufacture in the Middle Ages, see Henri Silbermann: Die Seide. Ihre Geschichte, Gewinnung, und Verarbeitung (vol. 1, Dresden 1897). F. S. Bodenheimer: Geschichte der Entomologie (vol. 2, 60–70, 1929; Isis, 14, 454). For Chinese sericulture, see Stanislas Julien: Résumé des principaux traités chinois sur la culture des mûriers et l'éducation des vers à soie (Paris 1837). The treatises studied by Julien are late ones (two Ming and one Ch'ing) but it is probable that they are not essentially different from the earlier ones and in any case they may help us to understand the latter. Otto Franke: Kêng Tschi-t'u. Ackerbau und Seidengewinnung in China (194 p., 102 pl., 57 ill., Hamburg 1913). James Westfall Thompson: An economic and social history of the Middle Ages (by index, New York 1928)

purpose. These bestiaries belong to the history of folklore and of comparative literature rather than to the history of science. In volume 2 I shall speak of only a few of them, those which I encountered in the course of my investigations. It is probable that their number could easily be increased.

It is very curious that the six bestiaries dealt with were all written by Frenchmen, five of them in French, in spite of the fact that I did not pay more attention to Frenchmen or to French texts than to others. As I did not try to make a complete survey of the bestiaries I can draw no conclusion from this, except that the French bestiaries were very probably more numerous.

A bestiary was composed in Anglo-Norman verse by Philip of Thaon for Queen Adelaide, Henry Beauclerc's consort. The Latin bestiary ascribed to Alan of Lille is certainly not his, except perhaps the second part; the first part, on birds, was probably written by Hugh of Fouilloy (de Folieto, in Picardy; d. c. 1174); the third and fourth, by the Dominican William Perault (d. bef. 1260).[38] To return to the French texts, at least three were composed in the first half of the thirteenth century, by Peter of Beauvais, William the Clerk, and Gervase of Bayeux. These were among the last "moralized" bestiaries. Peter's was very popular until the fifteenth century. The sixth one, anterior to 1260, was the Bestaire d'amour, an erotic composition of Richard de Fournival.

I shall come back to bestiaries presently in section 43.

41. *Falconry, hunting, and fishing*—The Muslims were very fond of the chase which they practised with the help of dogs, cheetahs and falcons, or other birds of prey. Falconry was especially popular with them. They had not invented it; it was a very old sport, witness Egyptian frescoes of the XVIIIth Dynasty and possibly earlier ones (Isis, 14, 222). However it seems probable that they had improved the technique of it. Unfortunately no early Arabic texts have yet been found; the earliest of which I know is one of uncertain date and authorship which may date back to the eleventh century (vol. 1, 731). We have a poem on hunting by the philosopher Ibn Bājja of Saragossa, but it is unpublished and I do not know whether it deals with or refers to falconry. The earliest datable Arabic book dealing with falconry and with the chase in general is the Kitāb al-i'tibār, being the reminiscences written in his old age by the great Syrian soldier and sportsman, Usāmah ibn Munqidh. There are at least three other Arabic treatises dating possibly from the second half of the twelfth century, but they have not yet been properly investigated, and their origin is uncertain. One of them may have been composed by the Persian historian, 'Imād al-dīn of Ispahan (d. 1201). There is also a Hebrew treatise, obviously of Arabic origin, dating from the end of the twelfth century.

In short though we have good reasons to believe that falconry was practised in the Near East from time out of mind,[39] our Arabic sources are thus far very poor. It is possible that additional researches will fill the gap, and such researches are very desirable.

It is clear that as long as the Arabic literature is not better known it is impossible to decide whether western European falconry was of Arabic origin or not; as it is

[38] Histoire littéraire (vol. 16, 422, 1824).

[39] It is very probable, for example, that the Beduin practice of falconry goes back to pre-Islāmic times, to the days of al-jāhilīya. For a description of their methods see Alois Musil: The manners and customs of the Rwala Beduins (31–35, and passim, New York 1928; Isis, 14, 444–446).

we have Latin references to falconry anterior to the dated Arabic ones (e.g., in Aelfric, second half of the tenth century). But even if the Latin references could be traced back to Arabic ones, this would not yet prove the whole case. Assuming that European falconry was of Oriental origin, it may have been transmitted from Egypt to the Mediterranean countries and thence to other parts of Europe, or across the Caucasus to Russia, Scandinavia, etc., by other and earlier channels than the Muslim. One may also conceive of independent origins in various places. The history of falconry is after all but a chapter in the history of domesticated animals, and the beginnings of that history will always be lost in mystery.

The earliest extant Latin treatise on falconry is the one composed by Adelard of Bath. As it seems innocent of Arabic influence it probably dates from Adelard's youth when he was still an abacist. Another early treatise was written by one William, falconer to Roger II of Sicily, but only fragments of it have come down to us. Additional information on western falconry can be derived from the hunting code of Sancho el Sabio (1180).

By far the most elaborate treatise we owe to the emperor Frederick II of Hohenstaufen. This is not simply the best treatise of its kind, but one of the best zoological works of the Middle Ages. It deals not only with the breeding and training of falcons, but with their anatomy, and contains the account of many original experiments. Indeed, Frederick's Ars venandi is one of the most conspicuous monuments proving the final emergence of the true scientific spirit in Latindom. The emperor was well acquainted with the earlier writings whether in Latin, Arabic or Persian. One of them was translated for him from the Arabic by his astrologer and secretary, Theodore of Antioch. Arabic and Persian treatises were translated from Latin into French by Daniel of Cremona for Frederick's son, Enzio. Another son of his, Manfred, revised the Ars venandi. We also have treatises in Provençal and in Catalan. Even if western Europe first knew of the sport through non-Muslim channels, it is highly probable that its interest in it remained relatively small until it had been stimulated to a much higher pitch by Muslim contacts. How else could we explain the sudden expansion of the relevant literature in the second half of the twelfth century and in the thirteenth century?

The most important treatise after Frederick's was written in Greek a little later by Demetrios Pepagomenos. As in every other treatise of the kind, much attention was paid to the care of falcons which were distempered or diseased. Demetrios made on this subject remarkable helminthological observations. Three other Greek treatises may date from the same time.

Next to the books on falconry, the most interesting accounts of hunting are those relative to the herring fisheries by Thomas of Cantimpré, to the seals and walruses in the Konungs skuggsjá, to whaling in Albert the Great's zoology.

It is strange that there are no Latin and vernacular writings on fishing (as opposed to the fisheries mentioned above).[40] I know a Greek treatise of the first half of the twelfth century, a commentary on Oppian's poem by John Tzetzes.

42. *Treatises devoted to special animals*—As we remember the curious treatises which Chinese scholars devoted to special plants (see section 39), we may hope to find in their literature other treatises equally unusual dealing with sundry animals. Let us thus begin our survey in the Far East; we shall not be disappointed. I found nothing in the twelfth century which might be compared with

[40] C. H. Haskins: The Latin literature of sport (Speculum, 2, 235–252, 1927; revised in Studies in mediaeval culture, 1929; Isis, 14, 434).

the treatise on crabs written in 1059 by Fu Kung, but the thirteenth century brings us a brilliant compensation. From time immemorial the Chinese had been exceedingly interested in insects; this enabled them to discover the function of the silkworms and to apply it with great ingenuity to their own purposes (sericulture was dealt with in section 38, together with husbandry). They were very familiar with other insects, especially with crickets about which they made many extraordinary observations. The earliest treatise wherein these observations were collected was written in the first half of the thirteenth century by Chia Ssŭ-tao, and in the course of time Chia's treatise was followed by many others.

The Chinese were also deeply interested in birds. Ornithological treatises may have been written by them in early days, perhaps as early as the Han or even the Ch'in dynasty, but the earliest text which has come down to us, the Ch'in ching, cannot be much older than the end of the Sung dynasty.

The most interesting Arabic treatises of this category were devoted to horses: one was written by Ibn al-Jawālīqī of Baghdād in the first half of the twelfth century; another by the Egyptian 'Abd al-Mu'min of Damietta in the second half of the thirteenth century. These books are far remote from the kind which would appeal to naturalists, for they are concerned mainly with traditions, and with literature and lexicography. However it should be possible to derive from them a modicum of information on Arabian horses.[41]

Al-Māzinī of Granada traveled extensively in the Near East and what was more remarkable, in Russia. During his stay in the Volga region he witnessed the trade in fossil bones (ivory?) which were exported to Persia and beyond.

In the west of Europe, the encyclopaedists of the thirteenth century gave accounts of all kind of animals, as much as they could. For example out of the nineteen books constituting the De natura rerum of Thomas of Cantimpré, nine deal with the animal kingdom, and of these the first three form a sort of anthropological introduction. In the Norwegian Konungs skuggsjá there is naturally some information—not found in other books—on the Arctic fauna. Various animals were observed for the first time by Albert the Great in the course of his long pastoral wanderings across Europe. However the most curious news was brought back by the travelers to the Far East, especially William of Rubruquis and Marco Polo. In fact some of their stories were passing strange and even beyond mediaeval credulity, and yet they have been confirmed by modern science.

A Greek treatise on dogs is ascribed to Demetrios Pepagomenos. This is a mediocre production inferior to the ancient works of the same kind.

43. *Zoological iconography*—The study of zoological iconography would suggest remarks similar to those I have made with regard to botanical iconography (section 37). In fact it would be expedient to investigate the two subjects at the same time, and the more so because the same MSS. would more than once require consideration from both points of view. For example many of the herbals contain representations of animals.

There are quite a few illustrated bestiaries of the twelfth and thirteenth centuries but their illustrations are generally very conventional, and thus more interesting for the study of artistic than of scientific traditions.[42] We need hardly consider

[41] More information on horses will be found in the sections 38 and 60 respectively devoted to husbandry and farriery.

[42] Montague Rhode James: Catalogue of the Pierpont Morgan collection of MSS. (vol. 1, no. 107, p. 165–167, 2 figs., London 1906; describing a bestiary of c. 1170); A Peterborough psal-

them. Naturalists will be more pleased with the sketches of animal life (molluscs, crustacea, insects, birds, porcupine, lion, etc.) preserved in the album of the Villard de Honnecourt, a French architect who flourished about the middle of the thirteenth century, but these sketches are truly exceptional vestiges of that time.

There are curious pictures of animals of various kinds in the Arabic and Persian MSS. of such works as al-Qazwīnī's cosmography, and the Manāfi' al-ḥayawān of 'Ubaidallāh ibn Jibrīl ibn Bakhtyashū'. Most of these figures, though pleasing to the eye, are of little if any scientific value, but there are a few exceptions.[43]

The greatest illustrators of that time were the Chinese, who represented birds, fishes, and even insects with astounding faithfulness. Their purpose was purely artistic, sometimes religious, for their love of nature and of living things, whether animals or plants, was inspired by their Buddhist doctrine; it was never scientific. Yet some of their paintings are so good that it should be possible to identify the genera represented. I do not believe that any attempt has yet been made to analyze the Sung and early Yüan paintings from that point of view; it would be worth while but far from easy, the main difficulty being to date even approximately the paintings themselves. But even if it were not always possible to distinguish between, say, a Sung original and a Ming or Ch'ing copy, the purely zoological interest would still be considerable. Which animals attracted the fancy of Chinese artists? Which birds and fishes did they know best? And how do these early representations compare with to-day's fauna? Similar investigations might be applied to the Japanese paintings of the Fujiwara and Kamakura periods.

44. *Transmission of Aristotelian Zoology. General theories*—One can find in many Arabic and Persian writings speculations on the order of nature as far as the distribution of the three kingdoms is concerned. The Muslims, with but few exceptions, were hardly interested in the scientific aspect of these matters, but rather in their theological implications; they were not thinking so much of evolution from the human or naturalistic point of view as of creation from the divine one. How did all the creatures of God come into being? Was the act of divine creation a continuous or an instantaneous performance, and in the second case, to what extent did it involve the future? It is not probable that they were acquainted with St. Augustine's theory of potential creation, but some of their philosophers developed a very similar one; this was not so surprising after all, and no contact is needed to account for the occurrence of the same logical deductions in distant places. For example al-Naẓẓām (first half of the ninth century) explained the idea of a creation which is largely hidden; only a part of it appears at a time, generation after generation, though the creation was complete from the outset. This is truly a theory of evolution, and the word evolution was first used by Charles Bonnet about 1762, with that very acceptation. Charles Bonnet's idea was far more technical than al-Naẓẓām's but not very remote from it: both conceived an extreme view of creation. All that has ever happened or will ever happen is but

---

ter and bestiary of the fourteenth century (Roxburghe Club, Oxford 1921); facsimile reproduction with description and discussion of the tradition. Alexandra Konstantinowa: Ein anglisches Bestiar des zwölften Jahrhunderts (Kunstwissenschaftliche Studien, 4, 32 p., 32 ill., Berlin 1929; Isis, 16). Helen Woodruff: The Physiologus of Bern. A survival of Alexandrian style in a ninth century manuscript (The art bulletin, vol. 12, 226–253, 45 figs., 1930; Isis, 16).

[43] Arabic figures of insects may be seen in F. S. Bodenheimer: Geschichte der Entomologie (vol. 1, figs. 40–47, pl. IV, 1928; Isis, 13, 388).

an unfolding, a rolling out, an "evolution" of something which was absolutely inclusive and final from the very beginning. Other speculations on fundamental biological problems—such as the struggle for existence and adaptation—are found in the Kitāb al-ḥayawān of al-Jāḥiẓ (second half of the ninth century). The idea that all the objects of nature could be arranged in a progressive series "from mineral to plant, from plant to animal and from animal to man" was a commonplace in Islām. It is clearly expressed, e.g., in the Kitāb al-tanbīh wal-ishrāf of al-Mas'ūdī (first half of the tenth century), but that arrangement should not be confused with our modern idea of gradual transformation of one species into another.[44]

So much by way of introduction. We may expect these various speculations to reappear in the Arabic and Persian literature of our period. For example some of them are referred to about the middle of the twelfth century in the Persian discourses of Niẓāmī-i-'Arūḍī and the philosophical romance of Ibn Ṭufail. Niẓāmī conceived of intermediate stages between the three kingdoms of nature: corals between minerals and plants, and date-palms between plants and animals. This suggests that he was beginning to realize the sexual nature of date fructification which had been subconsciously assumed from time out of mind.[45] Ibn Ṭufail discussed spontaneous generation.

In the meanwhile Aristotelian zoology had been transmitted to the whole European and Arabic world. The part of that world which knew it least was the Greek. Byzantine scholars had but little interest in science in spite of the fact that the treasures of ancient science were readily available to them; it is true the Latin conquest of Constantinople in 1204 had destroyed many of these treasures or moved them out of reach.[46] At any rate the Byzantine tradition of Aristotelian zoology was almost insignificant: all that we have for this period is a commentary on the Parts of animals ascribed to John Tzetzes.

We may thus say that Aristotelian zoology was almost entirely transmitted

[44] See vol. 1 (p. 383, 559, 597, 638). For a deeper discussion of Muslim views on creation, see D. B. Macdonald: Continuous recreation and atomic time in Muslim scholastic theology (Isis, 9, 326–344, 1927). For creation in general and Bonnet, see Edwin Tenney Brewster: Creation. A history of non-evolutionary theories (Indianapolis 1927; Isis, 9, 462–465). For the biological views of al-Jāḥiẓ on the struggle for existence, etc., see Miguel Asín Palacios: El Libro de los animales de Jāḥiẓ (Isis, 14, 20–54, 1930).

[45] I have just discovered a curious passage relative to the sexuality of plants in St. Thomas' commentary on the Book of sentences of Peter the Lombard. I quote it verbatim:

"In his enim quae habent vitam perfectam, distinguuntur agens et patiens in generatione propter perfectam generationem in eis. In plantis autem quae imperfectam vitam habent, est in eodem utraque virtus, activa scilicet et passiva: quamvis forte in una planta dominetur virtus activa, et in alia virtus passiva: propter quod dicitur etiam una planta masculina, et alia feminina." (Sancti Thomae Aquinatis Commentum in quatuor libros sententiarum; Liber III, Dist. III, Quaest. II, Art. 1; Opera omnia ad fidem optimarum editionum accurate recognita, Tomus VII, p. 42, Parmae, 1857.)

It is not surprising that these views of the Angelic Doctor have remained unknown to botanists and historians of science, for who would hunt for them in that ponderous commentary? The article in which they appear is entitled "Utrum Virgo aliquid active ad Christi conceptionem operata fuerit." Considering that many people had an empirical knowledge of the sexuality of certain plants (dates and figs) from time immemorial, the astounding fact is not that some scientists or philosophers like Theophrastos, Pliny, Niẓāmī, St. Thomas had a vague notion of plant sexuality, but that one had to wait until the end of the seventeenth century (Rudolph Jacob Camerarius, 1694) for the transformation of that vague notion into scientific knowledge. For the early history of plant sexuality, see Julius von Sachs: History of botany (2d. impression of the English translation, 376–385, Oxford 1906).

[46] M. R. James: The wanderings and homes of manuscripts (14, London 1919).

through Arabic channels (the "almost" is added because of William of Moerbeke). The real fountain-head of Aristotelian zoology, East and West, from the eleventh century on was the Arabic summary of the nineteen books by Ibn Sīnā. In a sense we might even say that Ibn Sīnā was indirectly the main fountain-head of mediaeval zoology, for every serious treatise on zoology naturally took the form of a commentary on Aristotle, i.e., on Ibn Sīnā; hence the Aristotelian or Avicennian tradition carried with it the highest thoughts on the subject. Another source was the jāmi' of books XI–XIX (Parts and generation of animals) completed by Ibn Rushd at Seville in 1169.

The new knowledge filtered rapidly into Latindom. Alfred of Sareshel wrote a commentary on the Parva naturalia. Another Englishman, Michael Scot, was the first to write a Latin translation of the nineteen books; he did this in Toledo probably before 1220, and he translated also Ibn Sīnā's summary in Sicily a little before 1232. A third translation partly based on Scot's and on Ibn Rushd's commentary was made by the Spanish Franciscan, Peter Gallego, about the middle of the century. In 1260 a direct translation of the History and generation of animals was made from the Greek by William of Moerbeke.

The time was now ripe for further elaborations.

Two Latin commentaries were based upon Michael Scot's version at about that time, the one by Peter of Spain, the other by Albert the Great. Peter's work does not seem to have much scientific value; on the contrary, Albert's is one of the most important zoological works of the Middle Ages. To the nineteen Aristotelian books, Albert added seven more containing abundant information derived from other sources, some of it from his own observations. Frederick II and Albert the Great were the first leaders of zoological research in Christendom.

The transmission of Aristotelian zoology to the Hebrew world was neither as complete nor as rapid. I say advisedly Hebrew, not Jewish, for the Jews of Spain and of the East did not need any translation from the Arabic. They could read Ibn Sīnā and Ibn Rushd in the original, and we are sure that they did read them for we have many manuscripts in Hebrew script. One of these Spanish Jews, Judah ben Solomon ha-Kohen of Toledo, wrote an encyclopaedic treatise in Arabic and in Hebrew, and included in it an elaboration of books XI–XIV. One Abū-l-Faraj Ibn al-Ṭayib[47] collected liquṭim (gleanings) from the Aristotelian zoology, and these were used by Shem-ṭob ben Joseph ibn Falaquera. Finally Ibn Rushd's synopsis was translated into Hebrew by Jacob ben Maḥir in 1302.

MEDICINE

45. *Introductory remarks*—Some remarks which might be made apropos of every aspect of mediaeval thought apply with special force to medicine. We can misjudge the Middle Ages in at least two ways: first by expecting too little from them, second, by expecting too much. The first mistake would lead us to believe that what the leeches did or left undone during the twelfth and thirteenth centuries is hardly worth considering; the second would cause us to visualize a progress of such magnitude and to anticipate so many discoveries that we would necessarily be disappointed.

The first mistake is very common but our readers need no warning against it; the second is less common but far more insidious. To protect ourselves it will suffice to bear in mind that not only in our period but almost until the nineteenth

[47] M. Steinschneider: Hebraeische Übersetzungen (144, 1893).

century medicine was hardly a science; it was essentially an art. It is still an art today but the proportion of scientific knowledge upon which it is based has steadily increased, so much so that modern medicine is poles apart from the mediaeval one. Now an art does not progress in the same way that a science does; very often it does not seem to progress at all, or its progress is erratic and interrupted by moments of standstill or regression. Whatever progress occurs is largely due not so much to the art as to the scientific knowledge upon which it is based. That scientific knowledge is objective, and susceptible of increase and transmission; the art on the contrary is highly personal and as such untransmissible. One can teach the medical sciences, but the art itself, the medical intuitions, are unteachable. In that sense one may say that a doctor is born, not made. However true that may be to-day, it was far more true in the Middle Ages. Indeed the mediaeval physician had hardly any means of checking his intuitions; on the contrary his modern colleague has a whole arsenal of instruments which enable him to measure some of the variables, to eliminate contingencies, and to determine his problem in many ways. To illustrate, consider but one of these instruments—the clinical thermometer, and let the modern physician imagine how perplexed he would be without it. Now the thermometer is a very late acquisition: reliable ones date only from the beginning of the eighteenth century; during that century a few men gave indications of its medical use[48] but the first to give an elaborate account of clinical thermometry was C. R. A. Wunderlich in 1868,[49] and in that same year the first pocket thermometer—short and rapid—was introduced by Thomas Clifford Allbutt: that is, hardly more than 60 years—two generations—ago!

The number of physicians has always been considerably greater than that of all the other men of science put together, and the quantity of medical publications is proportionately large. The writings registering definite steps forward—tangible discoveries—are relatively easy to appraise, but those far more numerous which are simply restatements or rearrangements of available knowledge are very difficult to deal with. Some of them are very long and their true value could only be measured by minute comparison with several others of the same age and equal length, a formidable task indeed which has never been attempted and seems hardly worth the effort. In most cases we assume that a work was really important if it was deemed to be so by contemporaries or by the following generations; we well know that such standards are misleading, but the historian must take into account extrinsic as well as intrinsic importance. If a mediocre treatise was considered very important by many generations of thoughtless doctors—well, it was important for it helped to shape their minds. Because of this the medical part of my survey is bound to be less accurate than the other parts, and also less complete. I shall not attempt to quote all of the medical works involved in each section, but simply to quote a few—the most conspicuous in my own eyes—by way of illustration.

Treatises on materia medica have already been discussed in the section on herbals (no. 35).

46. *Translations*—In order to appreciate the creative work of the physicians of this period we must first find out how well they knew the results of past, i.e., Greek and Arabic, efforts.

[48] The two Dutch physicians, Boerhaave (c. 1736) and Anton van Haen (c. 1758), and the Scotch one, James Currie (1797).

[49] It should be added that Wunderlich had begun his investigations in 1842 and that his famous treatise of 1868 was the result of more than 25 years of labor.

Many Hippocratic treatises were translated from the Arabic into Latin by Gerard of Cremona and Marc of Toledo; from the Greek into Latin by Burgundio of Pisa and William of Moerbeke; from the Arabic into Hebrew by Shem-ṭob ben Isaac and Nathan ha-Me'ati.

The bulk of the Galenic corpus, which had been translated or edited in Arabic by Ḥunain ibn Isḥāq and his school in the second half of the ninth century, was translated from the Arabic into Latin by Gerard of Cremona, Marc of Toledo, and Faraj ben Salīm; from Greek into Latin by Burgundio of Pisa and William of Moerbeke; from Arabic into Hebrew by al-Ḥarizi, Zeraḥiah Gracian, Nathan ha-Me'ati and Solomon ben Nathan; from Arabic or from Hebrew into Latin by Armengaud son of Blaise.

The De natura hominis of Nemesios of Emesa was translated from Greek into Latin by Burgundio of Pisa. So much for Greek medicine.

Let us now consider Arabic knowledge. The Sirr al-asrār was translated by John of Seville, Philip of Tripoli, and Theodore of Antioch; a treatise of al-Kindī, Ibn Māsawaih's Aphorisms and Yaḥyā ibn Sarāfyūn's Breviarium, by Gerard of Cremona. Speaking of Galen, I have already mentioned the Arabic canon edited by Ḥunain ibn Isḥāq. Ḥunain's own introduction to it, the Isagoge ad Tegni Galeni, was translated into Latin by Marc of Toledo, and into Hebrew, about a century later, by Moses ben Tibbon.

Please notice that I am dealing with these Arabic texts in rough chronological order; we thus come to one of the greatest physicians of Islām, al-Rāzī. His Kitāb al-Manṣūrī was translated into Latin by Gerard of Cremona and into Hebrew, about a century later, by Shem-ṭob ben Isaac. Other treatises of his were translated into Hebrew by Moses ibn Tibbon and perhaps by Nathan ha-Me'ati. Finally, his Kitāb al-ḥāwī—the Continens, the largest encyclopaedia of Greco-Arabic medicine—was translated into Latin by Faraj ben Salīm in 1279.

The theoretical part of another great encyclopaedia, the Kitāb al-malikī of 'Alī ibn 'Abbās, had been translated into Latin under the title Pantegni by Constantine the African; another part, the surgery, was translated by one of Constantine's disciples, John the Saracen, and by Rusticus of Pisa; an entirely new Latin version of the whole work was completed by Stephen of Antioch, c. 1127.

The main surgical treatise of Islām, the Kitāb al-taṣrīf of Abū-l-Qāsim al-Zahrāwī was translated into Latin by Gerard of Cremona, and into Hebrew, about a century later by Shem-ṭob ben Isaac. Other contemporary Hebrew translations were made by Meshullam ben Jonah and perhaps by Nathan ha-Me'ati. The materia medica of the Taṣrīf was translated from the Arabic, or more probably from the Hebrew, into Latin by Simon of Genoa with the assistance of Abraham ben Shem-ṭob.

An early Latin version of the Zād al-musāfir (Viaticum peregrinantis) of Ibn al-Jazzār is ascribed to Constantine the African; it was again translated into Latin by Stephen of Saragossa and into Hebrew by Moses ibn Tibbon. One gathers from Moses' introduction that an earlier Hebrew version had been made from the Latin! This illustrates the complexity of the Latin-Hebrew interchanges.

Passing to the first half of the eleventh century, we shall keep Ibn Sīnā for the climax and dispose first of a series of less important yet very popular authors. The treatise on drugs of Ibn al-Wāfid was translated into Latin by Gerard of Cremona and another—on purgatives and emetics—by Māsawaih al-Māridīnī was translated into Hebrew by Samuel ben Jacob of Capua. One of the best early Arabic treatises on eye diseases, the one by 'Ammār ibn 'Alī was translated into Hebrew by Nathan ha-Me'ati. 'Alī ibn Riḍwān's famous commentary on the Tegni was translated into Latin by Gerard of Cremona, and into Hebrew, before the end of the same century, by Samuel ibn Tibbon.

And now—Ibn Sīnā, the illustrious shaikh, the prince of all learning! His medical encyclopaedia—the Qānūn, which was for centuries a sort of medical bible—was put into Latin by Gerard of Cremona. Partial Hebrew translations were made by Zeraḥiah Gracian and Moses ibn Tibbon; the complete text became available in Hebrew only in 1279, thanks to Nathan ha-Me'ati. By that time the Latin version was already a century old. The Qānūn was so large and so forbidding that it was hopelessly out of reach of the majority of physicians, whether Christians or Jews, but every one of them knew of it and thought of it as the supreme monument of medical learning and wisdom. Whether they could avail themselves of it or not did not matter so much after a time, because most of the medical writers were sooner or later dominated by it. From the second half of the thirteenth century we may assume general knowledge of the Qānūn, either directly or indirectly. Moreover, Ibn Sīnā was known also by smaller works, chiefly the very popular Arjūza (or Cantica), to which Ibn Rushd had added a commentary. Both the poem and the commentary were translated from Arabic into Hebrew by Solomon ibn Ayyub and by Moses ibn Tibbon, and from Hebrew into Latin by Armengaud son of Blaise.

We are now coming to Arabic writings of the twelfth and thirteenth century which were translated within that very period. The closeness of the Arabic and Hebrew traditions is very apparent in them. For example, the greatest physician of the first half of the twelfth century was the Spaniard Ibn Zuhr. His most important work, the Taisīr, was written in Arabic of course, but our Latin versions were made from the Hebrew, the first by John of Capua, the second by Paravicius. Another book of his, the Kitāb al-aghdiya was translated into Hebrew by Nathan ha-Me'ati. A new medical encyclopaedia, the Kullīyāt (Colliget) of Ibn Rushd, was translated from the Arabic (or from the Hebrew?) into Latin by Bonacosa within less than a century. The original Jewish medical treatises of the twelfth century were composed in Arabic but promptly translated into Hebrew, and often from Hebrew into Latin. Those of Maimonides were translated into Hebrew by Zeraḥiah Gracian, Moses ibn Tibbon and Nathan ha-Me'ati, and into Latin by John of Capua and Armengaud son of Blaise. The treatise on gynaecology of Sheshet Benveniste was translated into Hebrew within a single generation.

Finally we have the two mysterious treatises ascribed respectively to Serapion the Younger and to Mesuë the Third. Both are best known in the form of Latin and Hebrew texts ostensibly translated from the Arabic, yet their Arabic origin has been questioned. If they were passed off as translations for the sake of publicity, their authors are excellent witnesses of the prestige of Arabic science in their days. Whether we consider them as genuine translations or not, the fact that they were far more popular in Latin and in Hebrew makes of them fitting symbols of this age of transition.

In this review, I have not spoken, except in two instances, of the translations of Constantine the African, because they occurred before the beginning of this period, yet we must bear them in mind, for they constituted the main treasure of Arabic medicine until the time of Gerard of Cremona, that is, almost until the end of the twelfth century and remained in use for many centuries. Thanks to the intellectual apathy of most physicians and the inertia of the early printers, thousands of people continued to read Arabic medicine in its Constantinian garb until the end of the sixteenth century. Constantine was the first initiator of the Latino-Arabic revival; he died in 1087; the second was Gerard of Cremona who died in 1187, i.e., exactly a century later; and the main characteristics of twelfth century medicine (that is, of Salernitan medicine in its golden age) were due to its being at once post-Constantinian and pre-Gerardian. Gerard gave two fundamental texts to the Latin world: the Kitāb al-manṣūrī and the Qānūn. For another century, Jewish physicians were obliged to read these two texts either in Arabic or in Latin. Two other great landmarks were the Latin translation of the Kitāb al-malikī by Stephen of Antioch, c. 1127, and that of the Kitāb al-ḥāwī by Faraj ben Salīm in 1279. The last named was too late to influence the physicians of our period; its fruits belong to the fourteenth century and the Renaissance.

47. *Commentaries on Greek and Arabic medicine*—The ancient medical traditions to which our period fell heir do not appear only in the form of translations; they were also represented by various kinds of elaborations and commentaries. Most of these were made upon the basis of the translations which were thus the initial stage in the passing on of knowledge from one crew to another. A complete account of these elaborations and commentaries is out of the question, for it would be very long and tedious and it would be sometimes difficult to draw the line between commentaries and original works. The titles may easily deceive us: a commentary may be more original in fact than a treatise giving itself out as a novelty. It will suffice to quote a few examples to illustrate how the ancient knowledge was transmitted.

In Byzantium, John Tzetzes wrote commentaries on the Theriaca and Alexipharmaca of Nicandros.

There are many Arabic commentaries on Hippocrates and Galen, by Yūsuf ibn Ḥasdai, an Egyptian Muslim of Hispano-Jewish ancestry, David ben Solomon, an Egyptian Qaraite, Ibn al-Quff, a Christian Syrian, and Ibn al-Nafīs. The Arabic writing physicians attached at least as much importance to the great classics written in their own tongue as to the Greek ones. For example, we have Arabic commentaries on the Qānūn by Ibn al-Sā'ātī, the Samaritan Muwaffaq al-dīn, Ibn al-Quff, Ibn al Nafīs, and Quṭb al-dīn al-Shīrāzī.

The Jewish philosopher, Nathan ben Joel Falaquera, compiled a large collection of extracts from the Greek and Arabic medical writings in Hebrew translation under the title Ẓori ha-guf. The same purpose was accomplished by Latin collections such as the Revocativum memoriae of John of Saint Amand and the Aggregator brixiensis of William Corvi. Maurus wrote a commentary on Hippocrates' Aphorisms. Abundant commentaries on Greek and Arabic medicine were published by Peter of Spain, Taddeo Alderotti and Arnold of Villanova. Taddeo had made special efforts to reach the original texts; he criticized severely Constantine's translations and insisted upon the necessity of translating the Greek classics not from the Arabic but from the Greek as was done by Burgundio of Pisa, whom he praised accordingly.

It should be noted that all of the writers thus far quoted, whether Christian,[50] Jewish, or Muslim, had essentially the same medical background, the same tradi-

[50] It would be more correct to say Western Christian or Latin, for the Byzantine physicians —the Greek writing ones— were hopelessly behind the times.

tions. By the middle or the end of the thirteenth century the same medical classics might already be found in the libraries of Paris, Montpellier, Bologna, Salerno, Granada, Cairo, Damascus or Baghdād. In no other way can the achievement of these two centuries be better measured. At the beginning of the twelfth century in spite of Constantine's translations—which were then eagerly studied in Salerno and began to percolate into other countries—the Latin world was still considerably behind the Arabic. Its knowledge not only of the Arabic medicine but also of the Greek was rudimentary. Saracenic doctors could consider their Christian colleagues, who followed the Crusaders, as barbarians. By the end of the thirteenth century the situation had entirely changed. The Muslims were still ahead in many respects, but one feels that their supremacy would not last much longer, for the Christians, not to speak of the Jews, were now fully informed and ready to forge ahead. In fact with regard to one branch of medicine at least—surgery—the Christians were already in tbe van of progress.

The three main medical traditions—Jewish, Christian, Muslim—were now largely amalgamated. If we proceed further East outside of the Dār al-Islām in India and the Far East, in the real—Buddhist—Asia, we come across entirely different traditions.

An art as complex as medicine needs the backing of social experience. Each individual makes experiments to be sure, but however numerous these may be and however able he himself may be to improve his opportunities, his own experience is utterly insufficient and he must needs fall back upon the traditions handed down to him by his predecessors. Hence in each civilized country medical traditions were eagerly transmitted, but the traditions which we are now going to consider were independent of the western (Greek-Arabic-Latin) ones.

In India, Ḍallana wrote a commentary on the Suśruta-saṃhitā and, somewhat later, Hemādri wrote one on the Ashṭāṅgahṛidayasaṃhitā of Vāgbhaṭa (vol. 1, 76, 480).

In China, the main commentator was apparently Liu Wan-su who flourished during the Chin dynasty of the Nü-Chên Tartars (1115–1260). Many of his writings were devoted to the ancient medical classics, the Huang Ti Nei-ching su-wên and the Shang-han-lun (vol. 1, 122, 310).

It is of course probable that common elements would be found in these three divergent traditions: the Western (Greek-Arabic-Latin), the Hindu, and the Chinese if only because the fundamental problems of health and disease were the same all the world over; it is even possible that a few of these common elements might be traced back to a single origin, but that would not affect the independence of these traditions very much. Let us hope that thorough comparisons between them may some day be accomplished; they are still out of the question and long investigations will be needed to make them possible.

48. *General medicine*—After the translations and commentaries, going up another step, we shall now examine the general medical treatises, those which may be assumed to be more or less original—though I must repeat that in some cases more originality is to be found in the commentaries than in the new treatises.

The most important of these treatises were written in Arabic. Let us begin with them. We shall deal first with the treatises written in the East by Muslims or by Jews; then with those of western origin.

The earliest physician we come across is Sa'īd ibn Hibat Allāh of Baghdād who died at the very beginning of the twelfth century. He wrote a medical summary, the Mughnī fi tadbīr al-amrāḍ, and a discourse on the creation of man, Maqāla fī khalq al-insān, wherein a number of physiological questions are discussed. Other treatises were written in the twelfth century by 'Adnān al-'Ainzarbī, the Kāfī fī 'ilm al-ṭibb; by Ibn Hubal, the Mukhtār fīl-ṭibb; by the great encyclopaedist, Ibn al-Jauzī, the Luqaṭ al-manāfi' fīl-ṭibb. The two last named were Baghdādites; the first, 'Adnān, spent also many years in Baghdād but he came from Asia Minor. To these Arabic treatises should be added those written in Persian, namely the immense Dhakhīra al-Khwārizmshāhī of Ismā'īl al-Jurjānī, and the medical portions of the encyclopaedias of Fakhr al-dīn al-Rāzī. In the thirteenth century various Arabic treatises were composed by Najīb al-dīn of Samarqand, notably his Kitāb al-asbāb wal-'alāmāt, whose influence may be followed in the East for at least five centuries, and by Ibn Ṭarkhān of Damascus. The latter's Tadhkira al-hādiya also enjoyed a very long popularity. It is often called after its author, the Tadhkira Ibn Ṭarkhān.

Barring their respective doxologies the medical writings of Eastern Jews can hardly be distinguished from those of the Muslims. In the twelfth and thirteenth centuries Egyptian medicine was largely Jewish. Important treatises were written in Arabic by a number of Egyptian Jews: the Irshād li maṣāliḥ al anfās wal-ajsād of Ibn Jamī', completed by his son Abū Ṭāhir Ismā'īl; the Fuṣūl fīl-ṭibb of Maimonides; the Minhāj al-dukkān of al-Kūhīn al-'Aṭṭār (extremely popular); the Kitāb al-muntakhab of Solomon Cohen.

These Muslim and Jewish physicians of Egypt, Syria and farther East, formed undoubtedly an imposing group. Those of the Maghrib were less numerous, but equally distinguished. There was first of all the famous family of the Ibn Zuhr; one of the finest examples of medical heredity in the whole past. The two greatest members of that family, Abū-l-'Alā' Zuhr and his son Abū Marwān ibn Zuhr (Avenzoar), flourished in the first half of the twelfth century. Abū-l-'Alā' wrote many treatises on materia medica and at least one of a more general nature, the Kitāb al-nukat al-ṭibbiya. His illustrious son, Abū Marwān, is best remembered by the Taisīr which was meant to be a sort of counterpart to the Kullīyāt of his friend Ibn Rushd. Those two treatises, the Taisīr and the Kullīyāt (Colliget) are among the most valuable of their kind in mediaeval times. Though Ibn al-Baiṭār spent almost thirty years of his life in the East and died in Damascus, this cannot cancel the fact of his birth in Malaga and his Spanish education. He was primarily a pharmaceutist, but his two works were so important, that they may be counted here among the general treatises. They were truly standard works but partly because of their relative lateness (middle of the thirteenth century) their influence however great in Islām was negligible outside of it.

The only Hebrew treatise deserving to be quoted in this section is the Ẓori haguf composed by Nathan ben Joel Falaquera in the second half of the thirteenth century.

The twelfth century was the golden age of the Salernitan school. Its remembrance is perpetuated by a few Latin treatises which do not bear comparison with the Arabic ones of the same time; yet we are deeply interested in them because however crude and elementary they are the beginnings of European medicine. The Practica brevis of John Platearius the Younger dates from the end of the eleventh century. Other Practicae were composed by Archimatthaeus, Bartholomew of Salerno, Petronius, and John of Saint Paul. A more ambitious author was Urso of Calabria who discussed medico-philosophical questions as the Arabic writers loved to do. An independent tradition more purely Latin and Benedictine, folkloric, was represented by Hildegard of Bingen, the most original medical writer of Latindom in the twelfth century.

During the following century Salernitan knowledge spread gradually across the Alps. Giles of Corbeil was its main expositor in Montpellier and later in Paris, and Henrik Harpestraeng, in Denmark. The English people heard of it through Alfred of Sareshel, Robert Grosseteste, Gilbert the Englishman, Richard of Wendover. The most important Latin treatises of the first half of the thirteenth century were due to these Englishmen: the De motu cordis to Alfred, the Micrologus to Richard, and the Lilium to Gilbert.

In the second half of the century the main work was done by Italians and by a solitary Portuguese. The latter, Peter of Spain (pope John XXI in 1276–1277), wrote a little textbook, the Thesaurus pauperum, which enjoyed an immense popularity, not only in Latin but in sundry other languages, including Hebrew. The medical initiation of Christian Europe had been accomplished by Southern Italians, the Salernitan masters of the eleventh and twelfth centuries; the foremost Latin writings of our period were composed by other Italians, but this time, Northerners, toward its very end. William of Saliceto wrote his Summa conservationis et curationis after 1275; Simon of Genoa's dictionary, the Clavis sanationis, dates probably from the last decade of the thirteenth century. Under the influence of the law school of Bologna, Taddeo Alderotti began to write medical treatises in the scholastic manner. This new tendency was strongly accentuated in the Aggregator brixiensis of William Corvi, and in the Conciliator and the Lucidator of Peter of Abano. These works bring us already into the following century, though both men, being born in or about 1250, certainly belong to the thirteenth century. In fact, Peter's works were completed in the first decade of the fourteenth century.

The Summa conservationis, the Clavis sanationis, the Aggregator, the Conciliator, and the Lucidator may be said to close this period in a spiritual as well as in a purely chronological sense: the period of reorganization of medical knowledge after the assimilation of the main Arabic writings, also the first period of independent Latin or European medicine. It is remarkable that these monuments were constructed by men belonging to a relatively small region, the quadrilateral whose summits are Genoa, Brescia, Padua and Bologna.

Another Christian offshoot of the Arabic tree, was the Armenian represented by a treatise written in 1184 by Mekhitar of Her and by other anonymous ones which date possibly from the same time. These texts are of archaeological and linguistic interest, but are scientifically negligible, not however because of their intrinsic value which is not much below the Latin standard of the twelfth century, but because of their sterility. The poorest Latin treatises were stepping stones which led gradually to the summits of modern medicine; the Armenian ones led nowhere, not even to modern Armenian medicine, which is derived from the West. Mekhitar flourished in the New Armenian Kingdom (ancient Cilicia) and his treatise was a part and symbol of the Armenian renaissance. Great Armenia was under Muslim rule, and Arabic was spoken there as much as the old national language. I know of but a single physician who practised in that country, the Muslim Ibn Hubal who was attached for a time to the court of the Shāh of Akhlāṭ, at the western end of the lake of Vān. Another Muslim physician, whom we have already mentioned, 'Adnān al-'Ainzarbī, hailed from Anazarbos in Cilicia, Dioscorides' birthplace.

The main general treatises in Chinese seem to be those of Ch'ên Yen, Liu Wan-su, and Chang Tzŭ-ho. They contain elaborations of the complicated symmetries and analogies so pleasurable to the Chinese mind, fantastic and premature rationalizations of little if any scientific value. We can evoke the spiritual conditions represented by these treatises by trying to imagine what would have happened if the theory of microcosmos and macrocosmos had been allowed to develop in Europe without any kind of experimental counterweight. The Chinese were accomplished virtuosi in the field of arbitrary theorization. It was with them like "l'art pour l'art," theorization for its own sake with hardly any reference to reality. Such thinking in a sort of spiritual vacuum is doomed to sterility: Chinese medicine is a gigantic illustration of this.

49. *Medical tables*—A Christian physician of Baghdād, Ibn Buṭlān, had the idea about the middle of the eleventh century of summarizing medical knowledge in the form of synoptic tables, Taqwīm al-ṣiḥḥa.[50a] This was imitated a little later in the work of another Christian Baghdādite, Ibn Jazla, and thus originated a tradition which was continued in the twelfth century, witness the Arabic tables of Ibn Biklārish, a Jew of Saragossa, and the Latin ones of Salernus.

50. *Anatomy*—Anatomical progress was almost exclusively due to Christian efforts, which is not surprising considering the Semitic abhorrence of blood. This progress was initiated by the school of Salerno, and is—together with the surgical progress closely connected with it—its chief glory. The earliest Salernitan—and European—anatomy is the one ascribed to one Copho. It dates from the beginning of the twelfth century (or the end of the eleventh century) and is based upon the dissection of the pig. The Anatomia porci was followed one or two generations later by another conventionally called the Second Salernitan Demonstration, which is of essentially the same kind as the first but more elaborate. A third text, the Anatomia Mauri, shows a little more independence than the earlier ones but is still porcine. A fourth one, the Anatomia Ricardi, marks a distinct step forward because it describes, or at any rate purports to describe, human anatomy. A fifth Salernitan anatomy may possibly be ascribed to Urso of Calabria. These five texts enable us to measure the advance of a whole century. The progress may seem very small, but we must not forget that the beginnings are always very difficult, especially when the way is blocked by religious opposition and sentimental prejudice. Rapid progress was possible only when (and as soon as) these prejudices were removed; it involved a complete spiritual volte-face. The intensity and depth of these prejudices can be appreciated by the time it took not to destroy them (they still exist and ever will) but simply to neutralize them: it was not a matter of one century but of four. We must always bear that in mind when we judge the fruits of the first century; all considered they were remarkable, and they were entirely due to the school of Salerno.

As that school declined rapidly after the twelfth century, we must look elsewhere for the subsequent achievements. However in the thirteenth century anatomical progress was strangely jeopardized by the triumph of Aristotelianism. The opinions of Aristotle were victoriously opposed to those of Galen though the latter were generally nearer to the truth. This is reflected in the Anatomia vivorum ascribed to Richard of Wendover. That new anatomy dating from about the middle of the thirteenth century was largely derived from the Qānūn but in controversial questions Aristotle's authority was upheld against Galen's. The Anato-

[50a] Lynn Thorndike and George Sarton: Tacuinum, taqwīm (Isis, 10, 489–493, 1928).

mia vivorum was apparently the main source of Albert the Great who reproduced almost verbatim its anti-Galenic conclusions.

This regression due to philosophical conceit was happily compensated toward the end of the period by the opening or reopening of experimental sources, without access to which anatomical progress was impossible. These sources were human dissection and post-mortem examinations. Human bodies were dissected occasionally (very rarely it must be admitted) in the second half of the thirteenth century; some evidence of such dissection is found in the Cyrurgia of William of Saliceto (1275). By the way this William was the first to write what might be called a topographical (or surgical) anatomy. Anatomy and surgery walked hand in hand: better anatomy made better surgery possible; on the other hand, surgical experience was one of the best sources of new anatomical knowledge. Toward the end of the century under the influence of the law school of Bologna, the value of post-mortem examinations began to be recognized. An autopsy made for a purely legal purpose was (or might be) nevertheless very interesting from the anatomical or medical point of view. However the post-mortems made in the thirteenth century were too few in number to have any practical importance. We simply record the germ of a method which would give abundant fruits many centuries later. Indeed pathological anatomy could never have developed as it did without the evidence afforded by numerous autopsies.

The practice of human dissections prepared the anatomical renaissance of the fourteenth century, symbolized by the name of Mondino de' Luzzi. We shall deal with him in volume 3, for the Anathomia Mundini was only completed in 1316. However we may recall that Mondino was born in Bologna about 1275 and that in his youth he must have witnessed some of the anatomical, surgical, or legal demonstrations referred to above.

The early anatomical texts included many physiological facts and observations. An organ and its function were described together. Anatomy and physiology were hardly separated. Sometimes however the physiological point of view would dominate, as in the Motus cordis of Alfred of Sareshel (before 1217). General medical treatises often contained an anatomical and surgical introduction; this was the case for example for Ibn Sīnā's Qānūn which remained the medical bible of Christendom until modern times and of Islām until yesterday or even to-day. Hence a complete history of anatomy and physiology in the twelfth and thirteenth centuries should include a survey of all the medical treatises not specifically devoted to other subjects.

Very little was accomplished in the field of comparative anatomy. The emperor Frederick II made some excellent remarks on the anatomy of birds in his treatise on falconry (e.g., pneumaticity of their bones, peculiar form of the sternum). Albert the Great's anatomy—mentioned above—was included in his De animalibus; he compared the organs of various animals with those of man.

Muslim and Jewish views on anatomy and physiology are found in their medical encyclopaedias; they are simply restatements and elaborations of Galenic and Avicennian knowledge. For example a summary of Galenic anatomy was composed by the Egyptian Hibatallāh ibn Malkā, a Jew who had embraced Islām, under the title Ikhtiṣār al-tashrīḥ. A positive addition to our knowledge was made by another Egyptian, 'Abd al-Laṭīf, who had an opportunity of examining a large quantity of human ossements: he observed that the lower maxillary is made of one piece not of two, and that the sacrum is generally consolidated into a single bone.

Chinese anatomy would hardly deserve to be discussed, but for the fact that it affords an excellent illustration of the danger and the stupidity of premature rationalization (Isis, 14, 257).

51. *Surgery*—The transition from anatomy to surgery is natural enough. Surgeons needed a more intimate knowledge of anatomy than any other medical practitioner, and conversely, the very exercise of their profession gave them opportunities of increasing their knowledge.

The relative importance of the surgery of this time will be indicated at once by stating that whatever medical progress was accomplished was largely surgical. That progress was almost exclusively creditable to Christian doctors, most of them Italians. To be sure these doctors were familiar with the Greco-Arabic tradition, yet their achievements were original to a degree. After all a surgeon cannot get away with a shibboleth; he must work with his hands—and hands are far more honest than brains, one cannot fool them, nor induce them to pretend. They work or they do not, and the results of their actions are not far remote. There is no chance of bluffing, and mistakes are paid for in cash.

As for medical practice in general, we must divide the history of Christian surgery into two periods, the Salernitan, covering the twelfth century and the beginning of the thirteenth, and the post-Salernitan, covering the rest of the thirteenth century.

Surgery did not begin in Salerno as early as general medicine, the earliest and greatest surgeon being Roger who flourished about 1170. This delay is understandable enough. In the first place, the assimilation of Arabic knowledge and the organization of general practice were more urgent tasks and they taxed the energy of Salernitan practitioners to the limit for more than a century; in the second place, the surgical revival was to a large extent a result of the Crusades—war is the mother of surgery!—but it took a little while for that result to be felt and for the new surgery to develop. All considered we could hardly expect the Salernitan textbook of surgery, the Post mundi fabricam, to appear much earlier than it did, toward the end of the third quarter of the twelfth century. Up to that time Salernitan surgery had been purely Constantinian as far as literary sources were concerned, and Roger was naturally well acquainted with Constantine's versions, but in the writing of his treatise he took full advantage of his own experience and that of his brother surgeons. Hence the Post mundi fabricam is far more than an elaboration of Arabic surgery; it is truly the first monument of European surgery.

The following steps were made outside of Salerno. A disciple of Roger's, Roland of Parma, carried Salernitan surgery to Lombardy. The Chirurgia rolandina was not essentially different from Roger's Practica, except that it was perhaps a little more Arabicized. In the meanwhile indeed Arabic surgery had become far better known through the translation of its masterpiece, the surgical part of Abū-l-Qāsim's Taṣrīf, by Gerard of Cremona. A little later still the Rogerina and the Rolandina were commented upon by four masters whose names are unknown. The Arabic tendencies are still somewhat more accentuated in their commentary, the Glossulae quatuor magistrorum super chirurgiam Rogerii et Rolandi.

Another elaboration of the Rogerina was composed in the first half of the thirteenth century by John Jamatus in South Italy; this was probably the last surgical fruit which could be directly ascribed to Salerno. After this time Salernitan knowledge blossoms and fructifies in other places. We have already said that Roland of Parma took it to North Italy; the "quatuor magistri" were probably French.

The main offshoot of Salerno was the school of Bologna, established by Hugh Borgognoni, and continued by his sons, chiefly Theodoric. In its Bolognese or North Italian phasis, surgery became more and more experimental. At about the same time Salernitan surgery was expounded by a master of Montpellier, William of Congenis.

By the middle of the thirteenth century a great step forward was made by Bruno da Longoburgo in Padua. The latter's Chirurgia magna (1252) continued the evolution thus far described in the same two directions—it was at once more experimental and more Arabic. Its progressive nature illustrates once more the fertility of theory combined with practice. Learning is a very dangerous thing when dissociated from experience: Arabic astrology had played havoc with so many European minds for that very reason. On the contrary, Arabic surgery (or in a more general way, Arabic medicine) had been assimilated by European doctors gradually in proportion to the growth of their own experience. The more the Italian surgeons knew experimentally, the more Arabic learning they were able to assimilate and to profit by.

Bruno's efforts were continued by William of Saliceto in Bologna and Verona, and by the latter's disciple, Lanfranchi, in Milan. Toward the end of the thirteenth century Lanfranchi was banished from that city, and the latest developments of Italian medicine were introduced by him into France. He became one of the greatest medical teachers of the University of Paris.

It is curious that the main medical advance was due to surgeons, who constituted a despised class of practitioners and were looked down upon by other physicians. For example skin diseases were abandoned to them as being too disgusting for self-respecting doctors. This may seem paradoxical at first view, but the paradox is easily explained. The highbrow doctors who spent more time in reading Galen and Ibn Sīnā than in collecting observations and in trying to interpret them, were hopelessly jeopardized. How could they ever progress without experimental methods? They might become more and more "learned"—yet they learned nothing; their "learning" tended to become more and more bookish and empty. On the contrary the humbler-minded surgeons were all the time interrogating nature, receiving and collecting her answers.

It should be noted that these Italian surgeons were surprisingly well educated; they were not simply surgeons in the narrow sense of the word; their treatises embraced the whole of medicine. Their point of view was surgical or experimental, but their field extended to every kind of discomfort or suffering. In fact one of them, William of Saliceto, wrote not only a Cyrurgia, he also composed a general treatise on medicine.

These writings were very much appreciated, witness the number of manuscripts and translations. It is typical that most of them were translated into Hebrew. Indeed we have Hebrew translations of the works of Roger of Salerno (?), Roland of Parma, Theodoric Borgognoni, William of Congenis, Bruno of Longoburgo, William of Saliceto, and Lanfranchi. One of them at least was a very early one, Bruno's Chirurgia magna being translated by Hillel ben Samuel before the end of the century.

To these Latin and Hebrew treatises should be added the mysterious Arabic one ascribed to Mesuë the Third. The original Arabic text is lost and its reality has even been doubted, but we have a Latin translation (or edition) of it made by Faraj ben Salīm and a Hebrew one prepared a few years later by Jacob ben Joseph ha-Levi (1297). The only other Arabic treatise on surgery of this period which I can think of is the 'Umda fī ṣinā'at al-jirāḥa of Ibn al-Quff, who was an Eastern Christian! Thus in this instance even the Arabic works were witnesses of the growing superiority of Christendom.

52. *Pulse and urine*—The two methods of diagnosis which were the most popular in our period were the examination of the patient's urine and the feeling of his pulse.

Both methods were ancient. The Hippocratic writings contain many remarks on urine but none is specifically devoted to it; there are various Galenic writings on the subject but their authenticity is uncertain.[51] The Περὶ οὔρων ascribed to Galen was possibly written by one Magnos of Emesa who flourished somewhat later (fourth to sixth century). The Greek doctrines on urine were collected and reexplained by Theophilos Protospatharios (first half of the seventh century), whose treatise was very much used. However it is difficult to say how much of the mediaeval urological tradition was directly derived from Theophilos (or Philaretus, Philotheus, as he was also called). There is a strong probability that most of it reached Latin Christendom only indirectly through the Arabic elaboration, the Kitāb al-baul, prepared by an Egyptian Jew, Isḥāq al-Isrā'īlī, about the end of the ninth or the beginning of the tenth century. The Kitāb al-baul was translated into Latin by Constantine the African, and into Hebrew. This work was so popular—witness the large number of Latin and Hebrew manuscripts of its own text and of various summaries or elaborations—that the study of its tradition is very difficult. For example it would seem that some Hebrew texts were derived from the Arabic and others from the Latin. Whatever the exact means of transmission, there is no doubt that the whole Middle Ages, whether Christian or Muslim, obtained their urological knowledge from Theophilos Protospatharios and Ishāq al-Isrā'īlī, and that that knowledge was essentially Galenic.[52]

Of course every Practica dealt with urine, but there were also a few treatises specifically devoted to it. The earliest seem to date from the second half of the eleventh century, namely a Greek synopsis by Symeon Seth and Latin ones by John the Saracen and John Platearius the Younger (Regulae urinarum).

More Latin treatises on urology were published by Matthaeus de Archiepiscopo, Maurus, Urso of Calabria, Giles of Corbeil, and Michael Scot. The fact that Giles' De urinarum judiciis was written in verse helps to explain its enormous popularity; it continued to be read and conned until the sixteenth century. Maurus' treatise was translated into Hebrew. A Greek treatise is ascribed to Maximos Planudes.

Sphygmology is even older than urology and more universal. The early Egyptian physicians were already aware of the pulse: there are references to it in the Smith and Ebers papyri dating from the seventeenth and sixteenth centuries but representing the knowledge of earlier times (the Old Kingdom, or Pyramid age, say, thirtieth to twenty-sixth century). Indeed the author of the text of the Smith

[51] In C. G. Kühn's Greco-Latin edition of Galen (vol. 19, Leipzig 1830): Galeno adscriptus liber de urinis, περὶ οὔρων (p. 574–601). Galeni de urinis compendium (p. 602–608). De urinis ex Hippocrate, Galeno et aliis quibusdam (p. 609–628). None of these treatises is included in the Arabic canon established by Ḥunain ibn Isḥāq (Isis, 8, 685–724).

[52] M. Steinschneider: Die hebraeischen Übersetzungen (757, 833, 1893). E. Desnos: Histoire de l'urologie (Encyclopédie française d'urologie, vol. 1, Paris 1914; Isis, 2, 466). The mediaeval part of Desnos' account is utterly insufficient, yet it contains interesting data. Johannes Peine: Die Harnschrift des Isaac Judaeus (Diss., Leipzig 1919; Isis, 4, 579).

papyrus was not only aware of the pulse but fully realized its importance.[53] Strangely enough in spite of that long Egyptian experience Greek sphygmology was rather slow in shaping itself. There are references to the pulse (φλεβοπαλία) in Democritos and in the early Hippocratic treatise περὶ τροφῆς, but for a clearer appreciation of it we have to wait until the days of Praxagoras and Herophilos. The most significant Greek treatise on the subject was written by Rufus who flourished under Trajan. There is an abundant Galenic literature including five long treatises and three shorter ones,[54] the greatest part of which was available in Arabic before the end of the ninth century. Moreover Greek knowledge was summed up by Theophilos Protospatharios in the first half of the seventh century, and Theophilos' account was soon translated into Latin and into Hebrew.

Greek sphygmology was thus transmitted to the Arabic, Latin, and Hebrew readers as fully as one would wish. This may help to explain the relative scarcity of original writings in these languages. To be sure every general treatise on medicine discussed the pulse, but I know only of a very few special treatises on the subject. The only Arabic one on nabḍ (pulse) I have come across is anterior to our period; it is the one by Abū Sahl al-Masīḥī, a Christian physician, Ibn Sīnā's teacher, who died at the very end of the tenth century. A very popular Latin treatise was the one written in verse by Giles of Corbeil.

Hindu and Chinese physicians devoted considerable attention to the pulse. There is an elaborate analysis of it in the Śārṅgadharasaṃhitā. The Chinese study of the pulse goes back at least to the time of Chang Chung-ching, who was one of Galen's contemporaries; it may be much older. Chinese sphygmology was elaborated to the point of absurdity: they distinguished 27 kinds of pulse, while the Greeks distinguished at most 15. Considering their extraordinary interest in the pulse, it is strange that they paid hardly any attention to urine.[55]

53. *Bloodletting and purgation*—The two favorite methods of treatment—methods of almost universal application—were bloodletting and purgation. Both methods had been used from time out of mind.

Bloodletting was practised in three ways: by venesection, by cupping, and by the application of leeches. Venesection may have been discovered accidentally in prehistoric days; it was practised in ancient Egypt and Babylonia, probably also in ancient India. Cupping is also of great antiquity. Primitive people used animals' horns as cupping-glasses. The use of leeches seems to be of somewhat later origin. For example, none of the Hippocratic writings is specially devoted

[53] James Henry Breasted: The Edwin Smith surgical papyrus (Chicago University Press, 2 vols., 1930; Isis, 15, 355–367).

[54] The following are included in Kühn's edition: (1) Galeni de pulsuum usu liber (vol. 5, 149–180, 1823); (2) De pulsibus libellus ad tirones (vol. 8, 453–492, 1824); (3) De pulsuum differentiis libri IV (vol. 8, 493–765); (4) De dignoscendis pulsibus libri IV (vol. 8, 766–961); (5) De causis pulsuum libri IV (vol. 9, 1–204, 1825); (6) De praesagitione ex pulsibus libri IV (vol. 9, 205–430); (7) Synopsis librorum suorum de pulsibus (vol. 9, 431–549); (8) De pulsibus ad Antonium disciplinae studiosum ac philosophum (vol. 19, 629–642, 1830). All of these writings but the last one are included in the Arabic canon established by Ḥunain ibn Isḥāq. See G. Bergstraesser's edition of it (Leipzig 1925), or M. Meyerhof's analysis of it (Isis, 8, 685–724), under the nos. 41, 5, 16 (four treatises), and 66.

[55] Eugène Vincent: La médecine en Chine au XXe siècle (300, Paris 1915). J. Dyer Ball and E. Chalmers Werner: Things Chinese (187, London 1926). Franz Hübotter: Die chinesische Medizin zu Beginn des XX. Jahrhunderts und ihr historischer Entwicklungsgang (Leipzig 1929; Isis, 14, 255–263); On the Mo-ching and the Mai-chüeh ascribed to Wang Shu-ho (Isis, 15, 202).

to bloodletting, but they mention venesection and cupping very often; on the contrary I found no reference in them to the medical use of leeches.[56] Pliny was acquainted with that use, and there are many references to it in Galen. The latter provided the main literary sources of mediaeval knowledge on bloodletting.[57]

In the period now under review the practice of bloodletting was dominated by the Galenic knowledge transmitted by the Arabians, and by all the astrological fancies which had gradually clustered around it. According to the complaint to be cured venesection had to be done at this or that point of the body, which was selected for good and bad reasons, and it had to be done at a propitious time in a propitious manner. Such a method gave ample scope for the elaboration of astrological rules. In general the Greeks practised venesection on the same side as the complaint to be cured; another method, called derivative bleeding, consisted in opening a vein on the opposite side and as far as possible from the seat of trouble. The Arabians are credited with the development of that second method but I have not yet been able to determine their share of responsibility in the manner, nor to find which were the earliest Arabic writings recommending derivative bleeding. The respective merits of both methods caused a tremendous controversy in the first half of the sixteenth century.

To return for a moment to the leeches, the importance of their use in early mediaeval times, at least in England, is symbolized by their very name. The Anglo-Saxon word læce (hence, our leech) meant at once the animal (annulate worms of the class Hirudinea) and the physician making use of it. Which one was named after the other? Many variants of that word would suggest that there were originally two separate words which were assimilated through popular etymology.[58] However interpreted, the confusion of both words, or the existence of but one for both ideas, proves that leeches were in common use. It may be recalled that that ancient practice became immensely popular in the first half of the nineteenth century, chiefly under the influence of the French physician François Joseph Victor Broussais (1772–1838), and later fell into almost complete desuetude.[59] It is a strange irony of fate that within recent years leeches have again been hunted for, because their saliva contains an haemolysin—hirudin—preventing the coagulation of blood.

Needless to say every general textbook on medicine or hygiene of our period contains an account of bloodletting or some references to it. There were also a few treatises entirely devoted to it. For example, the Arabic one entitled Al-maqāla al-Amīnīya fīl-faṣd, by the Christian Baghdādite Ibn al-Tilmīdh; or the

[56] In Littré's edition (vol. 9, 45), Prorrhetic (book 2, chapter 17), there is a reference to a leech (βδέλλα) accidentally stuck in the throat.

[57] Kühn's edition includes the following treatises: (1) De venae sectione adversus Erasistratum (vol. 11, 147–186, 1826); (2) De venae sectione adversus Erasistrateos Romae degentes (vol. 11, 187–249); (3) De curandi ratione per venae sectionem (vol. 11, 250–316); (4) De hirudinibus, revulsione, cucurbitula, incisione et scarificatione (vol. 11, 317–322). These treatises 1 to 3 or 1 to 4 are sometimes considered as one bearing the title of the first. (5) De venae sectione (vol. 19, 519–528, 1830). The treatises 1 to 3 were included in the Arabic canon established by Ḥunain ibn Isḥāq as one item under the title Kitāb fīl-faṣd.

[58] See Murray's New English dictionary, sub voce. The earliest example of the word leech = animal is dated "before 900"; the earliest example of the word leech = physician is dated "about 900." Cf. Icelandic, læknari, Danish, læge, Swedish, läkare, Russian, lekar, lechit (to heal).

[59] Not so fast however. When I was a child Belgian country doctors were still keeping quantities of leeches in readiness for their patients.

Latin ones by Maurus, John of Aquila and Peter of Dacia. Maurus' treatise was translated into Hebrew.

As far as I know, bloodletting was not practised in China but was replaced by another technique without equivalent in the West, acupuncture, consisting in pricking definite parts of the body with needles and inserting these needles more or less deeply into the tissues and into the organs. Even as every Latin or Arabic treatise on general medicine devoted some space to bloodletting, even so, every Chinese one—unless it be specifically dedicated to some other special subject—may be assumed to contain an account of acupuncture. The analogy with bloodletting is much closer than one would think for the practice of acupuncture was soon regulated by a system of rules of increasing complexity, similar to the astrological rules of the West, but even more arbitrary and intricate. An idea of the complication of acupuncture is given by the fact that the number of places hsüeh[4]* (4840) in the body wherein needles may be inserted is as high as 308 or even 650 with certain authorities, each having its definite indications. My earliest reference to acupuncture in vol. 1 (p. 342) was relative to Huang Fu who flourished in the second half of the third century, but the practice was possibly much older. From China it spread to Japan, at least as early as the tenth century, for it is already explained in the oldest Japanese treatise which has come down to us in its original form, the Ishinhō of Yasuyori Tamba, c. 982 (vol. 1, 683). It is continued to this day in both countries.

The bloodletting calendars and images of the West were replaced in the East by anatomical drawings indicating every hsüeh and the peculiar virtues of each. In 1027 Wang Wei-tê was ordered by the emperor to make two copper figures of the human body illustrating the details of acupuncture (vol. 1, 732).[60]

Acupuncture is often associated with moxibustion, that is, cauterization by means of moxa.[61] Moxibustion was already explained by Sun Ssŭ-mo (second half of the seventh century) but it could probably be traced to earlier times (vol. 1, 499).

My statement as to the absence of bloodletting in China must be qualified by a curious restriction. It is said that the Ch'i T'an Tartars, a Mongol race which ruled China during the Liao dynasty (907–1125) drank human blood: the husbands drinking from the living bodies of their wives by cutting a small slit in their back.[62]

Passing to purgation, it is easy to imagine that primitive people discovered the virtues of certain plants and substances and learned to make use of them even before the dawn of historical times. Purgatives and emetics were probably among the earliest drugs of mankind. Even the use of enemata and clysters, which was much less obvious, is very ancient. Pliny would have us believe that men learned

[60] Eugène Vincent: La médecine en Chine (42, 1915). J. Dyer Ball and E. Chalmers Werner: Things Chinese (10, 1926). Franz Hübotter: Die chinesische Medizin (Leipzig 1929; Isis, 14, 255–263). Hübotter's work contains many acupuncture images. The existence of such copper figures as the one of 1027 is confirmed by the fact that the treatise on acupuncture of Chiang[1] T'ing[1]-lü[2] (1233, 11284, 7522) tzŭ[4] (12324) Kung[1]-wang[4] (6568, 12509), was entitled Hsin[1] chien[1] t'ung[2] jên[2] chên[1] chiu[3] t'u[2] ching[1] (4574, 1649, 12285, 5624, 615, 2275, 12128, 2122), meaning "classic of the copper acupuncture man recently engraved." That treatise is divided into seven books plus a supplement, and contains 20 full-page figures of the body in various positions. The Library of Congress has a reprint of it made in 1700 by Liu[2] Hsi[2]* (7270, 4157). See Report of the Librarian for 1929–1930, p. 385.

[61] In Chinese ai[4] huo[3] (32, 5326), escharotic substance obtained from the leaves of the Chinese wormwood, Artemisia moxa, and similar plants.

[62] J. D. Ball and E. C. Werner: Things Chinese (396, 1926).

bloodletting from the hippopotamus and clystering from the ibis who uses his own beak for the purpose![63] At any rate this proves that the practice was already immemorial in Pliny's time. In fact, there are many references to it in the Hippocratic writings. Ancient knowledge on purgatives was transmitted to the West, via the usual Arabic channels, together with the Galenic[64] corpus, Dioscorides and the herbals. The tradition of the herbals has been discussed in section 35. I should have spoken then of Dioscorides, but it may not be too late to do it now. The first Arabic translation of his work was made in the second half of the ninth century by Stephanos son of Basilios, whose task was completed by Ḥunain ibn Isḥāq. A century later the Dioscoridean text was improved in the East by Al-Ḥusain ibn Ibrāhīm, and in the West by Ḥasdai ibn Shaprut and Ibn Juljul. The work of Ḥasdai and his collaborators was a fine symbol of the great Spanish renaissance of that time. Practically all the translations from the Greek into Arabic had been made in the East, but for Dioscorides a Greek manuscript was actually brought to Cordova and used by the translators for the revision of the Arabic text (vol. 1, 680, 682).

It is remarkable that during our period the Arabic text of Dioscorides was not translated into Latin and Hebrew, but transmitted by way of adaptations and commentaries. One of the main interpreters in the West was Mesuë the Younger, "pharmacopoeorum evangelista" (d. 1015), whose works were known only in Latin and Hebrew. One of these works dealt exclusively with purgatives and emetics; it was translated into Hebrew by Samuel ben Jacob of Capua in the second half of the thirteenth century. Treatises specifically devoted to purgatives were few, but every medical treatise and every herbal dealt with them. Some of the treatises on materia medica—notably the Mughnī of Ibn al-Baiṭār—were arranged in pharmacodynamical order and then purgatives would naturally be grouped together.

In this respect Chinese practice was not essentially different from the Muslim and European; the Chinese attached due importance to laxatives (as also to diaphoretics and emetics), but naturally their armamentarium contained other drugs.

There was some amount of discussion among doctors, East and West, as to the relative importance of purgation, but in general they were more likely, all of them, to abuse than to neglect it. For the Chinese aspect of that controversy see, e.g., my notes on Liu Wan-su and Chang Tzŭ-ho.

In the West the practice of bloodletting and clystering was largely abandoned to barber-surgeons, a circumstance which helped to discredit surgery and to keep the surgeons for centuries in a position of social and professional inferiority as compared with other physicians.

54. *Erotics*—The historian of medicine, especially of oriental medicine, must consider a class of books which would seem at first view to lie outside of his field, yet touch it in many points. I am referring to the erotic books of which there were as many, relatively speaking, in mediaeval times as in any other. These books might be compared to the "sex" books of our own days—to the whole gamut of

[63] Natural history, book 8, chapters 40 and 41 (or 26 and 27).

[64] There are abundant references to purgation in Galen, but he devoted only two short treatises to it. De purgantium medicamentorum facultate (Kühn's edition, vol. 11, 323–342, 1826); Quos, quibus catharticis medicamentis et quando purgare oporteat (vol. 11, 343–356). The first was included in the Arabic canon of Ḥunain ibn Isḥāq, no. 44 in Bergsträsser's edition and Meyerhof's analysis.

them, from the most innocent, which tender helpful advice to troubled adolescence or to the young married people, to the most wicked, which are nothing but literary aphrodisiacs.

The books on the Ars amandi in the Ovidian manner do not concern us, on the other hand those on gynaecology and obstetrics will be discussed in the following section. We are now concerned with an intermediary group half-medical half-erotic which is almost exclusively represented by Arabic (or Persian) publications. These books contain in various proportions advice on sexual intercourse, gynaecological prescriptions, proverbs on men and women in love, recipes for all kinds of aphrodisiac or anaphrodisiac foods and drugs, smutty anecdotes, etc. It is clear that the goodness or wickedness of the book depends entirely on the proportions of the various ingredients, on the author's avowed or hidden intention, on his morality. I have not examined these books carefully enough to attempt a classification of them, which would be delicate, and tedious, and hardly worthwhile. A good example of the best kind of such books is the Maqāla fīl-jimā' which Maimonides composed for one of Saladin's nephews. It was written in Arabic but translated at least twice into Hebrew. Two other important treatises were published at about the same time, the one by Samū'īl ibn 'Abbās, an Islāmized Jew who came from the Maghrib but died in Adharbāyjān, the other by 'Abd al-Raḥmān ibn Naṣrallāh of Shīrāz. The first was half-erotic, half-gynaecological, the second, entitled "Explanation of the secrets of married life" was probably more strongly erotic. Some of the best known Arabic works on this subject were written about the middle of the thirteenth century by the Egyptian lapidarist al-Tīfāshī. I know of only one Latin book of this class (but there are probably more), namely the De coitu of Arnold of Villanova, but the Secreta mulierum ascribed to Albert the Great was partly meant to gratify the same kind of itching curiosity.

Another aspect of Muslim eroticism is revealed by their treatises on materia medica which always contain a very rich assortment of aphrodisiacs and anaphrodisiacs. The same is true of every oriental pharmacopoeia, e.g., of the Chinese pên-ts'ao. As far as Islām is concerned it is probable that the institution of polygamy had something to do with that. Of course there are dissolute people everywhere, but my point is that in Islām even the least profligate were irresistibly led to abuse their sexual vigor. A pious Muslim was bound to treat his wives equally; if he was of a generous temperament this led him easily to over-indulgence and to exhaustion. Hence the need of aphrodisiacs, whether in the form of drugs or of literature, was perhaps greater in Islām than in Christendom.

55. *Women's diseases and midwifery*—Erotical books often contain information on normal and abnormal menstruation, on pregnancy and confinement; on the other hand gynaecological treatises may include remarks on women and love which are more erotical than medical: hence these two classes of books might to some extent have been discussed together. I can but repeat that my classification, like any other, is somewhat artificial. Each important book mentioned in any section might properly be introduced into half a dozen other sections and considered from as many angles, but this would confuse our survey rather than clarify it.

The study of women's diseases is one of the oldest branches of medicine. The earliest medical texts extant (the Kahun papyri and the Gardiner fragments dating from the beginning of the second millennium)[65] already contain gynaecological

[65] Francis Llewellyn Griffith: The Petrie papyri, hieratic papyri from Kahun and Gurob (London 1898). J. H. Breasted: The Edwin Smith surgical papyrus (vol. 1, Chicago 1930; Isis, 15, 355–367).

recipes. Every general treatise had necessarily its gynaecological section. There were also special treatises of which the most famous Latin one was the mysterious "Trotula" or Liber de passionibus mulierum. Do we have to take the word Trotula as a sort of title or trademark or as the name of the author? There was a famous "mulier salernitana" bearing the name of Trotula, but was she really the author of this book or was the book named after her to capitalize her fame? An earnest and convincing plea for her authorship has recently been made by another woman physician.[66] Whether Trotula wrote the Trotula or not, that book is very precious because it gives us a definite idea of Salernitan midwifery. It is practically the only Latin textbook of our period, if it is not somewhat earlier. The only other I can think of, is the Secreta mulierum ascribed to Albert the Great; one might also quote the treatise on generation prefacing Michael Scot's Physionomia, but these two works are largely irrelevant, and they are insignificant as compared with Trotula. Judging by the number of manuscripts and of references to it in later works the latter was very popular.

The main independent gynaecological treatise in Arabic was written toward the end of the twelfth century or in the first years of the thirteenth by a Jew, Sheshet Benveniste of Barcelona. The fact that it was written by a Jew would hardly call for notice, but it is remarkable that the author was a Catalan Jew, for by that time the majority of his brethren had already forgotten the use of Arabic. The anomaly was promptly repaired by al-Ḥarizi who translated Sheshet's treatise into Hebrew.

Chinese gynaecology and obstetrics are represented by the writings of Ch'ên Yen who flourished in the last quarter of the twelfth century and half a century later by the elaborate treatise of Ch'ên Tzŭ-ming.[67]

56. *Children's diseases*—In every literature, the discussion of women's complaints and their confinement was generally followed by one or more sections explaining the care of infants. The student of early pediatrics should thus make a close examination of gynaecological literature, but he should consult also other sources. The main pediatrical treatise of the early Middle Ages was the one written by al-Rāzī, which was translated into Latin and into Hebrew. These translations cannot be dated; the Latin one was not made by Gerard of Cremona, but possibly by a member of the latter's school.[68] Moreover there is at least one other early Latin text, dating from the twelfth century or earlier, the Practica puerorum ("Passiones puerorum adhuc in cunabulis iacentium . . .") which did not find its way into print until recent years but was circulated in MS. and used by one of the authors of incunabula pediatrics, Cornelis Roelans of Malines.[69]

[66] Kate Campbell Hurd-Mead: Trotula (Isis, 14, 349–367, 1930).

[67] Additional information may be probably obtained from a much later treatise, the Ch'an[3] k'o[1] hsin[1] fa[2]* (360, 6089, 4562, 3366) by Wang[1] Chê[2]* (12497, 572). Preface dated 1780. It is a work in 2 chüan including two short supplements. The Library of Congress has a copy on yellow paper dated 1870. A. Wylie: Notes on Chinese literature (104, Shanghai 1902). Report of the Librarian of Congress for 1929–1930 (386, 1931).

[68] Al-Rāzī's De curis puerorum in prima aetate was first printed in the Opuscula Rhazis (Milano 1481) and often reprinted. Facsimile edition in Karl Sudhoff: Erstlinge der pädiatrischen Literatur (pls. II to VIII, München 1925). Fragments Englished in John Ruhräh: Pediatrics of the past (19–21, New York 1925; Isis, 8, 386–388). For the MSS. of the Hebrew translation, see M. Steinschneider: Hebraeische Übersetzungen (728, 1893).

[69] Roelans' Liber de aegritudinibus infantium (Louvain c. 1485) was the third treatise on pediatrics to appear in print. I shall discuss it in a later volume. The Practica puerorum was edited by K. Sudhoff: Die Schrift des Cornelius Roelans von Mecheln über Kinderkrankheiten und eine ihrer handschriftlichen Quellen (Janus, vol. 14, 467–485, 1909); Erstlinge der pädiatrischen Literatur (p. xli, 1925).

A Chinese treatise on children's diseases was published by Ch'ien-i (vol. 1, 773), just before the beginning of our period, about 1093, but more information on Chinese pediatrics may be derived from the general treatises and those treating of women's diseases.

57. *Eye diseases*—Next to surgery the most progressive branch of medicine was ophthalmology, but while surgical advance was due to Western Latin doctors, the ophthalmological must be credited primarily to Eastern Muslim ones. Here again we must not forget that both subjects were somewhat mixed, for much of the ophthalmological work was surgical; e.g., Egyptian and Syrian eye doctors developed better methods to operate the cataract; on the other hand the Latin surgical treatises generally contained sections relative to the treatment of eyes.

The superiority of oriental eye doctors is partly explainable by the fact that eye diseases have always been more prevalent in eastern countries than in Western Europe. The problems to be solved were far more pressing in the East, hence it is but natural that the best solutions should have been discovered there. It is significant that the greatest oculists were not simply Muslims, but Eastern Muslims.

The latest oculist to be dealt with in volume 1 (p. 772) was Zarrīn Dast whose Nūr al-'uyūn was written in Persian in 1087. All the Muslim works of our period were written in Arabic. Let us consider these works first together with those composed by Eastern Jews. Indeed those Jewish treatises were also written in Arabic and were not essentially different from the Muslim ones. The only Western Muslim to be quoted in this section was not an eye doctor but a philosopher and general practitioner—no less a person than Ibn Rushd. In the anatomical introduction to his Kullīyāt he recognized the function of the retina.

Arabic ophthalmology began magnificently in the ninth century; we have many treatises of that first golden age by Ibn Māsawaih, Ḥunain ibn Isḥāq, Khalaf al-Ṭūlūnī, 'Alī ibn Rabban al-Ṭabarī, al-Rāzī.[70] The tenth century was a period of rest. More treatises appeared in the eleventh century which might be called a second golden age, witness the excellent Tadhkirat al-kaḥḥālīn of 'Alī ibn 'Īsā, and the Muntakhab fī 'ilāj amrāḍ al-'ain of 'Ammār ibn 'Alī al-Mawṣilī, and other treatises by 'Alī ibn Ibrāhīm ibn Bakhtyashū' and Ibn Sīnā (a part of the Qānūn). The twelfth century was a second period of fallowness but not of final decadence, for the following century saw a renewal of activity which was so remarkable that we might call it a third golden age. Observe the rhythm of that evolution: the ninth, eleventh and thirteenth centuries being the crests of the wave; the tenth and twelfth, the troughs.

The only Arabic work of the twelfth century worth quoting was a collection of observations by a Jewish-Egyptian oculist, Ibn al-Nāqid. In the thirteenth century on the contrary we have a whole series of Arabic treatises, of which two at least were excellent. The renewal was gradual; during the first half of the thirteenth century there was but one distinguished oculist Aḥmad ibn 'Uthmān al-Qaisī; in the second half of the century, I counted four: Ibn Kammūna, Ibn al-Nafīs, Khalīfa ibn abī-l-Maḥāsin and Ṣalāḥ al-dīn ibn Yūsuf. Ibn Kammūna was a Jew, the others Muslims; all of them were Egyptians or Syrians. Khalīfa's treatise, Al-kāfī fīl-kuḥl, and the Nūr al-'uyūn of Ṣalāḥ al-dīn were of special importance. It would seem that these Arabic treatises were generally illustrated; some of the illustrations representing sections of the brains and eyes, the eye nerves,

[70] See the introduction to M. Meyerhof's edition of Ḥunain's treatise (Cairo 1928) or my review of it (Isis, 13, 106–109).

and surgical instruments have come down to us in the manuscripts, but the exact date and nature of the original drawings is difficult if not impossible to determine. These late Arabic treatises were largely derived from the earlier ones of the ninth and the eleventh centuries; the fact remains that during our period ophthalmological knowledge and practice were far more developed in Egypt and Syria than in the rest of the world.

The Jewish physicians of Spain continued the Arabic traditions and carried them across the Pyrenees. Jewish eye doctors became famous in Western Europe. In the thirteenth century there were three kinds of oculists in Latindom: the Judaeus, the rusticus, and the chirurgus expertus in oculis.[71] The rusticus was the empiricist —male or female—using popular remedies, miraculous waters or relics; the chirurgus was the ordinary surgeon who treated a few eye troubles, such as ophthalmias, ulcers, cataracts, etc. Almost every one of the Latin surgical treatises named in section 51 contains some chapters devoted to eye surgery. The Judaeus—generally a Spanish Jew—was the real specialist; his knowledge of Arabic enabled him to obtain his scientific information from the best sources. However the anti-Semitism which was a result of the Crusades in general and of the Crusade against the Albigenses in particular drove him out of France. In 1246 the Council of Béziers forbade Christians to employ Jewish physicians, yet such was the prestige of Jewish oculists that a few years later Alphonse of Poitiers, St. Louis' brother, caused one Habrahym (Abraham) of Aragon to come "ex terra Saracenorum" with a safe-conduct in order to cure him of some eye trouble.

The most important Hebrew work was the translation of the Kitāb al-muntakhab fī 'ilāj amrāḍ al-'ain of 'Ammār ibn 'Alī al-Mawṣilī (Canamusali), one of the best Arabic eye doctors. This was done by Nathan ha-Me'ati, probably in Rome and toward the end of the thirteenth century for another Roman Jew, Isaac ben Mordecai, alias Maestro Gajo, who was physician to Nicholas IV (or Boniface VIII), and much respected by the Jewish community. An earlier Latin text, ascribed to David the Armenian, was partly derived from the same Muntakhab but was not a translation of it.

This brings us back to Christendom. By and by there grew up a small class of Christian oculists who had obtained some knowledge of Arabic ophthalmology. How had they obtained it? The treatise of Ḥunain ibn Isḥāq[72] translated by Constantine the African, remained for some time the only Arabic treatise on the subject available in Latin, but much ophthalmological knowledge was contained in the general treatises, notably in the Kitāb al-malikī of 'Alī ibn 'Abbās, the whole of which could be read in Latin before the middle of the twelfth century. The earliest Latin writers on eye diseases Benvenutus Grassus (or Grapheus) of Jerusalem, Zacharias of Constantinople, David the Armenian, all of whom seem to have been associated with Salerno, derived their Arabic knowledge mainly from Ḥunain. However it is possible that David at least was able to read Arabic and thus to reach other sources.

About 1159, a Christian of Toledo, "Alcoatim," compiled a new treatise, the

[71] Pierre Pansier: Collectio ophtalmologica veterum auctorum (fasc. 6, 104, 1908).

[72] Ḥunain's treatise is really a collection of ten treatises preserved pseudonymously, nine of them in the Liber de oculis Constantini Africani (Opera Ysaac, Lyon 1515), and all of them in the Galeni de oculis liber a Demetrio translatus (included in many Latin editions of Galen, e.g., in the nine Juntine 1541 to 1625). The Arabic text was discovered only recently (1908) by Max Meyerhof and published by him for the first time (Cairo 1928; Isis, 13, 106–109).

Congregatio de oculis, which was either originally written in Arabic or made up by means of translations from the Arabic. In any case the Congregatio released a new budget of Arabic knowledge. This fact, as well as the complete availability of the Kitāb al-malikī, may be said to open a second period in the history of European ophthalmology. The main Latin treatise of that second period was the Liber de morbis oculorum of Peter of Spain. Peter's main Arabic source was the Kitāb al-malikī; he made use also of some Latin texts embodying the traditions of the "rustici" and of the alchemists on the healing virtues of the "twelve" waters (including aqua vite and aqua ardens). Two other Latin treatises dating probably from the same time (second half of the thirteenth century) are the anonymous Tractatus de egritudinibus oculorum ex dictis sapientium veterum compilatis, and the Tractatus de quibusdam dubiis circa dicta oculorum concurrentibus, wherein are quoted Hippocrates, Galen, al-Rāzī, Sābūr ibn Sahl, Jibrīl ibn 'Ubaidallāh ibn Bakhtyashū', Isḥāq al-Isrā'īlī, 'Alī ibn 'Abbās, Ibn Sīnā (chiefly the last named).[73] Still another treatise of that time is the Tractatus de oculo morali of Peter of Limoges (c. 1272). Though its purpose is moral rather than medical it includes a description of the eye and a brief account of eye diseases and their treatment. Finally we may still quote the Libellus regiminis de confortatione visus of Arnold of Villanova, though it dates only from about 1308. The technical part was entirely copied from the Grabadin of Māsawaih al-Māridīnī.

58. *Fevers and other diseases*—It would take too long and would hardly serve our purpose to consider each kind of disease; it will suffice to mention sundry monographs and to present a few remarks.

Skin diseases were traditionally abandoned to surgeons, as being too far below the dignity of the doctors. Thus it was mainly surgeons who experimented with mercurial ointments and other similar preparations. We are not surprised that the peculiar salivation resulting from the abuse of mercury was first observed by a surgeon, Theodoric Borgognoni. By the way, some historians cannot read a reference to mercury in a mediaeval text without thinking of syphilis. This is absurd: mercurial salts were used[74] (and are still used today) for various complaints (e.g., ringworms) which have nothing to do with syphilis; it was on the contrary the successful application of mercury in other cases which suggested its use to combat the syphilitic pandemy in the sixteenth century. (I have not yet come across an unmistakable reference to syphilis anterior to the fifteenth century.)

[73] These two treatises were first published by P. Pansier: Collectio ophtalmologica veterum auctorum (fasc. 6, 99–155, Paris 1908). The first contains 15 chapters, and the second originally contained 8, of which hardly more than 3 have been preserved.

[74] Mercury was known to Egyptians of the eighteenth and nineteenth Dynasties (H. Schelenz: Geschichte der Pharmazie, 41, 1904). There is no mention of it in Littré's edition of the Hippocratic corpus. Theophrastos knew how to obtain it from cinnabar; and that knowledge was transmitted to Dioscorides. Galen considered mercury a poison and did not dare to experiment with it (Kühn's edition, vol. 11, 767; vol. 12, 237).

Hellenistic alchemists were so familiar with mercury that they gave to it (as well as to sulphur) a special importance in their theory of metals; that theory was developed by Muslim alchemists (vol. 1, 532; Isis, 11, 166). Maslama ibn Aḥmad al-Majrīṭī described a quantitative transformation of mercury into mercuric oxide (vol. 1, 669).

Mercury and mercurial preparations were introduced into our pharmacopoeia by Eastern Muslims, such as Ibn Qutaiba, al-Rāzī, Abū Manṣūr, Ibn Sīnā, for skin-troubles and delousing.

Hindus (e.g., Suśruta) and Chinese (e.g., Ko Hung) seem to have been early acquainted with mercury and its medical use.

For more information on the early history of mercury, see E. O. v. Lippmann: Entstehung und Ausbreitung der Alchemie (vol. 1, 600–607, Berlin 1919; vol. 2, 175–180, 1931).

Speaking of skin-diseases, the first recognition of the itch-mite is generally credited to the great Spanish physician, Ibn Zuhr, but in this he was anticipated by a Persian physician, Aḥmad ibn Muḥammad al-Ṭabarī, two centuries earlier.

Ibn Rushd's medical work was naturally eclipsed by his philosophical fame, or else it was considered as a purely synthetic achievement. Yet Ibn Rushd deserves credit for a few concrete discoveries. For example he was apparently the first to recognize that an attack of smallpox confers immunity against ulterior attacks. The contagious nature of that disease was first indicated about the middle of the thirteenth century by Gilbert the Englishman.

It is remarkable that the two greatest philosophers of the twelfth century (indeed two of the greatest of the Middle Ages) were also great physicians—not simply medical philosophers or philosophical physicians, but genuine and ingenious practitioners. Of the one, Ibn Rushd, I have just spoken; the other, his exact contemporary, Maimonides, was one of the best mediaeval physicians. Both wrote general treatises which remained medical classics for centuries and whose popularity facilitated the transmission of Greco-Arabic knowledge. Maimonides also wrote what might be called monographs, on poisons and antidotes, on asthma, on haemorrhoids. These treatises were originally written in Arabic, but promptly and repeatedly translated into Hebrew; so much so that the original Arabic texts are comparatively insignificant, and that it is perhaps more correct on the whole to count them as Hebrew writings. Another Hebrew treatise on haemorrhoids was written almost a century later by Solomon ibn Ayyub.

A valuable monograph was produced in Byzantium, and this is the more remarkable because of the general sterility of the Greek medical writings of this period. I am referring to the treatise on gout written by Demetrios Pepagomenos, physician to Michael Palaeologos. The same Demetrios made curious helminthological observations already mentioned in section 41 on falconry. Byzantines were apparently well acquainted with the gout, for even a woman—a very learned one to be sure—like Anna Comnenè was able to discuss it intelligently.

Another medical specialty to which the reader's attention should be attracted is what might be called, if this were not too ambitious, psychopathology: the spiritual causes and results of diseases, and the spiritual means of curing them. Psychological and psychopathological traditions can be traced back to the earliest times of which we have any records. Incubation as practiced in the Egyptian and Greek temples was largely a psychical treatment, and we may assume that some of the doctors attached to the sanctuaries of Imhotep and Asclepios were conscious of their opportunities to cure their patients sometimes and to improve their own knowledge always.[75] The rich fruits of temple medicine were garnered in the Hippocratic writings. One of the finest, as well as one of the earliest, classics of Greek medicine is Hippocrates' treatise on the "sacred disease" (*περὶ ἱερῆς νόσου*), epilepsy. The Hippocratic, Aristotelian, and Galenic corpora are full of notes on psychologic subjects. In fact ancient physiology and psychology were to a large extent undissociated. The theory of humors or temperaments which dominated ancient medicine was psychological to a degree. Even to this day its technical terms—melancholic, choleric, phlegmatic, sanguine—evoke psychological as well

[75] For the Egyptian incubation see Jamieson B. Hurry: Imhotep, the vizier and physician of King Zoser (Oxford 1926; 2d ed., 49–56, 105–111, Oxford 1928; Isis, 13, 373–375).

For Greek incubation, Mary Hamilton: Incubation or the cure of diseases in pagan temples and Christian churches (228 p., London 1906).

as physiological ideas. Psychological traditions were handed down from age to age in a series of treatises on the soul, and in the humbler but abundant literature on dreams and on physiognomy. The study of psychical diseases and of the psychical means of combatting them appealed strongly to the Muslim imagination. For example they had carefully studied the effects of music and had even introduced its practice in some of their hospitals for therapeutic purposes.[76]

The titles of various standard medical books reveal the Arabic interest in "spiritual" medicine. For example, the Kitāb al-iqtiṣād fī iṣlāḥ al-anfās wal-ajsād (dealing with the restoration of souls and bodies) of the Spanish Muslim, Ibn Zuhr, and the Kitāb al-irshād li-maṣāliḥ al-anfās wal-ajsād (Direction for the improvement of souls and bodies) of the Egyptian Jew, Ibn Jamī'. A famous Baghdādite physician, Ibn al-Jauzī, wrote a treatise specially devoted to spiritual medicine, Kitāb al-ṭibb al-rūḥānī. Moreover every general treatise includes a psychological summary and abundant psychological remarks.

Arabic psychotherapy ('ilāj rūḥānī, tadbīr nafsānī) is illustrated by anecdotes relating the remarkable cures effected by al-Rāzī, Hibatallāh ibn Malkā, Ibn Sīnā, and others, by purely psychological means.[77]

Down to modern times a good many diseases were hidden, undifferentiated or badly differentiated, under the general label, fevers. The general symptoms of any fever were clearly recognized: increase in bodily temperature, acceleration of the pulse, thirst, loss of appetite, etc.; but until the introduction of clinical thermometers hardly more than half a century ago (see section 45), all of these symptoms were qualitative, except one, and many were rather elusive and misleading. The single exception was the acceleration of the pulse which could be measured. Herophilos of Chalcedon (first half of the third century B. C.) was the first to use a clepsydra for that purpose. However the pulse lore of ancient and mediaeval times remained largely in the qualitative stage: a number of arbitrary distinctions were gradually introduced into it and its general barrenness was not compensated, but rather aggravated, by this artificial over-elaboration (see section 52). Nowhere is the utter dependency of progress on experimental and quantitative methods more obvious. The use of the thermometer has replaced all these complicated and fantastic distinctions by a single one which is of the utmost simplicity: the exact measurement of the temperature of the body. A lay patient who measures his temperature at regular intervals and plots it on a chart, has some essential information on the course of his illness, which was absolutely beyond the reach of the wisest physicians of the past. To be sure they were familiar with the periodicity of certain fevers, which is often discussed in the Hippocratic treatises, but that knowledge was crude and confusing. To be sure their scientific ignorance might be compensated in individual cases by long experience, intuitive diagnosis, and deep medical wisdom, but that was art, and at best incommunicable and precarious.

As these ancient physicians derived some of their safest indications for the diagnosis and differentiation of fevers from the pulse, it is natural enough that their

[76] On the effects of music as observed by the Muslims see D. B. Macdonald: Emotional religion in Islām as affected by music and singing (Journal R. Asiatic Society, 195–252, 705–748, 1901; 1–28, 1902). H. G. Farmer: History of Arabian music (35, London 1929; Isis, 13, 375). On the medical use of music, Ahmed Issa bey: Histoire des bimaristans (Comptes rendus du Congrès international des maladies tropicales, Cairo 1929; e.g., p. 130; Isis, 14, 535).

[77] Some of these anecdotes are told by Edward G. Browne: Arabian medicine (Lecture 3, Cambridge, 1921; Isis, 4, 349).

knowledge of them was largely impregnated with that artificial body of facts and ideas called sphygmology (ars sphygmica).[78] In fact sphygmology and the doctrine of four humors and temperaments formed the scientific core around which a vast amount of clinical observations of fevers had been gradually collected. However as long as the real key to the understanding of these observations was hidden, they remained essentially unrelated and meaningless.

Ancient knowledge of fevers was summed up at about the same time (second half of the second century) in the East by Chang Chung-ching (we shall come back to him presently) and in the West by Galen. The chief Galenic work on the subject was the Περὶ διαφορᾶς πυρετῶν (De febrium differentiis), the tradition of which was continued in the Greek world by Alexander of Tralles and Stephanos of Athens. By that time it had already been translated into Syriac by Sergios of Resaina; in the second half of the ninth century it was translated into Arabic by Ḥunain ibn Isḥāq.[79] The Galenic tradition was continued in the Kitāb al-ḥummayāt of Isḥāq al-Isrā'īlī (first half of the tenth century), and many other Arabic writings; in Latin treatises by John the Saracen, John Ferrarius, Taddeo Alderotti, etc. in an Armenian one, by Mekhitar of Her; and in countless versions and elaborations in Hebrew and various vernaculars.

In fact the Galenic conception of fevers continued to reign supreme, more or less elaborated or disguised, until clinical thermometry and bacteriology radically transformed it. The hazy descriptions of various feverish diseases were gradually replaced by correct nosological definitions, and fever was reduced to the rank of a symptom, a most comprehensive symptom to be sure, a sort of natural integration, yet a symptom, not a disease, a result, not a cause. One of the earliest "fevers" to be recognized as a separate entity was smallpox, remarkably well described by al-Rāzī; another was measles described by Ibn al-Jazzār, etc. The old conception of fever is preserved in our language, for there are still quite a few diseases which we call fevers in spite of the fact that their nature has been very clearly analyzed and defined (e.g., scarlet fever, yellow fever, typhoid fever).

The Chinese knowledge of fevers was not very dissimilar from the Western except that it remained in the qualitative stage—that it never grew up. The standard text, which was as fundamental in China as its contemporary Galenic treatise in the West, was the Shang-han-lun of Chang Chung-ching.[80] In China even as in the West the diagnosis of fevers was largely based on the pulse but the Chinese sphygmology was even more fantastic than the Western. The Shang-han-lun is divided into ten books of which the first is a sort of scientific (sphygmological) introduction to the others. It exerted a deep influence upon the medical thought and practice not only of China, but of the Far East in general. It was one of the earliest Chinese medical works to be translated into Japanese, under the title Shō-kan-ron. Many other treatises on fever were published in Chinese, notably by P'ang An-shih toward the end of the eleventh century and by Liu Wan-su in the

[78] Of course sphygmology was rational enough in its purpose but it was encumbered with many irrational or irrelevant distinctions. Quantitative sphygmology dates only from the time of Karl v. Vierordt (Die Lehre vom Arterienpuls in gesunden und kranken Zuständen, Braunschweig 1855) and the invention of the sphygmograph by Etienne Jules Marey (1860).

[79] For the Greek text and the Latin translation, see C. G. Kühn's edition (vol. 7, 273–405). The Arabic text is no. 17 in Ḥunain's Galenic canon (Isis, 8, 692).

[80] Vol. 1, p. 310. Fr. Hübotter: Die chinesische Medizin (13–14, Leipzig 1929; Isis, 14, 255–263).

twelfth or thirteenth century. As I referred above to the Arabic knowledge of smallpox, it is proper to add that the Chinese were also acquainted with it even in earlier days. What is more remarkable, it is said that as early as the beginning of the eleventh century they were already used to protect themselves against it by inoculation.[81]

59. *Hygiene*—Most medical treatises devoted a certain amount of space to prophylaxy, but some written for laymen were primarily prophylactic: treatises on diet, regimina, etc. The line is not always easy to draw; a regimen composed at the request of a gouty patron might easily become a treatise on gout.

Let us consider a few examples of regimina and similar works in various literatures. The earliest to draw our attention in this period are the Greek. "Ptochoprodromos," the poor Prodromos, wrote a poetical calendar containing dietetic advice for each month of the year. A similar work was composed by Hierophilos the Sophist. This type of literature still exists to-day, for our "farmers' almanacs" often include sanitary rules for man and beast.

Contemporary Latin works were as usual on a much higher level. For example Peter of Musanda, a teacher of Giles of Corbeil, gave us an excellent treatise on the proper diet for feverish people. Salernitan teachings are also represented by a treatise of John of Saint Paul and above all by the Regimen sanitatis, a poem which enjoyed an immense popularity for centuries and is still living to-day in the form of homely proverbs in many languages. A significant novelty was the elaborate treatise written by Adam of Cremona for the emperor Frederick II, wherein he explained special hygienic rules to be followed by bodies of soldiers or pilgrims. This was a result of the Crusades; the early Crusaders had paid dearly for their ignorance of elementary sanitation. Rules for travelers by land or sea were added by Gilbert the Englishman at the end of his Lilium medicinae. A good example of a general medical treatise attaching special importance to prophylaxy was the Summa conservationis et curationis of William of Saliceto. The most successful popular treatise on medicine in Latindom was the Thesaurus pauperum of Peter of Spain (pope John XXI).

One of the most remarkable treatises on hygiene was written in French by an Italian—the Régime du corps of Aldobrandino of Siena (1256). It is one of the earliest monuments of French scientific literature.

As illustrations of the Arabic literature, I would select first of all the Tadbīr al-siḥḥa of Maimonides (c. 1198), containing rules for mental as well as for physical well-being, and also simple therapeutic advice for use in emergencies when physicians are out of reach. This excellent work was soon translated into Hebrew and into Latin. Another good example is the Kitāb jāmi' al-gharaḍ fī ḥifẓ al-ṣiḥḥa wa daf' al-maraḍ of Ibn al-Quff, explaining the means of preserving health and avoiding disease. Still another is the treatise on diet, Kitāb al-mukhtār min al-aghdhiya,

[81] Vol. 1, p. 732. J. Dyer Ball and E. Chalmers Werner: Things Chinese (698–707, London 1926).

The Library of Congress has recently acquired two Chinese treatises on smallpox: (1) The Tou^4 chên^3 chêng^4 tsung^1 (11414, 600, 687, 11976) by Sung^4 Lin^2-hsiang^2 (10462, 7186, 4277), tzŭ Chung^1-yo^4* (2891, 12953), republished in 1743 by a member of the Manchu imperial family, Hung^2 Chün^4 (5282, 3279) tzŭ Hua^2 ch'uan^1 (5005, 2728); (2) A revised edition of an illustrated treatise on smallpox entitled Tou^4 chêng^4 ching^1 yen^2 pi^4 yao^4 (11414, 691, 2133, 13025, 8932, 12889) by Yüan^2 Chü^4 (13739, 2947) tzŭ Ta^4-hsüan^1 (2688, 4805). Preface dated 1753. The date of the earlier edition is not given. Report of the Librarian of Congress for 1929–1930 (385, 1931).

of Ibn al-Nafīs. It is curious that these three treatises which I chose without regard to the personalities of the authors, were written by three Syro-Egyptian physicians, and that the first was a Jew, the second a Christian, and the third, a Muslim. They represent very well the complex civilization of the Near East of those days, and even of our days.

The treatises mentioned in this section do not contain medical novelties; their purpose was popular rather than scientific. They help us to appreciate the diffusion of medical knowledge. They are perhaps of greater value to the historian of culture than to the historian of medicine.

60. *Veterinary medicine*—A number of treatises on veterinary medicine were written in Sicily and possibly in Spain. The scope of these treatises was restricted to horses. The ailments of cattle and other domestic animals are briefly dealt with (if at all) in the books on husbandry (section 38), those of hounds and hawks in the books on the chase and falconry (section 41).

With the exception of a few Spanish treatises on farriery which have not been properly studied and are not exactly dated, it is very remarkable that all the treatises which have come within the purview of my observations were written in Sicily about the second half of the thirteenth century. The chief of these treatises is the Liber marescalchiae dedicated by Jordan Ruffo to the memory of the emperor Frederick II soon after the latter's death. It continued the Greco-Roman tradition, represented by the Mulomedicina Chironis; apparently that tradition had never been interrupted in South Italy. Its immense popularity is proved by an abundance of manuscripts in many languages. It is not certain whether the original text was Latin or Italian. The Greek treatise of Hierocles (second half of the fourth century) was translated into Latin by Bartholomew of Messina. There is also an Italian text written by Bartholomew Spadafora of Messina (are these two texts and these two Bartholomews identical?) The pseudo-Hippocratic treatise on the subject was put into Latin for Charles of Anjou by Moses of Palermo. Finally a new treatise was composed, probably for the same king, by Boniface of Gerace. It is not quite clear whether this last treatise was originally written in Greek or in Latin. It also exists in Italian, and some manuscripts of it contain abundant illustrations.

It is curious that we don't have Arabic treatises of the same kind, for Muslims were passionately interested in horses. In fact we have Arabic treatises on horses (see section 42) but they are far more literary than scientific or medical. The only Arabic treatise on hippology and hippiatry I came across is the Kitāb al-Nāṣirī written by Ibn al-Mundhir al-Baiṭār for the Baḥrī Mamlūk sulṭān al-Nāṣir Muḥammad ibn Qalā'ūn who ruled three times, in 1293, from 1298 to 1308, and from 1309 to 1340; it may thus date from the end of our period, but it more probably dates from the first half of the fourteenth century. By the way the author's name al-Baiṭār (or Baiṭar) means the farrier or veterinary surgeon. This is not the first time that we meet it; one of the greatest botanists and pharmacists of the Middle Ages was named Ibn al-Baiṭār, the farrier's son. The name proves two things: firstly that the profession existed and who could doubt it; secondly that it was of foreign origin, for the word baiṭār is derived from the Greek *ἱππίατρος*. To be sure the badāwī (bedouins) had already an extensive empirical knowledge of the diseases of animals (chiefly camels and horses), witness their abundant pathological vocabulary, but more systematic information and an improved technique were brought to them by itinerant surgeons straying from the Byzantine provinces. After all the veterinary art is but a branch of medicine; the knowledge of human physiology and pathology needed but little modification to be applied to the higher animals; the fundamental principles provided the same guidance in every case. These itinerant surgeons attended the great fairs where the badāwī assembled; they treated men as well as beasts, for the pre-Islāmic poets used the word baiṭār in the sense of leech.[82] Realizing the extreme conservativeness of nomadic people, it is not surprising that the badāwī were satisfied with their own crude farriery and with the additional information obtainable at the fairs from the foreign bayāṭira. For a more systematic knowledge expressed in Arabic one had to wait until the urban and military needs had made themselves felt long enough. The Kitāb al-Nāṣirī was the first book to answer those needs.

A glimpse into Japanese farriery is given to us through the illustrations prepared by Seia in 1267 with the help of an artist. For the Sino-Japanese medical care of insects (silkworms, crickets), see the treatises mentioned in sections 38 and 42.

61. *Medical philosophy*—This subject has been partly discussed in section 48, for the general medical treatises usually included an introduction which was more or less philosophical, and which reflected the author's philosophy or lack of it. However a few authors stand out in this respect, and contributed far more than the others to the development and organization of medical thought.

In the twelfth and thirteenth centuries medical philosophy was essentially determined by the writings of three great physicians of earlier days: Hippocrates, Galen, and Ibn Sīnā. This does not mean that there were no medical thinkers; as we shall see presently there were a few very good ones, but they were hopelessly overshadowed by those three giants. Much of the new activity in this direction took the form of commentaries on the Hippocratic, Galenic, and Avicennian writings (section 47).

Two great medical philosophers appeared in the second half of the twelfth century, the Muslim, Ibn Rushd and the Jew, Maimonides, but they were but secondary prophets who reaffirmed the medical ideals of the three great masters with but little variation. In that century no Latin writer reached the level of those two illustrious sons of Cordova. The most philosophical master of Salerno, Urso of Calabria, was but a child as compared with them.

In the following century the tables were already turned; whatever philosophy there was was explained more abundantly and authoritatively in Latin than in Arabic. In the second half of that century, the intellectual triumph of Latindom and Christendom is complete. Under the influence of scholasticism and of the legal renaissance of Bologna, physicians like Taddeo Alderotti, William Corvi, Peter of Abano do their best to raise medical thought to a higher level. In fact they overdo it: they forget that medicine, unlike law or theology, is an experimental science which must not be imprisoned into too rigid a frame, that in this case freedom of growth is far more important than classification and systematization. And yet in spite of its exaggeration and of its prematureness their effort was neither unnecessary nor sterile: it was but a phasis in the everlasting cycle from analysis to synthesis and vice versa. Did I say "prematureness"? In a sense every synthesis is premature until we know the whole truth; in another sense no synthesis is premature as long as we know a part of the truth. The Alderottis

[82] J. Hell: Baiṭār (Encyclopaedia of Islām, vol. 1, 599, 1911). Alois Musil: The manners and customs of the Rwala bedouins (New York 1928; Isis, 14, 444–446). See p. 368–370 for camels, and p. 382–383 for horses; many Arabic technical terms are explained.

and Corvis were encouraged by the circumstance that medical knowledge had enormously increased since the incorporation of the Arabic writings. The time had come for a new synthesis wherein all the information derived from Greek, Latin, Arabic, and popular sources would be neatly collected, collated, and classified, and made as available in its entirety and its details as possible.

Another kind of synthesis was accomplished on a humbler scale by Peter of Spain. Moreover Peter was a very successful writer not only in the field of medicine but in that of philosophy proper. His Summulae logicales was the most popular treatise on logic of the Middle Ages; nor was its fame restricted to Latindom, for it extended to the Greek and Hebrew worlds. He also composed an elaborate treatise on psychology, which is of special interest to us because Peter did not forget that he was a physician when he wrote it: the physiological or medical point of view pierces through quite often.

The logical revival due to the fact that the Aristotelian organon was now completely available had produced (or helped to produce) admirable results, notably the development of the law school of Bologna, the Summulae of Peter of Spain, Taddeo Alderotti's teaching, the Aggregator brixiensis. It also produced other results which were less admirable. Indeed every movement may be perverted, and if it be sufficiently popular, it is bound to be perverted in some way or another. The new logic went to the head of some men as if it were too strong a wine: because it proved efficacious, they soon expected it to work miracles. The best symbol of that logical perversion was the Catalan Ramon Lull. He labored under the delusion that medicine could be organized and demonstrated on a purely logical basis.

Bacon wrote various medical treatises most of which are disappointing, but in one of them at least, the De erroribus medicorum, he gave proof of considerable wisdom and outlined the principles of experimental medicine. I shall come back to it in section 63.

Our appreciation of Hebrew medical writings will vary considerably according to whether we take those of Maimonides into account or not. Both procedures may be justified, for Maimonides wrote in Arabic but his works were promptly translated into Hebrew and exerted more influence in their Hebrew than in their Arabic form. If Maimonides is included, the Hebrew medico-philosophical literature was very strong; without him, it was rather poor. The chief writer besides Maimonides was another Spaniard (but a northern one)—one might perhaps call him a Catalan—Shem-ṭob ben Isaac of Tortosa. Shem-ṭob was primarily a translator, one of the greatest medical translators of the Middle Ages, but he was almost as deeply interested in philosophy as in medicine.

62. *Medical astrology*—The progress of mediaeval medicine was not handicapped so much by the lack of scientific knowledge, as by its mistaken confidence in a pseudo-science, astrology. This is not said in a captious or disparaging spirit. As I have explained above (section 12) astrology could not be dissociated from astronomy. One of the results of the Arabic conquest of intellectual Europe had been to reinforce very strongly the astrological tendencies which already existed—they were an integral part of the Roman traditions—but only in a subdued form. The Arabic treatises gave these tendencies the scientific prestige which was all they needed to flourish luxuriantly. All sorts of superstitions clustered around them and shared their prosperous growth. If the astronomers did not know better, can we blame the physicians for being fooled? Astrology became a branch

of medical propaedeutics as important as physiology. As no man could be isolated from the stars, every case involved a consideration of two worlds, the microcosmos represented by the patient, and the macrocosmos outside of him. The little world was explained in terms of physiology, but astrology was required to account for the great world and for the relationships of both.

The learned physicians read the astronomical and astrological literature which was then available (many were astronomers in their own right) but it was soon found necessary to publish astrological treatises for the special use of ordinary leeches. These treatises would be less technical than the others and devote more attention to the medical applications. (Even as to-day we have physical or chemical textbooks prepared with special reference to medical needs.) As these treatises are of little scientific interest, it will suffice to quote a few examples.

The most remarkable Latin specimens are perhaps the Astrologia de urina non visa of William the Englishman and the Secreta mulierum et virorum wrongly ascribed to Albert the Great.

The most typical Arabic work is the Kitāb fī mā yaḥtāj al-ṭabīb min 'ilm al-falak (What the physician needs to know of astrology), by 'Adnān al-'Ainzarbī. The title makes one think of sundry modern books, such as, "What the physician needs to know of X-rays."

The astrological ideas explained in Latin and Arabic were essentially the same, and the identity was not restricted to the principles but extended to most of the details. On the contrary the strange astrology which permeated Chinese medicine was of an entirely different kind. Arabico-Latin and Chinese astrology had nothing in common except the fundamental postulate of the existence of relationships and correspondences between the microcosmos and the macrocosmos. On that basis the Chinese astrologers and physicians had built a superstructure of infinite complexity and fantastic symmetry. See, for example, the writings of Liu Wan-su and Chang Tzŭ-ho.

The fact that similar, though independent and different, aberrations had developed East and West is highly significant. The human spirit craves for scientific knowledge, and if the right kind is unavailable, men's desires may easily overcome their prudence. Nowhere are those desires stronger and wilder than in the medical field, for is not health the greatest blessing, and the lack or loss of it, the greatest misfortune? This explains also why medical quackery has always flourished and will continue to do so as long as there are distressing and incurable diseases. As indicated in the Introductory remarks (section 45), medicine remained an art almost until our own days. The lack of scientific knowledge of a truly objective, dependable, and transmissible nature, caused a sort of vacuum inviting the introduction of any kind of knowledge which was sufficiently consistent and plausible, and seemed to work. Did medical astrology work? Of course it did, partly because most of it was harmless anyhow (in many cases it simply caused a postponement of medical intervention), partly because it was often tempered with clinical experience and common sense. Moreover who could ever prove that the astrology was wrong? In case of accident, it was so much easier to blame the doctor, or the patient, or—fate.

Every mediaeval physician was somewhat of an astrologer, but some had a genuine knowledge of astrology, while others knew it only in a second-hand manner, as a collection of recipes to be followed more or less blindly. From the point of view of their time the difference was enormous; but as we now realize that it was based on false values, we consider it negligible. The great physicians of our period were great, not because but in spite of their astrology. Yet we can imagine the prestige obtained by men who had obtained fame at once as astronomers and as physicians. The average good doctor enjoyed much authority over his patients; think of his prestige with them if he could prove his familiarity not only with their own microcosmos, with their own little secrets, but also with the secrets of the universe? This helps us to understand the power which so many medical astrologers exerted upon their papal or royal patrons, e.g., Nāṣir al-dīn al-Ṭūsī upon Hūlāgū Khān.

63. *Clinical observations and the seeds of experimental medicine*—Medical astrology, however popular, was doomed to sterility. Fortunately there were a few physicians who were not entirely swept off their feet by the prevalent delusion. They were not bold enough to say, or even to think, that astrology was nonsense; the highest degree of genius could not have given them the courage and the vigor to resist the universal tendencies of their age. In proof of this it will suffice to remark that even the wisest of men accepted astrology, even as they accepted alchemy; they made reservations to be sure and rejected many of the superstitions which had been gradually associated with the main theory, but with that theory itself they could not help acquiescing. The physicians of whom I am going to speak now accepted the principles of astrology, as a matter of course, but their own attention was directed elsewhere. They were primarily physicians, and they realized more or less consciously that the progress of medicine would depend to a large extent upon the collection of good clinical observations.

This was a very small movement to begin with, one which was neither very attractive nor brilliant, but rather inconspicuous. In the past even more than to-day, textbook writers attracted an undue share of attention while genuine investigators were left in the shadow. That was all right after all. Everybody got what he wanted and what he deserved. The popular writers needed fame, and they got it: receperunt mercedem suam, vani vanam. The investigators and the original thinkers would have cried with Carlyle, "Silence and secrecy!" and they got both.

The clinical spirit was not a new thing of course; admirable examples of it may be found in Epidemics I and III, which is one of the most authentic works of the Hippocratic corpus. Every great physician had made clinical observations, yet throughout the Middle Ages there was an ever-increasing and dangerous tendency to depend too much on the "authorities" of earlier times, chiefly Hippocrates, Galen, and Ibn Sīnā, but also on many others. Here again as in other departments of science, a protracted war was being fought between the literary minded people and the "authorities" on one side, and the experimenters and the free discoverers on the other. For centuries the latter were hopelessly on the losing side; their case was especially hopeless, because even the boldest of them were not half bold enough. They too were enthralled by the authorities. How else could astrology have lasted so long? Indeed it is only within recent times that the battle has been finally won by the experimenters, and they have won it only for themselves; the mass of the people is still and will probably ever remain enslaved. It is only within our own lifetime that the complete gospel of science has been proclaimed: there are no authorities whatever, no final authorities, mankind is ever on its way toward the goal, ever replacing incomplete truths by others which are less so; the goal itself, perfect truth, will probably never be reached though we may come indefinitely nearer to it.

To return to medicine, a hopeful if small revival of clinical observations may be detected first in the Arabic world in the twelfth century, then in the following century in Latindom.

The Arabic renaissance is evidenced by the publication, alongside with the more pretentious treatises, of collections of experimental facts, e.g., the Mujarrabāt of Abū-l-'Alā' Zuhr of Cordova (Avenzoar's father); the Mujarrabāt of the Baghdādite Christian, Ibn al-Tilmīdh; the Mujarrabāt of the two Egyptian Jews, Ibn al-Mudawwar and Ibn al-Nāqid. I have repeated these identical titles on purpose. All of these books were significantly called mujarrabāt, meaning experimenta. To be sure we must not take those mujarrabāt at their face value; the experimental spirit was exceedingly slow in finding itself. We may assume that the word mujarrabāt even as its Latin equivalent was often used in vain by people who did not know exactly what experiments were. In fact the meaning of the word experiment (and its equivalents) must have varied as the experimental methods themselves were gradually unfolded and as the experimental spirit grew up and slowly reached its maturity. However crude the earliest use may have been, these mujarrabāt are very impressive: we may consider them the humble symbols of the experimental rebirth. It would take many centuries for the new spirit to develop into the experimental spirit of modern science, but the beginnings of great things are necessarily slow; however humble they be we cannot admire them too much.

The mujarrabāt were apparently on a higher level than the experimenta, for the Latin word had been frightfully misused.[83] A better equivalent of the Arabic mujarrabāt was the consilia medicinalia of which we have at least two interesting collections dating from the second half of the thirteenth century, the one by Taddeo Alderotti and the other by William Corvi. It is curious that these clinical records should have been written by men of that type, but this only illustrates the complexity of human nature. Taddeo and William were very intelligent men who understood at once the need of a new medical synthesis and of more experiments: these were not conflicting but complementary needs, which it was equally necessary to answer in order to make further progress possible.[84]

However interesting the consilia, we have even better proofs of the experimental renaissance in the Latin writings of the second half of the thirteenth century, proofs without exact counterpart in Arabic. Physicians like Peter of Spain and John of Saint Amand were actually discussing the experimental method. In his logical treatise Peter opposed the via experimenti to the via rationis. The best defender of the new method, and to that extent the true protagonist of modern medicine was Roger Bacon. His medical writings were generally mediocre, except one, the De erroribus medicorum, wherein he showed the superiority of experiment over authority or argument. It may be objected that Bacon did not practice what he taught, and it is a great pity he did not, but that does not destroy the value of his advice.

The mujarrabāt, the consilia, and the discussions of scientific methods were less in the nature of true achievements than of promises, but such promises are worth recording. We may truly say that the seeds of experimental medicine, and of experimental science in general, were sown in the thirteenth century.

[83] See my note on Nicholas of Poland. See also Isis (6, 80, 1924).

[84] Critical editions of the Arabic mujarrabāt and of the Latin consilia would be very instructive. In their absence my remarks are necessarily tentative.

64. *Medical education and hospitals. Bedside manners and deontology. Balneology*—Hospitals date back at least to the time of Constantine the Great (first half of the fourth century) but they remained relatively insignificant for centuries. The earliest larger hospitals were probably those associated with the medical school of Jundīshāpūr, not very far from Sūs (ancient Susa), N. W. Khūzistān in the sixth century (vol. 1, 435). As that school was in many respects the cradle of Arabian medicine, it is not surprising that hospitals of increasing magnitude and perfection were established in the main urban centers of the Dār al-Islām. Some of these hospitals were very elaborate indeed.[85]

The organization of similar institutions in the West was probably one of the results of the Crusades. Once more a Christian and Greek idea had needed to be transplanted into the Muslim soil to attain a sufficient maturity. It was now coming back to Christendom for further development. A great many hospitals were established in western Europe in the twelfth and thirteenth centuries. During that time they continued to develop in Islām; for example one of the greatest Islāmic hospitals, the Bīmāristān al-Manṣūrī was founded in Cairo by the Baḥrī Mamlūk sulṭān al-Manṣūr Qalā'ūn at the end of the thirteenth century; parts of its spacious buildings are extant to this day.

Leprosy is a very ancient disease; probably the very one (or one of the diseases) discussed in Leviticus. It was endemic in western Europe long before the Crusades, but its extension seems to have increased considerably in the twelfth and thirteenth centuries, after which it decreased again. Its extraordinary prevalence in those two centuries may be partly explained by the Crusades, which caused people of many countries to be mixed on an unparalleled scale, and multiplied indefinitely the chances of contagion.[86] Certain it is that besides the hospitals proper, a great many leper houses were established in the twelfth and thirteenth centuries; after that time many more hospitals were created but fewer leper houses, and the number of European lepers steadily diminished. The best mediaeval account of leprosy may be found in the Lilium medicinae of Gilbert the Englishman (fl. 1250).

Medical deontology and etiquette (εὐσχημοσυνή) were essentially established by a series of writings of the Hippocratic corpus: the Oath, the Law, the Physician, Decorum, and Precepts. The tradition of these writings is difficult to retrace. The Oath is probably of high antiquity; its substance may even be pre-Hippocratic (vol. 1, 97, 101), yet Galen never alluded to it. It may be called the first charter of the medical profession; it has never been abrogated, and in that respect, as in many others, Hippocrates fully deserves to be called the Father of medicine.[87] The Middle Ages added little if anything to this; the Oath appeared in slightly modified forms to satisfy Christian or Jewish creeds, but the substance remained unaltered. The most interesting document of early mediaeval deontology is the

[85] Ahmed Issa bey: Histoire des bimaristans à l'époque islamique (130 p., Cairo 1929; Isis, 14, 535).

[86] In spite of its bacterial nature leprosy is not by any means as contagious as was formerly believed. Casual contacts are not sufficient to transmit it, long and close contacts are necessary. It is far less infectious than tuberculosis.

[87] W. H. S. Jones: The doctor's oath (62 p., Cambridge 1924; Isis, 11, 154). Includes Greek, Arabic, and Latin texts, and facsimiles of MSS. The Arabic version is taken from the 'Uyūn al-anbā' of Ibn abī Uṣaibi'a, dating from the middle of the thirteenth century, but there must be earlier texts than that.

Formula comitis archiatrorum ascribed to Theodoric, king of the Ostrogoths from 475 to 526.[88] To come down to our period, the best account of Salernitan bedside manners was given by Archimatthaeus, in a quaint little treatise entitled De instructione medici (or De adventu medici ad aegrotum). The physician's prayer ascribed to Maimonides, whether genuine or not, gives us a good insight into the Jewish conception of medical duty.

Bathing was far more common in the Middle Ages than is usually supposed. Public bathing in the Roman style was discountenanced by the Church, but various forms of private bathing continued: the main obstacles to their diffusion were technical rather than moral.[89] A curious result of the Crusades was the introduction into Europe of public baths in the Muslim style, hot steam baths or ḥammāmāt. In the thirteenth century such baths were available in the main cities of Western Europe. The ḥammām reintroduced the practice of public bathing which soon degenerated into a dangerous kind of sexual dissipation. The fears of the Church proved to be more than justified. Instead of favoring health, the baths became centers of physical and moral disease.

Balneology proper, by which is meant the therapeutic use of natural springs, hardly existed in our period. To be sure springs have always played a very important part in mythology, folklore, popular religion and healing, but that was another matter.[90] The earliest balneological text I came across is the De balneolis Puteolis, a poem celebrating the waters of Pozzuoli (near Naples), ascribed to Peter of Eboli and also to Alcadino of Syracuse. Whichever ascription be the correct one, the poem dates from the end of the twelfth century or the beginning of the thirteenth. Later treatises are credited to John of Saint Amand and Arnold of Villanova.

Medical teaching was provided in an ever increasing number of centers, e.g., Cairo and Damascus in the East; Salerno, Montpellier, Bologna, Paris in the West. The more theoretical and philosophical forms of medicine were transmitted through the lectures delivered in those or other universities. Empirical medicine, and the various medical techniques, were largely transmitted in private, from father to son, from master to apprentice. The Hippocratic oath was not only the foundation of medical deontology; it created a special guild; it established the medical profession. The secrets of the art as well as the professional duties were handed down from one individual to another in an endless succession.

However with the better organization of the universities, the medical profession received a sort of official consecration. The title of doctor of medicine, first used by Giles of Corbeil, with reference to Salernitan graduates, became the badge of honor of the most learned physicians. Graduation ceremonies were made as

[88] Vol. 1, 438. Text of the Formula in Cassiodori Senatoris Variae epistolae (book 6, chapter 19). Theodorus Mommsen's edition (Mon. Germ. hist., auct. antiq., tomus 12, p. 191–192, Berlin, 1894).

[89] On bathing in the early Middle Ages, see K. Sudhoff's articles in Johannes Hoops: Reallexikon der germanischen Altertumskunde (vol. 1, 153–155, Strassburg 1911–1913).

[90] The literature on springs and more generally on water-lore is very abundant. A great many memoirs are devoted to the springs of particular regions, or to particular springs.

James Reuel Smith: Springs and wells in Greek and Roman literature, their legends and locations (745 p., New York 1922). Karl Weinhold: Die Verehrung der Quellen in Deutschland (Abhdl. Preuss. Ak., 69 p., Berlin 1898). Berthold Rein: Der Brunnen im Volksleben (185 p., ill., München 1912). Edward Schröder: Brunnen (Reallexicon der germanischen Altertumskunde, vol. 1, 335–338, Strassburg 1911–1913).

impressive as possible. A very definite idea of the organization of medical studies in Salerno in the first half of the thirteenth century is given by the regulations promulgated by the emperor Frederick II. Our period thus saw the transformation of a profession organized on a purely individualistic basis, mainly controlled by the rules and ideals of its own brotherhood, into one consecrated and protected by academic and governmental regulations and privileges.

65. *Forensic medicine*—The relations between law and medicine are many even if we take into consideration only lay jurisprudence, and exclude sacred regulations, such as are essential parts of the Jewish and Muslim religions (e.g., circumcision, dietary laws).

The earliest lay medical regulations are included in the Babylonian code of Hammurabi (XXIst century); they refer to such matters as the physicians' rewards in case of success and their penalties in case of failure. Similar regulations may be found in later codes but nowhere as elaborately.

Other points of contact between law and medicine were afforded by the organization of medical teaching and the needs of restricting the profession to persons who were properly qualified to exercise it; this had to be done for the common protection of the patients and of the physicians themselves. The best mediaeval example of such regulations is the ordinance promulgated by the emperor Frederick II Hohenstaufen in 1240.

Cases of civil law might require medical advice, e.g., the determination of sexual impotence or sterility. However the largest field of medical jurisprudence was the application of criminal law. Such questions as to whether a man's death was due to natural causes, and, if not, how it had been brought about; whether a woman had been raped or not, etc., fell distinctly within the physician's province. Under the influence of the law school of Bologna, post-mortems began to be made, but they were apparently very rare. Within our period we found references to but two or three, all of which occurred in northern Italy probably in the last quarter of the thirteenth century (see notes on William of Saliceto, Taddeo Alderotti, and Fra Salimbene). Indeed popular prejudices were strongly opposed to autopsies and these remained uncommon until the end of the sixteenth century.

No regulation of forensic medicine existed in Europe until the beginning of the sixteenth century when laws were published by the bishop of Bamberg (1507) and the elector of Brandenburg (1516) to that effect. These laws led a little later to the promulgation of the Constitutio criminalis carolina by the emperor Charles Quint (1532). On the other hand an elaborate treatise on the subject was written in Chinese about the middle of the thirteenth century: the Hsi-yüan lu of Sung Tz'ŭ. In the course of time revised editions of it appeared which have been used by Chinese coroners to this day.[91]

66. *History of medicine*—If forensic medicine was essentially a Chinese subject, the study of the history of medicine was a Muslim one. Latin books might occa-

[91] Heinrich Zoepfl: Die peinliche Gerichtsordnung Kaiser Karl's V., nebst der Bamberger und der Brandenburger Halsgerichtsordnung sämmtlich nach den ältesten Drucken und mit den Projecten der peinlichen Gerichtsordnung Kaiser Karl's V. von den Jahren 1521 und 1529 beide zum ersten male vollständig nach Handschriften herausgegeben (first edition, preface dated 1841; 3d synoptic edition, 216 p., Leipzig 1883). J. Kohler und Willy Scheel: Die peinliche Gerichtsordnung Kaiser Karls V. Constitutio criminalis carolina. Ausgabe für Studierende (144 p., Halle a. S., 1900); with glossary, and analytical index.

For Chinese forensic medicine, see my note on Sung Tz'ŭ, and Eugène Vincent: La médecine en Chine (119–122, Paris 1915).

sionally contain brief historical notices, as may be found in modern scientific publications, but even these were rare and generally of little value. Perhaps the best example of the history of science in the West is the thirteenth or last part of Peter of Spain's treatise De anima containing a history of Greek and Arabic psychology, with many references to its physiological and medical aspects. The Latin chronicles of which there is an abundance do not help us much, for the information which they have to offer on scientific subjects could not be more meager than it is.

On the other hand, the Muslims had a deep interest in learning, and some of their historical works took naturally the form of biographical collections, wherein a large place was left to theologians and philosophers, some of whom were also scientists. The most elaborate Arabic collection of that kind, within our period, was the Wafayāt al-a'yān of Ibn Khallikān, which has been compared to our modern dictionaries of national biography. More precious even to the historian of science are two collections more exclusively devoted to learned men: the Ikhbār al-'ulamā' of Ibn al Qifṭī and the 'Uyūn al-anbā' of Ibn abī Uṣaibi'a. The first includes some 414 very unequal biographies of Greek and Muslim physicians, men of science, and philosophers; the second includes even more biographies and is restricted to physicians. Thanks to these two works we can realize how much the Muslim East knew of the Greek philosophers and scientists; but what matters even more, we owe to them a substantial part of our knowledge of Muslim medicine and science. The authors of these collections, Ibn al-Qifṭī, Ibn abī Uṣaibi'a, and Ibn Khallikān, were Syro-Egyptians who flourished in the thirteenth century.

CONCLUSIONS

I did my best to keep this survey of scientific thought in the twelfth and thirteenth centuries as brief as possible. For example I kept out of it a large quantity of items which deeply affected that thought in many ways, yet are not scientific stricto sensu; I did not refer to a number of religious, philosophical, historiographical, philological, and sociological questions, which are discussed in the present work. In spite of that, this survey is so long that it may have taxed the reader's patience to the utmost.

What shall we conclude from it? First of all, that the scientific activity of these two centuries, if small as compared with that of our own days, was nevertheless considerable. By way of illustration I might mention that the main personalities dealt with in these two volumes are more than eight hundred in number,[92] and each of these represents a host of others. The variety and complexity of that activity are even more striking than its mere size. My survey is truly encyclopaedic in its scope: the mediaeval scientists whose works I was studying have obliged me to consider one after another every scientific question which was at all conceivable in their days.

In the second place, the internationalism of that activity is very obvious. The progress of mankind was not due to the efforts of this or that nation, this or that race, this or that sect; it was due to their combined efforts. The leaders in the twelfth century were most of them Muslims, but Muslims hailing from a great number of countries stretched all the way from Central Asia to the Far West. When their intellectual hegemony was broken, they were replaced by Christians, but again, Christians of every kind: Frenchmen, Italians, Spaniards, Englishmen,

[92] To be more accurate some 360 in the twelfth century and some 455 in the thirteenth.

Germans, and many others. In the meanwhile some of the richest fruits of scientific research were due to Jews. In spite of the obloquy to which they were subjected in Christendom, the Jews contributed far more than their share to the common undertaking. Indeed, the scientific quest, even as the artistic and religious ones, is of such a nature that it would be impossible to restrict it within any kind of boundaries, even if one tried in every possible way. The human spirit cannot be restricted to this or that. It must be entirely free, and if it is restrained in any manner it must needs regain its freedom sooner or later. It is regulated only by the laws of its own activity, which are identical for all sound minds, and by the laws of nature, which are the same all over the world.

So it is that not only science in general, but each branch of it, was gradually improved by an unconscious and unorganized coöperation involving the civilized people of the whole planet. The continuity of that collaboration in spite of wars and other calamities, is very impressive; its spontaneity is even more so, for it proves that the evolution described in these volumes is something like a cosmic phenomenon. Each of the great men dealt with in them was striving to accomplish a purpose, which he saw more or less clearly yet which remained unrelated to the other purposes. I have tried to show their abundant and complex relationships, and thus to evidence the greater purpose of which these men were the unconscious tools: the discovery of the truth, the gradual revelation of nature and of God.

APPENDIX TO INTRODUCTORY CHAPTER

NOTES ON TRANSLITERATION

The following notes complete those previously published (vol. 1, 46–51) relative to (1) Arabic, (2) Chinese, (3) Greek, (4) Hebrew, (5) Japanese, (6) Persian, (7) Sanskrit, (8) Syriac.

The guiding rule was clearly expressed in volume 1. "The supreme desiderata of any system of transliteration are consistency and simplicity. I have been guided always by the written language, which is relatively fixed, rather than by the spoken, which may vary considerably. That is, I have tried to write foreign words in such manner that the original written form might be easily reconstructed or found in a dictionary."

As this has been misunderstood I add a few explanatory remarks. The problem of transliterating written words is difficult enough, why complicate it by trying to reproduce exactly the pronunciation? The phonetic ideal leads to endless inconsistencies. For example, Arabic is written everywhere in the same way but pronounced differently. If we want each Arabic word to be represented always in the same way, we are bound to disregard phonetic differences and to consider only the written word.

This may be illustrated without reference to oriental languages. I have found that such names as Maeterlinck and Ruysdael are pronounced differently in almost every country which I have visited. I have been gradually led to pronounce my own name (yet so simple!) differently in French-speaking and in English-speaking countries, because I naturally wish to be understood (in both cases I pronounce the vowels and place the accent as in the French and English word "pardon"). Happily these unavoidable changes in the pronunciation do not affect the written form which remains constant, or at any rate varies less and more slowly.

It is true that in the past, when dictionaries were not available or were rare and expensive, orthography was not as fixed as it is to-day. Some languages are more fluid than others in this respect. For example the fact that vowels are generally unwritten in the Semitic languages causes naturally much fluctuation in their vocalization. But we need not go so far: there are endless variations in most of the European names, chiefly perhaps in the Italian and Portuguese ones. In such cases it is well to select one form—the best or most popular—and to stick to it. For languages written by means of another script, one written form should be selected once for all, and vocalized always in the same manner.

The first requisite of a good transliteration is consistency, the second is simplicity. There are two pitfalls to avoid: the one is the use of too many letters to represent a foreign one (e.g., the German use of four letters, dsch, to represent the Arabic jīm); the other, is the abuse of diacritical signs. The Arabic and the Hebrew shīn are generally represented in English by the digraph sh; it would be of course more correct to indicate by some typographical sign (e.g., underlining) that these two letters are really one sound (as in shape) and not two (as in mishap), but is the typographical complication worth while? I believe that it is not, and that it is simpler to indicate the exceptional cases where the letters sh are not to be pronounced together, even as in an English primer a footnote might warn the reader that the word mishap should be pronounced mis-hap. Diacritical signs should be used as sparingly as possible, as the reader is likely to misunderstand them, and they always risk being dropped by writers or printers. For example it may be less ambiguous to represent the second Sanskrit sibilant sha by ṣ than by sh, but what if the ṣ degenerates into s? The English sh (as in share or shun) represents the letter and the sound exactly, and the h will not be forgotten or disregarded as easily as the mysterious and unwelcome dot.

In short our transliteration of foreign languages should be as consistent and as simple as possible; and if in addition to that our system suggests the average pronunciation in our own language, so much the better. Every attempt at orthographic or phonetic refinement leads to additional inconsistencies and absurdities. Nowhere does the old French saying "Le mieux est l'ennemi du bien" find a better application.

Some niceties of script are necessarily lost in any simple transliteration. Instead of trying to preserve them at the cost of futile complications I would prefer to publish eventually oriental indices in the original scripts; one index for each script.

I hope philologists and especially phoneticians, phonologists and orthophonists will forgive me for trespassing upon their premises, but I could not help it. Every historian using texts written in another script than his own must face the problem of transliteration, and solve it in one way or another.

One more remark. I have done my best to avoid a practice, unfortunately common enough in English, which consists in forming the plural of foreign words by the addition of an s. This is erroneous and misleading, except in the case of words which are sufficiently Anglicized. One may write viziers or vizirs, but not wazīrs; if one uses the Arabic word at all, one must use the correct Arabic plural wuzarā' or awzār; again one may write sultans or salāṭīn, but not sulṭāns. This applies to every language.

We may now pass to the consideration of separate languages.

1. ARABIC

See vol. 1, 46. I am afraid I have not always been consistent in the representation of the final and silent hā (or tā marbūṭa) following a fatḥa; sometimes I have written an *h* (or a *t*) sometimes not. This matters but little, because final letters do not affect the position of words in the index.

The forms fā'il and fa'īl are sometimes equivalent. For example the name Nāṣir is sometimes written Naṣīr, both words having the same meaning. I have always written Nāṣir.

I have generally translated Arabic titles, but not always. These translations are not always easy, as the Arabic conception of a title was absolutely different from ours. Instead of a clear title, they preferred a metaphoric and symmetrical one and they loved alliterations and rhymes so much that they were sometimes tempted to sacrifice sense to sound.

In the writing of a name such as Marwān ibn Zuhr, ibn is written with a minuscule i if ibn Zuhr simply means the son of Zuhr; it is written with a capital i if Ibn Zuhr has become a patronymic, if Zuhr is not the father but a distant ancestor. (Compare the family name Macdonald, derived from macDonald meaning the son of

Donald). The distinction is not always easy nor even possible; it cannot occur in the Arabic script because the latter lacks capitals; one should not attach too much importance to it. In the index of this volume every name beginning with Ibn is classified under the following word.

Due to the fact that vowels are generally unwritten, the vocalization is not always certain. Some Arabic words (e.g., proper names) may be and are actually vocalized in different ways. The same remark applies to other Semitic languages. Hence if a name does not appear at its place in the index, it is sometimes worthwhile to try again with other vowels. If you don't find madkhal try mudkhal, etc. (In our transcription there are but three Arabic vowels: a, i, u.)

4. HEBREW

My decision to follow the Authorized Version for proper names opened the doors to many inconsistencies. Happily it matters but little, for the exact form of these names can be found at once in any Hebrew Bible.

For other words I have followed the system of the Jewish Encyclopedia (12 vols., New York 1901–1906), except in my use of the letter q instead of dotted k. That system has the advantage of being very simple; but maybe the simplification has been carried a little too far.

The translations from Arabic into Hebrew, together with the Hebraization of many Arabic words which was a result of them, created new difficulties not foreseen in vol. 1. The Arabic letters jīm and ṣād were represented by j and ṣ while the Hebrew letters gīmel and ẓādē, being pronounced somewhat differently though etymologically equivalent, were represented by g and ẓ. This was of no importance until the same words began to occur in both languages. For example the Greek word ἀστρολάβος was successively Arabicized and Hebraized: in Arabic it reads aṣṭurlāb, in Hebrew, aẓṭurlab; the second letter in both words is really the same, but our different systems of transliteration dissociate it. In the same way the word reading Giqaṭilia in Hebrew, reads Jiqaṭīla in Arabic; the Hebrew word ẓaddiq, meaning just, righteous, is the equivalent of the Arabic ṣādiq, yet they would be widely separated in the index.

Other ambiguities, unavoidable ones, this time, are due to the fact that the Hebrew tāv corresponds to the Arabic tā and thā; the Hebrew ḥēth, to the Arabic ḥā and khā; the Hebrew dāleth to the Arabic dāl and dhāl; the Hebrew ẓādē to the Arabic ṣād and ḍād; the Hebrew gīmel to the Arabic jīm and ghain; the Hebrew ṭēth to the Arabic ṭā and ẓā. The confusion was considerably increased by the fact that the Arabic speaking Jews wrote their Arabic in Hebrew script.[1] They used pointed letters in their transliterations (even as we do) to compensate the deficiencies of their own alphabet—e.g., a pointed ṭēth to represent a ẓā, a pointed gīmel to represent a jīm, a pointed ẓādē to represent a ḍād—but there were too many dots already in the Hebrew script and dots have a way of getting out of place or of disappearing altogether in the manuscript tradition.[2]

So much for what may be called the Arabico-Hebrew ambiguities; others due to the contacts between Hebrew on the one hand and Greek or Romance languages on

[1] Oriental Jews do so to this day. Refer to my remarks on the religious importance of script vs. language (vol. 1, 152, 333).

[2] For a good example of the textual difficulties involved see Harry Austryn Wolfson: Crescas' Critique of Aristotle. Problems of Aristotle's Physics in Jewish and Arabic philosophy (351, Cambridge, Mass., 1929; Isis, 14, 240–244).

the other may be called Greco-Hebrew or Latino-Hebrew ambiguities (in general when two languages are used simultaneously, there is inevitably some attrition between them, and each damages the other). Many mediaeval Jewish names were Romanized very early, and these Romance forms written in Hebrew script. If we retransliterate them according to our system we obtain a new form different from the original. To illustrate, the name Crescas is spelled Qresqas or Qreskas in the Hebrew script, the name Astruc is spelled Astruq, Astrug, Aṣtruq, etc. (and the s in that word is sometimes a sāmekh, sometimes a sīn), the name Caslari is spelled Qaslarī. Now all of these names are of Romance origin. Crescas is connected with the Latin root cresco; astruc is a Provençal word meaning happy, itself derived from aster (cf. the forms benastruc, malastruc); Caslari is derived from the name of a place, Le Caylar, in Hérault, Languedoc.

Another famous Jewish name, Calonymos (Kalonymus, etc.) is derived from the Greek. It was a poor Greek translation of the common Jewish name Shem-ṭob meaning good name (i.e., the divine name). The Greek form was transcribed in Hebrew Qalonimus.

Some Jewish names were Romance translations of Hebrew ones, as Gracian which is the equivalent of Ḥen (grace), or Hebrew translations of Romance ones, like Caspi (or silver) derived from the place Largentière, not very far from Nîmes, and Me'ati translated from the place-name Cento, near Ferrara. This particularity was not purely Jewish. Christians also translated their names, e.g., Agricola for Bauer, Melanchthon for Schwarzerd, Regiomontanus for "he of Königsberg." The same practice has probably occurred whenever two languages were in contact; indeed we see it happen under our own eyes.

Even purely Hebrew names were gradually corrupted. It will suffice to think of the name originally spelled in Hebrew Kohen (or Ha-kohen, the priest). Countless varieties of it have developed under the influence of almost every language: Cowen, Cowan, etc., in England; Cohn, Kahn, Kohn, etc., in Germany; Cahn, Caen, Cahun, etc., in France; Cohan, Cone, etc., in America; Coen, in Italy, etc.

In the face of all these conflicting usages how could one be always consistent?[3]

9. ICELANDIC

During the period covered in these volumes, the most important European vernacular, next to French and Spanish, was Icelandic. This was not due so much to the intellectual vigor of the Icelandic people, remarkable as it was, as to the fact that the learned books produced in other countries of Western Europe were most of them written in Latin.

In the spelling of Icelandic words I have been obliged to introduce two special letters, þoddn and eð, corresponding to the English lisping sounds, because of the ambiguity of the English th; þ, which occurs mostly at the beginning of words, corresponds to the voiceless spirant, as in (the English words) *thin*, *thing*, *length;* ð, which never occurs at the beginnings of words, corresponds to the voiced spirant, as in (the English words) *the*, *bathe*, *with*. No great mistake would be made by replacing these letters þ and ð by th; and this has been done in the index.

For other details of pronunciation, consult Icelandic grammars, e.g., Helen McMillan Buckhurst: An elementary grammar of old Icelandic (112 p., London 1925).

[3] A very useful list of Hebrew names in (Hebrew) alphabetic order is appended to the first Catalogue of the Hebrew books in the British Museum, compiled by Joseph ben Jonathan Zedner (821–827, London 1867).

10. RUSSIAN

The Russian alphabet will be transliterated as follows: a, b, v, g (h, v), d, e (ye), zh (j), z, i, i, i (or omitted), k, l, m, n, o, p, r, s, t, u (or ou), f, kh, ts, ch, sh, shch, (omitted), y, y (or omitted), e (or ye), e, you, ya, th (or f), y.

The letters represented in Western Slavic languages by ž, č, and š (or by the same letters with other diacritical signs) are transliterated respectively zh, ch, and sh.

For the letters like the fourth (gheh), for which there is more than one alternative it is best to be guided by the origin of the word. The problems involved are very similar to those indicated in my note on Hebrew.

A great many Russian words are of Greek or more exactly Byzantine origin; many others are of "European" (i.e., Western European, Germanic or Romance) origin. Those of the former group are generally very old, and thoroughly Russified. It would be pedantic to re-Hellenize them. Hence we shall write Vasili rather than Basil, Irod rather than Herodes, Feodor rather than Theodore, Ksenia rather than Xenia, Filaret rather than Philaret.

The "European" words on the contrary are generally modern, and our transliteration should not disguise their origin. We shall write Hofmann rather than Gofmann, Henri or Henry rather than Anri, Jungmeister rather than Youngmeister, journal rather than shurnal.

Similar remarks apply to the other Slavic languages written in the Cyrillic script (vol. 1, 590).

These remarks will bring it home to the reader that when so many languages adulterated one another in a number of ways, absolute consistency in transliterating them is out of the question. One might perhaps be absolutely consistent in the transcription of a pure language (if there be such a thing), but no system can remove the inconsistencies which have been introduced into each language by its contacts with others. This has been made sufficiently clear in my notes on Hebrew and Russian. However much we may try, our system will fail in this or that respect, and will have to be corrected by exceptions, and by exceptions to the exceptions, etc., because languages are living things and life laughs at consistency. After all consistency, however valuable, is not the highest virtue. We have done our best to be consistent, but we have always preferred to be inconsistent rather than pedantic.

PART I
THE TWELFTH CENTURY

BOOK ONE

The Time of William of Conches, Abraham ibn Ezra, and Ibn Zuhr

(First Half of Twelfth Century)

Mens hebes ad verum per materialia surgit.

—*Suger of Saint Denis*

(De rebus in administratione sua gestis, cap. xxvii, c. 1146)

CHAPTER I

SURVEY OF SCIENCE AND INTELLECTUAL PROGRESS IN THE FIRST HALF OF THE TWELFTH CENTURY

I. INTRODUCTION

The end of the eleventh century was a turning point in the history of mankind. From the end of the eighth century to the end of the eleventh the intellectual leaders had been most of them Muslims, and the most progressive works had been written in Arabic. It is not too much to say that during these three centuries the Arabic language had been the main vehicle of culture.

But by the time which we have now reached, these conditions had changed considerably. There were still, as we shall see in this and following chapters, great scientists in Islām, but they were becoming exceptional. Scientific renaissance due to Muslim initiative was growing less enthusiastic and its expansion was damped by theological obscurantism. Its spirit was weakened from within and from without. In the meanwhile Jewish and Christian efforts were increasing in vigor and quality. It would seem as if the spirit which had inspired the greatest intellectual endeavors of Islām was filtering away under orthodox pressure into the minds of Jewish and Christian doctors.

Be it as it may, the fact is that in the twelfth century we can not speak any longer of a Muslim or Arabic supremacy, but we can not yet speak of another supremacy. It is distinctly a period of transition. Culture is being transmitted as fast as possible from one group of mankind to another.

Let us close our eyes for a moment and try to see things in a very simplified manner, as they would appear from a great distance, in a sort of vision. The stately chariot which carries the highest hopes and the noblest thoughts of mankind has been stopped to change horses in the neighborhood of an inn. The old Muslim postillions are being thanked and new ones are taking charge. The chariot is stopped, but the fresh horses are pawing the ground impatiently. A last glass to the driver and the barmaid bids him Godspeed. In a moment they will be gone. It is the same old chariot, but the horses and postillions are changed from time to time, and the people riding in it change too, one by one. . . . . . But, mark this, *it is a chariot that never comes back.* It goes on and on as the spirit of mankind moves it; it has been driven by Greeks, by Romans, by people of all kinds, lately by Muslims, now by Jews and Christians. Nor does it matter much who drives if it goes safely forward in the right direction.

To return to our subject, in my first volume I used to give to each chapter a title recalling one of the main personalities of the period concerned. I did this chiefly for mnemonic reasons. I was going to do the same in this volume, but the increasing number of personalities, the increasing complexity of the picture, suggested that it would be better to name in the title two or three persons representing the different types of competing civilizations. Thus we shall call this age The time of William of Conches, Abraham ibn Ezra, and Ibn Zuhr.

This title will be fully justified later, but it may at once be stated that Abraham ibn Ezra was not only one of the noblest minds of that period, but also a good representative of its translating activity. Some Christian translators were perhaps more important but, as far as we know, they do not represent the period so well. Moreover, thanks to a poetical accident, English readers are very familiar with him already, for he is no other than the Rabbi ben Ezra sung by Browning. Ibn Zuhr, a Spanish Muslim, was one of the greatest physicians of the Middle Ages. William of Conches was one of its most original thinkers; less bold and less influential than Abaelard, but the latter died as early as 1142. William symbolizes at once the Norman spirit and one of the most lovable mediaeval schools, the School of Chartres. Englishmen called him Shelley, and I was wickedly tempted to entitle this chapter The Time of Shelley, but it did not seem fair to confuse our literary friends more than was necessary. But perhaps that other title would have clung better to their memories? If so, let them remember that the Time of Shelley was the first half of the twelfth century.

From the purely chronological point of view these three great men represent our period very well. Even Ibn Zuhr, who was the youngest, was at least seven years old when the century began, Abraham was ten, and William twenty; they grew up with the century and lived well beyond its middle, William until 1154, Ibn Zuhr until 1161, and Abraham until 1167.

II. RELIGIOUS BACKGROUND

1. *Christendom*—The end of the eleventh century and the beginning of the twelfth was a period of revival in Christendom. The Crusades were at once a symptom and an additional cause of renewed religious fervor. It was not simply a period of revival, but also of spiritual unrest. The creation of a number of new religious orders is a proof of this.

I ought to have spoken in volume I of the foundation of the Carthusian Order in 1084 by Bruno of Cologne. It was in that year that he began the establishment of the Grande Chartreuse near Grenoble. Carthusian life was a sort of compromise between the two historical types of monasticism, the coenobitic and the eremetic, both of which can be traced back to the very beginnings (first half of the fourth century; vol. I, 346). The wisdom of this foundation is attested by the fact that it has withstood the vicissitudes of time with less need of modification than almost any other religious order. A few years earlier, in 1078, St. Stephen of Muret had started another community equally austere, the Good Men of Grammont (or Grandmontains). The rule was written partly upon the Camaldulian model, in 1141, after St. Stephen's death.

In my chapter devoted to the first half of the tenth century I explained the Reform of Cluny which gave a new vigor to the Benedictine Order. However, by the beginning of the twelfth century this old order was again dangerously declining and a new reform became urgent. This was undertaken by Robert of Molesme in 1098, at Cîteaux in Burgundy; hence the movement was called Cistercian Reform. Robert's effort was admirably continued by the third abbot of Cîteaux, St. Stephen Harding (who drew up the Carta caritatis, 1119), and was brought to its climax by the greatest religious leader of the age, St. Bernard of Clairvaux. The Cistercian reform was essentially an austere reaction against Clunisian laxity and luxury; that is, Harding's ideal was very similar to that which had inspired Bruno and St. Stephen of Muret. The triumph of the Cistercians affected the whole of western civilization very deeply and in many ways. It promoted the Christian faith, but jeopardized the amenities of Christian life; it improved the agricultural and commercial organization, but discouraged learning; it mitigated the evils of serfdom, but threatened intellectual freedom; it put an end to many artistic velleities, yet gave the world some architectural masterpieces. The federal organization of Cîteaux, equally opposed to the dangerous autonomy of the early Benedictine monasteries and to the Clunisian centralisation, was a political discovery of great value. The Cistercian Order enjoyed a marvelous prosperity until the fifteenth century, but its moral climax had already been reached by the middle of the twelfth century.

Still another order must be quoted, the Premonstrants, founded in 1120 by Norbert of Gennep. This was a community of canons regular rather than of monks; its rule was largely inspired by the Cistercian charter of love. Norbert also established a nunnery exclusively for noblewomen, and an auxiliary society anticipating the Franciscan tertiaries.

The number of these foundations and their success prove the intensity of the religious needs which were then felt in western Europe. It should be noted that this revival was not restricted to any single country. To consider only the leaders, Bruno was a German; St. Stephen of Muret was a son of central France; Robert of Molesme came from Champagne, and St. Bernard from Burgundy; Stephen Harding was an Englishman; Norbert of Gennep came from the Duchy of Cleves.

The activity of all of these men and of their innumerable followers represents only one type of religious devotion, the orthodox, conservative, and submissive. They were keenly sensitive to the sins of their time and to the many shortcomings of the Church, and tried to cure them by increased austerity and fervor. But naturally enough, other men of a different temper reacted in a different way; instead of submitting to the Church they withdrew from her bosom. Heterodox Christendom was apparently very much alive in the twelfth century. Witness the wide diffusion of many strange sects such as the Cathari, East and West. The study of these sects is of considerable cultural interest because most of their ideas were simply survivals of older ones, or oriental notions such as Manichaean dualism and Hindu metempsychosis in western garb. Unfortunately these heretics were so thoroughly persecuted, and so few of their writtings were allowed to subsist, that our knowledge of them is bound to remain very limited.

Heretodox Christendom of that time was largely anonymous, but the spirit of revolt is well symbolized by the romantic figure of Arnold of Brescia who withstood vigorously the temporal power of the popes and the cupidity of the priests, but was finally defeated and was hanged in Rome in 1155.

To return to orthodoxy, Christian education had hitherto been dispensed for the most part in monasteries, but the rapid growth of cities increased the importance of cathedrals, and the schools attached to these cathedrals became more and more influential. This implied gradually deep changes in education itself. The urban cathedral being more closely in touch with the outside world than the rural abbey, education in general became a little more worldly. The cathedral schools prepared the birth of the first universities in the subsequent period.

Under the tremendous stimulation of the Crusades an entirely new type of organization developed—the religious orders of knighthood. The earliest was the Order of St. John of Jerusalem, founded in 1099 when the Christian hordes conquered the Holy City. By the middle of the twelfth century this order had already become a universal institution endowed with considerable wealth and power. The Knights Templars were organized a little later, in 1119, and their constitution was drawn up in 1127 with St. Bernard's assistance. The Templars became even richer and more powerful than the Knights of St. John; their secret power was felt all over Latin Christendom. Thanks to the strength and discipline of their order, and to its ubiquity and secrecy, they constituted until the beginning of the fourteenth century the leading financial organization of the world. Indeed, so great was their power that it created corruption within and jealousy without. The king of France and the pope united to destroy it in 1307–1312. Both orders were children of the Church and of War; they combined the ideals of chivalry and monasticism; they were at once military and religious institutions. Considering this inherent conflict of ideals, their shortcomings were far less astonishing than their success.

Apart from St. Bernard, the leading personalities of the Christian world were Peter the Venerable, who was the last of the seven great abbots of Cluny; and Suger, thanks to whose genius the abbey of St. Denis near Paris became one of the cultural centers of that age. It is noteworthy that these three great men, who were then the finest representatives of Christian endeavor, were Frenchmen.

To complete this picture of Christendom it is necessary to say a few words of the admirable development of Romanesque art, which was to a large extent a creation of the church and became in itself an educational agency of which it is hardly possible to exaggerate the importance. Remember that the proportion of literate people was exceedingly small. The decoration of the cathedrals was encyclopaedic in its scope. There were probably as many intelligent men and women then as now; most of them could not read but they could see, and the walls and windows of the churches were their Bible and their school-books.

2. *Israel*—The Crusades are generally thought of as a holy war against Islām. Most people visualize the Crusaders as noble knights who fought the infidels in the most chivalresque manner and incidentally brought with them western civilization to the East. Unfortunately the reality was very different from that beautiful vision. To begin with, the Christian hordes were on the whole less civilized than the Saracens whom they encountered. Secondly, chivalry was the exception rather than the rule. The conquest of Jerusalem in 1099, by Godfrey of Bouillon, instead of being the pure glory and blessing which it was supposed to be, was made odious by the wholesale murder of Muslims and Jews. The greed and brutality of the Christian conquerors was a glaring contrast to the moderation shown by the caliph 'Umar when he had taken the Holy City in 637, and even to the relative generosity of which Ṣalāḥ al-dīn gave proof when he reconquered it in 1187.

But the saddest part of this shameful story is that the Crusades, while outwardly a war against the Crescent, created opportunities to persecute other "infidels," notably the Jews. The criminal phasis of anti-Semitism may be said to date from that time. Each of the first three Crusades was accompanied by violent anti-Jewish outbreaks (regular "pogroms") in France, Germany, and later in England. These troubles were followed by special anti-Jewish regulations which perpetuated the original injustice and the hatred, warped Christian and Jewish souls in various ways, and initiated untold misery and wickedness.

3. *Islām*—In Islām as well as in Christendom this period was more remarkable for religious organization than for theological activity. Peter the Venerable, Suger, and even St. Bernard, were more interested in edification and clerical or monastic organization than in abstract theology. However, the greatest theologian of Islām, al-Ghazzālī,[1] died only in 1111, and thus a part of his activity belongs to the twelfth century.

[1] vol. I, 753.

It is convenient to consider separately Eastern and Western Islām. To begin with the East, the activity of the Crusaders could but fan Muslim faith and stimulate Muslim endeavor. The best illustration of this unwelcome result of the Crusades was given by the Ismā'īlīya sect of the Ḥashīshīyūn (or Assassins),[2] which became very powerful in the twelfth century. Their first leader, al-Ḥasan ibn al-Ṣabbāḥ, who had conquered Alamūt in 1090, died in 1124. The Shaikh al-Jabal (the old man of the mountain) of whom students of the Crusades hear so often, was the chief of the Syrian Hashīshīyūn.

The foundation of the earliest order of dervishes at Baghdād about 1130 is traditionally ascribed to 'Abd al-Qādir al-Jīlī, and this order was named Qādirīya after him. The dervishes are the Muslim counterparts of the Christian monks. Their organization answered exactly the same purposes and the same psychological needs as the organization of monastic orders in Christendom. It is probable that Muslim monasteries existed before this time, but the Qādirīya is the only order of which the history can be traced as far back as the first half of the twelfth century.

'Umar al-Nasafī composed a catechism which remained exceedingly popular in the East (more exactly in Hanīfite countries) almost until our own days. Finally the Ash'arite al-Shahrastānī wrote a valuable history of religions and of Muslim sects. Apart from al-Ghazzālī, who died in 1111, al-Shahrastānī was the greatest Muslim doctor of the first half of the twelfth century.

The only western personality which deserves to be quoted in this summary is the Berber fanatic Ibn Tūmart, the Mahdī of the Almohades. His main disciple 'Abd al-Mu'min was the founder of that dynasty; before the end of his reign (1130–1163) 'Abd al-Mu'min ruled the whole of Muslim Spain and North Africa from Egypt to the Atlantic. This is a chapter of political history but it was based, like the early Muslim conquests, upon religious enthusiasm.

4. *Buddhism*—The first Buddhist sect which may be called Japanese is the Nembutsu shū founded by Ryōnin at the beginning of the twelfth century. The tenets of the eight previous sects had been imported from China and were simply Japanese modifications of Chinese ideas. But by the beginning of the twelfth century Buddhism was becoming dormant and declining in China, and on the other hand, Japan had grown more and more independent of Chinese influence. Ryōnin's activity marked the beginning of a great Buddhist revival, the Great Awakening. The Nembutsu was essentially Amidaist, that is, salvation was expected primarily from constant prayer to Amida.

III. THE TRANSLATORS

A large part, we might almost say the largest part, of the intellectual energy in mediaeval times was spent not in the creation of new intellectual values but in the transmission of older ones. In consequence the activity of translators was of paramount importance. To realize this more clearly, it suffices to transport oneself into any one of the countries of the modern world where mediaeval conditions still obtain, for example, Abyssinia. The historian of a few centuries hence who attempts to explain the intellectual progress of that country will have to find out which scientific works were gradually translated into Amharic. Of course foreign knowledge might be introduced into Abyssinia in different ways, but if it be introduced, as seems most likely, by means of translations, the history of these translations will

[2] vol. I, 752.

at once assume an especial importance. This was exactly what happened in the period now under review. Much of the knowledge which became available in the first half of the twelfth century was obtained not by fresh and independent investigation, but by translation from foreign books, chiefly Arabic.

Thus, after our brief description of religious events, which was necessary to evoke the spiritual atmosphere, our next task must be to speak of the chief translators and to give a general view of their work. To be sure, we shall deal again with some of these translators in the sections devoted to separate sciences; our present purpose is simply to speak of them in a general way and to show how much they accomplished. We shall witness knowledge and culture being, as it were, poured out from one vessel into another.

These translators were so numerous that we must divide them into many groups. The most natural classification is that according to languages. We shall begin by the most important group, then deal with the one second in importance, and so forth, the translations being finally arranged as follows: Arabic into Latin, Greek into Latin, Arabic into Hebrew, Hebrew into Latin, Celtic into Latin, Latin into French. This brief enumeration illustrates the complexity of the cultural exchanges involved, but it should not blind us to the fact that during the period under consideration the first group of translations—from Arabic into Latin— was far more important than all the others put together.

1. *From Arabic into Latin*—One of the earliest as well as one of the greatest of these translators was the Englishman, Adelard of Bath. In 1126 he translated the astronomical tables of al-Khwārizmī, revised by Maslama ibn Aḥmad al-Majrīṭī; he produced the earliest Latin translation of Euclid's Elements—the fifteen books; and he was probably also the translator of the mathematical encyclopaedia, the Liber ysagogarum alchorismi, ascribed to al-Khwārizmī. There is no evidence that Adelard resided in Spain; it is more probable that he obtained his Arabic knowledge in Sicily or in the East. Thus he stands alone in contrast with the imposing group of translators who worked in Spain.

Before speaking of the latter, we may mention Peter the Venerable who traveled in Spain to inspect Clunisian monasteries. He was not an Arabist, but he realized how necessary it was to be acquainted with Muslim thought. He caused the Qur'ān to be translated and refuted. His interest was purely religious, but that does not matter. He helped to build a bridge between Islām and Christendom.

The center of translation in Spain was Toledo. This was natural enough. The ancient Visigothic capital had been but lately reconquered from the Moors. Though it was now again Christian, it had been in Muslim hands for almost four centuries (712–1085). It probably contained an abundance of Arabic writings; but what matters even more, a large amount of its population, including Jews, Christians, Muslims, Mozarabs (assimilated Christians) and Mudejars (assimilated Muslims), used Arabic as their own language. The great opportunity which was thus offered to the Christian conquerors to study the superior culture of their enemies was eagerly improved by the wise archbishop Raymond I (1126–1151). He gathered around him a school of translators working in coöperation with dragomans. The latter would translate from Arabic into Castilian, and their work would be completed by others whose forte was Latin rather than Arabic. This procedure is still often followed for translations from an eastern into a western language, or vice versa; for western scholars need native assistance to make sure that they have not misunderstood the idiomatic meaning. Thus, translators generally worked in pairs and it is often difficult if not impossible to appreciate the value of each partner's contribution.

The greatest of these pairs was that formed by Domingo Gundisalvo and John of Seville, a converted Jew. The latter acted as dragoman but also, it would seem, as translator. We must think of them together. The translations ascribed to them are so abundant that it is impossible to enumerate them here even briefly, and one cannot help conjecturing that some of them were made, at least partly, by other people, as will easily happen in a school. It must suffice to indicate the most important of them: an arithmetical treatise, al-Farghānī's astronomy, the neo-Platonic treatise De causis, and the philosophical writings of al-Fārābī, Ibn Sīnā, Ibn Gabirol and al-Ghazzālī. These translations were chiefly John's work, or were made under his direction and responsibility, but he was helped and guided by Gundisalvo who was more of a philosopher. Gundisalvo's activity revealed itself less in straightforward translations than in "original" treatises which were hardly more than elaborations of the translated works. At any rate, it is through these translations as well as through Gundisalvo's adaptations or elaborations, that much of Muslim and Jewish philosophy was introduced into Latin Christendom.

I must speak more rapidly of other translators of the Spanish school. To Hermann the Dalmatian we owe versions of astronomical and astrological works, notably of Ptolemy's Planisphere (1143). Together with Robert of Chester he prepared a translation of the Qur'ān. Hugh of Santalla, who worked under the patronage of Michael, bishop of Tarazona, translated treatises on astrology, geomancy and alchemy. Robert of Chester, who flourished even further north, in Pamplona, translated a number of treatises on similar subjects, notably one on alchemy (1144), one of the earliest works of its kind to be imported from Islām into Christendom. However, he is chiefly remembered because of his versions of the Qur'ān (1143), and of al-Khwārizmī's algebra (1145). Rudolf of Bruges, a pupil of Hermann the Dalmatian, was, like his master, more interested in astronomy; he translated a treatise on the astrolabe by Maslama ibn Aḥmad. Plato of Tivoli, who was established in Barcelona, translated writings on astrology, astronomy and geometry; he was helped by the Jew, Abraham bar Ḥiyya.

All of these translators, with the possible exception of Adelard of Bath, obtained their Arabic knowledge in western countries. However, one great translator lived in the East, the Italian physician Stephen of Antioch, who made an entirely new version of the Kitāb al-malikī of 'Alī ibn 'Abbās.

To this long list might be added the mysterious "Artephius," who is said to have translated two alchemical treatises, but it should be noted that the exact time of his activity is unknown.

2. *From Greek into Latin*—Those who have realized the immense superiority of Arabic culture from the second half of the eighth century to the second half of the eleventh—a superiority which was fully acknowledged in the twelfth and thirteenth centuries by some of the leading thinkers of Christendom[3]—will not be surprised by this abundance of translations from the Arabic. But while this was going on with increasing vigor there began also to appear a new series of translations made directly from the Greek.

Thus while John of Seville and Gundisalvo were revealing Muslim and Jewish Aristotelianism to the western world, James of Venice was translating the "New

[3] Isis, 10, 68.

Logic"—the Topics, the Prior and Posterior Analytics, and the Sophistici elenchi —from Greek into Latin. It would seem that Boetius' lost version of the same works had reappeared shortly before James' translation, and the latter was followed by still another, the anonymous Toledan translation (probably after the middle of the twelfth century). Finally, another version was made from the Arabic by Gerard of Cremona (second half of the twelfth century). The points to remember are, first, that knowledge of the "New Logic" spread rapidly among the learned men of Europe; second, that in this particular case the direct translation from the Greek was ahead of the indirect one from the Arabic.

The other translators are far less important than James of Venice. Anselm of Havelberg, Moses of Bergamo and Burgundio of Pisa had been present with James at the theological disputations between Latin and Greek churchmen held in Constantinople in 1136 before Joannes II Comnenos. Each contributed his modest share to the interpretation of Greek thought for Latin readers. Anselm wrote an account of the disputations. Moses was so well acquainted with both aspects of the controversy that he "was chosen by all to be a faithful interpreter for both sides." Burgundio will be discussed in the next chapter. Still another Hellenist might be mentioned, Hugh of Saint Victor, who wrote a commentary on the Celestial hierarchy of Dionysios the Areopagite.

3. *From Arabic into Hebrew*—Translations from Arabic into Hebrew were not yet numerous because Eastern and Spanish Jews were still sufficiently well acquainted with Arabic not to need such translations. In fact, Eastern Jews and most of the Spanish ones had a better knowledge of Arabic than of Hebrew. Yet two great translators appeared, the philosopher Abraham ibn Ezra and the mathematician Abraham bar Ḥiyya. Both were Spaniards. Rabbi ibn Ezra translated three treatises on grammar by Judah Ḥayyuj; two treatises on astrology by Māshāllāh (before 1148); and a commentary by al-Bīrūnī on al-Khwārizmī's tables (1160), which is known only through this Hebrew version. Abraham bar Ḥiyya is said to have translated from Arabic into Hebrew a treatise on music; his own writings were essentially Hebrew adaptations of Arabic ones; furthermore he helped Plato of Tivoli, and perhaps others, to translate Arabic works into Latin.

The Jewish translators did for their brethren of Christian Europe—who, unlike the Spanish Jews, did not know any Arabic—exactly what the other Spanish translators did for the Christians themselves. The translations from Arabic into Hebrew were the counterparts of those from Arabic into Latin. Thus Muslim science penetrated western Europe along two parallel channels which it will be our task in the following chapters to examine more closely and to compare.

4. *From Hebrew into Latin*—St. Stephen Harding started a revision of the Vulgate with reference to the Hebrew text made clear to him by Jewish assistants. I have already said that Peter the Venerable, abbot of Cluny, caused a translation of the Qur'ān to be made. He was one of the first churchmen to think of that; he was also one of the first to encourage investigations of the Talmud, which were carried out with the assistance of baptized Jews. Of all the translators thus far mentioned, Plato of Tivoli is the only one who published Latin translations of both Arabic and Hebrew writings. In 1145 he translated from Hebrew into Latin the famous Liber embadorum, a treatise on practical geometry by Abraham bar Ḥiyya.

5. *From Celtic into Latin*—Two Welsh chroniclers, Geoffrey of Monmouth and Caradog of Llancarvan, translated Cymric accounts and stories and inserted them into their own writings, whence they were distributed all over western Europe.

This is of great importance for the history of letters and of arts, as many of these Celtic romances such as the Grail, Perceval, Lancelot, Tristram, and the Round Table, obtained an immense popularity and are still very much beloved to-day. It is possible that Caradog's chronicle was originally written in Welsh (the original text is lost), but if so it was promptly translated into Latin.

6. *From Latin into French*—The Anglo-Norman writer Philip of Thaon wrote in "langue d'oïl" a number of popular treatises adapted from the current Latin literature. They are not real translations, but Philip may be quoted as a translator of Latin knowledge into French.

IV. PHILOSOPHIC BACKGROUND

As I have many times explained in volume I, the dividing line between philosophy and theology is not always easy to draw. Most mediaeval philosophers were theologians, and vice versa; the differences between them were rather quantitative than qualitative. Some were primarily theologians, some were not even interested in abstract theology but only in practical religion or in ecclesiastical organization. These are discussed, if they fall at all within the purview of this work, in the section on religious background. Other theologians will be considered presently.

1. *Eastern Muslim*—The greatest Muslim theologian and one of their greatest philosophers, al-Ghazzālī, died only in 1111. I have spoken of him in volume I, but it is well to remember that his gigantic figure is standing, as it were, upon the threshold of this chapter.

Muḥammad ibn Aḥmad al Qazwīnī wrote a popular encyclopaedia, the Mufīḍ, in 1132. The Ḥanīfite doctor 'Umar al-Nasafī composed a catechism which was extremely popular in the East. The physician Ismā'īl al-Jurjānī showed the vanity of worldly desires in his Munabbih. Al-Zamakhsharī wrote a commentary on the Qur'ān, called Al-kashshāf. These four men were Persians, but wrote mainly if not exclusively in Arabic, except Ismā'īl who wrote an immense medical encyclopaedia in Persian. They represent four different types; the first and third were encyclopaedists, the second, a theologian; the third, a moralist; the fourth, an exegete.

2. *Hispano-Muslim*—With the exception of al-Ghazzālī, who stood head and shoulders above every other philosopher of his time, the Persians were far less original than their contemporaries of Spain. For example, there is a very interesting treatise, the Ḥadā'iq, by al-Baṭalyūsī, which we only know through a Hebrew translation. It contains elaborations of neo-Platonic views on the universe, on the theory of the eternal return, etc. None of this was truly progressive, but it made some impression upon Muslim and Jewish doctors at least until the second half of the fourteenth century. Partly because of the negligence of scribes, and partly because of the consideration of which he was the object, al-Baṭalyūsī was finally confused with Ptolemy!

A much greater man was Ibn Bājja, the Avenpace of Latin writers. He too was an encyclopaedist, but he was less of a dreamer and more of a genuine man of science than al-Baṭalyūsī. The reality of his philosophic and scientific interests is confirmed by the persecutions for "atheism" of which he was the victim. His chief philosophical works were the Tadbīr al-mutawaḥḥid (the Guide of the solitary), and a farewell letter (Risālat al-wadā') to a friend. The former is known only through a Hebrew analysis. Ibn Bājja's influence was felt indirectly through the writings of Ibn Rushd and of Albert the Great.

Two Spanish physicians were interested in logic: Yūsuf ibn Ḥasdai, a Muslim of Jewish ancestry, wrote a summary (ijmāl) on logic; and Abū-l-Ṣalt Umaiya wrote another one entitled Taqwīm al-dhihn. Finally we must still mention, because of the breadth of their studies, the political writer Abū Bakr al-Ṭurṭūshī; and the jurist and educator Ibn al-'Arabī.

3. *Hispano-Jewish*—From the Spanish Muslims we turn naturally to the Spanish Jews who shared their cultural background to a considerable extent. All of them knew Arabic as well as Hebrew, one or two knew it better. As far as their different faith permitted, their philosophy was essentially the same as that of their Muslim neighbors—neo-Platonism and Aristotelianism in their Arabic garb.

The first of them, Baḥya ben Joseph ibn Paquda, is placed here tentatively; some scholars place him a little earlier, in the eleventh century. He wrote in Arabic an ethical treatise, Hidayat ilā farā'iḍ al-qulūb (the Guide to the duties of the heart), which was the earliest Jewish book of its kind and one of the best of mediaeval times. His main sources of inspiration were the Scriptures and Muslim neo-Platonism. One section of the Hidayat is an encyclopaedic summary of positive knowledge. This work enjoyed considerable popularity, chiefly in its Hebrew translation and in other versions derived from the latter.

Moses Sephardi, best known under his baptismal name Pedro Alfonso, will be discussed when I speak of Latin writers; but it should be noted that at least one of his works, the astronomical treatise on the Dragon, was written originally in Hebrew or in Arabic.

The mathematician Abraham bar Ḥiyya was one of the earliest translators from Arabic into Hebrew. He wrote in Hebrew a number of books treating not only of mathematics and astronomy but also of philosophy. His chief philosophical works are an ethical treatise, Hegyon ha-nefesh, and a sort of scientific encyclopaedia, Yesod ha-tebunah.

Moses ibn Ezra (probably a relative of Abraham ibn Ezra) wrote another encyclopaedia, the Ḥadīqat, which was of an entirely different type; it was philosophic and theologic rather than scientific, and the language was Arabic, not Hebrew. However, Moses is far better known by another Arabic work, the Muḥāḍarah, which is one of the rare specimens of Jewish "adab," an extremely popular branch of literature in Islām. Judah ha-Levi wrote, also in Arabic, the famous Kitāb al-Khazarī, wherein he defended the point of view of orthodox Jewish theology against other theologians and against lay philosophers. It is typical that this champion of Jewish orthodoxy was inspired by no one more than by al-Ghazzālī.

Both Moses ibn Ezra and Judah ha-Levi are known to most people as Hebrew poets. In fact, they are the greatest Hebrew poets of the Middle Ages, especially Judah ha-Levi, a great many of whose poems have become an integral part of the Jewish liturgy. This illustrates very well the bi-lingualism of the Spanish Jews. They used Arabic for philosophy and belles lettres, Hebrew for poetry and religion. Arabic was the language of their minds, but Hebrew that of their hearts.

Joseph ibn Ẓaddiq wrote a treatise on the microcosmos, 'Ālam al-ṣaghīr, wherein he developed the neo-Platonic views on the subject as they had been explained before by the Brethren of Purity. This was originally written in Arabic but is known only through a Hebrew version. It should be noted in a general way that though most of the philosophical works mentioned here were written in Arabic, they are known chiefly if not exclusively through Hebrew translations.

The latest[4] as well as the greatest of these Jewish philosophers was Abraham ibn Ezra, well known to English readers as Rabbi ben Ezra. Like the mathematician Abraham bar Ḥiyya, he wrote in Hebrew, and like him, was one of the earliest translators from Arabic into Hebrew. His works constitute one of the main channels through which the abundant stream of Greco-Muslim-Jewish knowledge reached the European Jews who lived beyond the Pyrenees, and indirectly western Christendom. He was one of the introducers of Muslim rationalism in Europe, and one of the forerunners of modern Biblical criticism. Ibn Ezra's rationalism was of course very moderate, and tempered by a large dose of mysticism, yet it was sufficient to cause strong reactions against him. In 1158 he wrote the Yesod mora, treating of the philosophy of religion.

The very length of this summary, in spite of my determination to keep it as short as possible, proves the abounding philosophical activity of the Spanish Jews, an activity which some of them were now beginning to carry into other parts of western Europe.

4. *French Jewish*—When I wrote the last chapter of volume I, I had not yet sufficiently realized the importance of Rashi's commentaries. That is, I had not yet measured their implications, and we cannot well judge a tree until we have tasted its fruits. Rashi died in 1105, and his influence dominated the first half of the twelfth century. He might be called the founder of rabbinical learning in France. The foremost French rabbis of the period were his two grandsons, the brothers Samuel ben Meïr ("Rashbam") and Jacob ben Meïr ("Rabbenu Tam"). Both continued their grandfather's work and improved upon it. Samuel, the elder brother, wrote a commentary on the Tōrāh which is considered one of the finest fruits of French Jewry. Rabbenu Tam is regarded as the founder of the school of Tosafists.

5. *Eastern Jewish*—The philosophical learning of the Eastern Jews is represented by an orthodox Egyptian and by a Qaraite, who lived in Constantinople. The Egyptian, Salāma ibn Raḥmūn, was a physician who wrote various treatises in Arabic. I call him a philosopher because of the variety rather than the depth of his interests; however, he wrote a sort of cosmology, the Niẓām al-mawjūdāt. The Qaraite, Judah ben Hadassi, wrote in Hebrew an encyclopaedic treatise on the decalogue, the Eshkol ha-kofer.

6. *Roger II of Sicily*—Before proceeding to examine the efforts of Christians, we may pause a moment to consider the beneficent activity of the most enlightened ruler of the age, Roger II, count and later king of Sicily until his death in 1154. Under his patronage Sicily became the leading center of cultural exchange. As far as the Muslim, Jewish and Latin civilizations were concerned it was less important than Spain; but to these civilizations were added, in Sicily, the Byzantine. Greek was actually spoken in Sicily and was one of the languages used by Roger's court. Thus in this privileged country (which included not only the island of that name but South Italy as well) the stream of Greek thought was allowed to flow not only through Arabic and Hebrew channels, but also from the original springs. The cultural importance of Sicily in the twelfth century can hardly be exaggerated. I may add that Roger was the patron of the greatest geographer of the century, al-Idrīsī; and it was during his reign, after 1147, that sericulture and the silk industries were introduced from the Peloponnesos into Sicily; this

[4] He died only in 1167; a good part of his activity belongs to the subsequent period.

was an important landmark in the long journey of silk from China to the westernmost end of the world.

7. *Byzantine*—As contrasted with the age of Psellos, the first half of the twelfth century was mediocre. The foremost Byzantine philosopher was Theodoros Prodromos—"Ptochoprodromos," as he was called. He wrote abundantly in vulgar Greek as well as in the literary language, in verse as well as in prose, but none of his writings has much importance. It will suffice here to mention his commentaries on Aristotle. The two brothers Tzetzes lived at about the same time. Both Isaac, the elder, and Joannes, wrote didactic poems. Their writings are difficult to differentiate, but Joannes was probably the chief author; he wrote a rhymed paraphrase of Porphyry's Isagoge.

8. *Latin*—It is very refreshing to turn from sleeping Byzantium to the Christians of western Europe who were now wide awake and whose activity, as we shall see in this and the succeeding chapters, was increasing at a tremendous rate.

In the chapter treating of the second half of the eleventh century I spoke briefly of the problem which engrossed the mind of schoolmen above all others, the problem of universals. The first protagonists in this new quarrel—or rather in this new phasis of a very old one—were still living when the twelfth century opened. St. Anselm, who defended the extreme realist point of view, died in 1109; the first champion of nominalism, Roscelin of Compiègne, who was almost twenty years younger, was still living in 1121. Thus one might well say that the mediaeval aspect of this famous controversy dates from the twelfth century. William of Champeaux, who founded the abbey of St. Victor near Paris about 1108 was a realist, but less absolute and more flexible than Anselm; he is often called the real father of Realism. Another doctor of the same house, Hugh of St. Victor, went even further than William, accepting Abaelard's compromise. He was a pluralist and conceived a complicated atomic theory. His was a very complex personality, for he was a mystic and yet deeply interested in scientific knowledge of which he grasped the need and the unity.

The leading Latin doctor was Peter Abaelard (1079–1142). He tried to solve the problem of universals by inventing a sort of compromise, the so-called conceptualism, which was hardly more than an attenuated nominalism. Now realism was the orthodox theory from the church's point of view, for it was easier to explain the dogma of the Trinity in realist terms than otherwise. Abaelard's eloquence gave considerable popularity to his compromise theory but could not save it from being condemned as heretic, even as nominalism itself. He was primarily a dialectician, and his vigorous and aggressive intellect sharpened the minds of Latin philosophers. In that respect he was one of the founders of scholasticism. By a strange coincidence his activity as a master of dialectics occurred at the very time when the "New Logic" and Muslim-Jewish philosophy were reaching western Europe through Latin and Hebrew channels. While he could hardly avail himself of the new Aristotelian knowledge, he contributed powerfully to prepare its reception.

So much for the early progress of nominalism and Aristotelianism. While this was going on, realism and Platonism developed vigorously in the school of Chartres. The first great master of that school was Bernard of Chartres, who was by temperament if not by actual knowledge a real Platonist. His younger brother Theodoric continued his teaching and wrote a treatise on the seven arts, Heptateuchon, and an Hexaëmeron. Gilbert de la Porrée was inclined to compromise, like Abaelard, and devoted most of his attention to the study of logic. William of Conches wrote various commentaries on the Timaeus and on Boetius' Consolation, and philosophical treatises which considerably enriched the Chartres teaching. For example, he introduced some of the views explained by Lucretius and Ḥunain ibn Isḥāq. He was deeply interested in scientific knowledge, discussing cosmological and atomic theories. Still another thinker can be attached to this school, namely Bernard Silvester, who lived about the middle of the century and wrote a neo-Platonic treatise on the microcosm and macrocosm. Unfortunately the activity of this admirable school did not last very long; perhaps its fervor was too intense to be maintained for any considerable time; the fact is that by the time of Theodoric's death about 1155 its golden age was already over.

I shall discuss in a later chapter the great conciliator Peter the Lombard, but it is well to recall here that he lived throughout the first half of the twelfth century. The converted Jew, Pedro Alfonso, was interested in mathematics, astronomy and geography, but his fame rests mainly upon two works of a more general nature, a vindication of Christian versus Jewish doctrines, and the Disciplina clericalis, a collection of tales derived from eastern sources. The latter enjoyed an immense popularity, being translated into many languages, and was the chief channel through which much oriental lore reached the west.

Adelard of Bath was not simply a great translator; he wrote original treatises, notably one on Identity and difference (before 1116), explaining neo-Platonism, and opposing extreme realism by a sort of compromise similar to the one suggested by Abaelard. He compiled a collection of Natural Questions which gave him another opportunity of publishing Arabic knowledge on a variety of subjects.

Many original treatises are also ascribed to Gundisalvo. These were essentially adaptations of Arabic writings, but he drew from many other sources as well. The De divisione philosophiae is especially valuable. It contains a classification of the sciences and scientific information which may be traced later in the works of Michael Scot, Albert the Great and Robert Kilwardby.

A third translator from the Arabic, Hermann the Dalmatian, wrote a treatise, De essentiis, dealing with categories.

These three philosophers of three different nationalities—Adelard of Bath, Domingo Gundisalvo, and Hermann the Dalmatian—were united by their knowledge of Arabic. We might call them Arabists, and Pedro Alfonso might possibly be considered an Arabist also.

A final group, which we might call German, includes three curious personalities, Honorius of Autun, Otto of Freising, and Hildegard. The German origin of the former is far from certain but is plausible. He wrote a theological treatise, the Elucidarium, which was exceedingly popular. On the other hand, the cosmography, Imago mundi, formerly ascribed to him, is probably the work of Honorius Inclusus (second half of the eleventh century). Otto of Freising was primarily a historian but was also a philosopher; he it was who introduced Aristotelianism into Germany, probably in its Boetian garb. His main historical work, Historia de duabus civitatibus, implied a philosophy of history derived from St. Augustine and Orosius. The most arresting personality of this group was Hildegard, a Benedictine nun, who, though their contemporary, lived until 1179. I shall discuss her in chapter XVIII.

All considered, the Latin philosophers of this period were far more active and more progressive than the Muslims and even than the Jews. Leaving out of the picture al-Ghazzālī who belongs rather to the previous generation, there was but one outstanding Muslim, the Spaniard Ibn Bājja. Turning to the Jews, we must leave out of account Rashi's school which was purely Biblical. The greatest Jewish philosopher was another Spaniard, Abraham ibn Ezra, a dominating figure to be sure, yet far less original, far less forceful, than Abaelard. The other Jewish philosophers, however important in other respects, do not begin to compare in point of vigor and originality with the best representatives of the school of Chartres, nor even with such men as Adelard of Bath, Gundisalvo, Hermann the Dalmatian, or Otto of Freising. Thus, so far as the general outlook is concerned, the Latin world seems already to have taken up with Islām.

9. *Vernacular*—To complete the philosophical or literary background of Christendom we have still to speak of some works written neither in Greek nor in Latin, but in some of those new languages which were perhaps the best symbols of the growing independence of Europe.

The new languages which were the best representatives of this period were, strangely enough, the "langue d'oïl" (French), and Icelandic. Various didactic poems were written in French by Philip of Thaon, the Anglo-Norman, who lived about 1119–1125.

The date of the Icelandic writings which form the Younger or Prose Edda, and the Elder or Poetic Edda, is far less definite, but we may be sure that a substantial part of these works dates from the period with which we are now concerned, if not from an earlier one. It is very remarkable that a great literature should have arisen in that frozen and inhospitable region of northern Europe long before it appeared in more favored countries. It is hardly possible to give an explanation of this which reaches the root of the matter. Most attempted explanations are nothing but commentaries; they describe but do not really explain. In our ignorance we cannot but repeat, "The wind bloweth where it listeth. . . . ."

V. MATHEMATICS AND ASTRONOMY

It is not expedient to treat mathematics and astronomy separately, as it would oblige us to reconsider twice substantially the same group of men. The astronomical work of the period consisted mainly in the compilation of tables, and trigonometric tables were inseparable from the purely astronomical. On the other hand the ethnic subdivision is very convenient, and it is also natural; the members of the same ethnic group were more likely to be somewhat related and to influence one another more than those of different groups. That is, the influence of one group upon another would not likely be immediate; its transmission would take more or less time and it would be felt not so much by contemporaries as by later generations.

1. *Eastern Muslim*—It is best to begin our survey with the eastern wing of Islām if only because one of the most original mathematicians of the Middle Ages, 'Umar al-Khayyāmī (Omar Khayyam), whom we chose as the standard bearer of the second half of the eleventh century, died only in 1123, in old age. He thus witnessed almost half of the period under consideration. Another mathematician of the eleventh century, Muḥammad ibn 'Abd al-Bāqī the Baghdādite, may have lived until about the same time. A commentary on the tenth book of Euclid, which was translated by Gerard of Cremona, is ascribed to him.

The great physicist al-Khāzinī compiled the astronomical tables, Al-zīj al-mu'tabar al-Sinjarī, which give the positions of the stars for the year 1115–1116, and the latitude of Marw.

Muẓaffar al-Asfuzārī, a collaborator of 'Umar al-Khayyāmī, wrote a summary of the fourteen books of Euclid's Elements.

Al-Badī' al-Aṣṭurlābī of Ispahan was the most famous maker of astrolabes of his time (hence his nickname); he directed astronomical observations and compiled tables; it does not seem that his work was of special excellence but he was excessively admired by Muslim biographers.

Muḥammad al-Kharaqī wrote treatises on astronomy and arithmetic, and revived a fantastic theory according to which the planetary spheres are not geometric abstractions but real things!

It is worth while to mention also the physician 'Adnān al 'Ainzarbī, who wrote a treatise on the application of astronomy to medicine. This should help us to remember that every self-respecting physician of those days was also an astrologer. Indeed, from their point of view astronomy was as essential as physiology, for the prescription of a rational treatment implied a sufficient knowledge of both.

2. *Western Muslim*—Turning to the West we come across another physician, Abū-l-Ṣalt, who wrote a treatise on the astrolabe. He was apparently a man of much higher caliber than 'Adnān al-'Ainzarbī; a philosopher rather than an astrologer. Like the two other astronomers of whom I shall speak presently, he was a Spaniard, but unlike them he lived in Egypt and Tunis.

Ibn Bājja (the philosopher Avenpace) was deeply interested in astronomy; he originated the criticism of Ptolemy which led somewhat later to al-Biṭrūjī's so-called theory of spiral motion.

The third Spaniard, Jābir ibn Aflaḥ (the astronomer Geber of Latin writers), was by far the greatest astronomer of the age. He too subjected the Ptolemaic theory, of which the shortcomings were becoming more and more apparent, to severe criticism. His astronomical treatise Iṣlāḥ al-Majisṭī was valued for centuries not only by Muslims but also, in its Latin and Hebrew versions, by Christians and Jews. The traditional trigonometric introduction was of special importance, as the part on spherics marked a real step forward; for example, it contained a new method of solving a right-angled spherical triangle. The invention of an astronomical instrument called turquet has been ascribed to Jābir; this is plausible but has not been proved.

3. *Hispano-Jewish*— There are but two Jewish mathematicians to consider, both Spaniards and both prominent. The first was Abraham bar Ḥiyya, often called Savasorda. His chief work, the Ḥibbur ha-meshiḥah, treating of practical geometry and algebra, is one of the most important mathematical books of the Middle Ages, not only because of its intrinsic value, but even more because of its influence. It contains the complete solution of the equation $x^2 + b = ax$. It was one of the earliest channels through which Muslim trigonometry reached the West. He wrote various astronomical works, and compiled tables derived from al-Battānī; his Sefer ha-'ibbur is said to be the earliest Hebrew treatise specifically devoted to the calendar. Unfortunately we have only fragments of his mathematical encyclopaedia, Yesod ha-tebunah.

The other Jewish mathematician was Abraham ibn Ezra (Rabbi ben Ezra). He wrote a number of treatises on mathematics and astrology, on the calendar, and the astrolabe. For example, he completed eight astrological tracts at Lucca in 1148. These tracts were very popular; witness the number of translations in French, Latin and Catalan. They were derived from Arabic models and thus helped considerably the diffusion of Muslim astrology in the West. Ibn Ezra was much interested in practical arithmetic and in the theory of numbers. His propensity to mysticism led him to study the occult properties of numbers and magic squares. He explained a decimal system of numeration and investigated the combinations of n things taken r at a time; he knew that $C_{n,r} = C_{n,n-r}$, etc.

It is important to realize that the scientific writings of Abraham bar Ḥiyya and of Abraham ibn Ezra were not in Arabic but in Hebrew. They were the earliest writings of their kind in that language. This is a landmark in the history of Jewish thought, for it symbolizes its gradual emancipation from Islām.

4. *Byzantine*—There is very little to say about Byzantine mathematics. All that I was able to find was a poem on astrology by Prodromos; and another by Isaac Tzetzes, or more probably by his younger brother Joannes. A commentary on Ptolemy is ascribed to this same Joannes.

5. *Latin*—There are a number of anonymous Latin treatises of this time (or let us say of the twelfth century) dealing with abacus, exchequer, algorism, compotus, etc. But none is sufficiently important to draw our attention from contemporary writings of known authorship.

The converted Jew, Pedro Alfonso, compiled astronomical tables and wrote a letter concerning astronomy to the Peripatetics. It is possible that these were originally written in Arabic or in Hebrew. At any rate, an astronomical treatise of his on the Dragon was translated into Latin in 1120 by the Englishman, Walcher of Malvern, or else Walcher adapted a translation made by somebody else, possibly by Pedro himself. This Walcher was a genuine astronomer who had observed lunar eclipses in Italy in 1091 and 1092, and compiled lunar tables about 1109. In these tables he used Roman fractions; in the treatise of 1120 he used degrees, minutes and seconds. As far as I know, Walcher was the first English astronomer; he was also the first of his nation (or one of the very first) to translate or adapt an Arabic treatise.

Walcher's tables call to mind others compiled a little later, about 1140, by Raymond of Marseilles. These were simply an adaptation of al-Zarqālī's tables; they seem to have passed almost unnoticed.

The arithmetical knowledge of the time may be measured by means of two treatises. The first was written by Ralph of Laon, a French educator who gave considerable lustre to the school of Laon directed by his brother Anselm and later by himself. It contains explanations of two methods of divison (divisio aurea, ferrea). The other was written by one mysterious Ocreatus, who was probably a pupil of Adelard of Bath. It is certainly of Arabic origin. Both treatises are of special interest because of their use of Roman numerals and also of Hindu numerals; in Ocreatus' treatise these are strangely mixed; or, more exactly, he combines the use of zero with that of Roman figures and of place value. Thus these treatises represent some sort of intermediary stage between an abacus and an algorism.[5]

To complete our account of Latin mathematics and astronomy, it is now necessary to recall the efforts of the translators from the Arabic, and those, very different, of the Chartres Platonists.

The value of the translators' activity can hardly be overestimated, inasmuch as the greater part of Latin mathematics and astronomy was derived from Arabic documents. Smaller portions were obtainable in earlier Latin writings, or translated from the Hebrew, but the main bulk came direct from the Arabic.

[5] For the distinction between an abacus and an algorism, or between abacists and algorists, see vol. I, 756.

To the Englishman, Adelard of Bath, belongs the rare honor of having produced the earliest Latin translation of the fifteen books of Euclid (the earliest translation from the Arabic, of course). He also translated in 1126 the astronomical tables of al-Khwārizmī, as revised by Maslama ibn Aḥmad al-Majrīṭī; and probably the Liber ysagogarum Alchorismi, the mathematical treatise of the same al-Khwārizmī. The tables introduced Muslim trigonometry, chiefly the use of the sine and tangent functions, into the West. Early in life, before his Arabic contacts, Adelard had written an abacus, and one of his latest works was a treatise on the astrolabe. His version of Euclid included the determination of the sums of the angles of stellated polygons.

A large number of other Arabic mathematical works were published in Latin during this period, because it happened that the most active translator, John of Seville, was especially interested in the mathematical sciences. I suspect that his main interest was astrology, and he was foremost in transmitting Muslim astrology to the West. He translated various treatises by Māshāllāh, Abū 'Alī al-Khaiyāṭ, Abū Ma'shar, al-Kindī, 'Umar ibn al-Farrukhān, Aḥmad ibn Yūsuf ibn al-Dāya, al-Battānī, Thābit ibn Qurra, al-Qabīṣī, and Ibn abī-l-Rijāl, and in 1142 he wrote an astrological summary derived from Arabic sources. In short, aided by Gundisalvo and possibly by other collaborators, he provided the Latin West with a whole astrological library! Of course astrology led him to astronomy and mathematics. We owe to him the translation of al-Farghānī's astronomy (1134); of a treatise on the astrolabe by Maslama ibn Aḥmad al-Majrīṭī; and of an algorism, Liber alghoarismi de practica arismetrice, which was an elaboration of al-Khwārizmī's earlier work. John was considerably more active than Adelard as a translator, but, unlike Adelard, he was not a mathematician; he added nothing of his own to our mathematical knowledge

As to John's main collaborator, Domingo Gundisalvo, his mathematics were mostly derived, as we would expect, from Arabic literature and from the Arabic Euclid, but a little of his arithmetical knowledge came from earlier Latin writings.

Astrology seems to have been the chief interest of the other translators also. This is certainly true of Hermann the Dalmatian whose activity as a transmitter of Arabic astrology, though much less than that of John of Seville or Plato of Tivoli, was nevertheless considerable. He translated treatises of Sahl ibn Bishr and Abū Ma'shar; and, in 1143, Ptolemy's Planisphere as preserved in the Arabic version of Maslama ibn Aḥmad al-Majrīṭī, this being the only tradition of that text. A translation of astronomical tables by al-Khwārizmī is also ascribed to him. Apropos of this, it may be observed that the compilation or adaptation of such tables might be considered purely astronomical work, yet the purpose was undoubtedly astrological. Allowing for a few exceptions, which will be noticed as they occur, mediaeval scientists considered astronomy a means to an end; the end was astrology.

The chief translation by Hugh of Santalla was al-Bīrūnī's commentary on al-Farghānī's astronomy. His astrological curiosity was extended to other occult subjects, such as geomancy and spatulamancy. He translated two of Māshāllāh's treatises.

Robert of Chester, who belonged to the same group, was a man of higher intellect. It is true he translated an astrological work of al-Kindī's but the rest of his activity was distinctly of a better type. For example, he was clearly attracted by the more scientific side of astrology; witness his translation of a treatise on the astrolabe (1147), his compilation of tables for the longitude of London (1149) derived from those of al-Battānī and al-Zarqālī, and his revision of the tables translated by Adelard of Bath. His main claim to our esteem, however, is his translation of the algebra of al-Khwārizmī (1145), a fundamental landmark in the history of that subject, as it may be considered the beginning of European algebra. Robert was the first to use the word sinus (sine) in its modern sense.

Hermann's pupil, Rudolf of Bruges, translated a book on the astrolabe by Maslama ibn Aḥmad, and is said also to have written original astronomical treatises.

The last but not the least of these translators was the Italian, Plato of Tivoli. His activity was second only to that of John of Seville. He was assisted by Abraham bar Ḥiyya, and translated mathematical works not only from the Arabic but from the Hebrew. In fact, his translation from the Hebrew of Abraham's Liber embadorum, completed in 1145, is his most important contribution. I have already spoken of that work, apropos of the original Hebrew edition (Ḥibbur hameshiḥah). It will suffice to add that the Latin version was later one of the main sources of Fibonacci, and thus one of the fountain heads of European mathematics. Though the texts translated by Plato from the Arabic were less important, two accredited to him deserve special mention: the Spherics of Theodosios of Bithynia, and the astronomy of al-Battānī. These are of course major works; for example, the second was one of the springs of Latin trigonometry; unfortunately we are not quite sure that Plato was their translator. We may still single out his translation of Ibn al-Ṣaffār's treatise on the astrolabe, but all the others are purely astrological: treatises by al-'Imrānī, Abū 'Alī al-Khaiyāṭ, Abū Bakr al-Ḥasan ibn al-Khaṣīb; aphorisms of unknown authorship, and Ptolemy's Tetrabiblon.

Though it would have been difficult to be briefer, my account of these translations from the Arabic is so long that it is necessary for the sake of clearness to sum it up. We may first observe that the great bulk of these translations is made up of astrological literature. It is important to bear that in mind; a real avalanche of astrology fell upon Europe. I use the word avalanche advisedly to suggest a catastrophe, which it was. It is not necessary to remember the details of that literature. But what else was translated? Very much. This is my second point. The large mass of astrological rubbish must not hide from our eyes the many valuable treatises which became then for the first time available to the Latin scholars. Let us consider them in order of subjects.

Geometry—The fifteen books of Euclid translated by Adelard of Bath; and the spherics of Theodosios of Bithynia, translated probably by Plato of Tivoli.

Arithmetic—Al-Khwārizmī's algorism, translated probably by Adelard; and another algorism, more elaborate than the first, translated by John of Seville.

Algebra—Al-Khwārizmī's algebra, translated in 1145 by Robert of Chester; and the algebra of Abraham bar Ḥiyya, translated from the Hebrew in the same year by Plato of Tivoli.

Astronomy—Al-Farghānī's treatise, translated by John of Seville in 1134; al-Bīrūnī's commentary on that treatise, translated by Hugh of Santalla; al-Battānī's astronomy, translated probably by Plato of Tivoli.

Astronomical tables—This implies the introduction of Arabic trigonometry, especially the sine and tangent functions. The tables of al-Khwārizmī, revised by Maslama ibn Aḥmad al-Majrīṭī, were translated in 1126 by Adelard of Bath; another translation was possibly made about 1140 by Hermann the Dalmatian; tables for London were compiled by Robert of Chester in 1149, and he revised Adelard's translation.

Astrolabe—I add a few treatises on the astrolabe, though a closer scrutiny of them would be needed to know how much of each is truly scientific, how much astrological. A treatise by Maslama ibn Aḥmad was translated by John of Seville, and another translation is ascribed to Rudolf of Bruges (it is possible that there are two different treatises). An anonymous treatise was translated in 1147 by Robert of Chester; and a treatise by Ibn al-Ṣaffār was translated by Plato of Tivoli. Adelard of Bath wrote, about 1140, a treatise on the same subject entirely derived from Arabic sources.

Some of these treatises were translated more than once, particularly the astrological ones which were naturally more popular. All of which illustrates the intensity of this movement.

To conclude: the translators from the Arabic and Hebrew of the first half of the twelfth century gave to the Latin world Euclid and Theodosios; the new arithmetic and algebra (including the complete solution of the quadratic equation); the astronomical knowledge of al-Farghānī and al-Battānī; the tables of al-Khwārizmī, revised by Maslama ibn Aḥmad, and to some extent those of al-Battānī and al-Zarqālī; finally, the beginnings of Arabic trigonometry, notably the use of sines and tangents.

It may seem a sort of anticlimax to pass from these great achievements to the Platonic meditations which were quietly pursued in the cloisters of Chartres. Yet this will serve to show the complexity of mediaeval thought. The spirit of that school was essentially neo-Platonic, but by the middle of the twelfth century Theodoric of Chartres and William of Conches were already aware of the new Aristotelian physics which was being poured out of its Arabic containers. Their cosmology was a mixture of their old Platonic dreams with this new knowledge. William was apparently as well informed as it was possible to be in Chartres in those days. He deserves special credit for drawing a sharp line between astronomy and astrology.

6. *Vernacular*—Very little was yet published in western Europe in other languages than Latin. I have nothing better to report than a few writings on the calendar, in French and in Icelandic.

About 1116 Philip of Thaon wrote a compotus in French verse.

Icelandic Easter tables date back to 1121 and 1140. An account of chronology is given by the great historian, Ari Fróði Þorgilsson, in his Islendingabók, about 1136. The poet, Stjörnu Oddi, wrote also on the compotus. Yet it is claimed that the earliest Icelandic treatise specifically devoted to that subject (rím) was written by Bjarni Bergþórsson who died in 1173; he will be discussed in Book II.

7. *Hindu*—I should have spoken in volume I of Śatānanda, who compiled some sort of astronomical tables for the year 1099 and following. This has but little importance. On the other hand, India produced at about this time a man of considerable genius, Bhāskara, who was certainly the most powerful and original mathematician of the age. The only one who could be compared to him in point of genius was 'Umar al-Khayyāmī, who belongs rather to the previous period as he was older by at least two or three generations. 'Umar, born about 1043, belongs to the end of the eleventh century and the beginning of the twelfth; Bhāskara, born in 1114, must be placed in the very middle of the century, as his main work was completed in 1150; he wrote a second work in 1178, thus we might have placed him in the subsequent period.

The Siddhāntaśiromaṇi, Bhāskara's masterpiece, is divided into four parts, the first two treating of mathematics, the last two of astronomy. The astronomical part is hardly more than a clearer restatement of the views explained in the Sūrya-siddhānta many centuries before;[6] it is thus behind the times and we need not worry about it. The mathematical part, on the contrary, is full of novelties, too many to be quoted: true nature of division by zero; convention of signs; general solutions of quadratic equations (though only positive roots are taken into account); solution of a few cubic and biquadratic equations; solution of indeterminate equations of the first and second degrees; elaborate tables of sines; etc. Perhaps the most striking characteristic of Bhāskara's algebra is its relative completeness. His geometry was also remarkable, though less advanced. The study of regular polygons with a great many sides had led him to find a good approximation of the ratio of a circumference to its diameter, and he had somewhat anticipated Kepler's method of integration.

An anonymous Sanskrit work, the Bakhshālī Manuscript, of the same time if not earlier, is also very interesting. It contains arithmetical and algebraical material similar to that found in the works of Mahāvīra and Bhāskara. As is true of so many Hindu monuments, its archaeological value is much diminished by the impossibility of dating it with any accuracy. If we date it by its mathematical contents, then clearly we cannot extract from them any information on the history of Hindu mathematics without arguing in a circle.

But the work of Bhāskara is sufficient to vindicate the scientific genius of the Hindus in the twelfth century.

VI. PHYSICS, TECHNOLOGY, AND MUSIC

1. *Physics*—I have shown in volume I that much Archimedean knowledge had reached the Muslim mathematicians. One item which found special favor with them was the hydrostatic principle, or rather its application to the determination of densities. This subject had been investigated by Sanad ibn 'Alī (first half of the ninth century), al-Rāzī (second half of the ninth century), al-Bīrūnī and Ibn Sīnā (first half of the eleventh century), and 'Umar al-Khayyāmī. An elaborate account of these studies was given by 'Abd al-Raḥmān al-Khāzinī in his Mīzān al-ḥikma, which is one of the fundamental treatises on mechanics and physics of mediaeval times. It includes a theory of gravity; tables of densities, not only of solids but also of liquids; observations on capillarity; etc. According to al-Khāzinī's own statement, densities were investigated also by the mathematician Muẓaffar al-Asfuzārī. It should be noted that all these students of specific gravity were Eastern Muslims; with the exception of Sanad who was a Baghdādite of Jewish ancestry, they were all of them Persians.

The Spanish physician Abū-l-Ṣalt dabbled in many sciences, including mechanics. During his long stay in Egypt (1096–1112) he tried to raise a ship sunk at Alexandria, but failed.

The great Hindu mathematician Bhāskara discovered, or rediscovered, the extension of oil upon the surface of water.

2. *Technology*—The oldest Artesian well of which the history is known is that dug in 1126 in Lillers, Artois. Such wells were far more ancient in the East, but they became more common at about this time in Western Europe.

[6] See vol. I, 386.

The craftsman Theophilus, presumably a German, wrote an encyclopaedia of the arts which is full of information for the historian of technology. For example, it contains the earliest western account of bell founding.

3. *Music*—It has been noted that Arabic writers on specific gravity were all of them Easterners. It is remarkable that the students of music, on the contrary, whether Muslim or Jewish, were Westerners. The physician Abū-l-Ṣalt wrote a treatise on music which is extant only in a Hebrew version; there are much fewer such treatises in that language than in Arabic. Ibn Bājja was deeply interested in music. Abraham bar Ḥiyya is said to have translated a musical treatise from Arabic into Hebrew, and of course his encyclopaedia Yesod ha-tebunah contained a section on music.

As to Latin treatises on music, I would first recall the Breviarium de musica and the Tonarius written by Frutolf of Bamberg who died in 1103. Adelard of Bath had studied music in France; and the mathematical treatise of al-Khwārizmī, which was in all probability translated by Adelard, included an account of music. Magister Leoninus, organist of Notre Dame in Paris, wrote the Liber organi de graduali wherein the different time values of notes are indicated. This notation was improved by his successor, Perotinus.

VII. CHEMISTRY

1. *Muslim*—Various treatises on alchemy are ascribed to the Persian poet al-Ṭughrā'ī who wrote in Arabic. He discussed Ibn Sīnā's sceptical views on the subject.

2. *Latin*—The mysterious Latin author "Artephius" may belong to the same time. His Liber secretus and his Clavis majoris sapientiae were probably translated from the Arabic. It is impossible to say anything more definite until the writings of al-Ṭughrā'ī and of Artephius have been thoroughly examined.

Theophilus' encyclopaedia contains much information on the preparation and use of oil colors, the making of glues, lakes, varnishes, dyes, etc., and also a recipe for ink which is essentially modern. Thus oil painting dates back at least to the first half of the twelfth century, but it was very imperfect because of the lack of siccative material.

Alchemical knowledge, like astrology, though in a lesser degree, became much more popular in Europe at this time on account of the appearance of various translations from the Arabic. We are on far more solid ground with regard to these than with regard to Artephius who was mentioned only because my note on al-Ṭughrā'ī suggested it. Leaving Artephius out of the picture, three translators of this period showed interest in alchemy. A revised edition of the Mappae clavicula is ascribed to Adelard of Bath. Hugh of Santalla produced the earliest Latin version of the famous Emerald Table. The most important alchemical treatise thus far published in Latin, the Liber de compositione alchemiae, was completed in 1144 by Robert of Chester; the original was supposed to have been written by Khālid ibn Yazīd (second half of eighth century) and to have been edited by Morienus Romanus. These translations, especially the last one, may be said to mark the beginning of European alchemy; their influence was not by any means as evil as that of the astrological treatises, for they contained more facts which were truly valuable in spite of wrong interpretations, and they did not divert students to the same extent from the real issue.

Bartholomew of Salerno may possibly be the author of a tract on distilled water which is best known by the German adaptation of Michael Puff (second half of the fifteenth century). Adelard's edition of the Mappae clavicula, mentioned above, contains one of the earliest references to alcohol. Another reference to it was made at about the same time by an unknown physician, Salernus, who lived at Salerno about 1130–1160. These are the earliest mentions of alcohol definitely known to me.

3. *Chinese*—Chinese claims of priority with regard to distillation and alcohol have not yet been fully substantiated. The claim was made in behalf of Tou P'ing (first half of the eleventh century). Another Chinese "chemist," Chu I–chung, is said to have written, about 1120, a treatise on the distillation of spirits.

Summing up this section, we see that alchemical progress in the first half of the twelfth century was partly theoretical and partly practical. The theoretical advance was due to the translations from the Arabic which were just becoming available, the first important one dating from 1144. The practical advance, far more significant, was caused by the experiments of craftsmen like Theophilus, and of physicians like Salernus, and Bartholomew of Salerno. It is probable that a similar development was taking place in China at the same time, but of this we know practically nothing.

VIII. GEOGRAPHY

1. *Eastern Muslim*—Three geographers of extremely different types illustrate this period. The first, Sahl ibn Abān, was of a type which we now meet for the first time, but of which there appeared many other examples during the following centuries until the supremacy of eastern seas was wrenched from Muslim hands by the western navigators. Sahl was a compiler of sea-voyages and route-books, who prepared instructions for the captains and pilots sailing to Cathay and the East Indies. He stands here as representative of a class, the members of which are generally as little known as are the authors of portolani.

An unknown Persian writer, Ibn al-Balkhī, wrote about 1110 in Persian a description of the province of Fārs, the Fārs nāmah.

The Persian grammarian al-Zamakhsharī compiled a number of Arabic glossaries, one of which was a dictionary of places, mountains and waters, that is, a geographical dictionary.

2. *Western Muslim*—We shall speak in this chapter of but one western geographer, Muḥammad al-Zuhrī of Granada, who wrote a general treatise on geography; but two others more important, to be considered more fully in the next chapter, began their activity in the first half of the twelfth century. It will suffice here to mention them: al-Idrīsī, the greatest of all mediaeval geographers, who was patronized by Roger II of Sicily; and al-Māzinī, who traveled extensively in the Near East and in Europe, including Russia.

3. *Latin*—Pedro Alfonso made a sketch map of the world, clearly derived from Muslim models, which shows the navel of the world surrounded by the seven climates, the south being placed at the top.

Henry of Mayence compiled in 1110 a treatise based upon the Imago mundi. This included a map which is in some ways comparable to the Hereford map (second half of the thirteenth century). The so-called Jerome maps which date from the middle of the twelfth century are closely related to the Henry map and are probably derived from the same prototype.

Another geographic encyclopaedia, the Geographica, was written in 1119 by

Guido the Geographer, probably an Italian; and still another, the Liber floridus, was completed at about the same time by Lambert of Saint Omer. Lambert was apparently the best of the three; he had some scientific knowledge; witness his belief in the sphericity of the earth. The older manuscripts, one of which was probably written by the author, contain very interesting maps.

To these cosmographical compilations might be added the De essentiis of Hermann the Dalmatian (1143), which includes astronomical and geographical information; and the De mundi universitate, written by Bernard Silvester about 1150, in which he emphasizes the influence of the soil upon plants and animals.

4. *Latin pilgrims*—The diffusion of accurate geographical knowledge was greatly encouraged in western Europe by the growing complexity of monastic organization which obliged abbots and monks to travel not infrequently to distant monasteries. The centralizing tendencies of the Church induced increasing numbers of regular and secular clergymen to report to the pope in Rome. Finally a constant procession of pilgrims was creating spiritual exchanges in the monastic centers such as Santiago de Compostela, Saint Martin of Tours, Rome, Chartres and many others. Pilgrims were especially numerous because it was now a well established custom in Christendom to start on a pilgrimage to obtain indulgences or the remission of sins. So many were the pilgrims that hospices were built to accomodate them, as on the Alpine and Pyrenean passes. (Some of these hospices were much older.) The influence of these pilgrimages cannot be overestimated. The pilgrimage roads stand in the same relation to the intellectual and artistic development of Christendom as the commercial roads to its economic organization.

The greatest pilgrimage of all was that to the Holy Land. These distant journeys were considerably stimulated by the Crusades, and visits to Jerusalem and other holy places of Palestine increased enormously while the Holy Land remained in Christian custody. On the other hand, one might claim that the Crusades were to a large extent a consequence of the pilgrimage impulse; they might be compared to immense pilgrimages organized in a military fashion and on a national or international scale. Certain it is that many of the best of the crusaders were at the same time pilgrims, and very conscious of it.

Now some of the pilgrims to the Holy Land wrote narratives of their experiences which are equally interesting from the historical and geographical point of view in spite of their general lack of criticism. These narratives ought to be completed of course by the chronicles of the Crusades, which will be considered in the section on history.

The earliest Latin account is that of an anonymous pilgrim, "Innominatus I," who visited Jerusalem before the conquest (1099). Two other anonymous narratives, those by "Innominatus IV" and "Innominatus VII," date respectively from the first quarter and the fifth decade of the twelfth century.

Two other pilgrim writers are better known: an Englishman called Saewulf who visited the Holy Land and the Near East in 1102–1103, and whose account is the earliest posterior to the First Crusade; and the Italian, Belardo d'Ascoli, who visited the Holy Land about 1116.

5. *Other Christian pilgrims*—Special importance must be attached to two other narratives written not in Latin, but in vernaculars. The first, by Daniel of Kiev who was a pilgrim to Palestine about 1106, is one of the earliest monuments of Russian literature; it compares very favorably with the Latin accounts. The second, the Sigurd's Saga, relates the adventures of the Norwegian king Sigurd the Cru-

sader, who in 1107 sailed all the way from his country to Palestine, and returned overland across Bulgaria, Hungary and Germany.

6. *Chinese*—Hsü Ching traveled to Korea in 1125 and wrote a description of that country and of its customs and institutions.

The two oldest Chinese maps extant were made in 1137, probably on the basis of earlier models. They are preserved in Hsi-an fu.

IX. NATURAL HISTORY

1. *Muslim*—The treatise on simples by Serapion junior and the antidotary of Ibn al-Tilmīdh must necessarily contain material of botanical interest.

For zoological information we have to turn to works of an entirely different type; first, to a book on the names of horses, Asmā' khail al-'arab, by Ibn al-Jawālīqī the grammarian; second, to a treatise on hunting, by Ibn Bājja the philosopher.

2. *Latin and Vernacular*—Marbode's Latin lapidary was probably composed before 1096, but it may be somewhat later and date only from the beginning of the twelfth century. At least one lapidary was written in langue d'oïl by Philip of Thaon. Two are ascribed to him; the so-called Alphabetical lapidary, and the Apocalyptic, but the ascription of the former and more important is less certain. The Alphabetical lapidary is at once the earliest and the most elaborate of the Anglo-Norman lapidaries. It is derived from the same sources as Marbode's Liber lapidum; that is, it is essentially pagan, including the old scientific and magic traditions, without Christian additions.

Turning to botany and husbandry, the outstanding fact is the immense agricultural progress due to the Cistercian reform and to the efforts of Suger of Saint Denis. It has been said that Cistercian farming changed the agricultural face of Europe. Suger, who was above all a great administrator, did much also by the example of his own monastery to raise the standards of French husbandry.

Information on herbs and other drugs is found in the Antidotarium Nicolai; and better still in the Circa instans of Matthaeus Platearius, which is primarily a herbal, 229 of the 273 chapters of the original text treating of plants.

Some of the Circa instans manuscripts are illustrated, and their influence can be measured by the fact that a quarter of the illustrations of the Gart der Gesundheit can be traced back to them. On the other hand, some of the earliest drawings of plants from life have come down to us in a manuscript of the De herbarum virtutibus of Apuleius Platonicus (a work of the fifth century), written at Bury St. Edmunds about 1120. This shows that the beautiful drawings of some of the early printed herbals were not as much of a novelty as is often thought; on the contrary, they were the culmination of a tradition which can be traced back at least to the first half of the twelfth century.

Zoological knowledge is represented mainly by treatises on falconry. Hunting with birds of prey is a very ancient sport which may have developed independently East and West. Aside from a dialogue in Aelfric's Colloquium (second half of the tenth century), the earliest Latin text on the subject is a treatise by Adelard of Bath, which seems independent of Arabic influence. However, even if western falconry was at the beginning independent of eastern, there is no doubt but that later it was very deeply influenced by eastern models. It is probable that in this, as in so many other things, the Crusades played an important part. The knights returning from Syria brought home with them a better knowledge of falconry and a deeper interest in it. After Adelard's, another Latin treatise was composed by William, falconer to King Roger ii of Sicily, but we know it only indirectly. It is probable that these Latin treatises were preceded by Arabic ones, but I have not yet been able to identify any such prototype with certainty.

The only other zoological document in western Europe was Philip of Thaon's French version of the Physiologos, Li bestiaire. In contrast with the early Latin and French lapidaries, which were pagan, the bestiaries continued the Christian traditions of their early Greek prototype. This illustrates once more the strength of tradition, or to put it otherwise, the narrow limitations of human originality. Twelfth century lapidaries and bestiaries were respectively pagan and Christian because of literary accidents which had happened at least a thousand years before!

3. *Byzantine*—Michael Glycas began his chronicle of the world's history with an elaborate account of creation which contains abundant information on stones, plants and animals, derived from the Physiologos, Aelianos and other sources. John Tzetzes wrote commentaries on Oppianos' poem on fishing, and possibly on Aristotle's zoology.

4. *Chinese*—Ch'ên-fu wrote in 1149 a treatise on husbandry which contains a section on sericulture. Of course a student of Chinese natural history will examine first of all their herbals or pên-ts'ao, but it will be more appropriate to discuss these in the section on medicine.

X. MEDICINE

1. *Serapion Junior, or Ibn Sarābī*—It is well to begin with Ibn Sarābī, or Serapion Junior, so mysterious that one does not even know to which race he belonged. It is very probable that the treatise on simples, which has come down to us under his name and is best known in its Latin form, was originally written in Arabic. Like many other Arabic-writing physicians, he may have been a Christian. However, it has been claimed that the Latin text was an original passed off as a translation from the Arabic for the sake of prestige. The date is equally uncertain; from internal evidence Ibn Sarābī must be placed after Ibn al-Wāfid who lived until 1074, and before Ibn al-Baiṭār who lived in the first half of the thirteenth century. I have placed Ibn Sarābī tentatively in the first half of the twelfth century, but he might belong to the second half of the eleventh or the twelfth century. Whatever its origin, the Liber Serapionis aggregatus was very popular from the end of the thirteenth century.

2. *Western Muslim*—Ibn Ḥasdai, who was in all probability a descendant of the famous Judeo-Spanish family Ḥasdai, was himself a Muslim. He wrote commentaries on Hippocrates and Galen. Abū-l-Ṣalt, who lived in Egypt and Tunis, wrote a treatise on simples. Another treatise on materia medica by the philosopher Ibn Bājja was often quoted by Ibn Baiṭār.

All of this is relatively unimportant, but a Muslim family established in eastern Andalusia since the beginning of the tenth century produced a series of physicians, the Ibn Zuhr, one of whom became one of the greatest physicians of mediaeval times. But before speaking of him, we must say a few words of his father, the wazīr Abū-l-'Alā' Zuhr (Alguazir Albuleizor), who died in Cordova in 1130. Though almost entirely eclipsed by his illustrious son, Abū-l-'Alā' was a very distinguished physician who wrote a number of medical treatises. His son, Ibn Zuhr (Avenzoar), was perhaps the greatest clinician of Islām (and of the Middle Ages), after al-Rāzī; Ibn Rushd considered him the greatest physician after Galen. The two foremost of his many writings are the Iqtiṣād (incomplete), treating of the reformation of *souls* and bodies (the beginning of it is a psychological summary); and the famous Taisīr. This second work seems to have been conceived by Ibn Zuhr and Ibn Rushd as a counterpart to the latter's Kullīyāt. The Kullīyāt was meant to be more philosophical; the Taisīr more practical. This double purpose was fully accomplished. The Taisīr is one of the most important books in the whole history of medicine. It is a treatise on pathology and therapeutics which is very valuable because of the many new clinical descriptions it contains, and because it deeply influenced the development of western medicine through Hebrew and Latin translations. The final part is an antidotary entitled Jāmi', sometimes considered a separate work. Ibn Zuhr has been called the earliest parasitologist after Alexander of Tralles, because the Taisīr includes among many other things a description of scabies (itch or mange) and of the mite causing it. However, with regard to the itch-mite he was anticipated by Aḥmad al-Ṭabarī (second half of the tenth century).

3. *Eastern Muslim*—'Adnān al-'Ainzarbī, who lived at the Fāṭimid court in Cairo, wrote a medical encyclopaedia and an astrological primer for the use of physicians. Ibn al-Tilmīdh was a physician at the court of al-Muqtafī in Baghdād. He wrote an antidotary, a treatise on bloodletting, and a collection of observations. It is worthwhile to observe that Ibn al-Tilmīdh, like his predecessors Ibn Buṭlān and Ibn Jazla, was a Christian, which shows that Christians were continuing to hold their own in the city of the caliphs.

Still further east, at the court of Khwārizm, was a third physician, Ismā'īl al-Jurjānī, the most interesting of the three. Soon after 1110 Ismā'īl completed an immense medical encyclopaedia in Persian, the Dhakhira al-Khwārizmshāhī. He wrote other medical works, but this one is the most important; it had the almost unique distinction (for a Persian work) of being translated into Hebrew.

4. *Jewish*—I have but two Jewish physicians to name, both writing in Arabic, the one in Spain, the other in Egypt. The Kitāb al-Musta'īnī which Ibn Biklārish wrote at Saragossa about 1106, was a medical compendium in the form of synoptic tables. Thus was the eleventh century Baghdād tradition of Ibn Buṭlān and Ibn Jazla continued in the far west. The Egyptian Salāma ibn Raḥmūn was an encyclopaedist whose interest in medicine was but one among many others.

5. *Byzantine*—Joannes Tzetzes was probably the author of commentaries on Nicandros' Theriaca and Alexipharmaca. Prodromos wrote a poetic calendar containing health rules for each month of the year. A work somewhat similar was written about the middle of the century by an unknown author, Hierophilos the Sophist; it is a treatise on diet, wherein the regulations collected by the author are arranged month by month.

6. *Latin*—The activity of Latin physicians was so considerable that it is necessary for the sake of clearness to divide them into groups. I shall discuss first the translators, then the Salernitan anatomists, other Salernitan physicians, and the oculists, and conclude with a brief account of hospitals.

The translators deserve the place of honor for their contributions were still of fundamental importance. European medicine was not yet ready to fly with its own wings; a large amount of preparatory work remained to be done; that preparatory work consisted to a large extent in pouring out medical experience from the Arabic into the Latin vessels.

One of the translators, John the Saracen, belongs possibly to the end of the previous century. He completed the translation, begun by Constantine the African, of the surgical part of the Malikī of 'Alī ibn 'Abbās; his work was ended in 1114 (?) with the help of a physician of Pisa called Rusticus. A new version of the Kitāb al-malikī was finished about 1127 by Stephen of Antioch. As John and Rusticus were working in Italy, and Stephen in Antioch, we may assume that their versions were entirely independent. Stephen was probably the author of the treatise entitled De modo medendi.

John of Seville was primarily interested in astrology and philosophy, but he translated at least a part of the Sirr al-asrār, under the title Epistola Aristotelis ad Alexandrum de conservatione corporis humani. This letter of Aristotle to Alexander is of special interest as a prototype of the famous Salernitan regimen. The translation of a treatise on pulse and urine is ascribed to Plato of Tivoli.

The Arabic knowledge thus introduced by Constantine and his followers was eagerly seized upon by the physicians of Salerno. Indeed we find many traces of it in contemporary Latin writings. For example, the earliest Salernitan anatomy, ascribed to Copho, dates from the end of the eleventh century, or more probably from the beginning of the twelfth. It was properly called Anatomia porci, its purpose being to conduct a public dissection of the pig. This treatise was a good specimen of an age of abrupt transition, for it combined traces of early Latin and of Arabic influence. We find in it some new anatomical terms, such as pia and dura mater. Another anatomical treatise, the so-called Second Salernitan demonstration, is probably anterior to 1150. It is similar to the first, though much longer and more elaborate. Some passages are taken in extenso from Constantine's Pantechni.

A number of Salernitan physicians illustrate this period. Archimatthaeus wrote a Practica, a treatise on bedside manners, and possibly also another on urine. Bartholomew of Salerno wrote another Practica which was very popular in Western Europe; he may also be the author of a tract on distilled waters.

The Antidotarium Nicolai, or Antidotarium parvum, which we ascribe to an unknown Nicholas of Salerno, was the standard antidotary of the school of Salerno. We must expect such works to be eclectic. The Salernitan antidotary was very eclectic indeed; it contained many recipes transmitted from antiquity or taken from early mediaeval writers, with additions and modifications borrowed from Arabic sources. It was immensely successful—witness the number of translations; it was even translated into Arabic, which is as remarkable as if an Arabic medical work of to-day were translated into English. It was in a sense the basis of all later works of the same kind, developed by a slow and gradual process of changes and additions, down to the monumental pharmacopoeias of our own times. It is impossible to go into the details of such a work; it will suffice to mention that it recommends the use of a spongia soporifera to induce anaesthesia.

Salernus composed medical treatises, one of which in tabular form may have been inspired by the taqāwīm of Ibn Buṭlān and Ibn Jazla. Matthaeus Platearius wrote the earliest commentary on the Salernitan antidotary, and a treatise on simples, usually called Circa instans, whose popularity until the sixteenth century was second only to that of the antidotary itself; for example, it was twice translated into Hebrew.

Two more works, though far less significant, deserve to be quoted. A small treatise on diet, by Petrus Musandinus; and one called Trotula, on midwifery and women's diseases, ascribed to a woman of that name, Trotula di Ruggiero. It is possible that Trotula was a Salernitan midwife who distinguished herself so much that her name was naturally chosen for the title of the Salernitan handbook summing up the special experiences of her profession; it is also possible that she was the real author.

Three eye doctors lived apparently at about the same time. It is strange that so little is known about any of them that they are all almost equally mysterious. One thing is clear, they were influenced by Arabic models; ophthalmology was one of the strongest branches of Muslim medicine. The greatest of the three was Benevenutus Grapheus, the most famous non-Muslim oculist of mediaeval times. He was probably a southern Italian, possibly a converted Jew; he lived in the twelfth century, probably in the second quarter, in Salerno and Montpellier. What we know of the two others is even less certain. Zacharias was probably also a Salernitan physician, but he lived in Constantinople about the middle of the century. David the Armenian lived in South Italy. In contrast with the other Salernitan physicians, these eye doctors are somewhat exotic—one is said to be a Jew, the second hails from Constantinople, the third from Armenia.

The achievements of the Latin physicians, though lacking in originality and power, were so remarkable that it is worth while to summarize them here.

To begin with, various medical treatises were translated from Arabic into Latin. The volume of translations was smaller than during the preceding period, but it included a work of the first importance, the Malikī of 'Alī ibn 'Abbās. By the middle of the twelfth century two Latin versions of it were available. Meanwhile the main textbooks representing the teachings of Salerno were being published in quick succession. Two editions of the anatomy had probably appeared before 1150. This anatomy, which naturally included elements of physiology and pathology, was derived not only from Arabic writings but was based on actual dissection of pigs. Practical treatises on medicine for the general practitioner were published by Archimatthaeus, Bartholomew of Salerno, and Salernus. Archimatthaeus taught doctors their duties and manners. The Antidotarium Nicolai was the main guide of apothecaries, and their knowledge of simples was expounded in the Circa instans of Matthaeus Platearius. A number of special treatises were written: on urine, by Archimatthaeus (?); on diet, by Petrus Musandinus; on midwifery and female disorders, by Trotula; on distilled waters, by Bartholomew (?); on eye diseases, by Benevenutus Grapheus, Zacharias of Constantinople, and David the Armenian. (For surgery, we shall have to wait a little longer). Observe that at least three of these treatises were not by any means ephemeral; Benevenutus' Practica oculorum, the Antidotarium Nicolai, and the Circa instans remained authoritative for many centuries.

To be sure, none of these Salernitan doctors was as impressive a personality as was Ibn Zuhr, but together they complemented one another very well and their total influence was greater.

To complete this picture of medical progress in the Latin West, a few words must be said of the hospitals. These can be traced back to the first half of the fourth century. The idea of systematic hospitalization was originally a Christian one, but it was very well understood also by Muslims. However, the Crusades gave a tremendous stimulus to it and from the beginning of the twelfth century a large number of hospitals and hospices of all kinds—but chiefly leproseries—were established all over Europe. In the beginning these "houses of God" (Hôtel Dieu) did not affect the progress of medicine, but they were bound to influence it deeply in later times.

7. *Hindu*—The only Hindu physician was Ḍallana, who wrote one of the earliest commentaries on the Suśruta-saṃhitā. I place him here tentatively. All that we know is that he lived probably in the twelfth century.

8. *Chinese*—Medical knowledge of the period is best represented by new stages of the traditional pên ts'ao or herbals, one of which, entitled Chêng lei pên ts'ao, was published in 1108 by T'ang Shên-wei, a physician of Ssŭ-chuan. It contains descriptions of some 1455 objects of the three kingdoms of nature. It is probable that these descriptions were illustrated; at any rate later editions were; for example, that of 1468 included 600 pictures of plants. Compare this with my remarks on Latin herbals in the section on botany.

A supplement to that herbal, the Pên ts'ao yen i, was compiled by K'ou Tsung-shih and added to the edition printed in 1111. It was revised at the end of the century.

XI. HISTORIOGRAPHY

As soon as a certain stage of civilization, which need not be very high, has been reached, the work of physicians and historians is bound to continue—which does not necessarily mean to progress. In the case of historiography it is even more difficult than in that of medicine to measure the real value of practical work and to determine whether there is any useful novelty in it. The best that we can hope to do is to indicate the main historical writings of the period, adding a few remarks here and there.

1. *Eastern Muslim*—The only historian of note was al-Shahrastānī, who wrote his chief work, the Kitāb al-milal wal-niḥal, in 1127. It is one of the best works of its kind, a very valuable history of the sects of Islām, and of other religions; scholarly, well arranged, and not unfair. Al-Shahrastānī also wrote a history of the philosophers.

2. *Western Muslim*— The Sirāj al mulūk, a political work by Abū Bakr al-Ṭurṭūshī, completed in 1122, contains many historical anecdotes. The Spanish physician Abū-l-Ṣalt wrote an account of the things and men he observed in Egypt. Ibn Bashkuwāl continued, in 1139, the biographical dictionary of learned Andalusians begun by Ibn al-Faraḍī (first half of the eleventh century).

3. *Western Jewish*—The Muḥāḍarah, written in Arabic by Moses ibn Ezra, contains much information on the Jewish settlements of Spain and on the literary activity of learned Jews. The fondness for biographical and bibliographical collections was really a Muslim trait, but it was natural enough for a Spanish Jew to acquire it.

4. *Byzantine*—One of the most interesting historical works of the period is the Alexias, the biography of Alexios Comnenos, emperor from 1081 to 1118; it was begun by his son-in-law Nicephoros Bryennios, continued by his daughter Anna Comnena, after her husband's death, and completed not long before her own death in 1148.

Joannes Zonaras compiled a historical summary from Adam down to the end of Alexios' reign. This is an important chronicle, and whatever knowledge we have of the first twenty-one books of Dion Cassios' Roman history is derived from it. A similar work covering the same period was produced by Michael Glycas, but it is distinctly less scientific and more anecdotic.

5. *Armenian*—The first golden age of Armenian culture occurred at the time of St. Mesrop (first half of the fifth century). A second began in the second half of the

twelfth century; a forerunner of this revival was the historian Matthew of Edessa, who compiled an Armenian chronicle from the middle of the tenth century to 1136, which was continued to 1162 by Gregory the Priest.

6. *French*—The greatest event of the end of the eleventh century was undoubtedly the First Crusade. Its implications were many and deep, some of them good, others evil. A few have already been mentioned. The main political results were the bringing together of East and West on a gigantic scale, and the realization of Catholic unity against the Infidels and the Greeks; the creation of a sort of European consciousness, or, in each nation (especially in France), of a national consciousness opposed to the regional loyalties. Europe was knit together by the ordeal.

Nowhere was this change of mind more apparent than in the writings of chroniclers. They were at once shaken out of their isolation and awed by the epic grandeur of the events which they had witnessed and which were still fresh in their minds. One of them, Robert the Monk, went so far as to say, "If we except the salutary mystery of the Crucifixion, what has happened since the creation of the world that is more marvellous than this which has been done in modern times, on this expedition of our men to Jerusalem? The more studiously anyone directs his attention to this subject, the greater will be his stupefaction."[7]

The First Crusade was initiated by Frenchmen and largely carried on by them; they were fully aware of their predominance, and so were their adversaries; witness that up to this day western Europeans are called Franks in the Near East.[8] The crusade being a French undertaking, it is natural that the chronicling of it appealed mainly to French imaginations.

Yet the author of the earliest account, the Gesta Francorum, was in all probability a native of South Italy. This account was imitated or used by a number of other writers: Guibert of Nogent, Orderic Vital, Ekkehard of Aura, Pierre Tudeboeuf, Baudri of Bourgeuil, Robert of Reims (Robert the Monk), Raoul of Caen, Hugues of Fleury, Gilon of Paris.

One adaptation is especially noteworthy, the so-called Song of Antioch, composed in French by Richard the Pilgrim at the beginning of the twelfth century and rewritten about a century later by Graindor of Douay. This was a regular *chanson de geste*,[9] and mark, it was the earliest to be devoted to a contemporary event. This shows how strongly the deeds accomplished by Christian knights in the fabulous and sacred countries of the East had caught hold of popular fancy.

Guibert of Nogent is known chiefly because of his history of the Crusades. But he wrote other works of unusual interest: a treatise on saints, wherein he expressed his scepticism concerning many relics; and one of the most important mediaeval autobiographies, consisting of three parts, the second and third treating of the history of his convent and of the commune of Laon.

Orderic Vital was born in England but lived at Saint Evroul in Normandy. He wrote a chronicle from the time of Christ to 1143, Historia ecclesiastica, which is considered the best historical work produced in France in the twelfth century.

Another chronicle, the Codex Calixtinus, written by a pilgrim to Santiago de Compostela for the use of other pilgrims, contains the earliest clear reference to

[7] As quoted by Dana Carleton Munro (American historical review, vol. 32, 220, 1927).

[8] Faranjī, Afranjī. Compare also the Persian-Arabic word Firangistān, to designate non-Turkish Europe.

[9] See my note on the Chanson de Roland in vol. I, 773–74.

the Basque people. It illustrates the relations between Galicia and France which a steady flow of pilgrims never allowed to be interrupted.

Robert of Torigny, the Norman, will be discussed more fully in the next chapter; but it should be noted here that as early as 1139 he revised the chronicle of the Dukes of Normandy. The Parisian philosopher, Hugh of Saint Victor, revived an old theory that civilization flows from east to west and when it reaches its westernmost limits the world will end. Suger of Saint Denis wrote the lives of Louis VI and Louis VII; but other works of his devoted to the explanation of his monastic administration are historically more valuable, in fact they are among the most significant historical documents of the age.

7. *Italian*—Leo of Ostia compiled a chronicle of Monte Cassino from its beginning in 529 to 1075 (1094?); this chronicle was revamped and continued to 1139 by Peter the Deacon.

8. *English*—Florence of Worcester wrote a chronicle covering the period from 450 to 1117, and John of Worcester continued it to 1141. But the best English chronicler of the time was William of Malmesbury, who published chronicles of England, of the English bishoprics, etc. He was one of the few mediaeval chroniclers who were not content to recite events but tried to explain them. He suggests comparison with Bede.

9. *Welsh*—It is to Geoffrey of Monmouth and his friend Caradog of Llancarvan that we are mainly indebted for the transmission from Cymric into Latin of an abundance of Celtic lore. This is of course important from the historical point of view, but vastly more so from the standpoint of pure literature, as I indicated when I spoke of these writers as translators. Geoffrey's history was abridged by Alfred of Beverley and translated into Anglo-Norman verse by Geoffrey Gaimar. English translations were somewhat later, but by the middle of the twelfth century the wonderful Celtic tales were available both in Latin and French.

10. *German*—With the possible exception of the French, the finest group of historians was the German. No less than four were notable men, and one of them was one of the greatest Latin historians of the Middle Ages.

Two of them wrote universal chronicles; Sigebert of Gembloux down to 1111, and Ekkehard of Aura to about 1125. Sigebert also wrote a history of the Benedictine abbey of Gembloux, and various biographies; he defended the imperial against the papal views. Ekkehard's chronicle was one of the best of its kind. His account of the first crusade has already been referred to.

Far greater than these two was the princely Otto of Freising, not simply a chronicler but a philosophic historian. He wrote a biography of his nephew Frederick Barbarossa, but his chief work was his Historia de duabus civitatibus, one of the best historical works of the Middle Ages, inspired by Augustine and Orosius, and probably also by Hugh of Saint Victor.

The fourth historian, Anselm of Havelberg, though not to be compared with Otto, was no less original. He wrote an account of the negotiations at Constantinople in 1135 between Greek and Latin theologians. Having witnessed these theological disputations, he returned to his bishopric in the North March where he had to take part in a much harder struggle, the protracted warfare between Germans and Slavs; his own bishopric had to be reconquered twice from the latter during his term of government.

11. *Bohemian*—Cosmas of Prague, the "Herodotos of Bohemia," wrote Latin chronicles of his country down to the time of his death in 1125. Though partial and uncritical, their importance is fundamental.

12. *Icelandic*—But strangely enough, one of the greatest historians of the time, Ari Fróði þorgilsson, was then living in remote Iceland, the northernmost and westernmost part of the civilized world. He wrote in Icelandic the Book of Kings, the Book of Icelanders (c. 1127), and the Book of Settlements. The last named contains an account of the Norwegian discovery and colonization of the island. Because of their historical content we may recall here the Eddas, discussed earlier.

13. *Russian*—The father of Russian history, Nestor of Kiev, wrote in Russian a chronicle from the Flood to 1110; this was continued to 1125 by Silvester of Kiev who is sometimes considered the real author or editor of the whole chronicle. Both accounts were derived from Byzantine sources and from other Slavic chronicles which are lost. Their importance cannot be exaggerated.

14. *Kashmirian*—The majority of Hindu chronicles have almost no historical value, because of their utter lack of impartiality, critical sense and chronology. We might extend this statement to apply to all the mediaeval chronicles of India, if we did not consider Ceylon in the south and Kashmir in the north as integrant parts of the country. Indeed the most valuable chronicles of India, we might almost say the only valuable ones, refer to these two extreme parts of it. They are the Mahāvaṃsa written in Pāli by Mahānāma (second half of the fifth century); and the Rājataraṅgiṇī (Stream of Kings), written in Sanskrit by the Kashmirian chronicler Kalhaṇa and completed in 1148; the latter is of essential importance for the study of Kashmirian history and archaeology.

15. *Chinese.*—The Chinese historical works form a very curious group which contrasts pleasantly with all the other works examined here.

Têng Ming-shih, with the help of his son Têng ch'un, compiled in 1134 a treatise on the origin and history of Chinese clans and families. This work was the basis of all ulterior investigations. We have not yet come across any similar treatise in the West, but I spoke in volume I of at least two other eastern books of the same type: the Kitāb al-nasab of Hishām ibn Muḥammad (second half of the eighth century), and the Shōjiroku (first half of the ninth century), treating respectively of Muslim families of Arabian origin, and of noble families of Japan.

Another Chinese antiquarian, Hung Tsun, published in 1149 the earliest extant treatise on Chinese coinage. This is probably the earliest independent work on numismatics in any language; I say independent, because accounts of the currency were included as a matter of course in the Chinese dynastic annals from the time of the Han.

Finally there are two archaeological works which are mentioned together here for the sake of convenience, though the second belongs to the subsequent period. Wang Fu compiled in 1107–1111 the Po ku t'u lu, a critical catalogue of the collections of the emperor Hui Tsung. A similar work, the Ku yü t'u p'u (illustrated description of ancient jades), was edited and prefaced by Lung Ta-yüan in 1176. Both works are eloquent proofs of the archaeological curiosity of the Chinese; there was nothing at all comparable to them in the West until a much later time.

16. *Japanese*—Fujiwara Tamenari compiled the O-kagami (Great mirror), a history of Japan from 851 to 1036. This is one of the three historical classics, Mitsu kagami (the Three Mirrors).

XII. LAW AND SOCIOLOGY

1. *Western Muslim*—The most remarkable Muslim treatises on government of the second half of the eleventh century had been written in the East by two East-

erners, al-Māwardī the Baghdādite, and Nizām al-Mulk the Persian. Those of the first half of the twelfth century were written by two Westerners who, however, spent a good part of their lives in the East; both were Spaniards and, naturally, Mālikites.

The first, Abū Bakr al-Ṭurṭūshī, made the Pilgrimage in his early twenties and remained in the East until the end of his life. His Sirāj al-mulūk, a treatise on practical politics, was written in Cairo in 1122.

The other, Ibn al-'Arabī, the Sevillian, was educated in the East but finally returned to his native city and later moved to Morocco. (Southern Spain and Morocco were then united under the Almoravide dominion). He was a professional jurist and wrote a commentary on the Kitāb al-muwaṭṭa'.

2. *Latin*—Manegold of Lautenbach, an Alsatian philosopher who died after 1103, wrote a pamphlet in defense of papal against imperial policies. This is one of the earliest mediaeval treatises on the philosophy of the state. Manegold claimed that the monarch's authority is limited by moral and social restrictions.

The protracted struggle between the emperor and the pope was one of the causes, perhaps the main one, of the revival of Roman law, which became the most significant development of that period. Hitherto law had been treated as a branch of rhetoric; it now became sufficiently important to be considered independently. The first mediaeval school of Roman law was founded in Bologna, either by Irnerius, or under his inspiration. At the beginning of his legal career Irnerius had defended the papal cause; after 1115 he adhered to the imperial party. His real interest was jurisprudence and his energy was mainly spent in writing glosses on the Corpus juris, especially on the Digest, and in other tasks of the same kind. His work was continued and the school of Bologna solidly established by his disciples, chiefly the "Four Doctors," Martinus, Bulgarus, Hugo and Jacobus. This revival of Roman law was extremely important because it contributed just as much as Abaelard's dialectics (if not more) to the development of stricter habits of thought. The influence of exact jurisprudence can be traced in many scientific writings of the ensuing periods; that influence was not free from evil, but it was apparently useful and necessary.

Though the endless political quarrels between Guelphs and Ghibellines made of Italy the natural cradle of this revival, it spread with amazing speed across the Alps. A treatise, the Brachylogus juris civilis, formerly ascribed to Irnerius, was probably a French work of the first quarter of the twelfth century. The author, whoever he was, had some acquaintance with the Corpus juris and also with Alaric's Breviary. Another legal work, Lo Codi, written about 1149 in southeastern France, is even more interesting, for it is the earliest treatise on Roman law written in a vernacular.

By the same time Roman law had already been introduced into England, for the Italian jurist Vacarius reached that country about 1143 and was teaching there before the middle of the century.

It is hardly necessary to say that feudal law was not displaced by Roman law except very slowly in the exact measure that the growing power of communes and of centralized governments made itself felt and obliged feudal institutions to give way to new political and legal ideas. In fact, various feudal constitutions date only from that very period.

The influence of the school of Bologna was not restricted to the civil law; it promptly caused a recasting of the canon law. This immense task was undertaken by Gratian, a pupil of Irnerius. In 1139 he published the first code of the laws of the church, the so-called Decretum. In the course of time the Decretum was followed by auxiliary codes, the collection of which formed the Corpus juris canonici, the ecclesiastical counterpart of Justinian's Corpus juris. The earliest commentary on Gratian was written, presumably before 1150, by one Magister Rolandus, the future Alexander III. This was the beginning of a new evolution which does not concern us, emancipating the canon law from its stem the civil law.

3. *Hindu*—Two Hindu legists deserve brief mention: Lakshmīdhara, who wrote one of the earliest commentaries on dharma; and Govindarāja, who wrote the most important mediaeval commentary on the laws of Manu. Both lived probably in the twelfth century, the former most likely in the first half of it.

XIII. PHILOLOGY AND EDUCATION

1. *Eastern Muslim*—The greatest philological activity occurred in the eastern part of Islām. I have shown in volume I with what eagerness eastern peoples, and chiefly Muslims, turned to philological investigations. This eagerness did not abate as fast as their scientific interest in other fields.

From the purely Arabic point of view, the greatest man of letters was al-Ḥarīrī, who wrote grammatical treatises, but is chiefly known as the author of a collection of stories, the Maqāmāt, which represents a very typical form of Arabic literature. Another grammarian of 'Irāq, Ibn al-Jawālīqī, wrote a commentary on Ibn Qutaiba's Adab al-kātib, and other grammatical treatises.

Two Persian grammarians, al-Maidānī and al-Zamakhshārī, were more interested in lexicography. The former compiled in 1104 an Arabic dictionary wherein the words were classified by subjects; he is best known for his collection of proverbs. The second compiled many dictionaries, notably one Arabic-Persian. Both knew Persian and added occasional explanations in that language; but their chief language was Arabic, and al-Zamakhshārī not only believed in its superiority but was a fanatic on the subject. This recrudescence of Arabic fervor is interesting when one recalls that al-Firdawsī and his nephew Asadī of Ṭūs had but just raised their national language to a very high level. But apparently it was impossible for Persian to compete with Arabic as a polite language, even in Persia!

Apropos of these lexicographical efforts, we may here recall "Stephen's Synonyms," the Greek-Arabic-Latin glossary which Stephen of Antioch appended to his translation of the Malikī.

2. *Western Muslim*—I do not know of any contemporary grammarian in the Maghrib worthy of mention, but the great jurist Ibn al-'Arabī deserves a place of honor in the annals of Muslim pedagogy. Instead of basing the whole of education upon the Qur'ān, a work hopelessly beyond the intelligence of children, he suggested teaching them first the three "r's"—reading, writing and arithmetic—and only then the Qur'ān. This is plain common sense, but it required imagination and courage to explain such views in his day, and his advice was so much ahead of the times that it remained unheeded.

3. *Western Jewish*—One of the greatest monuments of mediaeval scholarship, the 'Aruk, a Talmudic dictionary, was completed in 1101 by Nathan ben Jehiel, a Roman Jew.

A Spaniard, Isḥāq ibn Barūn, wrote a treatise in which he set forth the essential similarity of Arabic and Hebrew forms. This might be called the first comparative grammar of Semitic languages, for the epistle written three centuries earlier by Judah ibn Qarīsh was but a rudimentary anticipation.

The medical tables of Ibn Biklārish contain a glossary of remedies, the Arabic terms being translated into Syriac, Persian, Greek, Latin and Spanish. Such glossaries were frequently added to medical books, chiefly to herbals and antidotaries.

Nothing better illustrates the dependence of early mediaeval Jewish culture upon the Muslim, than the fact that some of the best treatises on Hebrew grammar were for a long time available only in Arabic. For example, Ḥayyuj, the father of Hebrew grammar (second half of the tenth century) had written only in Arabic. Three grammatical treatises of his were translated into Hebrew by Abraham ibn Ezra. Needless to say, Ibn Ezra's Biblical commentaries were also fundamental contributions to Hebrew philology. The same can be said of any important Biblical commentary—for example, those of Rashi and of his grandsons, Samuel and Jacob ben Meïr—because the correct interpretation of a text implies a grammatical analysis and a careful weighing of every word. Jacob ben Meïr became one of the leading Hebrew grammarians.

Latin scholars were beginning to study Hebrew; witness the efforts of Stephen Harding and Peter the Venerable.

4. *Byzantine*—The Alexias, written by Nicephoros Bryennios and his widow Anna Comnena, and completed in 1148, was the first great work exemplifying the Byzantine literary revival. It is characterized by conventional archaism and Atticism.

Students of early Slavonic culture must take Zonaras' Epitome into account, for it was soon translated into Slavonic languages and was one of the main channels through which historical knowledge reached the Slavs.

5. *Latin and Vernacular*—It is not surprising that the revival of Roman law should be accompanied by renewed study of the Latin language and classics. Wherever civilians went, Latin letters followed closely upon their heels.

I have already observed that glossaries were often appended to medical books; this was true not only of Arabic books but of Latin and others. For example, the Circa instans of Matthaeus Platearius includes a glossary of simples wherein the Latin names are translated into Greek, Italian and French. In an age when dictionaries were either inexistent or unavailable, each of these humble glossaries was like a bridge upon which knowledge could pass from one linguistic district into another.

A number of young vernaculars force themselves upon our attention. While the "langue d'oïl" was cultivated by Philip of Thaon, the "langue d'oc" was illustrated about 1149 by the publication of Lo Codi, the earliest treatise on Roman law in any vernacular (Provençal literature had begun in the eleventh century). Our earliest definite information on Euskara, the Basque language, appeared in the Codex Calixtinus about 1120. Celtic was introduced to the rest of the world by Geoffrey of Monmouth and Caradog of Llancarvan. The Eddas and the works of Ari Froði Þorgilsson symbolize the golden age of Icelandic.

At the same time we witness the birth of one of the greatest of the world's literatures, the Russian. Various translations from the Greek appeared in the first half of the twelfth century, chiefly one of the Jewish War of Flavius Josephus. Daniel of Kiev, the pilgrim, and Nestor of Kiev, the father of Russian history, proved the literary emancipation of their native tongue.

6. *Hindu*—I have nothing to report for this period; but it is well to bear in mind that the greatest lexicographer of India, Hemacandra, of whom I shall speak

in discussing the ensuing period, was living throughout the first half of the twelfth century.

7. *Manchu*—Emperors of the Chin dynasty (Nü-chen Tartars) tried to reduce their language to a written form by means of a modification of the Uighūr script, but the use of that script did not survive the Nü-chen dominion, and the Manchu language continued to remain unwritten until the time of the Manchu return to power in the seventeenth century.

XIV. CONCLUSIONS

Intellectual life in the twelfth century had become so complex that it is now necessary to bring out the outstanding facts of this survey in order to answer the following questions: Which were the main achievements of the period? To whom were they chiefly due? How did the activities of different peoples, or nations, compare?

The main work of translation was done by Christians who were helped by Jews, chiefly in Spain; they translated from the Arabic into Latin. However, Aristotelian logic was translated directly from the Greek, and a few texts were translated from the Hebrew. Thus Greek knowledge was being introduced into the West along three channels—a direct one, an indirect one via Arabic, and a third still more indirect, via Arabic and Hebrew. The most important channel was the second, the Arabic; with the result that much of Greek knowledge reached the West not in a pure state but transformed by Semitic minds—sometimes improved, sometimes debased.

The best synthetic effort was made by al-Ghazzālī, a Persian who belonged rather to the previous period but remained the greatest light of this one. The only other Muslim philosopher to be singled out is the encyclopaedist Ibn Bājja. Abraham ibn Ezra introduced Muslim rationalism into Jewish Europe. He and the mathematician Abraham bar Ḥiyya were the awakeners of those Jews living beyond the Pyrenees, who did not know Arabic and thus had remained as completely ignorant of the work and thought of three centuries as had their Christian neighbors.

With the exception of al-Ghazzālī, the work of Muslim and Jewish philosophers was insignificant compared with that of contemporary Christians. Abaelard's sharp criticism opened a new world; he prepared the minds for the immense scholastic effort of the succeeding century. The "New Logic" and his own dialectics appeared at the very time when they were most needed and provided a strong logical foundation for the edifice which schoolmen were almost ready to build. Meanwhile the school of Chartres was a sort of Platonic and humanistic stronghold the influence of which was to be felt long afterward. Not only "William Shelley," but also Bernard and Theodoric of Chartres, and Gilbert de la Porrée, were original minds who would have been conspicuous at any time. Adelard of Bath, Domingo Gundisalvo, Hermann the Dalmatian and Otto of Freising were also distinguished men, superior to their eastern colleagues except for the three or four outstanding personalities already mentioned.

Thus philosophic honors go to the Christian West for the first time in many centuries. After al-Ghazzālī's death in 1111, the leading philosopher for thirty years was Abaelard; and after Abaelard's death in 1142. the unquestionable leaders were Theodoric of Chartres, Gilbert de la Porrée and William of Conches. Abraham ibn Ezra, great as he was, did not compare with them, and his philosophical influence was restricted to the Jewish world; to the Christians he was known mainly as an astrologer.

Outside of India, the greatest mathematicians and astronomers were Muslim or Jewish, two of each. Of the two Muslims, one was the Persian poet 'Umar al-Khayyāmī, one of the most original algebraists of the Middle Ages, who died in 1123; the other was the Spanish astronomer Jābir ibn Aflaḥ. The two Jews were Abraham bar Ḥiyya, whose Ḥibbur ha-meshiḥah was the foremost mathematical treatise of the period; and Abraham ibn Ezra, who made an interesting contribution to combinatorial analysis. These two Abrahams wrote in Hebrew, and their works were the earliest important mathematical treatises in that language. Up to that time Jewish mathematicians had written in Arabic.

The activity of Latin mathematicians, though considerable, lacked originality; it consisted almost exclusively in translating foreign writings from the Arabic, and to a much smaller extent from the Hebrew. Thanks to their efforts, Euclid and Theodosios became partly available to Latin readers; as did also Muslim arithmetic and algebra, including the better use of Hindu numerals; and Muslim astronomy, including elementary trigonometry. The Ptolemaic system was more and more criticized by Muslims and thus the way was slowly prepared for the great revolution of the sixteenth century.

Though this summary is mainly restricted to progressive activities, it is necessary to add that the worst Arabic writings were translated as well as the best, and that a quantity of Muslim astrology and superstition found its way to the west. The scientific learning of the Muslims gave prestige to their scientific aberrations, and in a majority of cases it is those aberrations—astrology, geomancy, etc.—which received the most enthusiastic welcome in western Europe. Thus were nutritious food and poison mixed together in the Arabic pabulum, and the real progress of civilization considerably delayed.

The greatest mathematician of the age was the Hindu Bhāskara. I should have given his name to the period, but for the fact that he did not represent so much the first half as the two middle quarters of the century. His achievements were too many to be recalled here. He was at once the most original and the most complete mathematician, but unfortunately his astronomy was out of date.

The outstanding work in physics was al-Khāzinī's Mīzān al-ḥikma. A number of musical treatises were published in Arabic, Hebrew and Latin, none of them of great importance.

Arabic alchemy began to pour into Europe together with the astrological treatises. Western knowledge of distillation seems to date from this time and to be a western discovery; at any rate the earliest texts speaking of it are Latin. There are Arabic and Chinese claims to this discovery. The former are plausible enough, as experimental alchemy can be traced back in Islām at least to the second half of the ninth century (al-Rāzī), if not to a century earlier (Jābir ibn Ḥaiyān), but they have not yet been substantiated. The Chinese claims are too vague to be taken into consideration. The best chemical work was done by technicians like Theophilus, and by the Salernitan pharmacists. It is possible, nay probable, that men of the same type were experimenting also in other countries such as India and China, but we have no knowledge except of one, Chu I-chung.

There are no important geographical works to record, but Latin cosmographies contain curious maps, and the oldest Chinese maps extant date from that very time (1137). A description of Korea was published in 1125 by Hsü Ching.

Practical geographical knowledge was considerably extended in the Far East by Muslim sailors, and in the West by the increasing number of pilgrims many of whom wrote accounts of their experiences.

The Cistercian Reform and Suger's administrative genius contributed to improve European husbandry to the extent that one can speak of a real agricultural revival.

Botanical knowledge was increased mainly by the efforts of the herbalists, in the West as well as in the East. Some of the earliest plant illustrations from life date from that period and their influence can be followed down to the early printed herbals.

Whatever zoological knowledge was obtained was derived primarily from the chase, especially because birds of prey and other animals used and domesticated by huntsmen were the subjects of intimate studies. Treatises on falconry began to appear. The Crusaders brought back from the East a better knowledge of this sport and revived it all over Europe.

The contrast between the brilliant but waning culture of the Muslims and the youthful but vigorous efforts of the Latins is well illustrated in the medical field. The greatest physician of the time was undoubtedly the Spanish Muslim, Ibn Zuhr, illustrious scion of a great medical family. There was no one physician comparable to him in Salerno, but by way of compensation we find there a very active group of men whose total effort was considerable. In particular we witness an anatomical revival, still very humble but a definite promise of greater things. Indeed, this anatomical knowledge was at least partly experimental. The development of this branch of medicine was necessarily left to Christians, because strong religious prejudices made it impossible for Muslims or Jews to carry on anatomical investigations.

A large part of the activity of Latin physicians was in itself a tribute to the superiority of Muslim medicine, since it consisted in translating medical treatises from Arabic into Latin. The whole Malikī of 'Alī ibn 'Abbās—one of the three most important medical encyclopaedias of Islām—was now doubly available in Latin.

Under the combined influence of many religious revivals, and of the Crusades which had caused innumerable tragedies, the ideal and practice of hospitalization grew rapidly and very soon there was no town of any importance in Christendom that did not have its house of mercy.

I shall not attempt to speak again of the historians, but one of the outstanding facts of the age was the revival of Roman law in Lombardy and its spread into France and England. From the point of view of political history the significance of that event can hardly be exaggerated, but the point which I wish to emphasize is that it was exceedingly important also from the purely scientific point of view. The introduction of Aristotle's logic, Abaelard's dialectics, and the rebirth of Roman law, were three great events which favored clear and rigorous thinking; their coincidence could not have been entirely fortuitous, for each of them corresponded to the same definite stage in the maturity of European thought. I need hardly remind the reader that to appreciate them rightly they must be considered not from the point of view of the exact scientific thought of to-day, but from that of the eleventh or twelfth century philosophy. The intellectual progress marked by these three events was immense.

Let us now consider how much of mankind's supreme task was accomplished by people of different faiths, races or nations. It will be convenient to begin our survey in the Far East and move westwards.

I spoke of only two Japanese scholars: Ryōnin, the founder of the Nembutsu shū, the earliest autochthonous sect of Buddhism; and Fujiwara Tamenari the historian. The importance of these two was purely national.

A few Chinese were quoted: the chemist Chu I-chung; the geographer Hsü Ching, the authors of the maps of 1137; the two herbalists, T'ang Shên-wei and K'ou Tsung-shih; the agriculturist, Ch'ên-fu; the archaeologists and historians, Wang Fu, Têng Ming-shih and Hung Tsun.

Also a few Hindus: the mathematicians Śatānakanda and Bhāskara, the physician Ḍallana, the Kashmirian historian Kalhaṇa, the two jurists, Lakshmīdhara and Govindarāja. One of these, Bhāskara, was of international significance, one of the great men of science of the Middle Ages.

Further west we come to the Persians and other Eastern Muslims, and the Eastern Jews. The Muslims are so numerous that it is convenient to divide them into two groups; those of 'Irāq and west of it, and the others who might loosely be called the Persians. The latter outnumber the former considerably, but it is significant that with but two exceptions they all wrote in Arabic.

The two exceptions are Ibn al-Balkhī the unknown geographer, and Ismā'īl al-Jurjānī the great physician. These two were the only ones who used the Persian language. In spite of the fact that it had been glorified by al-Firdawī, Persian had not succeeded in becoming a learned language. The prestige conferred upon the Arabic language by Allāh's own book the Qur'ān was so great that any other language could be only a low vernacular in comparison. Thus it was as infradig for a philosopher or a physician to use Persian in the East as to use French or German in the West. Hence the astounding fact is less the paucity of Persian works, than the existence of such an enormous Persian encyclopaedia as Ismā'īl's Dhakhīra.

Quite a few scholars came from the easternmost provinces of Islām: the theologian 'Umar al-Nasafī came from the vicinity of Samarkand; the grammarian al-Zamakhsharī, from Khwārizm; the mathematician Muḥammad al-Kharaqī and the physicist al-Khāzinī, lived in Marw; the grammarian al-Maidānī came from Nīshāpūr; the mathematician Muzaffar al-Asfuzārī, and the historian of religions al-Shahrastānī, from other parts of Khurāsān. A fine group of men, to be sure; yet only two of them might be called great, al-Shahrastānī and al-Khāzinī. The latter was originally a Greek slave who had been adopted in a Muslim family.

In addition to the two Persians who wrote in their native language, Persia proper gave us 'Abd al-Qādir al-Jīlī, who is said to have founded the earliest ṭarīqa of dervishes; the encyclopaedist Muḥammad ibn Aḥmad al-Qazwīnī; the famous maker of astrolabes, al-Badī' al-Aṣṭurlābī; the poet and alchemist al-Ṭughrā'ī. To these we may perhaps add the geographer Sahl ibn Abān whose origin is unknown; and the falconer Jamāl Muḥammad al Ganjahī who came from the Caucasus.

The contributions of 'Irāq were relatively insignificant. I had occasion to mention only three 'Irāqians, and one of them, the physician Ibn al-Tilmīdh, was a Christian. The two Muslims, al-Ḥarīrī and Ibn al-Jawālīqī, were grammarians and men of letters. In the region west of 'Irāq we found but one, the physician 'Adnān al-'Ainzarbī who came from Anazarbos, Dioscorides' birthplace.

Undoubtedly the main center of Muslim culture at that period was in Spain, or rather in the Maghrib—Spain and North Africa, which were closely united. The following enumeration of the leading Hispano-Muslim scholars is sufficiently eloquent: the philosophers al-Baṭalyūsī and Ibn Bājja, the astronomer Jābir ibn Aflaḥ, the geographer Muḥammad al-Zuhrī, the physicians of the Ibn Zuhr family, the historian Ibn Bashkuwāl, and the jurists Ibn al-'Arabī and Abū Bakr al-Ṭurṭūshī. To these we might add the great Berber leader Ibn Tūmart; and two Spanish physicians established in Egypt, Abū-l-Ṣalt and Ibn Ḥasdai. Note first, that this list includes many of the most illustrious names of the age—Ibn Bājja, Jābir, Ibn Zuhr; second, that the majority of these men lived at least for a time in Seville. Indeed, Seville was then not only the leading city of Spain, but one of the most enlightened cities of the whole world.

The contrast between East and West was even greater for the Jews than for the Muslims. If eastern Muslims of the period were decidedly inferior to their western brethren, they still made an imposing show. On the contrary, eastern Jewry was reduced to very little. I mentioned only two eastern Jews: the orthodox Salāma ibn Raḥmūn who practised medicine in Egypt, and the Qaraite encyclopaedist Judah ben Hadassi who lived in Constantinople. Salāma wrote in Arabic, Judah in Hebrew.

But the western Jews could boast a number of great scholars. Indeed, there were so many that we are obliged to divide them into groups, and the best way of doing this is according to languages; some wrote in Hebrew, others in Arabic, still others used both languages. It is especially interesting to compare these groups.

Let us take the writers of Hebrew first. This included naturally the French Jews, Samuel and Jacob ben Meïr, Rashi's grandsons; and the two great Spaniards, Abraham bar Ḥiyya and Abraham ibn Ezra who took upon themselves the task of explaining Muslim science to their brethren living beyond the Pyrenees.

Two impressive personalities constitute the intermediate group: Moses ibn Ezra of Granada and Judah ha-Levi of Toledo, who are among the most famous poets of Israel, wrote their poetry in Hebrew but their philosophical treatises in Arabic. This illustrates the relation between the two languages. From the point of view of the Spanish Jews of that time, Hebrew was the liturgical, the sacred language, but Arabic was the language of science, of philosophy. Arabic was the key to this world, Hebrew to the next.

However, this was only an intermediate stage. As Jewish learning moved across the Pyrenees or northwards from Sicily, the relative importance of Arabic was bound to decrease. Abraham bar Ḥiyya and Abraham ibn Ezra were but the pioneers of a great intellectual migration.

Among the Spanish Jews who wrote in Arabic, four arrested our attention; two from Cordova in the South, and two from Saragossa in the North. The Andalusians were the philosopher Joseph ibn Ẓaddīq, and the grammarian Isḥāq ibn Barūn. The Aragonians were the philosopher Baḥya ben Joseph, and the physician Ibn Biklārish.

None of these four was of great moment, none was at all comparable to his Hebrew-writing brethren. This is extremely significant, and the more so if one considers that scientific books written in Hebrew were still very few. This is so true that most Jews had to refer to Arabic treatises even to study the grammar of their own language. In other words, the higher scientific education of every Jew was necessarily conducted in Arabic, yet the most prominent Jews of the time were already using Hebrew preferably to other languages.

It will suffice to say a few words of the Byzantine culture, which was relatively poor. It is true there were a few Greek historical works of some merit; those of Nicephoros Bryennios and Anna Comnena, of Zonaras and Glycas; but these were almost all. The polygraphs Theodoros Prodromos, Isaac and Joannes Tzetzes, and the physician Hierophilos were insignificant. We might recall here that the greatest physicist of the age, al-Khāzinī, educated in Khurāsān, was of Greek birth.

Russian culture was closely connected with the Byzantine. For example, Russian historiography was deeply influenced by some of the Greek chroniclers whom I have just mentioned. The earliest important Russian writings date from this time: a few translations from the Greek, notably one of Josephus' Jewish War; the account of the pilgrim Daniel of Kiev; and the chronicle of Nestor and Silvester of Kiev.

The revival of Armenian culture was but just beginning. I mentioned only one Armenian, the chronicler Matthew of Edessa.

I have left till the last the description of the new European culture, that of western Christendom, the vigorous growth of which was entirely independent of that of eastern Christendom. We witnessed the awakening of Europe in the second half of the eleventh century. The ensuing activity was immense, almost comparable to that of Islām during the second and third centuries of the Hegira. And like the Muslim revival, it was not focused upon a single point but upon many. To explain this in words would be tedious. I prefer to do it by means of the following tables which give a synoptic view of the whole subject. It will be seen that the countries which took the greatest share in this revival were France and Italy; third honors might be divided between England and Germany. The foremost names are italicized.

FRANCE

Religious leaders: Gerard of Jerusalem, Raymond du Puy, Hugues de Payns of Burgundy, Geoffrey of St. Omer, Stephen of Muret, Robert of Molesme, Albéric of Cîteaux, *Bernard of Clairvaux*, *Suger of St. Denis*, Peter the Venerable.

Philosophers and polygraphs: William of Champeaux, Hugh of St. Victor, *Abaelard*, Bernard of Chartres, *Theodoric of Chartres*, *Gilbert de la Porrée*, *William of Conches*, Bernard Silvester of Tours, Philip of Thaon.

Mathematicians: Ralph of Laon and Raymond of Marseilles.

Musicians: Leoninus and Perotinus, both in Paris.

Geographer: Lambert of St. Omer.

Historians: Let us quote first the two greatest, *Guibert of Nogent* and *Orderic Vital;* then Geoffrey Gaimar who translated Geoffrey of Monmouth; and the author of the Codex Calixtinus. The following wrote chronicles of the Crusade: Raymond d'Aguilers, Richard the Pilgrim, Peter Tudeboeuf and his anonymous continuer, Robert of Reims, Foucher of Chartres, Baudri, Ralph of Caen, Hugh of Fleury, Giles of Paris.

Jurists: The anonymous authors of the Brachylogus juris civilis and of Lo Codi.

I have named in all 40 scholars and scientists, from almost every part of France. All except four, wrote in Latin; Richard the Pilgrim, Philip of Thaon and Geoffrey Gaimar wrote in langue d'oïl; and the author of Lo Codi wrote in langue d'oc.

ITALY

Religious leader: Arnold of Brescia.

Translators: James of Venice, Moses of Bergamo. *Plato of Tivoli*, *Stephen of Antioch* (from Pisa).

Travelers and geographers: Belardo d'Ascoli, and Guido the Geographer.

Falconer: William the Falconer (?)

Physicians: Copho and the author of the second Salernitan anatomy, Archimatthaeus, Bartholomew of Salerno, *Nicholas of Salerno*, Salernus, *Matthaeus Platearius*, Petrus Musandinus, "Trotula," *Benevenutus Graphaeus*, (Stephen of Antioch). It should be noted that we have practically no biographical information on these Salernitan physicians; their nationality is generally unknown (Benevenutus was possibly a Jew). Yet they were all Italians by adoption, if not by birth.

Historians: The anonymous author of the Gesta Francorum, Leo of Ostia, and Peter the Deacon.

Jurists: *Irnerius* and his disciples; *Gratian*, and Magister Rolandus (Alexander III).

That is, 24 scholars, all of whom wrote in Latin. The tardiness of the Italian language was natural enough considering its greater propinquity to the Latin, both philologically and geographically. The emancipation of such a close vernacular was obviously much more difficult than that of distant ones. The French scholars were not only far more numerous than the Italians—40 against 24—but their contributions were of a very different nature. Not to speak of religious leaders who do not really belong to our subject, the prominent philosophers and historians were French, while all of the physicians and the chief jurists were Italians.

GERMANY

Religious leaders: Bruno of Cologne and Norbert of Gennep (of the Duchy of Cleves).

Philosopher: Honorius of Autun (nationality doubtful).

Chemist and craftsman: Theophilus Presbyter.

Geographer: Henry of Mayence.

Historians: Sigebert of Gembloux, Albert of Aachen, Ekkehard of Aura, Anselm of Havelberg, *Otto of Freising*.

Political writer: Manegold of Lautenbach.

All of these men wrote in Latin.

ENGLAND AND WALES

Religious leader: Stephen Harding.

Translators: *Adelard of Bath*, and *Robert of Chester*.

Mathematicians: Walcher of Malvern, Ocreatus, and the two translators mentioned.

Traveler: Saewulf of Worcester.

Historians: Florence of Worcester, *William of Malmesbury*, Geoffrey of Monmouth, Alfred of Beverley, Caradog of Llancarvan.

The English individuals are equal in number to the German—11 in each case—and all of them wrote in Latin, with the possible exception of Caradog whose original chronicle may have been in Celtic. The English and the Germans could each boast a great historian, William of Malmesbury, and Otto of Freising. Two of the most eminent translators of the age, Adelard of Bath, and Robert of Chester, were English.

SPAIN

Translators: *John of Seville, Gundisalvo of Segovia*, Hugh of Santalla.

Astronomer: Pedro Alfonso.

This seems little, but the translations of John of Seville and Gundisalvo's interpretations influenced very deeply mediaeval philosophy. Spain was then the greatest cultural center of the world, thanks to its Muslim and Jewish population.

SCANDINAVIA

Encyclopaedic literature: The Eddas.
Mathematics: Stjörnu Oddi.
Travelers: Skopti Ogmundson and Sigurd of Norway.
Historian: *Ari Fróði Þorgilsson.*
All the writings of these men were in Icelandic.

OTHER COUNTRIES

Bohemia: Cosmas of Prague, historian.
Flanders: Rudolf of Bruges, translator and astronomer.
Dalmatia: Hermann the Dalmatian, translator.
Armenia: David the Armenian, Salernitan oculist.
Byzantium: Zacharias, Salernitan oculist.

The total effort of Western Christendom, as I have described it here, was made by 100 scholars, of whom 40 were French, 24 Italian, 11 German, 11 English, 4 Spanish, 5 Scandinavian, etc. All of these wrote in Latin, except nine, four of whom wrote in French and five[10] in Icelandic. Strangely enough these two were the only vernaculars represented.

The precocity of Icelandic can be explained by the same argument as the tardiness of Italian and Spanish. It did not cost much trouble to South Europeans to understand Latin; but it was very hard, if not hopeless, for Scandinavians of that time to master a language as foreign to their own. Thus there was every inducement to write in Icelandic, and none to write in Italian or in Spanish. As to French, let us remember that the langue d'oïl was then the language of two countries, northern France and England; for some Anglo-Norman writers it must have had almost the prestige of a foreign and superior tongue. Moreover the French language had been ennobled by the creation of the Chanson de Roland. On the other hand, the English language which had already won its spurs under Alfred the Great (second half of the ninth century)—that is, before every other vernacular—was now thrown back into the darkness by the Norman supremacy.

After having thus considered the geographical distribution of all the scholars, it is interesting to examine that of the leading ones. The greatest mathematician of the age, Bhāskara, was a Hindu. At the beginning of the century the eastern Muslims could still boast two of the greatest personalities of the Middle Ages, al-Ghazzālī and 'Umar al-Khayyāmī; in addition to these they produced the physicist al-Khāzinī, and the historian of religions al-Shahrastānī, two original figures without counterpart anywhere in the world.

Spain gave us two of the leading philosophers, Ibn Bājja and Abraham ibn Ezra; two mathematicians, Jābir ibn Aflaḥ and Abraham bar Ḥiyya; two physicians, Ibn Zuhr, father and son; Isḥāq ibn Barūn, who may be called the founder of comparative Semitic philology; and two translators, John of Seville and Gundisalvo.

To Italy we owe a number of physicians and jurists: Nicholas of Salerno, Matthaeus Platearius, Benevenutus Grapheus, Irnerius and Gratian.

But the supreme leader of Christendom was France, whose fame was exalted by the genius of such men as St. Bernard, Suger of St. Denis, Abaelard, Theodoric of Chartres, Gilbert de la Porrée, William of Conches, and Orderic Vital.

[10] For the sake of simplification, the Eddas are counted as one writing.

England's contribution was very remarkable too: Adelard of Bath, Robert of Chester, William of Malmesbury. Two great historians, Otto of Freising and Ari Fróði þorgilsson, were given to the world respectively by Germany and by the Ultima Thule, Iceland.

Finally, one of the most significant features of the intellectual organization of Christendom was the creation (or continuation) of schools wherein the activity of individuals was improved and strengthened by collaboration, common criticism and teaching. At least five such schools must be mentioned: the translators' school of Toledo, the philosophical schools of Paris and Chartres, and the schools of Salerno and Bologna which were respectively the earliest school of medicine and the earliest school of Roman law in Europe. Toledo, Paris, Chartres, Salerno, Bologna—five nurseries wherein some of the highest destinies of Europe were being shaped.

CHAPTER II

RELIGIOUS BACKGROUND

(First Half of Twelfth Century)

I. CHRISTENDOM

THE CARTHUSIANS

As the foundation of the Carthusian Order really belongs to the end of the eleventh century, I ought to have spoken of it in volume I. However it is not too late to remedy the omission. The founder, Bruno, a German nobleman, was born at Cologne about 1030–1042, and educated in his native town, in Rheims and in Tours (?). He became chancellor of Rheims cathedral and head of its school; in 1080 he was offered and declined the archbishopric of Rheims, and set out with two disciples to establish a religious community in a suitable place. He stopped in various places, gathering more disciples, and finally in 1084 reached an Alpine valley near Grenoble where they built a hut which was the beginning of the "Grande Chartreuse" and the cradle of the Carthusian Order.

This order is a sort of compromise between western monasticism and eremitical tendencies. In spite of the severity of its rule it grew rapidly. The rule was somewhat mitigated in the course of time, yet it may be said that the Carthusians have remained more constantly faithful to their early purpose than any other Christian community. In 1089 Bruno left the Chartreuse to go to Rome; later he proceeded to Calabria where he established other hermitages and died in 1101.

The rule was put down in writing only in 1130, by Guido, fifth prior of the Grande Chartreuse, ex officio superior general of the order. A branch for women was established about the middle of the thirteenth century, but remained very small.

Life of St. Bruno in the Acta Sanctorum edited by the Bollandists (October 6).
Benedetto Tromby (1710–1788): Storia critico-cronologica diplomatica del patriarca S. Brunone e del suo ordine (10 vols., Naples 1773–1779). Charles Le Couteulx: Annales ordinis cartusiensis ab anno 1084 ad annum 1429, nunc primum a monachis ejusdem ordinis in lucem editi (8 vols. in 4to.; Monstrolii, typis Cartusiae S. Mariae de Pratis, 1887–1891). Hermann Löbbel: Der Stifter des Karthäuser-Ordens (256 p., Münster i.W., 1899). E. C. Butler: Encyclopaedia Brittannica (11th ed., vol. 5, 432–433, 1911). Ellen Scott Davison: Forerunners of St. Francis (33–46, Boston 1927)

THE GOOD MEN OF GRAMMONT

The Good Men of Grammont (or Grandmont)—Grandmontains, Grandmontines, Bonshommes—are a religious order the foundation of which is traditionally ascribed to St. Stephen of Muret, who was born in 1048 at Thiers, not far from Clermont-Ferrand. He was educated at Benevento where the fame of the Calabrian hermits reached him. In 1078 he returned to France and soon afterwards established an hermitage in Muret, near Limoges, where disciples gradually gathered around him, and where for almost half a century he led the most austere life. He died in 1124 and was canonized in 1189. After his death his disciples were driven out of Muret and established themselves in the "desert of Grandmont," also in Limousin.

The very austere rule of the order was written in 1141, probably on the basis of recommendations made by St. Stephen himself. It was largely eremitical, being inspired by the Camaldulians (or Camaldolese) established by St. Romuald (about 950–1027) in various parts of Italy. The monastery of Grandmont remained the main house of the order. In the course of time nunneries were also established in Limousin. As always, the worldly success of the order was only made possible when the original rule was sufficiently mitigated. But this process of mitigation went so far that in 1642 some of the brethren found it necessary to create a new order, the so-called Grandmontains de l'étroite observance.

To return to the original order, it deserves to be mentioned here in spite of the brevity of its heroic age, because it realized one of the best anticipations of the mendicant orders established a century later.

E. C. Butler: Encyclopaedia Britannica (11th ed., vol. 12, 349, 1911). Ellen Scott Davison: Forerunners of Saint Francis (69–76, Boston 1927; Isis, 11, 145).

DECLINE OF THE BENEDICTINE ORDER, AND THE CISTERCIAN REFORM IN 1116

It would seem that by the beginning of the twelfth century the old Benedictine Order had spent most of its energy. The golden age of famous monasteries like Luxeuil (near Lure, Franche-Comté), Bobbio (Lombardy), Corbie (near Amiens), St. Gall (Switzerland; see vol. I, 657) was already passed. Even the mother house, Monte Cassino, had reached its climax before the middle of the century. (See my notes on Leo of Ostia and Peter the Deacon, in the chapter on history). In the second half of the century the decline of the famous school of Bec in Normandy (see vol. I, 748) could not be denied. The last of the great abbots of Cluny, Peter the Venerable (see below), died in 1156.

This is the way of all human institutions, no matter how sacred the purpose or how intense the original enthusiasm; they must necessarily decline and perish unless new blood is periodically injected into them. The new reform of the Benedictine Order, which had become necessary at this time, was begun in 1098 by Robert of Molesme. He was a noble Champenois who had been prior of various Benedictine monasteries and finally, in 1075, of Molesme in the diocese of Langres. In 1098, however, accompanied by other monks including Alberic and Stephen, he established a new house with a stricter discipline at Cîteaux near Dijon in Burgundy—hence the name, Cistercian reform. Robert was soon obliged to return to Molesme, where he died; and Alberic, the second abbot of Cîteaux, died in 1110.

The third abbot of Cîteaux, the Englishman Stephen Harding (St. Stephen, d. 1134), is often regarded as the real founder. Born at Sherborne, Dorsetshire, he traveled and studied in Scotland, in Paris and in Rome. He assumed the Benedictine habit at Molesme. He was a great organizer and under his rule the Cistercian Order developed amazingly; he founded many new houses, instituted general chapters (1116, etc.), and drew up the admirable charter called Carta caritatis, establishing the *federal* government of the order. This rule was confirmed by Pope Calixtus in 1119. Stephen Harding revised the Latin text of the Old Testament, with the help of Jews who explained to him the meaning of the Hebrew original. It was under Stephen's rule that the Cistercians assumed in 1127 a white cowl instead of the black one of the other Benedictines; hence they are sometimes called White Monks.

William Hunt: Dictionary of National Biography (vol. 24, 333–335, 1890).

SAINT BERNARD

Bernard of Clairvaux

Bernardus Claravallensis. French theologian and religious leader. Born in 1090 at Fontaines, near Dijon, he joined the Cistercian community, and in 1115 left Cîteaux, with other brethren, to establish a new monastery in Clairvaux (Ville-sous-la-Ferté, Aube) which under his direction became the main house of the order. He died in 1153. St. Bernard took a leading part in the ecclesiastical and political affairs of his time, which obliged him to undertake many travels across France, Italy, and Germany. Thanks to his energy, wisdom, and prestige, the Cistercian Order prospered admirably. His abundant writings treating of almost every aspect of religious and political life need not be enumerated here. In 1140 he obtained Abaelard's condemnation; in 1145 he preached against the heretics of Languedoc, and soon afterwards was the chief promoter of the Second Crusade (1147–1149) which failed utterly. He had the courage to denounce and oppose the anti-Semitic tendencies of other leaders (Epistola 363).

Text—First attempt at a complete edition, by André Bocard (Paris 1508). Better edition by Jean Mabillon (Paris 1667; enlarged and improved in 1690, 1719, 1839). Migne's Latin patrology (vols. 182–85, Paris 1859).

On account of his immense political influence, his letters are particularly important (495 letters in Migne, vol. 182, 67–716).

Criticism—The early Vita by various contemporaries is included in Mabillon's and Migne's editions; Migne also published later elaborations and abridgments. Leopold Janauschek: Bibliographia bernardina (596 p., Wien 1891). Elphège Vacandard: Vie de St. Bernard (2 vols., Paris 1897; 4th ed., 1910). Potthast (149, 1896). George Gordon Coulton: Five centuries of religion (vol. I is devoted to St. Bernard, his predecessors and successors; Cambridge 1923). M. C. Slotemaker de Bruine: Het ideaal der navolging van Christus ten tijde van Bernard van Clairvaux (thesis, Groningen 1926). P. Tiburtius Hümpfner: Ikonographia S. Bernardi (2 vols., Augsburg 1927). S. Posener: Encyclopaedia judaica (vol. 4, 294, 1929).

THE CISTERCIAN RULE

The Cistercian reform was essentially an attempt to observe more literally St. Benedict's rule (first half of the sixth century; see vol. I, 419). It was a reaction not only against the laxity which had gradually invaded many Benedictine houses, but also against the increasing lack of austerity, and against the luxury which had insidiously grown under the Clunisian mantle, thanks to the love of art and the favor of princes.

From the point of view of general culture, the chief merit of the new observance lay in the fact that it attached great importance to agriculture. The Cistercian abbeys soon offered the best examples of mediaeval husbandry, and their good influence in that direction can hardly be overestimated. Agriculture conducted upon the large scale practised by the leading abbeys led naturally to better commercial organization. It also led to a marked diminution of serfdom. It is not too much to say that the Cistercians changed the agricultural aspect of Europe.

On the other hand, learning was not encouraged; rather it was discouraged. Stephen Harding's interest in Hebrew was an exception. Art also was discouraged. Each abbey had a scriptorium where the works needed for ritualistic purposes or for edification were copied, but these manuscripts were not illuminated. Abbatial buildings and ecclesiastical utensils and vestments had to be as simple as possible. It should be noted, however, that this did not necessarily mean an artistic loss; in architecture, for example, the very austerity of the requirements was sometimes the origin of real progress.

Walter Map, English author and wit of the second half of the twelfth century, hit the nail on the head when he compared Cîteaux and Cluny respectively with Martha and Mary. (De nugis curialium, Dist. 1, cap. 24; p. 36 in the edition by Montague Rhodes James, Anecdota oxoniensa, part 14, 1914).

Thanks to the federal organization of the order, each Cistercian house was largely independent, though not entirely so. Cîteaux (later Clairvaux), prima inter pares. This was a very wise compromise between the excessive independence of the early Benedictine abbeys and the Clunisian centralisation. Cistercian federalism marked a real progress; it was imitated by the Franciscans and the Dominicans.

The following facts will enable one to measure the rapid progress of Cîteaux. Within a few years (1112–1115) the four main daughter houses were established in La Ferté, Pontigny, Clairvaux, and Morimond. The Cistercians appeared in England in 1128; in 1134 when St. Stephen died there were already 30 Cistercian monasteries; in 1153 when St. Bernard died there were over 280; by the end of the twelfth century, over 500; and the maximum growth (about 750 houses) was reached in the fifteenth century.

Though the order continued to grow outwardly until the fifteenth century, its golden age was over before the middle of the thirteenth. For a century (from about 1125 to 1225) it succeeded Cluny as the leading organization of western Christendom. Later, though its material power increased, its moral prestige waned. Cîteaux was submitted to the same necessities of change and decay as other organizations, and the need of reform caused the appearance of various offshoots of the main Cistercian body, notably the Feuillants (or Improved Bernardines) in 1598; and the Trappists, representing the strictest observance, in 1663–1664.

The earliest Cistercian nunnery was that of Tart near Langres, founded in 1125; the most famous, that of Port Royal near Paris, founded in 1204.

To conclude, it is interesting to compare the activity of the Clunisians and Cistercians in the eleventh and twelfth centuries, with that of the Franciscans and the Dominicans in the thirteenth century. The contributions of the former were of a more practical nature; they were artisans and husbandmen, they reclaimed enormous tracts of land, they improved agriculture and architecture. The latter were more concerned with the defense of the faith, the struggle against heresy, with missionary work of various kinds. It is impossible to weigh these things against one another. Yet I can not help feeling that the activity of the former was on the whole more beneficial; it is probable that they did more good; it is certain that they did less harm.

Philippe Guignard: Les monuments primitifs de la règle cistercienne, publiés d'après les MSS. de l'Abbaye de Cîteaux (Analecta divionensia, vol. 10, 1878). Monasticon cisterciense, seu Antiquiores ordinis cisterciensis constitutiones a Juliano Paris collectae ac notis et observationibus adornatae. Ed. nova emendata et usque ad tempora nostra deducta a Hugone Séjalon. (863 p., Solesmis 1893).

For the early history of the order, see also the sources relative to St. Stephen and St. Bernard, already mentioned. See also Henri d'Arbois de Jubainville and Léon Pigeotte: Etude sur l'état intérieur des abbayes cisterciennes, et principalement de Clairvaux, aux XIIe et XIIIe siècles (508 p., Paris 1858). Henry Collins: Spirit and mission of the Cistercian Order (London 1866). E. C. Butler: Encyclopaedia Britannica (11th ed., vol. 6, 393–395, 1911). Hans Rose: Die Baukunst der Cisterzienser (148 p., 88 illustrations, 4 plates; Munich 1916). Ellen Scott Davison: Forerunners of St. Francis (46–68, excellent summary; Boston 1927; Isis 11, 145).

THE PREMONSTRANTS

The Premonstrants (or Praemonstratensians, White Canons, Norbertines) owe their origin to Norbert of Gennep in 1120. Norbert (Norbertus Magdeburgensis), son of Count Heribert, was born about 1080 at Xanten on the Lower Rhine in the Duchy of Cleves. He was educated in Xanten and Cologne, and became chaplain to Henry V (emperor from 1106 to 1125). In 1115 Norbert returned home and gave up his possessions, and after years of meditation and austerity founded in 1120 a new community at Prémontré in the forest of Coucy not far from Laon. It was a community of canons regular rather than of monks, and the rule finally adopted by Norbert was the Augustinian (vol. I, 748), made more severe by insistence upon absolute poverty, and by the incorporation of the Cistercian Carta caritatis. In 1124 he founded a nunnery open only to noblewomen; and also an auxiliary society, the Fratres et sorores ad succurrendum, thus anticipating the Franciscan tertiaries. The order was approved by the pope in 1124 and 1126. Norbert was elected archbishop of Magdeburg in 1126, and he died there in 1134.

This order was extremely successful. It is said that by the middle of the fourteenth century there were more than 1300 monasteries and 400 nunneries. The order played an important rôle in the Christianization of the eastern marches of Germany. The most important house existing to-day is at Tongerloo in Belgium.

Franz Winter: Die Prämonstratenser des 12. Jahrhunderts und ihre Bedeutung für das nordöstliche Deutschland (Berlin 1865). Bartholomaeus Wozasek: Der hl. Norbert (318 p., Wien 1914). Cornelius J. Kirkfleet: History of St. Norbert (380 p., ill., St. Louis 1916). André Léon Goovaerts: Ecrivains, artistes et savants de l'ordre de Prémontré (4 vols., Bruxelles 1899–1917). Ellen Scott Davison: Forerunners of St. Francis (76–95, Boston 1927); Isis, 11, 145)

THE CATHARI

It is impossible to give here a sufficient definition of the Cathari and other similar heresies,[1] because of the complexity and fluidity of the subject; yet something must be said of it, as a general warning to students of twelfth-century thought. The Cathari and similar heresies do not date from the twelfth century, but simply became more conspicuous then. In fact they can be dated back to the earliest times of Christianity, and many of their tenets and practices, far from being new,

[1] Bogomils, Paulicians, etc., in the East; Apostolics, Patarenes, Tisserands, Bulgars, Albanenses, Albigeois, etc., in the West. The German word Ketzer, meaning heretic, is derived from Cathari.

were survivals of ancient beliefs; their doctrine included vestiges of apostolic communism, of Manichaean dualism (see vol. I, 332), and even traces of the Hindu belief in metempsychosis.

The Cathari were divided into two main groups, the "consoled" or perfect, and the "credentes" or believers (cf. baptized and catechumens of the early church). Their ritual recalls the time when priestly ordination was not yet differentiated from confirmation. Their morality was excessively austere; for example, they insisted upon absolute chastity. They influenced the Roman Catholic Church very strongly, if indirectly; it was partly to counteract the Cathari that celibacy was finally imposed upon the clergy, the great mendicant orders were established, and the reading of the Old Testament by the laity was discouraged. It is possible that the Catholic sacrament of "extreme unction" is somewhat connected with the fundamental rite of the Cathari, the "consolamentum," an ultimate blessing which they tried to postpone as long as life permitted.

Catharan thought is but very imperfectly known by Catharan writings, for most of these have been destroyed; there remain only a Provençal translation of the New Testament (about the middle of the thirteenth century), and the fragment of a Provençal ritual of about the same time. More information, though naturally prejudiced, can be obtained from the writings of their enemies—letters and sermons, inquisitorial documents, and treatises directed against them. The most important treatises are those of the French Cistercian, Alan of Lille (second half of the twelfth century): Contra Albigenses, Valdenses, et Judaeos et Saracenos (c. 1203); and of two Italian Dominicans, Ranieri Sacconi of Piacenza and Moneta of Cremona (first half of the thirteenth century), both of whom were inquisitors, the former a converted Catharist. There are less important writings from two other converted Catharists: the French Ermengaud, and Bonaccorsi of Milan (both of the end of the twelfth century). To these might be added the Practica inquisitionis haereticae pravitatis, by the French Dominican, Bernard Guy (first half of the fourteenth century). Simon de Montfort's crusade against the Albigenses, a Catharan community of southern France, in the first half of the thirteenth century, attracted universal attention to them and was the cause of a considerable literature, some of which will be discussed in later chapters.

The consideration of the Cathari and other heretics of the twelfth century may be completed by a study of the romantic personality of Arnold of Brescia. He was born towards the end of the eleventh century; he was very ascetic, and opposed ardently the temporal power of the popes and the temporal possessions of the clergy; he was condemned in 1140, together with Abaelard, and was hanged in Rome in 1155. Arnold did not represent a definite sect, but simply the spirit of revolt against social injustice and ecclesiastical corruption—against sin.

Texts—(I quote only the texts to which I have already referred.) Léon Clédat: Le Nouveau Testament, traduit au XIIIe siècle en langue provençale, suivi d'un rituel cathare, édité en phototypie (Bibliothèque de la Faculté des Lettres de Lyon, vol. 4, Paris 1888).

Ermengaud: Opusculum contra haereticos (Migne, vol. 204, 1855). Alan of Lille: De fide catholica contra haereticos sui temporis (Migne, vol. 210, 1855). Moneta of Cremona: Adversus Catharos et Valdenses libri quinque, edited by T. A. Richinius (632 p., Rome 1743). Bonaccorsi: Manifestatio haeresis Catharorum, edited by Lucas d'Achéry (Spicilegium, vol. 1, Paris 1665), also by Migne (vol. 204, 1855). R. Sacconi: Summa de Catharis et Leonistis et Pauperibus de

Lugduno, in Ed. Martène and Urs. Durand: Thesaurus novus anecdotorum (vol. 5, Paris 1717).

Criticism—Charles Schmidt: Histoire et doctrine de la secte des Cathares ou Albigeois (2 vols., Paris 1849). J. J. I. von Döllinger: Beiträge zur Sektengeschichte des Mittelalters (2 vols., München 1890). Célestin Douais: Les hérétiques du Comté de Toulouse dans la première moitié du XIIe siècle, d'après l'enquête de 1245 (Paris 1891); L'Albigéisme et les Frères Prêcheurs à Narbonne au XIIIe siècle (158 p., Paris 1894). Paul D. Alphandéry: Les idées morales chez les hétérodoxes latins au début du XIIIe siècle (Bibliothèque de l'Ecole des Hautes études, sci. relig., vol. 16, Paris 1903). Achille Luchaire: Innocent III. La croisade contre les Albigeois (262 p., Paris 1905). Frederick Cornwallis Conybeare: Cathari (Encyclopaedia Britannica, vol. 5, 515–517, 1911); Moses Gaster: Bogomils (ibidem, vol. 4, 119–120, 1911). Edmond Broeckx: Le Catharisme. Etude sur les doctrines, la vie religieuse et morale, l'activité littéraire et les vicissitudes de la secte cathare avant la Croisade (Louvain thesis, 332 p., Hoogstraten 1916). Henry James Warner: The Albigensian heresy (94 p., London 1922). Ellen Scott Davison: Forerunners of St. Francis (201–236, Boston 1927; Isis, 11, 145). M. Wischnitzer: Albigenser (Encyclopaedia judaica, vol. 2 ,123–124, 1928).

For Arnold of Brescia, see Paul D. Alphandéry: Encyclopaedia Britannica (vol. 2, 632, 1911). E. S. Davison: The forerunners of St. Francis (96–167, Boston 1927).

THE RISE OF CATHEDRALS

The decline of so many monasteries, and the fact that so many others neglected intellectual pursuits, was partly compensated by the increasing importance of cathedral schools; this will be apparent in this book and the succeeding ones where such schools will be mentioned very often. The essential difference between the monastery and the cathedral as centers of education lies in the fact that the former was generally rural and often very isolated, while the latter was by definition urban; but this is only one aspect of a more general circumstance, for from that time cities became more and more important as cultural centers.

To indicate the significance of cathedrals, it will suffice here to recall a few whose names frequently occur in these pages. In France: Notre Dame of Paris, Chartres, Orléans, Rheims, Laon, Poitiers, etc. In England: Canterbury, and St. Paul of London. In Spain: Toledo. The relative importance of German and Italian cathedrals was considerably less in that age.

Charles Homer Haskins: The renaissance of the twelfth century (ch. 2, Cambridge 1927).

RELIGIOUS ORDERS OF KNIGHTHOOD

The military orders of knighthood and the customs of chivalry were to a large extent a product and became an essential part of the feudal system. They were later incorporated into the monarchical and even republican organizations and perpetuated within the modern world feudal ideas, some of them good and others evil. These orders are of little interest to the historian of thought.

However, during the Crusades many feudal institutions were shattered or materially transformed. Thus there arose a new conception of knighthood, distinct from the original feudal one. The notion of fealty to the liege lord was gradually extended, and under the influence of religious ideals local and exclusive loyalty tended to become universal in scope; loyalty to the liege was replaced or dominated by loyalty to God and service to one's brethren; feudalism by brotherhood. Thus the ideals of monachism and chivalry combined produced religious orders of knighthood. These orders played a not unimportant part in the development of civilization and must be mentioned here, however briefly.

The Knights of St. John of Jerusalem

Founded in 1099, at the time of the conquest of Jerusalem by the Latins, this was the earliest of these religious orders. It was probably a development of a hospital organization which had been functioning in Jerusalem for centuries for the care of pilgrims. Gerard (or Gerald), the head of this hospital, was the founder and first grand master of the order; but the religious organization was accomplished chiefly by Raymond du Puy who became the second grand master of the order after Gerard's death in 1120. By the time of Raymond's death about 1159 the order had grown tremendously in power and wealth and had become a universal institution.

The Order of St. John had its headquarters in Jerusalem until the conquest of that city by Saladin in 1187. It then took Acre where it remained but a few years; in 1291 it moved to Cyprus; in 1310 to Rhodes; finally in 1530 to Malta. This explains the different names of the order. The original name was Ordo fratrum hospitalariorum Hierosolymitanorum, or Ordo militiae Sancti Joannis Baptistae hospitalis Hierosolymitani. The knights were called Knights of St. John, or Hospitalers (Hospitallers). Later they were called Knights of Rhodes (1310–1523), and Knights of Malta (1530–1798). They wore a black mantle with a white cross—the Maltese cross. The order still survives in various forms, equally unimportant.

Joseph Delaville LeRoulx (d. 1911): Les archives, la bibliothèque et le trésor de l'Ordre de Saint-Jean à Malte (286 p., Paris 1883); Cartulaire général de l'ordre des Hospitaliers, 1100–1310 (4 vols., folio, Paris 1894–1906); Les Hospitaliers en Terre Sainte et à Chypre (Paris 1904); Les Hospitaliers à Rhodes jusqu'à la mort de Philibert de Naillac, 1310–1421 (458 p., Paris 1913). Also many other smaller publications by the same author.

Walter Alison Phillips: a brief history in the Encyclopaedia Britannica (vol. 24, 12–19, 1911). Popular accounts by Rose Georgina Kingsley: The Order of St. John, past and present (159 p., London 1918); and by Eva Mabel Tenison: A short history of the order from 1014 to 1918 (1st ed., London, 1914; 2nd. ed., London 1922).

Hans Karl von Zwehl: Über die Caritas im Johanniter-Malteser-Orden seit seiner Gründung (82 p., Essen 1929).

The Knights Templars

This order was organized in 1119 by Hugues de Payns (Hugo de Paganis) of Burgundy, and Godeffroi of St. Omer, as a religious community for the purpose of protecting the pilgrims going to the Holy Land. The Templars were also called Poor Knights of Christ, and Knights of the Temple of Solomon (Pauperes commilitones Christi templique Salominici). They wore a white mantle with a red cross. In 1127 they obtained the support of Bernard of Clairvaux who drew up their rule, or at least inspired it. By the middle of the twelfth century they were spread throughout Latin Christendom, and during the second half of that century and throughout the thirteenth their power and wealth increased enormously. This order became the greatest financial organization of the time and especially controlled the exchange of money between East and West. Its wealth was the cause of its ruin, internally because of the corruption which it fostered, and externally because of the jealousy which it excited. The Templars were denounced to the Inquisition for heresy and immorality, and those residing in France were arrested October 13, 1307, by order of King Philip IV le Bel, who was greatly in need of money. A long and atrocious trial followed. The order was dissolved and its enormous estates confiscated by Pope Clement V in 1312. The last grand master was burned to death in Paris in 1314.

The Templars were probably innocent of the abominable crimes ascribed to them, yet they constituted a secret society which was corrupted to the core by its very wealth and power, and had become a real danger to the state. The trial to which they were submitted paved the way for the iniquities of the witch persecutions of the subsequent centuries[2] in two ways: first, it increased the popular belief in witchcraft and devilry; second, it inspired the criminal procedure of the Inquisition, in particular the use of torture to wring "voluntary" confessions from the victims.

Abundant literature has been devoted to the trial of the Templars. A good summary of the case is given by Thomas Andrew Archer and Walter Alison Phillips in the Encyclopaedia Britannica (vol. 26, 591–600, 1911). Georges Lizerand: Le dossier de l'affaire des Templiers (Classiques de l'Histoire de France au Moyen Age, 2, 254 p., Paris 1923). Edward J. Martin: The trial of the Templars (London 1928). M. Dessubré: Bibliographie de l'Ordre des Templiers (344 p., Paris 1928)

PETER THE VENERABLE

Peter of Cluny, Petrus Cluniacensis dictus Venerabilis. Born in Auvergne in 1094; died in 1156. He was the Reformer of Cluny, and the last of its seven great abbots. He visited Rome six times, and traveled to Spain to inspect the monasteries of his order. While in Spain he recognized Muslim power, and caused the Qur'ān to be translated and refuted. He also ordered investigations of the Talmud, this being done with the help of Jewish renegades. His letters addressed to St. Bernard, Heloïse, etc., contain valuable information on his journeys, on Clunisian ideals and policies, on Christian views of Islām, etc.

Text—Epistolae, edited by Peter of Montmartre (Paris 1522); also in Migne's Patrology (vol. 189). Libri II adversus nefariam sectam Saracenorum (unpublished). Etc.

Criticism—Th. Schoell: Grande Encyclopédie (vol. 26, 901). Henri Quentin: Une correspondance médicale de Pierre avec Magister Bartholomaeus (Miscellanea F. Ehrle, 1, 80–86, 1923; Isis, 8, 740). Max Manitius: Zu Petrus' von Cluni patristischen Kenntnissen (Speculum, vol. 3, 582–587, 1928).

SUGER

Sugerus abbas. Born in 1081, lived mainly at St. Denis Abbey near Paris; died in 1151. He was the abbot of St. Denis from 1122 to 1151; statesman, diplomat and historian; counsellor and friend of Louis VI and Louis VII; and

[2] See my notes on the Inquisition in the first half of the thirteenth century, and on witchcraft in the first half of the fourteenth and second half of the fifteenth centuries.

one of the ablest administrators of his time. He reconstructed the church of St. Denis, and developed French husbandry. Under his direction and inspiration St. Denis became one of the greatest artistic centers of the age. His chief work is the Liber de rebus in administratione sua gestis, written in 1145; it contains valuable information on the customs of his time, on monastic administration, and on architecture. Before that, however (in 1144), he had written the Libellus de consecratione ecclesiae a se aedificatae; also a life of Louis VI the Fat, King of France from 1108 to 1137. He began the writing of a life of Louis VII.

Text—Complete works, edited by A. Lecoy de la Marche (510 p., Paris 1867). The two biographies have been edited by Auguste Molinier (195 p., Coll. de textes pour servir à l'étude etc., Paris 1887). The life of Louis the Fat was translated into French in Guizot's Collection de mémoires (vol. 9, 1–160).

Criticism—Potthast (1038, 1896.) Otto Cartellieri: Abt Suger (Berlin, 1898). Emile Mâle: La part de Suger dans la création de l'iconographie (Revue de l'art ancien et moderne, vol. 35, 91–102, 161–168, 253–262, 339–349, 1914); L'art religieux du XIIe siècle en France (Paris 1922; Isis, 6, 52–56).

DEVELOPMENT OF ROMANESQUE ART

My account of Suger leads naturally to a brief consideration of the extraordinary artistic development which graced Western Christendom in the twelfth century. The beginning of this development can be traced back to the end of the tenth century. I have shown (vol. I, 655) that the Byzantine renaissance which occurred during the Macedonian dynasty (867–1057) caused the birth of Russian art under St. Vladimir and stimulated the Ottonian renaissance in Germany. During the eleventh century many waves of this artistic revival spread all over Europe.

Some of the greatest monuments of Romanesque architecture date from the second half of the eleventh century; for example, the cathedral of Spires, completed in 1061; the cathedral of Pisa, begun in 1063; Westminster Abbey, 1065; St. Stephen, and Trinity, at Caen in Normandy (the churches of the Abbaye-aux-Hommes and of the Abbaye-aux-Dames), begun in 1066; Rochester cathedral and castle, 1077; Winchester cathedral, 1079–1093; St. Alban's Abbey church, about 1080; Colchester castle, about 1080; new Mayence cathedral, begun in 1081; St. Paul, London, begun in 1083; the great church of Cluny, begun in 1088; cathedral of Trondhjem, Norway, begun about 1090; Lincoln cathedral, 1074–1092; Durham cathedral, begun in 1093.

This is enough to show to how much artistic wealth the twelfth century was falling heir. That it was worthy of its inheritance is sufficiently proved by the following achievements: Abbey of Cluny, 1088–1109; Pisa cathedral, 1063–1118; Chartres, begun about 1120; new Lincoln cathedral, 1123–1147; Canterbury cathedral, 1070–1130; Norwich cathedral, 1096–1140; Abbey of St. Denis, 1144; Campanile of St. Mark, Venice, 1148–1154; Church of the Templars, Thomar, Portugal, about 1162; Temple (Round) Church, London, 1185.

Many of these dates are quoted from C. R. Beazley: A notebook of mediaeval history, A.D. 323–1453 (Oxford 1917). I have not attempted to check them all, but even if some need correction this will hardly affect the general impression.

The building of the cathedrals had much cultural significance in another way; their decoration stimulated the activity of painters and sculptors who worked under the general guidance of learned clerks. Christian iconography was to a large extent determined during this century. This is very important indeed if one realizes that church decoration was truly encyclopaedic in its scope, and that it represented the main vehicle of popular education.

These views have been admirably explained and illustrated by Emile Mâle in his many publications, chiefly in L'art religieux du XIIe siècle en France (Paris 1922; Isis, 6, 52–56). A. Kingsley Porter: Pilgrimage sculpture (American Journal of Archaeology, 26, 1–53, 1922; Isis, 10, 121); this illustrates the spread of artistic influences (see also my vol. I, 774). J. Puig i Cadafalch: Les origines de l'art roman (Bull. of the international committee of historical sciences, vol. 1, 694–710, 1928). Kenneth John Conant: Mediaeval Academy excavations at Cluny (Speculum, vol. 4, 3–26, 7 pl., 443–450, illus., 1929; vol. 5, 77–94, 2 pl., 1930; Isis, 13, 157).

II. ISRAEL

THE CRUSADES

It is not my purpose to deal with the Crusades in a general way, as the reader may be assumed to be sufficiently informed on the subject; but one aspect needs be considered because it is often overlooked and yet of great significance. That the Crusaders, in spite of their genuine religious enthusiasm, were not very different from any other horde bent on pillage and murder, is well known. The treatment meted out by them to the holy city of Jerusalem in 1099 was sufficiently convincing in this respect, and that was but one episode among many. The Crusaders massacred all the Muslims, and burned the Jews alive; it is claimed that they killed some seventy thousand people within a week. But long before reaching the Holy Land, the undisciplined mobs accompanying the Crusaders persecuted the Jews whom they encountered in France and Germany. Massacres and tortures of Jews were especially numerous and terrible in the Rhine region (Spires, Worms, Mayence, etc.) in 1096. These outrages were repeated during the Second Crusade (1145–1149), and during the Third, when they occurred also in England (1189–1190). It must be added that many bishops did all they could to protect the Jews in their dioceses; and that St. Bernard of Clairvaux raised his powerful voice in their behalf in 1146.

These anti-Jewish outbreaks of 1096 and 1146 are so important that they may be considered turning points in the history of Israel. Before that time Jewish persecutions had been exceptional in Western Europe. They now became more frequent, each persecution breeding its own share of hatred and revenge. Moreover they were the cause of anti-Jewish legislations by Innocent III (pope from 1198 to 1216) and by other rulers. The enormous amounts of money needed for the Crusades were partly obtained by special taxation of the Jews and confiscation of their goods. At the same time, Christian regulations against usury having become more severe, the banking business was more and more restricted to Jewish hands. Before the Crusades, Jews had been the main importers of Eastern products; their business was now jeopardized in various ways in order to favor the increasing number of Christian merchants trading with the East.

The main point is this: the Crusades were not simply a war against Islām; they turned out to be also, though less openly, a war against Israel. It is chiefly in that age that the seeds of the most virulent form of anti-Semitism were sown.

Joseph Jacobs: Jewish Encyclopaedia (vol. 4, 378–379, 1903); this contains a map of the Rhine region, showing sites and dates of the anti-Jewish outbreaks of

1096. Max L. Margolis and Alexander Marx: History of the Jewish people (Philadelphia 1927).

III. ISLĀM

'ABD AL-QĀDIR AL-JĪLĪ

'Abd al-Qādir al-Jīlī (or (Jīlānī) Muḥyī-l-dīn Abū Muḥammad ibn Abī Ṣāliḥ Zengi Dōst was born in 1077–1078, in the country called Jīl (or Jīlān), alluvial delta lands in the southwest of the Caspian. He studied theology and letters in Baghdād, and became a ṣūfī; he began to preach in 1127–1128, and soon afterwards a ribāṭ (a sort of monastery) was built for him in Baghdād, and he became also the head of a madrasa. He died in 1165–1166. Though a ṣūfī, he was entirely orthodox. He wrote in Arabic many religious works, chiefly sermons, some of them the best in Arabic literature, wherein he showed much elevation of spirit, and toleration.

He is quoted here chiefly as the reputed founder of an order (ṭarīqa) of dervishes (darwīsh) called after him, Qādirīya, the earliest order of dervishes still existing. Such religious fraternities may have existed before, but the Qādirīya is the earliest whose history can be traced. Before that time, disciples would gather around a ṣūfī teacher, and after his death would perhaps continue for one or two generations to congregate around the most prominent among themselves; but such a community had no permanence. Later, many more such fraternities were created either de novo or by secession from older ones, and they assumed enormous importance in Islām. The diversity of their forms and inspiration is as great as that in Christian monasticism. The purpose of this note is to draw attention to that essential aspect of Muslim life, which we have no time to analyze more deeply.

Further information together with abundant bibliographic references will be found in the following articles of the Encyclopaedia of Islām. D. S. Margoliouth: 'Abd al-Qādir (vol. 1, 41–42, 1908); Qādirīya (vol. 2, 608–611, 1924); Duncan B. Macdonald: derwīsh (vol. 1, 949–951, 1912); Louis Massignon: ṭarīqa (vol. 4, 667–672; 1929, including a list of the ṭuruq); also D. B. Macdonald: The religious attitude and life in Islām (145, 162, 199, Chicago 1909); Aspects of Islām (203, New York 1911).

'UMAR AL NASAFĪ

Abū Ḥafṣ 'Umar ibn Muḥammad ibn Aḥmad al-Nasafī Najm al-dīn was born in 1067–1068, in Nasaf (Persian Nakhshab, south of Samarkand, halfway to the Oxus). He died in 1142–1143. He was one of the most famous Ḥanīfite doctors of his time. He wrote a book on the fundamental articles of faith ('aqā'id)—a catechism—which was the most popular work of its kind and was extensively used in the Turkish public schools before the Great War.

This al-Nasafī is not to be confused with another, 'Abdallāh ibn Aḥmad, also an Ḥanīfite jurist (second half of the thirteenth century).

Text—The number of oriental editions of commentaries on al-'aqā'id is of course considerable. William Cureton: Pillar of the creed of the Sunnites, being a brief exposition of their principal tenets, by Hāfidh-uldīn Abū'lbarakāt Abd-ullah Alnasafi; to which is subjoined a shorter treatise of similar nature by Najm-uldīn Abū Hafs Umar Alnasafi (beautiful edition with short introduction; 44 p., London 1843).

French translation by Mouradgea d'Ohsson: Tableau général de l'empire othoman (vol. 1, Paris 1787). German translation by C. H. Ziegler: Türkischer Catechismus der Religion (Hamburg 1792).

Criticism—C. Brockelmann: Arabische Litteratur (vol. 1, 427, 1898). Carra de Vaux: 'Aqīda, in Encyclopaedia of Islām (vol. 1, 236–238, 1909); Penseurs de l'Islām (vol. 4, 181–186, 1923).

AL-SHAHRASTANĪ

See Chapter XI, Historiography.

IBN TŪMART

Berber-Muslim reformer, "the Mahdī of the Almohads." He was of Berber origin, of the Atlas tribe of Hintāta, and was born about 1077–1087 in the country of Sūs. He traveled to Spain and to the East, then returned to his own country. He was deeply influenced by the teachings of al-Ash'arī (first half of the tenth century), of al-Ghazzālī (second half of the eleventh century), and even more of Ibn Ḥazm (first half of the eleventh century). He began to preach, and to denounce the loose morals and narrow theology of his countrymen, his watchword being tawḥīd, the unity and incorporeality of God. He wrote a Berber treatise on tawḥīd, preserved in an Arabic version. Under the influence of Shī'a and Imāmīya ideas, he declared himself to be the Mahdī (the predestined guide), and began a war against the al-Murābiṭ rulers (Almoravides) of the Maghrib. He died in 1128 or 1130, and the struggle was continued by his chief disciple 'Abd al-Mu'min who was the founder of the new dynasty, al-Muwaḥḥid (Almohades)—or Unitarians. Before the end of his reign in 1163, 'Abd al-Mu'min had conquered the whole of Muslim Spain and North Africa from Egypt to the Atlantic.

Text—The Arabic text of the Tawḥīd al-bāri and other writings was edited by J. D. Luciani (Algiers 1903).

Criticism—René Basset: Encyclopaedia of Islām (vol. 2, 425–427, 1918). George Foot Moore: History of religions (vol. 2, 470–473, 1919). E. Lévi-Provençal: Documents inédits d'histoire almohade. Fragments manuscrits du "legajo" 1919 du fonds arabe de l'Escurial (Paris 1928; Isis, 13, 221).

IV. BUDDHISM

RYŌNIN

Posthumous name, Shō-ō-daishi. Japanese Buddhist. He was born in 1072 at Tomita, Owari, and lived at a Tendai monastery at Hiei-zan. After twenty-three years he founded the monastery Raikō-in, at Ōhara, Yamashiro, and later still the Dai-nembutsu-ji, at Sumiyoshi, Settsu. He died in 1132. He was the founder of a new Buddhist sect, the Yūzū nembutsu shū (or Nembutsu shū), at the beginning of the twelfth century. This was the first genuine Japanese sect, the Six Nara sects and the Tendai and Shingon sects having been introduced from China (vol. 1, 552). Ryōnin had studied the doctrines of the Tendai and Shingon sects, but they did not satisfy him. He often repeated the prayer Namu Amida butsu ("I adore thee" or "Have mercy upon me, Thou Buddha of eternal life and light"). Hence the name of the sect, nembutsu, means repeating that prayer; Yūzū nembutsu shū might be translated, "society of mutual benefit through nembutsu."

Ryōnin's activity was the beginning of the great religious revival, the Great Awakening, which shook Japan in the twelfth and thirteenth centuries. The Nembutsu shū was the first Japanese sect to give more definite expression to the

Amidaism which had been latent in Japan for centuries. Though it is the oldest of the four Amida sects, it is not the most representative, Japanese Amidaism being far better expressed by the Jōdo-shū (second half of the twelfth century), and the Jōdo-shinshū (first half of the thirteenth century).

The Yūzu nembutsu shū was represented about 1917 by 363 temples out of a total of 72,191. The central house is the Dai-nembutsu-ji, already mentioned.

E. Papinot: Historical dictionary of Japan (520, 762, Tokyo 1909). A. K. Reischauer: Studies in Japanese Buddhism (104, 111, 217, New York 1917).

CHAPTER III

THE TRANSLATORS

(First Half of Twelfth Century)

I. FROM ARABIC INTO LATIN

ADELARD OF BATH

Also called Æthelhard, Alard, etc. Adelardus Bathoniensis. Born in Bath, he was active at least from 1116 to 1142. He traveled in France, southern Italy, Sicily and the Near East. English philosopher, mathematician, scientist; the greatest before the time of Grosseteste and Bacon; one of the earliest translators from Arabic into Latin. Before 1116 he wrote a philosophical treatise on Identity and Difference (De eodem et diverso); and before 1137 (probably much earlier) a dialogue (Questiones naturales) divided into 76 chapters, each of which treats of a scientific question, the whole purporting to expound Arabic knowledge on these questions. In chapter 51, apropos of an experiment carefully described by him, he explains the impossibility of a vacuum by a theory of universal continuity (developed later by Roger Bacon). The Questions were translated into Hebrew by Berakya ha-Naqdan (second half of the twelfth century).

The De eodem et diverso is a dialogue explaining Platonic views similar to those of the School of Chartres and opposing exaggerated Realism: genera and species are nothing but individuals considered from different points of view (theory of the respectus). This attitude may be regarded as preparing Abaelard's conceptualism, but I do not know whether Abaelard was (or could be) actually influenced by it.

Adelard's most important contributions were in the field of mathematics. Early in life—before his Arabic contacts—he wrote a treatise on the abacus (Regule abaci). Later, in 1126, he translated from Arabic into Latin the astronomical tables of al-Khwārizmī, revised by Maslama ibn Aḥmad al-Majrīṭī; they included tables of sines. Thus was Muslim trigonometry, and more specifically the sine and tangent functions, introduced into the Latin world. He was also in all probability the "Magister A" who translated al-Khwārizmī's mathematical treatise (Liber ysagogarum Alchorismi). Thus Adelard was an abacist at the beginning of his career, and later became an algorist, the earliest (or one of the earliest) of them. Finally he translated from the Arabic Euclid's Fifteen Books, this being the earliest Latin translation known to us,[1] though he would seem to have made use of an earlier version from the Greek. There are many manuscripts of this, yet they are very divergent, and the exact nature of Adelard's original work—whether it was an abridgment, a close translation or a commentary—is not clear. His

[1] There is nothing to substantiate the story according to which some knowledge of Euclid had reached England two centuries earlier under the reign of Aethelstan, Alfred's grandson, about 925. See Florence A. Yeldham: The alleged early English version of Euclid (Isis, 9, 234–238, 1927).

translation of Euclid included the determination of the sum of the angles of stellated polygons. One of his latest writings was a treatise on the astrolabe (De opere astrolapsus; Bath?, c. 1142–1146). To complete this brief account of Adelard's mathematical activity, he was probably instrumental in introducing some knowledge of Muslim music into the West, for he had studied music in France, and al-Khwārizmī's mathematical treatise, covering the whole quadrivium, contains a section on music.

The revised edition of the Mappae clavicula is also ascribed to him. The earlier edition may be dated back to the second half of the eighth century (vol. I, 534). The edition ascribed to Adelard is much larger than the earlier one (293 recipes against 209); it is of special interest as containing one of the earliest references to alcohol.

At the time he was compiling his natural questions, he wrote also a treatise on falconry, the earliest Latin treatise of its kind which has come down to us. It shows no trace of Arabic influence; thus Adelard must have written it rather early or else he did not hear of eastern knowledge on the subject. My only reference to Arabic falconry at an earlier time concerns the treatise of 'Īsā ibn 'Alī al-Asdī, eleventh century (vol. I, 731), but the matter requires further investigation.

Text—Hans Willner: Des Adelard von Bath Traktat De eodem et diverso zum ersten Male hrg. und historisch-kritisch untersucht (Beitr. zur Geschichte der Philosophie des Mittelalters, IV, 1, 120 p., Münster 1903).

Questiones naturales perdifficiles. Louvain, without date (1480?), 1484, 1490. Hebrew adaptation by Berakya ha-Naqdan (second half of the twelfth century), edited by Hermann Gollancz, with a careless English version of Adelard's text (Oxford 1920; Isis, 4, 581).

Regule abaci, edited by B. Boncompagni in his Bullettino (vol. 14, 1–134, 1881).

Ezich Elkauresmi per Athelardum bathoniensem ex arabico sumptus. The trigonometrical part was edited by A. A. Björnbo in the Festskrift til H. G. Zeuthen (1–17, Copenhagen 1909). A complete edition prepared by Björnbo and R. Besthorn was published by Heinrich Suter (Danske Vidensk. Selsk. Skrifter, Hist. Afd., III, 1, 290 p.; Copenhagen 1914; Isis, 4, 502–503).

Liber ysagogarum Alchorismi in artem astronomicam a magistro A. compositus (also: Liber ysagogarum Alchoarismi ad totum quadrivium). First three books published by Max. Curtze: Über eine Algorismusschrift des 12. Jahrhundert (Abhdl. zur Geschichte der Mathematik, part 8, 3–27, 1898).

For other writings, see Haskins' Studies in mediaeval science, quoted below.

Criticism—S. Günther: Lo sviluppo storico della teoria dei poligoni stellati nell'antichità e nel medio evo (Bull. di bibliografia delle scienze mat., vol. 6, 313–340, 1873). H. Weissenborn: Die Übersetzung des Euklid aus dem Arabischen in das Lateinische durch Adelard von Bath nach zwei Hds. der Bibliothek in Erfurt (Z. f. Mathematik, hist. Abt., vol. 25, 141–166, 1880; comparing Adelard's translation with Campano's). J. L. Heiberg: Euklid's Elemente im Mittelalter (Z. für Mathematik, hist. Abt., vol. 35, 48–58, 81–98, 1890). M. Steinschneider: Hebräische Übersetzungen (463, 1893). A. Favaro: Intorno al presunto autore della Artis metrice practice compilatio edita da Mas. Curtze (Atti, Istituto Veneto, vol. 63, 377–395, Venezia, 1904; see Eneström in Bibliotheca Mathematica, vol. 5, 312, 1904, and P. Tannery, ibidem, vol. 5, 416, 1905; Mémoires, vol. 5, 342–345). C. H. Haskins: Adelard of Bath (English historical review, 491–498, July 1911; 515–516, July 1913; vol. 30, 56–69, 1915). P. Duhem: Système du monde (vol. 3, 112, theory of tides; 169, astronomical translations; 1915). Sir Thomas Heath: Greek mathematics (vol. 1, 362–364, 1921). C. H. Haskins: King Harold's books (English historical review, 398–400, July 1922). Apropos of Adelard's De avibus tractatus (Isis, 5, 213); Some early treatises on falconry (Romanic Review, vol. 13, 18–27, 1922; Isis, 5, 213); Lynn Thorndike: History of magic (vol. 2, 19–49, 1923). C. H. Haskins: Studies in mediaeval science (20–42, 113–129, 346–355, and by index, 1924; second edition, 1927, contains a few corrections). Henry George Farmer: Clues for the Arabian influence on European musical theory (Journal Asiatic Society, 69, 1925; Isis, 8, 508). M. de Wulf: History of mediaeval philosophy (vol. 1, 157, 1926). Franz Pl. Bliemetzrieder: Adelard von Bath (Graz 1927?, not seen).

PETER THE VENERABLE

See Chapter II, Religious background.

JOHN OF SEVILLE

John of Spain, John of Toledo. Joannes Hispalensis, Hispanensis, de Luna (Limia), Toletanus.[2] Hispano-Jewish translator from Arabic into Latin. He was converted to Christianity and his original Jewish name is unknown; it has been corrupted into the following forms: Avendeut, Avendehut, Aven Daud, Avendar, from which we may conclude that his father's name was David. His own name was possibly Solomon ben David (see below, and also my note on Gundisalvo). He flourished in Toledo about 1135–1153 and worked there under the patronage of Raymond I, archbishop of Toledo, 1126–1151. His translations were made with the assistance of Domingo Gundisalvo; it would seem that John translated from Arabic into the vernacular (Castilian), and Domingo from Castilian into Latin. In 1142 John compiled an astrological summary, Epitome totius astrologiae, derived from Arabic models; it is divided into an Isagoge, and a Quadripartitum, i.e., four books of judgments. He translated a good many Arabic treatises, the majority concerning astronomy, astrology and philosophy; one of them treats of arithmetic, and another may be called a medical treatise.

It should be noted that many of these translations present difficult problems relative to date and genuineness, because of the author's multiple names and because of the occurrence of many independent versions which have often been confused. As these translations are so numerous, it is necessary for the sake of clearness to classify them. I shall divide them into four groups: *Arithmetic*; *Astronomy and astrology; Medicine; Philosophy;* and in each group the material is arranged in the chronological order of the original texts. To simplify the account, printed editions have been indicated immediately after the mention of each translation.

Arithmetic—Liber alghoarismi de practica arismetrice. This is not al-Khwārizmī's arithmetic (first half of the ninth century) which was probably translated by Adelard of Bath, but an elaboration of it by a later Muslim writer. It is a pure algorism, professedly based on Hindu knowledge: zero; approximate extraction of square roots by means of decimal fractions (but no decimal notation, of course); no mention of abacus nor of complementary calculations; one magic square at the end. Edited by B. Boncompagni: Trattati d'aritmetica, II. Joannis Hispalensis liber algorismi de practica arismetrice (Rome 1857). Apparently the same work was also translated by Gerard of Cremona.

[2] There remains a possibility that the names Hispalensis, Toletanus, etc., do not always represent the same person.

Astronomy and astrology—1. Various treatises by the Jew Māshāllāh (second half of the eighth century): Epistola de rebus eclipsium et de conjunctionibus planetarum (alias, De ratione circuli; De circulo et stellis). Printed in Venice 1493, Basel 1533, Nuremberg 1549. This translation is also ascribed to Plato of Tivoli: De cogitationibus; De revolutione annorum mundi. Printed in the above-mentioned editions of 1493 and 1549; Super significatione planetarum in navitatibus. Also printed in 1493 and 1549.

2. The Kitāb fī ḥarakāt al-samāwīya wa jawāmi' 'ilm al-nujūm, by al-Farghānī (first half of the ninth century), translated in 1134–1135. Liber Alfragani in quibusdam collectis scientiae astrorum et radicum motuum coelestium et est xxx differentiarum (*i.e.*, chapters). Printed under the title Brevis ac perutilis compilatio . . . . totum id continens quod ad rudimenta astronomica est opportunum (Ferrara 1493). Later editions, Nuremberg 1537, Paris 1546. The translation of the same work by Gerard of Cremona, though more complete, remained unpublished. A French translation, probably of Gerard's version, was translated into Italian by Zucchero Bencivenni, in 1313.

3. Abū 'Alī al-Khaiyāṭ (first half of the ninth century): Albohali de judiciis nativitatum liber unus. This treatise was translated twice: by Plato of Tivoli in 1136, and by John in 1153. It is John's version which was printed under the above mentioned title (Nuremberg 1546, 1549). It was probably also John's version which was translated into French.

4. Abū Ma'shar (first half of the ninth century): Kitāb al-madkhal ilā 'ilm aḥkām al-nujūm. This was translated twice: by John about 1133, and by Hermann the Dalmatian. The printed text is probably Hermann's. Jacob ben Elia's Hebrew version is apparently derived from John's translation.

5. Al-Kindī (first half of the ninth century): Albumasar de magnis conjunctionibus et annorum revolutionibus ac eorum profectionibus (Augsburg 1489, Venice 1515). Treatise written by al-Kindī, plagiarized by Abū Ma'shar. The Flores astrologiae seem to be an extract from the Magnae conjunctiones.

6. 'Umar ibn al-Farrukhān (first half of the ninth century) or his son Muḥammad: De nativitatibus et interrogationibus. Printed in Venice in 1503. In a later edition (Venice 1525) the translator is called Solomon the Jew.

7. Aḥmad ibn Yūsuf ibn al-Dāya (second half of the ninth century): Commentary on Ptolemy's Centiloquium. Translated by John, or by Plato of Tivoli, about 1130–1136, the original text being ascribed by the translator to 'Alī ibn Riḍwān (first half of the eleventh century).

8. Al-Battānī (second half of the ninth century): Centiloquium, or Liber de consuetudinibus in judiciis astrorum. Printed with other works in 1493, 1507, 1533.

9. Thābit ibn Qurra (second half of the ninth century): De imaginibus astronomicis.

10. Al-Qabīṣī (second half of the tenth century): Kitāb al-madkhal ilā ṣinā'at aḥkām al-nujūm. Libellus ysagogicus Abdilazi, qui dicitur Alchabitius, ad magisterium judiciorum astrorum; often printed with a commentary by John of Saxony (first half of the fourteenth century), Venice 1481, 1485, 1491, 1521. French translation by Pelerin de Pousse, 1362.

11. Al-Qabīṣī: De conjunctionibus planetarum in duodecim signis. Venice 1485, 1511, 1521. French translation by Oronce Finé (Paris 1556 or 1557).

12. Maslama ibn Aḥmad al-Majrīṭī (second half of the tenth century): De astrolabio.

13. Ibn abī-l-Rijāl (first half of the eleventh century): Regulae utiles de electionibus. Uncertain.

Medicine—Epistola Aristotelis ad Alexandrum de conservatione corporis humani. Translated from the Sirr al-asrār, Secretum secretorum (probably first half of the ninth century; see vol. 1, 556). It is not certain that John translated the whole Secretum, but at any rate this translation was very popular. It is of great interest as a prototype of the famous Salernitan Regimen sanitatis. J. Pagel: Eine bisher unveröffentliche mittelalterliche Diätetik. Nach zwei Handschriften der K. Bibliothek zu Berlin (Pharmazeutische Post, 1907: reprint 11 p.; Latin text with German translation). Johannes Brinkmann: Die apokryphen Gesundheitsregeln des Aristoteles für Alexander den Grossen in der Übersetzung des Johann von Toledo (Diss., Leipzig 1914).

Philosophy—1. Pseudo-Aristotelian De causis (vol. 1, 404). Translated by John and by Gerard of Cremona; the printed text is probably Gerard's. Albert the Great considered John the original author.

2. Al-Kindī (first half of the ninth century): De intellectu, translated by John, or by Gerard of Cremona(?). Edited by Albino Nagy: Die philosophischen Abhandlungen des al-Kindī (Münster 1897).

3. Qusṭā ibn Lūqā (second half of the ninth century): Kitāb al-faṣl bain al-rūḥ wal-nafs (also ascribed to Ibn Sīnā). De differentia spiritus et animae. The Latin text has been ascribed to many authors: Constantine the African, Augustine, Alexander Neckam, Thomas of Cantimpré, Aristotle! Edited by Siegm. Barach: Excerpta ex libro Alfredi (Innsbruck 1878).

4. Al-Fārābī (first half of the tenth century): Kitāb iḥṣā' al-'ulūm. Translated by John, and also by Gerard of Cremona. Liber Alpharibii de ortu scientiarum. Edited by Clemens Baeumker (32 p., Münster 1916).

5. Ibn Sīnā (first half of the eleventh century): Partial translation of the Kitāb al-shifā'.

6. Ibn Gabirol (first half of the eleventh century): Yanbū' al-ḥayāt. Fons vitae. This translation is especially important because of its influence upon Christian scholasticism. Edited by Clemens Baeumker (Münster 1894–1895).

7. Al-Ghazzālī (second half of the eleventh century): Maqāṣid al-falāsifa. An encyclopaedia divided into three parts: logic, physics, metaphysics. Latin text printed in Venice in 1506.

The most important of these translations are the Arithmetic; al-Farghānī's astronomy (1134–1135); the Epistola de conservatione corporis humani, which marked the beginning of the western tradition of the Sirr al-asrār; and above all the philosophical writings—De causis, al-Fārābī, Ibn Sīnā, Ibn Gabirol, al-Ghazzālī—which were a real revelation to the Latin world and deeply influenced the development of scholastic philosophy.

Text—Epitome totius astrologiae. Nunc primum in lucem edita cum praefatione Joachimi Helleri Leucopetraei contra astrologiae adversarios (Nuremberg 1548).

The editions of John's translations have been mentioned when I spoke of each translation, for the sake of clearness.

Criticism—M. Steinschneider: Hebräische Übersetzungen (981–984, 1893). Meyer Kayserling: Jewish Encyclopaedia (vol. 7, 217, 1904). G. Eneström: Über den Bearbeiter oder Übersetzer des von Boncompagni hrg. Liber algorismi de practica arismetrice (Bibliotheca Mathematica, vol. 6, 114, 1905). M. Steinschneider: Die europäischen Übersetzungen aus dem Arabischen bis Mitte der 17. Jahrhundert. (Sitzungsber. der Ak. der Wiss., phil. Kl., vol. 149, 40–50, Wien 1904). Suzan Rose Benedict: Comparative study of early arithmetics (8, 121, 1914). P. Duhem: Système du monde (vol. 3, 177–183, 198–201, 1915; translation of al-Farghānī). Lynn Thorndike: History of magic and experimental science (vol. 2, 73–78, 94–98, 1923).

GUNDISALVO

Domingo Gundisalvo (or González). Dominicus Gundissalinus (Gondissalinus, Gondisalvi, Gunsalvus). Archdeacon of Segovia. Spanish philosopher and translator from Arabic into Latin in collaboration with John of Seville. I explained the nature of their collaboration when I spoke of John. It would be idle to try to divide honors between them; we must think of them together. It is possible that Gundisalvo used occasionally another dragoman than John, for with regard to the translation of a part of Ibn Sīnā's Kitāb al-shifā', his collaborator is called Solomon (of course this may have been John's original name, but we have no proof of it). It would seem that Gundisalvo was more of a philosopher than John of Seville. The latter wrote only one original treatise and this was an astrological summary. Some five philosophical treatises are ascribed to Gundisalvo: De divisione philosophiae, De immortalitate animae, De processione mundi, De unitate, De anima. The last three are largely based on Ibn Gabirol's Yanbū' al-ḥayāt, which Gundisalvo and John had translated (or were translating).

The most interesting is the De divisione philosophiae which is essentially derived from the Kitāb iḥṣā' al-'ulūm of al-Fārābī (first half of the tenth century), but is *not* a translation of it; it is more elaborate than the Iḥṣā'. Gundisalvo discusses various definitions of philosophy and states the principle: nulla est scientia quae philosophiae not sit aliqua pars. His classification of the sciences is as follows: *Propaedeutics*, divided into grammar, poetics (including history), and rhetoric. *Logic*. *Scientiae sapientiae*, including theoretical and practical branches. The theoretical branches are (a) Physics (scientia naturalis), divided into medicina, indicia, nigromantia, ymagines, agricultura, navigatio, specula, alquemia; (b) Mathematics, divided into arithmetica, geometria (and optics), musica, astrologia, scientia de aspectibus, de ponderibus, de ingeniis; (c) Metaphysics. The practical branches are politics, economics and ethics.

The influence exerted by this classification may be traced in the writings of Michael Scot, Albert the Great and Robert Kilwardby. Gundisalvo discusses each science in detail. His accounts of logic, geometry, astronomy and astrology are derived from Arabic authors and from the Arabic Euclid. The sections on arithmetic, music and medicine are partly of Arabic and partly of Latin origin; for example, the medical section is derived partly from Isidore of Seville (first half of the seventh century), and partly—so it seems—from Ibn Sīnā's Qānūn.[3] It is independent of the translation by Constantine the African, and of other early Latin translations, which had probably not reached Spain, or were despised in a place where reference to the original sources was relatively easy. The sections on poetics and rhetoric are derived exclusively from old Latin writings. The treatise De immortalitate animae shows traces of contact with Aristotle's Posterior ana-

[3] The Qānūn was translated only by Gerard of Cremona (second half of the twelfth century); but this translation made at Toledo must have occupied him for a great many years, and Gundisalvo was able to refer to the original text.

lytics. It was plagiarized by William of Auvergne (first half of the thirteenth century).

In general, Gundisalvo's philosophy is the Muslim Aristotelism and neo-Platonism as modified by Christian theology and individualism. We may say that Muslim-Jewish philosophy was introduced into Latin Christendom by his writings, as well as by the translations made by John of Seville and by himself.

Text—Ludwig Baur: De divisione philosophiae, herausgegeben und philosophiegeschichtlich untersucht nebst einer Geschichte der philosophischen Einteilung bis zur Ende der Scholastik (Beitr. zur Geschichte der Philosophie des Mittelalters, vol. 4, parts 2–3, 420 p., Münster 1903). Georg Bülow: Des D. Gundissalinus Schrift von der Unsterblichkeit der Seele (ibidem, vol. 2, part 3, 145 p., 1897); De processione mundi, herausgegeben und auf ihre Quellen untersucht (ibidem, vol. 24, part 3, 86 p., 1925). De processione mundi had been edited before by Menéndez y Pelayo: Historia de los heterodoxos españoles (vol. 1, 691–711, Madrid 1880). Paul Correns: Die dem Boethius fälschlich ausgeschriebene Abhandlung De unitate (Beitr. zur Gesch. der Philos. des Mittelalters, vol. 1, part 1, 1891). A. Löwenthal: Pseudo-Aristoteles über die Seele. Eine psychologische Schrift des 11. Jahrhunderts und ihre Beziehungen zu Salomon ibn Gabirol (144 p., Berlin 1891).

Criticism—M. Steinschneider: Die europäischen Übersetzungen aus dem Arabischen (32, 1904). Alessandro Levi: La partizione della filosofia pratica in un trattato medioevale (Atti, Istit. Veneto, vol. 67 (2), 1225–1250, 1908). P. Duhem: Système du monde (vol. 3, 177–183, 1915). M. de Wulf: History of mediaeval philosophy (vol. 1, 327–330, 1926).

HERMANN THE DALMATIAN

Also called Hermann the Slav, or the Carinthian. Hermannus Dalmata; or Secundus, probably with reference to Hermann the Lame (second half of the eleventh century). He studied at Chartres or Paris, and about 1138–1142 lived in Spain, and in 1143 in Languedoc. Philosopher, astrologer, and translator from Arabic into Latin. He was a pupil of Theodoric of Chartres. The intellectual origins of most translators are unknown; it is thus especially interesting to be able to link Hermann with the Platonic school of Chartres. He translated the following:

1. In 1138 an astrological treatise of the Jew Sahl ibn Bishr (first half of the ninth century), entitled Zaelis fatidica, or Pronostica, or Liber sextus astronomie.
2. About 1140, astronomical tables of al-Khwārizmī (uncertain).
3. About 1140, Abū Ma'shar (first half of the ninth century): Kitāb al-madkhal ilā 'ilm aḥkām al-nujūm. This translation, dedicated to Robert of Chester, is less slavish than that made by John of Seville about 1133. It was printed under the title, Introductorium in astronomiam Albumasaris Alabachii. (Augsburg 1489, Venice 1495, 1506).
4. About 1142, in Leon, two treatises against Islām: De generatione Muhamet et nutritura eius; Doctrina Mahumet. Printed in Bibliander's edition of the Latin Qur'ān (vol. 1, 189–212, Basel 1543). The second is a version of the apocryphal dialogue between the Jew 'Abdallāh ben Salām[4] and the Prophet. This work was probably done in conjunction with the translation of the Qur'ān, undertaken with Robert of Chester in 1141–1143.

[4] Abū-l-Ḥārith 'Abdallāh ben Salām, d. 663-664. See M. Steinschneider: Arabische Literatur der Juden (8-9, 1902).

5. Maslama ibn Aḥmad al-Majrīṭī (second half of the tenth century). Arabic translation of Ptolemy's Planisphaerium, with commentary. This was translated into Latin not by Rudolph of Bruges, but by Hermann. Hermann completed his translation at Toulouse in 1143 and dedicated it to his master Theodoric of Chartres. Maslama's translation and Hermann's version of it are the only channels through which the Planisphaerium has reached us. Edited by Jacob Ziegler in his collection: Sphaerae atque astrorum coelestium ratio, natura et motus; ad totius mundi fabricationis cognitionem fundamenta (Basle 1536). Ziegler ascribed it to Rudolph of Bruges. Independent edition without translator's name (Venice 1558). Critical edition by Heiberg: Ptolemaei opera astronomica minora (225–259, Leipzig 1907). There is also an anonymous Hebrew translation of Maslama's version, entitled Ma'amar more mofetim (or Mofete keli ha-habbaṭah), but as it dates only from the fifteenth century it may have been made from the Latin as well as from the Arabic. He also wrote:

6. De essentiis, an original treatise begun at Toulouse in 1143 and completed the same year at Béziers, dedicated to Robert of Chester.

Various other works—on meteorology (Liber ymbrium), arithmetic, geometry, the astrolabe, etc.—have also been ascribed to Hermann the Dalmatian.

The only independent treatise by Hermann, the genuineness of which is certain, is the De essentiis. It treats of the five essences which have a permanent existence—cause, motion, place, time, habitudo. These essences are different from those considered by al-Kindī (first half of the ninth century) in his De quinque essentiis (vol. 1, 560). Hermann's treatise contains miscellaneous information on astronomical and geographical topics.

Criticism—M. Steinschneider: Hebraeische Übersetzungen (535, 1893); Die mathematischen Wissenschaften der Juden (Bibliotheca mathematica, vol. 2, 76, 1901). G. Eneström (ibidem, vol. 2, 410, 1902).

A. A. Björnbo: Hermannus Dalmata als Übersetzer astronomischer Arbeiten (ibidem, vol. 4, 130–133, 1903). H. Bosmans: Hermann le Dalmate, traducteur des traités arabes. (Revue des questions scientifiques, vol. 56, 669–672, 1904). M. Steinschneider: Die europäischen Übersetzungen aus dem Arabischen bis Mitte des 17. Jahrhunderts. (Sitzungsber. der philos. Kl. der Ad. der Wiss., vol. 149, 33–34, Wien 1904. P. Duhem: Système du monde, (vol. 3, 171–176, 1915). C. H. Haskins: Hermann of Carinthia. Studies in mediaeval science (43–66, 1924).

HUGH OF SANTALLA

Hugo Sanccelliensis, Sanctallensis, Sandaliensis, Strellensis, de Satalia, etc. Born probably at Santalla—this is a common place-name in the northwest of Spain, especially in Galicia. Spanish astrologer, alchemist, and translator from Arabic into Latin, who worked under the patronage of Michel, bishop of Tarazona from 1119 to 1151. He does not seem to have been connected with the other translators living at Toledo at the same time. His translations include the following:

1. Al-Bīrūnī's (first half of the eleventh century) commentary on the astronomy of al-Farghānī (first half of the ninth century). This seems to be Hugh's chief work. A Hebrew translation of the same text was made by Abraham ibn Ezra about 1160.

2. A pseudo-Aristotelian treatise entitled Liber Aristotelis de 255 Indorum

voluminibus universalium questionum tam generalium quam circularium summam continens.

3, 4. Māshāllāh (second half of the eighth century). De nativitatibus; Liber ymbrium (meteorological predictions).

5. A treatise on geomancy (ars geomantie)—a system of divination by means of dots or lines, or other figures. This is distinctly a Muslim art, called in Arabic 'ilm al-raml, science of sand; a geomancer is called rammāl. Muslims ascribe its invention to Hermes Trismegistos and other remote personalities; however, there is no early Arabic work on geomancy which can be definitely dated. Ibn Khaldūn (second half of the fourteenth century) deals with it at considerable length in his Muqaddama. Hugh's treatise, of which two versions exist, is the earliest Latin work on the subject.

6, 7. Two shorter treatises on spatulamancy—divination by means of the shoulder-blades of animals.

8. Liber Apollonii de principalibus rerum causis.

9. Ptolemy's Centiloquium.

10. The earliest Latin version of the alchemical text called the Emerald Table (tabula smaragdina, lawḥ zabarjad).

Text—Two versions of Hugo's geomancy exist, the "ars geomantiae" and the "geomantia nova", both edited by Paul Tannery in the posthumous memoir quoted below.

Criticism—Paul Tannery: Practica geometriae (Bull. des sciences mathématiques, vol. 23, 140–145, 1899); Sur la Practica geometriae Hugonis (Bibliotheca mathematica, vol. 2, 41–44, 1901). Both papers reprinted in his Memoir scientifiques (vol. 5, 204–210, 308–313, 1922; Isis, 6, 432). The author of this Practica geometriae, edited by Max. Curtze (Monatshefte für Mathematik, vol. 8, 193–224, 1897), is probably neither Sanccelliensis, nor Hugues de Saint Victor who died in Paris in 1141, but is rather one Hugo Physicus who died in Paris in 1199 (?). M. Steinschneider: Europäische Übersetzungen (35–37, 1904). C. H. Haskins: The translations of Hugo Sanctelliensis (Romanic review, vol. 2, 1–15, 1911; revised edition in his Studies in mediaeval science, 67–81, 1924). This elaborate study of the subject is independent of Tannery's work. Paul Tannery: Le rabolion. Traités de géomancie arabes, grecs et latins (Mémoires scientifiques, vol. 4, 295–411, 1920; important memoir which Tannery had no time to complete, published posthumously by Carra de Vaux who has added to it an introductory chapter on Muslim geomancy. It contains the results of Tannery's studies on Hugo Sanccelliensis, the texts of the latter's treatises on geomancy, and of two Byzantine writings on the same subject for comparison (Isis, 4, 344). Julius Ruska: Tabula Smaragdina (Heidelberg 1926; Isis, 9, 375). Robert Steele and Dorothea Waley Singer: The Emerald Table (Proceedings of the Royal Soc. of Medicine, historical section, January 1928; Latin translation of an Arabic commentary on the Emerald Table; the authors are inclined to ascribe that translation to Plato of Tivoli: Isis, 12, 356).

ROBERT OF CHESTER

Robertus Castrensis, Cestrensis, Retinensis, Ketenensis, Ostiensis, Astensis, Anglicus. Robert the Englishman, Robert de Rétines. English mathematician, astronomer, alchemist, and translator from Arabic into Latin. He lived in Spain about 1141–1147; was archdeacon of Pamplona, Navarre, in 1143; lived in London about 1147–1150. He wrote the following:

1. A translation of al-Kindī's (first half of the ninth century) Judicia, dedicated to Hermann the Dalmatian.

2. The first Latin translation of the Qur'ān, begun in 1141 and completed in 1143, at the request of Peter the Venerable, with the assistance of Hermann the Dalmatian.

3. On February 11, 1144, he completed the translation of a treatise on alchemy, Liber de compositione alchemiae, supposed to have been written by Khālid ibn Yazīd (second half of the seventh century) and to have been edited by one Morienus Romanus.[5] This was one of the earliest Arabic alchemical treatises to be introduced to the Latin world. There is also a Mappae clavicula ascribed to Robert; and a translation of an Arabic commentary on the Emerald Table may be a work of his.

4. The first translation of the algebra of al-Khwārizmī (first half of the ninth century), dated Segovia 1145. The importance of this particular translation can hardly be exaggerated. It may be said to mark the beginning of European algebra.

5. A treatise on the astrolabe, dated London 1147. Revised in or after 1150. In some MSS. the treatise is ascribed to Ptolemy, and described as translated from the Arabic. (There are also Hebrew MSS. of a Ptolemaic treatise on the astrolabe).[6]

6. Astronomical tables for the longitude of London, 1149–1150, based on the tables of al-Battānī (second half of the ninth century) and al-Zarqālī (second half of the eleventh century).

7. Revision for the meridian of London, of the tables of al-Khwārizmī (first half of the ninth century) translated by Adelard of Bath.

Robert was the first to use the word sinus (sine), equivalent to the Arabic jaib, in its trigonometrical acceptation.

Text—Robert's and Hermann's translation of the Qur'ān was edited by Theodore Bibliander, with an introductory epistle by Maurice de Montboissier, notes and refutations, and a forewarning by Phil. Melanchthon (3 vols., Basel 1543, Zurich 1550 and (or) Basel 1550). The Italian version of the Qur'ān published in 1548 by the Venetian printer, Andrea Arrivabene: L'Alcorano di Mahometto tradotto dell'Arabo, was *not* translated from the Arabic, but from Robert's Latin version. Victor Chauvin's bibliography of the Qur'ān and ḥadīth in his Bibliographie des ouvrages arabes (vol. 10, 1907) gives no information on these early editions.

De compositione alchemie (Basle 1559, Paris 1564, Basle 1593). Reprinted in Artis auriferae quam chemiam vocant volumina duo (vol. 2, 3–37, Basel 1610), and in Jean Jacques Manget: Bibliotheca chemica curiosa (vol. 1, 509–519, Geneva 1702). For translations into German and French, see Ferguson. I do not know whether the following item, quoted by Ferguson (vol. 2, 108) refers to the same text; Morieni Romani De transfiguratione metallorum et occulta summaque antiquorum Philosophorum medicina. Libellus nusquam hactenus in lucem editus (Paris 1559). A seventeenth century English translation, Sloane MS. 3697, was edited by E. J. Holmyard: A romance of chemistry (Chemistry and industry, vol. 44, 1925; Isis, 9, 152).

[5] An account of this legendary personality, Morienus (Marianus, Mārīnūs), is given by Ferguson (op. cit.). Morienus the Roman was supposed to have been Khālid's teacher. There is nothing to substantiate that story (see vol. 1, 495). The date quoted by Ferguson, 1182, refers to the Spanish era; it corresponds to A.D. 1144.

[6] M. Steinschneider: Hebraeische Übersetzungen (536, 1893).

Adrien Romain: Commentaire sur l'algèbre de Mahumed ben Musa el Chowarezmi (1599). Only a fragment of this work has been preserved; see Henri Bosmans: Le fragment du Commentaire, etc. (Annales de la Société scientifique de Bruxelles, vol. 30, part 2, 1906). Frederic Rosen: The algebra of Mohammed ben Musa (London 1831, in Arabic and English). For other translations, see my vol. 1, 563. Louis Charles Karpinski: Robert of Chester's Latin translation of the Algebra of al-Khowarizmi, with an introduction, critical notes and English version (University of Michigan Studies, humanistic series, vol. 11, 164 p., New York 1915; excellent edition; Isis, 4, 504–505).

Criticism—T. A. Archer: Dictionary of national biography (vol. 48, 362–364, 1896). John Ferguson: Bibliotheca chemica (vol. 2, 108–109, 1906). C. H. Haskins: The reception of Arabic science in England (English historical review, January 1915; revised in Studies in mediaeval science, 120–123, 1924). Lynn Thorndike: History of magic (vol. 2, 83, 215–217, 1923). Richard Reitzenstein: Alchemistische Lehrschriften und Märchen bei den Arabern (Religionsgeschichtliche Versuche und Vorarbeiten, vol. 19, 61–86, Giessen 1923). Julius Ruska: Arabische Alchemisten. (1). Chālid ibn Jazīd (56 p., Heidelberg 1924; Isis, 7, 183). E. J. Holmyard: Mediaeval Latin versions of passages which occur in the Muktasab (Isis, 8, 424–426, 1926). Robert Steele and Dorothea Waley Singer: The emerald table (Proceedings of the Royal Soc. of med., vol. 21, historical section, 41–57, 1928; Isis, 12, 356). Julius Ruska: Zwei Bücher De compositione alchemiae und ihre Vorreden (Archiv für Geschichte der Mathematik, vol. 11, 28–37, 1928; Isis, 13, 221).

RUDOLF OF BRUGES

Flemish astronomer and translator from Arabic into Latin. The only known pupil of Hermann the Dalmatian. He lived in the second quarter of the twelfth century, partly in northern Spain. The translation of Maslama ibn Aḥmad's version of Ptolemy's Planisphere (Toulouse 1143) formerly ascribed to him, has been restored to his master, Hermann. He translated the treatise on the astrolabe of the same Maslama ibn Aḥmad al-Majrīṭī (second half of the tenth century): Descriptio cuiusdam instrumenti, cujus usus est in metiendis stellarum cursibus; and dedicated it to his friend Johannes David (John of Seville). Original astronomical works are also ascribed to him.

Criticism—L. Leclerc: Médecine arabe (vol. 2, 432, 1876). M. Steinschneider: Die europäischen Übersetzungen aus dem Arabischen (74–75, 1904). H. Bosmans: Hermann le Dalmate (Revue des questions scientifiques, vol. 56, 669–672, 1904); Biographie nationale de Belgique (vol. 19, 615, 1907). C. H. Haskins: Studies in mediaeval science (Cambridge, Mass., 1924).

PLATO OF TIVOLI

Plato Tiburtinus. Italian mathematician, astronomer, astrologer, and translator from Arabic and Hebrew into Latin. Lived in Barcelona about 1134–1145. It is not necessary to assume that he had a deep (or any) knowledge of either Arabic or Hebrew, for he was assisted in his work by the Jew Abraham bar Ḥiyya (Savasorda), in about the same way as Gundisalvo was helped by John of Seville. At any rate, Plato has the distinction among other translators of his age of having produced versions from the Hebrew as well as from the Arabic. Five of his translations are dated, as follows:

1. In 1133–1134, al-'Imrānī (first half of the tenth century): De electionibus horarum.

2. In 1136, Abū 'Alī al-Khaiyāṭ (first half of the ninth century): De nativitatibus, or De judiciis nativitatum. This was also translated by John of Seville in 1153. It is John's translation which was printed (Nuremberg 1546, 1549).

3. In 1136, Astrological aphorisms (fuṣūl). Almansoris Judicia seu propositiones . . . . , or, Centum propositiones . . . . , or, Capitula stellarum oblata regi magno Saracenorum Alchacham (ab) Almansore astrologo filio Abrahae Judei. Who was this Manṣūr? He has not yet been identified.[7] The Latin translation of these aphorisms was printed in 1484, and very often reprinted: 1492, 1493, 1501, 1519, 1533, 1551, 1581, 1641.

4. In 1138, Ptolemy's Quadripartitum, from an Arabic version; probably the one made by Ibrāhīm ibn al-Ṣalt and corrected by Thābit ibn Qurra and (or) Ḥunain ibn Isḥāq (second half of the ninth century). This is important, being the first of Ptolemy's works to be translated into Latin. The apocryphal Centiloquium (or Fructus) which is an abridgment of the Quadripartitum, had been translated two years earlier (1136) by John of Seville (translation formerly ascribed to Plato). The Quadripartitum being a very popular book, was translated again and again: in 1206 by an unknown translator; in the second half of the thirteenth century by Egidius de Thebaldis for Alfonso X; about 1305 by Simon de Bredon (first half of the fourteenth century); to which may be added a translation from the Greek quoted by Henry Bate in 1281. There were probably also other versions of the Centiloquium; I have already mentioned one made by Hugh of Santalla.

5. In 1145 (not 1116), from the Hebrew, the treatise on practical geometry: Liber embadorum by Abraham bar Ḥiyya. This translation is of fundamental importance as it was one of the main sources of Fibonacci (first half of the thirteenth century). Max. Curtze: Der Liber embadorum des Savasorda in der Übersetzung des Plato von Tivoli (Abhdl. zur Geschichte der Mathematik, vol. 12, 3–183, Leipzig 1902).

The following versions, being undated, are quoted in the chronological order of the writings translated.

6. Theodosios of Bithynia (first half of first century B. C.): version of the Spherics, from the Arabic. Another version was made by Gerard of Cremona.

7. Al-Battānī (second half of the ninth century): De motu stellarum. This translation was published together with al-Farghānī's Elements, Albategnius de motu stellarum ex observationibus tum propriis tum Ptolemaii omnia cum demonstrationibus geometricis et additionibus Ioannis de Regiomonte (Nuremberg 1537). Printed alone (Bologna 1645).

8. Abū Bakr al-Ḥasan ibn al-Khaṣīb (second half of the ninth century): De revolutionibus nativitatum.

9. Ibn al-Ṣaffār (first half of the eleventh century): Liber Abulcasim de operibus astrolabiae. This translation was dedicated to John of Seville.

10. Unidentified treatise on geomancy: Alfakini arabici filii quaestiones geomanticae. Published in the Fasciculus geomanticus (Verona 1687; 1704).

11. Aeneas de pulsibus et urinis. Aeneas might be Ḥunain ibn Isḥāq (second

[7] Steinschneider (Europaeische Übersetzungen, 64, 1904), suggests that it might be Yaḥyā ibn abī Manṣūr (first half of the ninth century), but this does not seem plausible. Another possibility is Abū Naṣr Manṣūr ibn 'Alī (second half of the tenth century). But I would rather read the title " . . . regi magno Alchacham Almansori (ab) astrologo filio Abrahae Judei." The king would be al-Ḥākim al-Manṣūr, Fāṭimid caliph from 996 to 1020, and the author a contemporary Egyptian Jew converted to Islām.

half of the ninth century). At any rate, this is the only medical translation ascribed to Plato, and the ascription is very doubtful. Gerard of Cremona was possibly the translator.

Leaving this last translation aside, it will be observed that most of the writings which Plato published in Latin were astrological. However, one of these (no. 4) happens to be the earliest Ptolemaic treatise to appear in Latin. Plato deserves special credit for his translation of al-Battānī (no. 7), of great importance in the history of Latin trigonometry; and even more for his translations of Theodosios (no. 6), and of Abraham bar Ḥiyya (no. 5). The publication of the Liber embadorum[8] is a landmark in the history of mathematics, and it is of special interest as having been translated not from the Arabic but from the Hebrew. This translation lost some of its value, and Plato some of his fame, when Haskins showed that its date was 1145 and not 1116. For example, the sine table included in it, which was believed to be the earliest Latin table of its kind, is antedated by Adelard's translation of al-Khwārizmī's tables (1126). Yet the Liber embadorum is still the earliest Latin writing wherein the complete solution of a quadratic equation is found. I must add that the ascription to Plato of the translations of al-Battānī and Theodosios needs confirmation.

Criticism—Baldassare Boncompagni: Delle versioni fatta da Platone Tiburtino (Atti dell Accad. Pontificia, vol. 4, 249–286, 1851). M. Steinschneider: Hebraeische Übersetzungen (1893); Europaeische Übersetzungen (62–66, 1904). A. v. Braunmühl: Geschichte der Trigonometrie (vol. 1, 48, 50, 93, 130; 1900). P. Duhem: Système du monde (vol. 3, 198–201, 1915; vol. 4, 577, 1915). C. H. Haskins: Studies in the history of mediaeval science (11, 14, 51, 68, 110; 1924).

STEPHEN OF ANTIOCH

See Chapter X, Medicine.

"ARTEPHIUS"

See Chapter VII, Chemistry.

II. FROM GREEK INTO LATIN

JAMES OF VENICE

Jacobus Clericus de Venetia. Lived about 1128–1136. In 1136 he was in Constantinople. About 1128 he translated directly from the Greek into Latin the Topics, the Prior and Posterior Analytics, and the Sophistici elenchi, and he commented upon them. These parts of the Aristotelian Organon which he was thus the first (after Boetius) to reveal to the Latin West, were called the "New Logic," in opposition to the "Old Logic," *i.e.*, the Categories and De interpretatione, which constituted all that remained of Boetius' translation and were the only parts of the Organon known in the West before this time. When the Latin text of the New Logic made its appearance it was generally ascribed by contemporaries to Boetius. Another anonymous translation of the "New Logic," represented by a Toledo MS., appeared a little later.

Thus it would seem that the New Logic was revealed in Latin during the second quarter of the twelfth century in three ways: (1) the reappearance of Boetius'

[8] Embadum or emdadon (ἔμβαδον) means area. The word was used by Roman surveyors (gromatici).

version; (2) a little later, James's version; (3) still later, the anonymous Toledan one. It is possible, but not probable, that (1) and (2) are identical, and that (3) occurred somewhat later than the middle of the century. Knowledge of the New Logic spread rapidly: in 1132, Adam du Petit Pont (later bishop of St. Asaph) was discussing the Prior analytics; at about the same time Gilbert de la Porrée was quoting them. Most of the Organon was known to Theodoric of Chartres, and by 1159 Theodoric's disciple John of Salisbury knew the whole of it; it was introduced into Germany by Otto of Freising. I may add that the New Logic reached the West a little later through still another channel, the translation from the Arabic by Gerard of Cremona (second half of the twelfth century).

Criticism—C. H. Haskins: Mediaeval versions of the Posterior analytics (Harvard studies in classical philology, vol. 25, 1914); The Greek element in the Renaissance of the XIIth century (606, 1920); Studies in mediaeval science (223–241, 1924; second ed., p. XIV, 1927). Sandys: History of classical scholarship (vol. 1^3, 527, 557, 1921).

ANSELM OF HAVELBERG

Italian or Lotharingian priest who was, from 1129 to 1155, bishop of Havelberg (on the Elbe) and then to the time of his death in 1158, archbishop of Ravenna. He was one of the diplomats sent to Constantinople in 1135 to negotiate with the Greek theologians. About 1150 he wrote an account of his discussion with Nicetas (Νικήτας) archbishop of Nicomedia (Libri tres dialogorum s. 'Αντικειμένων). I mention this Anselm for two reasons: he illustrates the Byzantine influences which reached the Latin West through the activity of church diplomats; he illustrates also the fight between Germans and Slavs in the North March (east of the Elbe), for Anselm's bishopric had to be reconquered twice from the Slavs (1130, 1147).

Text—Migne's Latin patrology (vol. 188, 1163–1248).
Criticism—H. Prutz: Allgemeine deutsche Biographie (vol. 1, 478, 1875).

MOSES OF BERGAMO

Italian historian and humanist who lived in the Venetian quarter of Constantinople about 1130–1136. He had made a collection of Greek MSS. which was lost in the burning of his house in 1130. He composed in Latin verse a description of his native place, Bergamo, (Pergaminus) 372 rhyming hexameters. According to Anselm of Havelberg, Moses was one of the Latin doctors present at a theological disputation held before Joannes II Comnenos, in 1136, the others being James of Venice, Burgundio of Pisa, etc. "Moses was chosen by all to be a faithful interpreter for both sides." He was equally versed in Greek and Latin and wrote studies on Greek grammar and theology. He is quoted here as an interesting representative of Latin humanism in Constantinople and a link between Greek and occidental culture.

Text—Pergaminus, carmen de laudibus Bergomi, in Marius Mucius: Theatrum carminum Achillis Mucii (Bergomi 1596). L. A. Muratori: Rerum italicarum scriptores (vol. 5, 523–536).
Criticism—C. H. Haskins: Moses of Bergamo (Byzantinische Zeitschrift, vol. 23, 133–142, 1914); Studies in the history of mediaeval science (Cambridge, Mass., 1924; Isis, 7, 121–124).

HUGH OF SAINT VICTOR

See Chapter IV, Philosophic Background.

III. FROM ARABIC INTO HEBREW

ABRAHAM IBN EZRA

See Chapter IV, Philosophic Background.

ABRAHAM BAR ḤIYYA

See Chapter V, Mathematics and Astronomy.

IV. FROM HEBREW INTO LATIN

See my notes on Stephen Harding and Peter the Venerable, in Chapter II, Religious Background; and on Plato of Tivoli, in this chapter, above.

V. FROM CELTIC INTO LATIN

See my notes on Geoffrey of Monmouth and on Caradog of Llancarvan, in Chapter XI, Historiography.

VI. FROM LATIN INTO FRENCH

PHILIP OF THAON

See Chapter IV, Philosophic Background.

CHAPTER IV

PHILOSOPHIC BACKGROUND

(First Half of Twelfth Century)

I. EASTERN MUSLIM

MUḤAMMAD IBN AḤMAD AL-QAZWĪNĪ

Jamāl al-dīn Abū 'Abdallāh Muḥammad ibn Aḥmad al-Qazwīnī. Lived about 1132. Persian encyclopaedist writing in Arabic. He wrote, in 1132–1133, a popular encyclopaedia entitled Mufīḍ al-'ulum wa mubīd al-humūm (the giver of knowledge and destroyer of cares) treating of religion, ethics, politics, natural history, geography, and history.

Criticism—C. Brockelmann: Arabische Litteratur (vol. 1, 499, 1898).

'UMAR AL-NASAFĪ

See Chapter II, Religious Background.

AL-ZAMAKHSHARĪ

See Chapter XIII, Philology.

ISMĀ'ĪL AL-JURJĀNĪ

See Chapter X, Medicine.

II. HISPANO-MUSLIM

AL-BAṬALYŪSĪ

Abū Muḥammad 'Abdallāh ibn Muḥammad ibn al-Sīd al-Baṭalyūsī. Born in Badajóz, Estremadura, in 1049–1050, or 1052–1053; lived in Valencia, and died there in 1127. Hispano-Muslim theologian, who wrote in Arabic various treatises on philosophical and theological subjects. One of these treatises, the Kitāb al-haḍā'iq (the Orchard), apparently lost in Arabic, is of special interest. It contains a comparison of the world with an imaginary sphere and develops the old Greek idea of eternal return, which is also found in the Epistles of the Ikhwān al-ṣafā' (second half of the tenth century), combined with neo-Platonic number mysticism. This treatise is known through the Hebrew translation by Moses ibn Tibbon (second half of the thirteenth century), and also through an incomplete Hebrew version (ch. 1–4) published by Samuel ibn Moṭoṭ (Guadalajara 1370). Al-Baṭalyūsī's name was corrupted by Jewish authors to the extent of being finally confused in the fourteenth century with Ptolemy!

Text—Moses' translation, together with Moṭoṭ's fragment, was edited by David Kaufmann: Die Spuren des al-Batlajusis in der jüdischen Religionsphilosophie (Budapest 1880).

Criticism—Ibn Khallikān (de Slane, 2, 61–63, 1843). M. Steinschneider: Hebraeische Übersetzungen (286–288, 1893). C. Brockelmann: Arabische Litteratur (vol. 1, 427, 1898).

IBN BĀJJA

Abū Bakr Muḥammad ibn Yaḥyā ibn al-Ṣā'igh (son of the goldsmith). Generally called Ibn Bājja, hence the mediaeval Latin name Avenpace (or Avempace). The significance of this nisba is unknown; Ibn Khallikān derived it from a Frankish name meaning silver? Hispano-Muslim philosopher, scientist, physician, and commentator on Aristotle. Born in Saragossa about the end of the fifth Muslim century—that is, before 1106; lived in Granada, Saragossa, and Fez; persecuted because of his "atheism;" died, poisoned (?), in Fez, 1138–1139. He wrote many small treatises on medicine, geometry, astronomy, natural science, alchemy, and philosophy. He criticized some of Ptolemy's assumptions, thus preparing the way for Ibn Ṭufail and al-Biṭrūjī (second half of the twelfth century). A treatise of his on materia medica was very frequently quoted by Ibn al-Baiṭār (first half of the thirteenth century). He composed a poem on hunting, Ṭardīya. He was deeply interested in music, a skilful lute ('ūd) player, and his (lost) treatise on music was as much appreciated in the West as al-Fārābī's in the East. The two writings of his which are best known (we might say the only ones which are known) are two philosophical treatises, the Kitāb tadbīr al-mutawaḥḥid (De regimine solitarii, Guide of the solitary) and a farewell letter, Risālat al-wadā', to a friend who was leaving Spain to go to Egypt. The Tadbīr is known only through an analysis in Hebrew by Moses ben Joshua (second half of the fourteenth century). The Risāla was translated into Hebrew by Ḥayyim ibn Vives (or Vivas) for David ibn Bilia (first half of the fourteenth century), and the Hebrew version was put into Latin, Epistola expeditionis, by Abraham de Balmes (second half of the fifteenth century).

Ibn Bājja exerted much influence upon Ibn Rushd and Albert the Great. A study of his extant scientific writings is much needed; in the meanwhile it is not yet possible to appraise his scientific importance.

Text—The Tadbīr is the only published work; it was edited by D. Herzog: Die Abhandlung des Abū Bekr Ibn al-Sāig Vom Verhalten des Einsiedlers (Beitr. zur Philosophie des Mittelalters, vol. 1, Berlin 1896; this is Moses ben Joshua's analysis).

Criticism—Ibn Khallikān (de Slane, 3, 130–133). Wüstenfeld: Geschichte der arabischen Aerzte (93, 1840). S. Munk: Mélanges de philosophie juive (383–410, 1859). Leclerc: Médecine arabe (2, 75–78, 1876). M. Steinschneider: Hebraeische Übersetzungen (356–361, 1893). C. Brockelmann: Arabische Litteratur (1, 460, 1898). H. Suter: Die Mathematiker und Astronomen der Araber (116, 1900). De Boer: Geschichte der Philosophie im Islam (156–160, 1901). Léon Gauthier: Une réforme du système astronomique de Ptolémée (Journal Asiatique, 14, 483–510, 1909; important). P. Duhem: Système du Monde (2, 130–132, 1914, criticism of Ptolemy; 4, 520–532, 1916, on the unity of human intellect). Encyclopaedia of Islām (2, 366, 1916). Henry George Farmer: History of Arabian music (222, 1929; Isis, 13, 375).

For Ibn Ḥasdai and Abū-l-Ṣalt, see Chapter X, Medicine; and for Abū Bakr al-Ṭurṭushī and Ibn al'Arabī, see Chapter XII, Law and Sociology.

III. HISPANO-JEWISH

BAḤYA BEN JOSEPH

Baḥya ben Joseph ibn Paquda. Hispano-Jewish philosopher and moralist, writing in Arabic. He lived at Saragossa in the eleventh or twelfth century. There is much discussion about the date of his activity. The discussion centers upon this: there are many points of contact between Baḥya on the one hand, and Ibn Gabirol (first half of the eleventh century) and al-Ghazzālī (second half of the eleventh century) on the other. Was Baḥya inspired by them, or they by him? The first hypothesis seems more probable and obliges me to place him at a later period (say the beginning of the twelfth century) than was done before.

His main work is the Kitāb al-hidayat ilā farā'iḍ al-qulūb (Guide to the duties of the heart), wherein much emphasis is laid upon the inner duties beyond the requirements of the law and of conventional morality. It was the first Jewish book of its kind and one of the best ethical works of the Middle Ages. Baḥya's philosophy was essentially the Judeo-Muslim neo-Platonism as developed by the Ikhwān al-ṣafā' and by Ibn Gabirol; he was acquainted with Muslim Aristotelism, through the works of Saadia ben Joseph. Of course his whole outlook was dominated by the Jewish faith. The "Heart duties" is divided into ten sections or gates, of which the second, called in Hebrew Sha'ar ha-beḥinah (Gate of reflection), is of special importance to us, being in fact a summary of scientific knowledge—cosmology, microcosm and macrocosm, botany, zoology, physiology, and psychology.

This work was very poorly translated into Hebrew by Judah ibn Tibbon (second half of the twelfth century), under the title Torah ḥobot ha-lebabot. The translation of the first gate had already been completed about 1161, this being one of the earliest translations from Arabic into Hebrew. Another translation was made by Joseph Qimḥi (second half of the twelfth century). Versions in many other languages—not only Ladino and Yiddish, but Portuguese and Italian as well—were derived from the Hebrew.

Another Arabic work, Ma'ānī al-nafs (Inner meaning of the soul) had been ascribed to Baḥya, unrightly, it seems. It was translated into Hebrew under the title Torot ha-nefesh.

Text—Earliest edition of Ibn Tibbon's translation, Naples 1489. More critical edition of it, Mantua 1559. New edition, together with the extant part of Joseph Qimḥi's translation, by Isaac Benjacob and Ad. Jellinek (Leipzig 1846).

Arabic edition by A. S. Yahuda (538 p., Leyden 1912). See also Yahuda's Prolegomena to that edition (Frankfurt a. M., 1904).

Spanish translation by Joseph Pardo (Amsterdam 1610). Portuguese translation by Samuel ben Isaac Abbas (Amsterdam 1670). Ladino translation by Ẓaddiq ben Joseph Firmon (Venice 1703). Hebrew text with German translation and commentary by R. Fürstenthal (Breslau 1835). German translation by Mendel E. Stern (Vienna 1856). Etc. English translation of selected passages by Edwin Collins (Wisdom of the East, 58 p., 2d. impression, London 1909). Isaac Broydé: Les réflexions sur l'âme (Paris 1896; Hebrew text with French summary).

Criticism—M. Steinschneider: Hebraeische Übersetzungen (372–378, 1893); Arabische Literatur der Juden (132–135, 1902). Isaac Broydé and Kaufmann Kohler: Jewish Encyclopaedia (2, 447–454, 1902; they place Baḥya in the first half of the eleventh century). K. v. Zetterstéen: Review of Yahuda's edition

(Le monde oriental, 8, 250–252, 1914). Isaac Husik: Mediaeval Jewish philosophy (80–113, 1918). P. Kokowzoff: The date of life of Bahya ibn Paqoda (Livre d'hommage à la mémoire de Samuel Poznanski, 13–21, Warsaw 1927; Isis, 13, 422, 522); concluding that the Duties of the heart cannot be later than about 1080–1090.

PEDRO ALFONSO

See subsection VIII, Latin, in this chapter.

ABRAHAM BAR ḤIYYA

See Chapter V, Mathematics and Astronomy.

MOSES IBN EZRA

Moses ben Jacob ha-Sallaḥ ibn Ezra. In Arabic: Abū Hārūn Mūsā al-Gharnāṭī. Hispano-Jewish theologian, philosopher, and poet. Born at Granada about 1070; died after 1138. He was a friend of Judah ha-Levi and probably related to Abraham ibn Ezra. He wrote two important works in Arabic. First, a philosophical treatise entitled Kitāb al-ḥadīqah fī ma'ānī al-majāz wal-ḥaqīqah (Book of the garden, on the true and metaphorical meanings). It is divided into seven parts: (1) God and man, philosophy; (2–4) theology; (5) motion; (6) nature; (7) intellect. It is derived from Hermes, Pythagoras, Socrates, Plato, Aristotle, pseudo-Empedocles, al-Fārābī, Saadia Gaon, Ibn Gabirol, etc. It was translated anonymously into Hebrew, under the title 'Arugat ha-bosem. This work was entirely eclipsed by the second, Kitāb al-muḥāḍarah wal-mudhākarah, which is particularly interesting as being almost the only Jewish representative of the adab[1] writings so immensely popular in Islām. The only other remarkable example is the Taḥkemoni written by al-Ḥarizī (first half of the thirteenth century) *in Hebrew*. The Muḥāḍarah is divided into eight chapters, of which the fifth and sixth contain much information on the history of Jewish settlements in Spain, their literary activity (with list of authors and works), and their culture. Moses is chiefly known as a Hebrew poet; he was one of the very greatest poets of his time.

Text—The Kitāb al-muḥāḍarat was partly edited by Paul Kokowzow (ch. 1–4, St. Petersburg 1894). Specimen in Hartwig Hirschfeld: Arabic chrestomathy in Hebrew characters (London, 61–63, 1892).

The Tarshīsh, or 'Anaq (or in Arabic, Zahr al-riyāḍ—Flowers of the gardens), a collection of poems, was edited by David Günzburg (Berlin 1886). Partial German translation in Saul Isaac Kaempf: Nichtandalusische Poesie andalusischer Dichter aus dem elften, zwölften und dreizehnten Jahrhundert (2 vols., Prague 1858).

Criticism—Leopold Dukes: Moses ben Ezra. Darstellung seines Lebens und literarischen Wirkens nebst hebräischen Beilagen und deutschen Übersetzungen (Altona 1839). S. Munk: Mélanges de philosophie juive (262–265, 515–517, 1859). M. Steinschneider: Catalogus librorum hebraeorum in Bibliotheca Bodleiana (p. 1801–1814, 1860); Die arabische Literatur der Juden (149–151, 1902). M. Schreiner: Le Kitab al-mouhadara (Revue des études juives, vol. 21, 98–117, 1891; vol. 22, 62–81, 1892; analysis of the work). Isaac Broydé: Jewish Encyclopaedia (vol. 6, 525, 1904).

[1] The word adab is difficult to translate: belles lettres, urbanity. The popularity of that branch of literature in Islām—pure literature, we might call it—and its relative unpopularity in Israel are profoundly significant.

JUDAH HA-LEVI

Jehudah Halevy. In Arabic, Abū-l-Ḥasan al-Lawī. Hispano-Jewish poet and philosopher, the greatest post-Biblical poet of Israel. Born at Toledo about 1085; lived at Lucena, Toledo, and Cordova; died near Jerusalem after 1140. Of his Hebrew poems, a great many of which have been included in the Jewish liturgy, the most famous is the Ẓion ha-lo tish'ali (Ode to Zion) written at Damascus about 1140. His claim to our attention, however, is based chiefly on a philosophical treatise, originally written in Arabic, the Kitāb al-ḥujjah wal-dalīl fī nuṣr al-dīn al-dhalīl (Book of argumentation and proof in vindication of the despised religions), commonly called Kitāb al-Khazarī. It is cast in the form of a dialogue between the king of the Khazars[2] and a Jew, and the purpose is to defend revealed religion against philosophy, Judaism against other religions, and traditional Judaism against Qaraism. For example, he defends the Biblical account of creation against the Aristotelian theory of the eternity of matter. It is divided into five parts or discourses (ma'amar), of which the fifth is devoted to a critical study of various philosophical systems. Outside of purely religious questions, Judah's point of view is very similar to that of al-Ghazzālī (second half of the eleventh century). The Kitāb al-Khazarī was soon translated into Hebrew by Judah ibn Tibbon (second half of the twelfth century): Sefer ha-Kuzari (Lunel 1167); it was translated a second time by Judah ben Isaac ibn Cardinal[3] about 1211, but this second translation was entirely overshadowed by the first. Through these Hebrew translations it exerted a deep influence upon Jewish thought.

Text—Judah ibn Tibbon's translation was first published in 1506 at Fano. Many later editions. David Cassel edited the Hebrew version of Judah Cardinal with German translation and commentary. (Leipzig 1853), twice reprinted. (Leipzig 1869). Critical edition of the original Arabic text and of the Hebrew version by Judah ibn Tibbon, by Hartwig Hirschfeld (Leipzig, 1887).

Latin translation from the Hebrew by Johann Buxtorf (Bale 1660). Spanish translation from the Hebrew by Jacob Abendana (Amsterdam 1663). German translation by Heimann Jolowicz and David Cassel (Leipzig 1841). German translation from the Arabic by Hartwig Hirschfeld (Breslau 1885). English translation from the Arabic by Hartwig Hirschfeld (318 p., London 1905).

For the poems, see the Jewish Encyclopaedia. I quote only (because of its convenience) the volume of Selected poems recently published in Hebrew and English (texts side by side) by Nina Salaman (220 p., Schiff Library of Jewish Classics, 2; Philadelphia 1925; Isis, 8, 540).

Criticism—M. Steinschneider: Hebraeische Übersetzungen (402–405, 1893); Arabische Literatur der Juden (152–154, 1902). Max Schloessinger and Isaac Broydé: Jewish Encyclopaedia (vol. 7, 346–353, 1904). David Neumark: Jehuda Hallevi's philosophy (91 p., Cincinnati 1908). Harry A. Wolfson: Maimonides and Halevi (Jewish quarterly review, vol. 2, 1912). Emil Berger: Das Problem der Erkenntnis in der Religionsphilosophie Jehuda Hallewis (Diss., München; Berlin 1915). Isaac Husik: Mediaeval Jewish philosophy (1918, 150–183). J. Heller: Jehuda Cardinal (Encyclopaedia judaica, vol. 5, 43, 1930).

JOSEPH IBN ẒADDĪQ

Joseph ben Jacob ibn Ẓaddiq. Joseph ha-Ẓaddiq ben Jacob. Abū 'Umar Yūsuf ibn Ṣadīq. Lived at Cordova, and died there in 1149. Hispano-Jewish

[2] About the Khazars, see my note on Ḥasdai ibn Shaprut (second half of the tenth century), in my vol. I, 680.

[3] Spelled in Hebrew, Gardinal or Qardinal.

philosopher. He wrote in Arabic on logic and on religious philosophy. His chief work is a treatise called Kitāb al-'ālam al-ṣaghīr (Microcosmos) inspired by Muslim philosophy, chiefly by the writings of the Ikhwān al-ṣafā' (second half of the tenth century). The theory of the microcosm and macrocosm is fully developed in it. The Arabic original is lost, but we know it through a Hebrew version, Ha-'olam ha-qaṭon, probably made by Nahum ha-Ma'arabi, a Jewish Moroccan poet of the thirteenth century.

Text—First edition of the Hebrew text by Ad. Jellinek (Leipzig 1854). New critical edition by S. Horovitz (Jahresbericht des Jüd. Theol. Seminars; Breslau 1903).

Criticism—M. Steinschneider: Ersch und Grubers Allgemeine Encyklopädie (reprinted in Gesammelte Schriften, vol. 1, 180–183); Hebraeische Übersetzungen (407–410, 1893); Arabische Literatur der Juden (151, 1902). Isaac Broydé: Jewish Encyclopaedia (vol. 7, 264–265, 1904). Isaac Husik: Mediaeval Jewish philosophy (125–149, 1918).

Max Seligsohn: Jewish Encyclopaedia (vol. 8, 233, 1904), on Nahum Ma'arabi (or Maghrabi), quoting other translations of this Nahum.

IBN EZRA

Abraham ben Meïr ibn Ezra. Aben Ezra. Abū Isḥāq Ibrāhīm ibn al-Majid. Abenare, Avenare. Abraham Judaeus. Born in Toledo about 1089–1092. He traveled extensively: Rome 1140, Salerno 1141, Mantua 1145, Verona 1146, Lucca 1148, Béziers 1156, London 1158, Narbonne 1160. He died in 1167, probably at Calahorra. Hispano-Jewish philosopher, astrologer, translator from Arabic into Hebrew, and Hebrew grammarian. One of the greatest Biblical commentators of the Middle Ages, one of the forerunners of modern criticism, and much admired by Spinoza on that account. He was one of the first to translate writings of Muslims into Hebrew. He wrote various books on mathematics and astrology, on the calendar, and on the astrolabe; eight treatises on astrology were completed at Lucca in 1148. One of his main titles to fame is that through his wanderings in Provence, France, and England, he helped to propagate among the Jews of Christian Europe (who, unlike their Spanish brethren, did not know Arabic) the rationalistic and scientific points of view which had been developed in Spain by Muslims and Jews on the basis of Greco-Muslim knowledge.

He translated from Arabic into Hebrew three treatises on grammar by Judah Ḥayyuj (second half of the tenth century), Rome 1140; two treatises on astrology by Māshāllāh, before 1148; al-Bīrūnī's commentary on al-Khwārizmī's tables, Narbonne 1160. The last mentioned is known only through Ibn Ezra's version.

Ibn Ezra's mind was a strange mixture of rationalism and mysticism. His writings show his deep interest in magic squares and the mystical properties of numbers. He explained a decimal system of numeration: the first nine letters of the Hebrew alphabet, plus a circle for the zero, with place value. Problem involving the product of complex fractions. Account of the *regula infusa,* ascribed to one Job ben Solomon, to solve equations. For example, given

$$m(ax + b) + c = o$$

let

$$ax + b = y$$

then

$$my + c = o$$

$$y = -c/m$$

$$ax + b = -c/m$$

which can easily be solved.[4] One of the earliest forms of the traditional arithmetical problem known as "Turks and Christians." Combinations of n things taken r at a time. Ibn Ezra knew that $C_{n,r} = C_{n,n-r}$.

His astrological treatises exerted a great deal of influence not only upon the Jews but also upon the Christians. Their popularity in Christendom is attested by the existence of many translations. The earliest of these was a French translation made in 1273 by a Jew called Hagin,[5] in Henry Bate's house in Malines. This French version was the basis of many Latin translations: by Henry Bate, 1281–1292; by Peter of Abano, 1293;[6] and by Arnold of Quinquempoix at the beginning of the fourteenth century. The Hebrew text was translated also into Catalan by Martin of Osca (or Huesca), Aragon; and one treatise of the Catalan version was translated into Latin in 1448 by Louis de Angulo. Thus did the Arabic astrological knowledge, collected by Ibn Ezra in Hebrew, reach the Latin world through many channels.

Though they do not directly concern us, Ibn Ezra's commentaries on the Old Testament were so influential, even outside of their own sphere, that something must be said of them. He explained his methods in the introduction to his commentary on the Pentateuch (Firush ha-Torah); he distinguished between the peshaṭ, simple or literal meaning; the derash, common sense explanation; and the midrash, more philosophic explanation; trying hard to steer a middle course between excessive literalism and loose interpretations. As an instance of his boldness, I may mention his conclusion that the Book of Isaiah contains the sayings of two prophets, a view confirmed by modern criticism. The popularity of his commentaries is attested by the large number of super-commentaries.

Aside from his translations of Ḥayyuj's writings, he wrote treatises on Hebrew grammar.

Finally, in 1158, he wrote a treatise on religious philosophy, the Yesod mora (Foundation of awe).

Texts and translations—The Sefer ha-eḥad (on the peculiarities of the numbers 1 to 9) has been edited by S. Pinsker and M. A. Goldhardt (Odessa 1867). The Sefer ha-mispar (or Yesod mispar), by Moritz Silberberg: Das Buch der Zahl. Ein hebräisch-arithmetisches Werk von Rabbi Abraham ibn Ezra. Zum ersten Male hrg., im Deutsche übersetzt und erläutert (148 p., 80 p. in Hebrew; Frankfurt a. M., 1895; Bibliotheca mathematica, 91, 1895). The Sefer ha-'ibbur (on the calendar), by S. J. Halberstam (Lyck 1874). The Keli ha-neḥoshet (on the astrolabe), by H. Edelmann (Königsberg 1845).

D. E. Smith and Jekuthial Ginsburg have published an English translation of Ibn Ezra's introduction to his Hebrew translation of al-Bīrūnī's work on the astronomical tables of al-Khwārizmī. Rabbi ben Ezra and the Hindu-Arabic problem (American mathematical monthly, vol. 25, 99–108, 1918). This is an interesting account of the introduction of Hindu mathematics into Islām. The Hebrew title of this translation is Ta'amē lūḥōt al-Chowārezmī; part of the Hebrew text with German translation had already been published by M. Steinschneider (Z. der deutschen morgenl. Ges., vol. 24, 325, 1870)

[4] This example is borrowed from D. E. Smith: History of mathematics (vol. 2, 442, 1925). The ascription of the *regula infusa* to Ibn Ezra was made by Guglielmo Libri: Histoire des sciences mathématiques en Italie (vol. 1, 312, 1838). Smith questions the correctness of that ascription.

[5] See my note on Hagin Deulacres (second half of the thirteenth century).

[6] This was the only complete Latin version. It was published in Venice in 1485 and in 1507, by two different printers.

The "Liber augmenti et diminutionis vocatus numeratio divinationis ex eo quod sapientes Indi posuerunt, quem Abraham compilavit et secundum librum qui Indorum dictus est composuit," edited by G. Libri: Histoire des sciences mathématiques en Italie (vol. 1, 304–371, 1838)—possibly the translation of an original work of Ibn Ezra? It has also been ascribed to Abū Kāmil. It contains applications of the regula elchatayn (regula duorum falsorum). (See Cantor, 1^3, 730–732).

The commentary on the Pentateuch was first printed at Naples in 1488. The commentary on Isaiah was edited by M. Friedländer, with notes and glossary, and translated into English (London 1877; 1873). Various commentaries of Ibn Ezra are included in rabbinical editions of the Old Testament.

The Yesod mora was first printed at Constantinople in 1529.

For editions of other works, see the Jewish Encyclopaedia.

Criticism—M. Steinschneider: Abraham Judaeus. Savasorda und Ibn Esra. Zur Geschichte der mathematischen Wissenschaften im 12. Jahrhundert (Zeitschrift für Mathematik und Physik, vol. 12, 1–44, 1867; Gesammelte Schriften, vol. 1, 327–387); Ist Ibn Esra nach Indien gewesen? (Z. der deutschen morgenländischen Gesellschaft, vol. 20, 427–432, 1866; Gesammelte Schriften, vol. 1, 498–506); Abraham ibn Esra, Abraham Judaeus, Avenare (Suppl. zur Zeitschrift für Mathematik und Physik, vol. 25, 57–128, 1880; very elaborate study; reprinted in Gesammelte Schriften, vol. 1, 407–498); Hebraeische Übersetzungen (869, 1893); Arabische Literatur der Juden (156, 1902).

Israel Abrahams: Jewish life in the middle ages (385, 1896), on arithmetical puzzles ascribed to Ibn Ezra. G. Orchanski: Abraham ibn Esra als Philosoph (Breslau 1900). P. Tannery: Sur le Liber augmenti et diminutionis compilé par Abraham (Bibliotheca Mathematica, vol. 2, 45–47, 1901; Mémoires, vol. 5, 304–307; Isis, 6, 433). W. Bacher: Jewish Encyclopaedia (vol. 6, 520–524, 1904). P. Duhem: Système du monde (vol. 3, 125–127, 1915), the astronomical hypothesis of Heraclides of Pontos). Isaac Husik: History of mediaeval Jewish philosophy, 184–196, 1918). D. E. Smith: History of mathematics (vol. 2, 1925). M. Wilensky: Ibn Esra's books Sefer ha-yesod and Sefat yether (Kirjath Sepher, 3rd year, 73–79, Jerusalem 1926; in Hebrew). Raphael Levy: The astrological works of Ibn Ezra (174 p., Baltimore 1927; Isis, 11, 171; 13, 158). J. Freimann: Abraham ha-Chose (i.e., ha-Ḥozeh) (Encyclopaedia judaica, vol. 1, 437, 1928). Raphael Levy: The position of Abraham ibn Ezra in Judaeo-Romance (The Jewish forum, 16–23, 1930).

IV. FRENCH JEWISH

SAMUEL BEN MEÏR

Often called Rashbam, from the initials of his name Rabbi S. b. M. Judaeo-French commentator on the Old Testament and the Talmud. He was a grandson of Rashi, on his mother's side. Born at Ramerupt near Troyes about 1085; died about 1174. He knew French and Latin, but not Arabic. He continued his grandfather's work, and from a certain point of view improved upon it. He insisted even more than Rashi upon the literal interpretation, the simple meaning—the peshaṭ, as opposed to the midrash.[7] From that point of view his commentary on the Tōrāh may be considered the masterpiece of Judaeo-French exegesis.

During the preparation of this volume, I was made to realize more deeply the immense importance of Rashi (second half of the eleventh century) as a Biblical and Talmudic commentator. His commentary on the Tōrāh is especially im-

[7] Peshaṭ means simple; cf. the Syriac word pĕshiṭṭā (vol. 1, 291). The Midrash is a body of tradition auxiliary to the Talmud (vol. 1, 402); in this case midrash means exegesis.

portant. His commentaries are almost always printed together with Tōrāh and the Talmud. The influence exerted upon Jewish thought by these clear and well balanced commentaries can hardly be exaggerated. If I had to rewrite my volume I, the note on Rashi (p. 752) would be far more elaborate.

Criticism—Schulim Ochser: Jewish Encyclopaedia (vol. 11, 22–24, 1905).

JACOB BEN MEÏR

Jacob ben Meïr Tam, Rabbenu Tam. Born at Ramerupt in 1100; died at Troyes in 1171. Younger brother of Samuel ibn Meïr. Head of a Talmudic academy at Ramerupt. Founder of the French school of Tosafists and one of the greatest Talmudic scholars of his time. He was also one of the leading Hebrew grammarians.

The term tosafot (meaning additions) designates marginal glosses on the Talmud, which were generally written opposite Rashi's notes. The authors of these glosses were called Tosafists (ba'ale ha-tosafot); most of them were French.

Text—His main work, Sefer ha-yashar, containing some tosafot and responsa, was edited very badly in Vienna in 1810. Better edition by F. Rosenthal for the Meqiẓe Nirdamim (Berlin 1898).

His grammar, Sefer ha-hakra'ot, was edited by H. Filipowski, together with the Maḥberet of Menaḥem ben Saruq, second half of the tenth century (London 1854).

Criticism—Max Schloessinger: Jewish Encyclopaedia (vol. 7, 36–39, 1904).

V. EASTERN JEWISH

SALĀMA IBN RAḤMŪN

Salāma ibn Mubārak ibn Raḥmūn ibn Mūsā. Jewish physician and philosopher who lived in Egypt about the beginning of the twelfth century, for Abū-l-Ṣalt Umaiya al-Andalusī (first half of the twelfth century) met him there. He wrote various treatises in Arabic: Kitāb niẓām al-mawjūdāt (Arrangement of the universe); Maqāla fī-l-sabab al-mūjib li qillut al-maṭar bi Miṣr (Causes of the scarcity of rain in Egypt); another maqāla discussing why Egyptian women become stout when they grow old; a treatise on theology, Maqāla fī-l-'ilm al-ilahī.

Ibn abī Uṣaibi'a (vol. 2, 106). M. Steinschneider: Arabische Literatur der Juden (176–178, 1902).

HADASSI

Judah ben Elijah ḥa-Abel Hadassi. Born in Jerusalem (?), he lived in Constantinople about 1148. Qaraite encyclopaedist and theologian. He was the last Qaraite writer of note, with the exception of a much later one, Isaac ben Abraham Ṭroqi (1533–1594). His chief work is the Eshkol ha-kofer, or Sefer ha-peles (Cluster of cypress flowers), a treatise on the Decalogue, of encyclopaedic scope, written or begun in 1148. It is a summary of natural history, cosmology, physics, geography, religious history, controversy, exegesis, and grammar. It is written in rhymed acrostics. The earliest grammatical writing of Abraham ibn Ezra, called Moznayim, the scales (Rome 1140), is included in it without acknowledgment.

Criticism—M. Steinschneider: Bodleian Catalogue (1327, 1860). Max Seligsohn: Jewish Encyclopaedia (vol. 6, 132, 1904). For another Qaraite theologian and grammarian, somewhat earlier, see my note (Appendix) on 'Alī ibn Sulaimān (lived c. 1103).

VI. ROGER II OF SICILY

Born in 1093. Norman count of Sicily and duke of Calabria since 1101, king of Sicily (or of the "Two Sicilies"—Apulia and Calabria constituting the second one) from 1130 until his death at Palermo in 1154. The most enlightened monarch of his time. Patron of science and art. The main scientific glory of his reign was due to his patronage of al-Idrīsī, of whom I shall speak in the next chapter. Indeed al-Idrīsī had been helped by him since 1138 (or a few years before), but his two maps of the world were completed only in 1154 and 1192. Roger's kingdom was the seat of the most extraordinary mixture of civilizations: Latin, Byzantine, Jewish, and Muslim; to be complete one should say Greek and Byzantine, for there existed also in Sicily a pre-Byzantine Greek population. The Jewish colony was important; about 1170 Benjamin of Tudela counted nearly 1500 of his people in Palermo. Sicily was one of the main centers of diffusion of Greek and Muslim knowledge.

The cultural importance of Sicily will appear in subsequent pages, but it is worth while to mention at once the following interesting illustrations: (1) the earliest extant paper document from Europe is a deed of count Roger, written in Arabic and Latin, dated 1109; (2) the earliest coin the date of which is expressed by means of Hindu numerals, is one of Roger's, dated 1138, and bearing an Arabic inscription; (3) sericulture and the weaving of silk, which had been introduced from China into the Byzantine Empire under Justinian about 552 (vol. 1, 452), were imported from Greece into Sicily by Roger after his war against Manuel Comnenos in 1147. This increased considerably the wealth of Sicily.

Erich Caspar: Roger II und die Grundüng der normannisch-sicilischen Monarchie (Innsbruck 1904). Edmund Curtis: Roger of Sicily and the Normans in lower Italy (495 p., illustr., New York 1912). C. H. Haskins: The Normans in European history (Lowell lectures, 265 p. Cambridge, Mass., 1915); The Sicilian translators (Studies in mediaeval science, 155–193, Cambridge, Mass., 1924).

D. E. Smith and L. C. Karpinski: Hindu-Arabic numerals (139, 1911). T. F. Carter: Invention of printing in China (100, 1925; Isis, 8, 361).

VII. BYZANTINE

PRODROMOS

Theodoros Prodromos. Θεόδωρος ὁ Πρόδρομος, "Ptochoprodromos," "the poor Prodromos." Lived in Constantinople at the court of the Comnenoi in the first half of the twelfth century. A very prolific writer; the best representative of the Byzantine civilization of his day. Most of his writings are of no interest to us, but it is well to quote (1) an astrological poem (593 political verses); (2) a poetical calendar, Στίχοι εἰς τοὺς δώδεκα μῆνας, with dietetic and meteorological advice for each month; and (3) commentaries on Aristotle's categories. He wrote many poems in modern Greek, and is one of the few Byzantine authors who attained distinction by their use of the vulgar as well as the literary language.

Texts and translations—(1) E. Miller: Notices et extraits (vol. 23, 1–39, 1872). (2) Fr. Boissonade: Notices et extraits (vol. 11, 181 sq., 1827). J. L. Ideler: Physici et medici graeci minores (vol. 1, 418 sq., 1821). New critical edition by Bruno

Keil: Die Monatscyclen der byzantinischen Kunst in spätgriechischer Literatur (Wiener Studien, vol. 11, 94–142, 1889). (3) J. A. Cramer: Anecdota graeca (vol. 3, 204–215, Oxford 1836). P. Tannery: Sur le grand et le petit (Annuaire de l'association pour l'encouragement des études grecques en France, 104–119, 1887; also Mémoires, vol. 4, 207–222; Isis, 4, 342).

The most complete collection of Prodromos' writings is that of La Porte du Theil: Notices et extraits (vol. 6, 496–566, 1801; vol. 7, 235–260, 1804; vol. 8, 78–220, 1810. It contains analyses of and extracts from a good many writings. See also Migne: Patrologia graeca (vol. 133, 1003–1424).

E. Jeanselme and L. Oeconomos: La satire contre les Higoumènes. Poème attribué à Prodrome. Essai de traduction française (Byzantion, vol. 1, 317–339, 1924).

Criticism—There is no complete study of Prodromos' work, and one would be difficult because of the lack of critical texts; it would be even more difficult to investigate his writings from our particular point of view, yet such investigation is very desirable. C. Neumann: Griechische Geschichtschreiber und Geschichtsquellen im zwölften Jahrhundert (Leipzig, 37–77, 1888). K. Krumbacher: Geschichte der byzantinischen Litteratur (749–760, 804–806, and passim, 1897). E. Jeanselme et L. Oeconomos: Où il est établi que Prodrome fut atteint de la variole (1. Congrès de l'art de guérir, 3 p., Anvers 1920; Isis, 4, 582).

TZETZES

Two brothers of that name, whose activities are not easy to differentiate, lived in the first half of the twelfth century. The elder, Isaac, Ἰσαάκιος ὁ Τζέτζης, died in 1138 in Rhodes; the younger, Joannes, Ἰωάννης, was born in Constantinople in 1110. A didactic poem on astronomy bears Isaac's name but is more probably the work of his brother, *Ἰσαακίου στίχοι περὶ ἀνατολῆς καὶ δύσεως τῶν ἄστρων ἰαμβικοί*. Joannes is far better known, but his abundant writings are superficial and mediocre. The only ones deserving to be quoted here are his scholia to Oppianos' poem on fishing (Ἁλιευτικά)[8] and (probably) to Nicandros' Theriaca and Alexipharmaca (first half of the third century B. C.; vol. 1, 158); and his rhymed paraphrase of Porphyry's Isagoge. Commentaries on Aristotle's De partibus animalium and on Ptolemy's astronomy are also ascribed to him.

The writings here quoted are still unpublished; they need investigation, though we cannot expect to find in them much that is valuable. Gustav Hart: De Tzetzarum nomine, vitis, scriptis (Jahrbücher für classische Philologie, supp. vol. 12, 1–75, 1881). Christian Harder: De Ioannis Tzetzae historiarum fontibus (Diss., 90 p., Kiel 1886). K. Krumbacher: Byzantinische Litteratur (526–536, 1897).

A. B. Drachmann: Isaac Tzetzae De metris pindaricis commentarius (Danish academy, hist. comm., vol. 9, 3; 129 p., Copenhagen 1925); see edition of that text in Byzantion (vol. 3, 501, 1926).

VIII. LATIN

WILLIAM OF CHAMPEAUX

Guillaume de Champeaux. Guilelmus de Campellis, or Catalaunensis (after his bishopric). Born at Champeaux, Seine-et-Marne, in the second half of the eleventh century, lived at or near Paris. Bishop of Châlons-sur-Marne, Champagne,

[8] I ought to have spoken in vol. I of this Oppianos, who lived in the second half of the second century. This omission has been repaired in Isis (vol. 11, 413).

from 1113 until his death in 1121. French philosopher. Realist of a more scientific type than Anselm, he is often considered the real founder of Realism.

About 1108 he founded the abbey of Saint Victor in Paris. This was one of the three great schools out of which grew gradually the University of Paris; the two others were the school of the cathedral of Notre Dame, and that of the collegiate church of Sainte Geneviève. Abaelard was one of Champeaux's pupils at Saint Victor.

Eugène Michaud: Champeaux et les écoles de Paris au XIIe siècle d'après des documents inédits (2e ed., 550 p. Paris 1867). Georges Lefèvre: Les variations de G. de Champeaux et la question des universaux (84 p., Lille 1898). M. de Wulf: History of mediaeval philosophy (vol. 1, 149–150, 1926).

HUGH OF SAINT VICTOR

Hugo de S. Victore. Augustinian canon, theologian, humanist, and educator. Born probably near Ypres about 1096, he was taken at a very early age to Saxony; later he lived in Marseilles; finally, about 1118, he went to the abbey of St. Victor in Paris, of which he became the pedagogical director about 1125, and where he died in 1141. He wrote various mystical treatises, including a commentary on the Celestial Hierarchy of Dionysios the Areopagite (second half of the fifth century), which he knew through the Latin translation of John Scotus Erigena (second half of the ninth century). His most important work, from our point of view, is a sort of encyclopaedia of sacred and profane knowledge, entitled Didascalicon de studio legendi (or Eruditio didascalica), in six books. It includes a classification of knowledge, which is already the Aristotelian. Hugh strongly realized the need of scientific and coordinated knowledge. In this respect he may be considered a forerunner of the Christian encyclopaedists of the following century. With regard to the problem of universals, he adopted Abaelard's compromise. Moreover, he was a pluralist, and these views led him to conceive a complicated atomic theory.

His treatise on Noah's ark, De arca Noë, contains the curious theory that civilization flows from east to west, even as the sun and stars, and that when it reaches its westernmost limits—that is, the Atlantic Ocean—the Day of Doom will occur. This was a theological counterpart of the modern "westward course of empire." Verily, there is nothing new under the sun. The theological notion can be traced back to the fourth century.

A Practica geometriae, sometimes ascribed to Hugh, is probably somewhat later (see second half of the twelfth century).

The Summa sententiarum formerly ascribed to Hugh of Saint Victor was composed by another Hugh sometime between 1138 and 1158, very probably after the Sententiarum libri of Peter the Lombard (1152). The author may have been Hugh of Mortagne, prior of the Benedictine monastery of Saint Martin in Séez (13m. NNE Alençon, on the Orne), who died about 1180.

Text—Complete works edited by the Canons of St. Victor (3 vols. folio, Rouen 1648). Reprinted in Migne's Patrologia latina (vol. 175–177, 1854). Joseph Freundgen: Das Lehrbuch. Übersetzt, eingeleitet und erläutert (Sammlung der bedeutendsten pädagogischen Schriften, 23, Paderborn 1896).

Criticism—Barthélemy Hauréau: Hugues de Saint Victor (216 p., Paris 1859).

Alphonse Le Roy: Biographie nationale de Belgique (vol. 9, 675–680, 1887). A. Mignon: Les origines de la scolastique et Hugues de Saint Victor (2 vols., Paris 1895). Potthast (625, 1896). Heinrich Ostler: Die Psychologie des Hugo (Beitr. zur Gesch. der Philos. des Mittelalters, vol. 6, 1; 191 p., Münster 1906). P. Duhem: Système du monde (vol. 3, 38, 1915). Lynn Thorndike: History of magic (vol. 2, 8–16, 1923); treating chiefly of Hugh's classification, and his views on magic; Hugh considered magic unscientific. Marcel Chossat: La Somme des sentences, oeuvre de Hugues de Mortagne, vers 1155. Préface et introduction par J. de Ghellinck (Spicilegium sacrum lovaniense, 5; 212 p., Louvain 1923; Isis, 13, 423). J. K. Wright: Geographical lore (234, 1924). M. de Wulf: Mediaeval philosophy (vol. 1, 171–173, 201, 212, 1926).

ABAELARD

Pierre Abelard (Abailard). Petrus Abaelardi. Born in 1079, of a noble family in Pallet near Nantes; died at the abbey of St. Marcel near Chalon-sur-Saône, in 1142. French philosopher; one of the most original and romantic personalities in the Latin West. He studied under William of Champeaux, and perhaps also under Roscelin of Compiègne; he taught with considerable success in Paris and in other places, including his hermitage called Paraclete, near Nogent-sur-Marne. He defended a sort of compromise between Roscelin's nominalism and Champeaux's extreme realism; this middle doctrine, called conceptualism, was a sort of mitigated and disguised nominalism (universals exist, but only as concepts in the minds of men, and previous to that, in the mind of God). Partly because of Abaelard's eloquence and dialectical power, partly because of its intermediate nature, this doctrine became very popular; it remained for three centuries (the twelfth to the fourteenth) the favorite solution of the problem of universals. Though Abaelard's views were less objectionable to the Church than pure nominalism,[9] they were repeatedly condemned: at Soissons in 1121; at Sens in 1141; finally in Rome in 1142. Abaelard's philosophy is best expressed in his Glossulae super Porphyrium. His dialectical attitude is illustrated by the Sic et non, a collection of scriptural and patristic extracts showing the pro and con of a number of theological and casuistic questions. Abaelard exposed these contradictions without trying to solve them. He was essentially a dialectician and may be considered one of the founders of the scholastic method; his teaching prepared for the reception of Aristotle and the Aristotelian supremacy. His own work was done before the arrival of Arabic philosophy— either in Latin or in Hebrew; it is interesting to note that he deplored the fact that the latter language was generally unknown.

It is impossible not mention his love affair with the learned Heloïse, and the terrible punishment (castration) meted out to him by her uncle, canon Fulbert. After this, Abaelard became a monk (1119) and Heloïse a nun. They remained faithful to one another unto death. The collection of their love letters is one of the most popular classics of mediaeval literature. Heloïse, born in Paris in 1101, died at the Paraclete in 1164; she was buried there at the side of her lover. They are now supposed to be buried in the Père Lachaise, Paris, where their tomb is shown to visitors, but this is far from certain. Abaelard wrote (before 1136) a history of his misfortunes, Historia calamitatum (Libellus de calamitatibus suis; Epistola ad amicum), which betrays his inordinate conceit, restlessness and aggressiveness, but also his genuine love of learning and his intellectual ardor.

[9] Roscelin had been condemned in 1092, for tritheism. Indeed nominalism, strictly applied to theology, dissolved the Trinity into three persons.

Text—Victor Cousin: Oeuvres inédites (880 p., Paris 1836). Petri Abaelardi Opera hactenus seorsim edita nunc primum in unum collegit textum recensuit nota argumenta indices adjecit Victor Cousin, adjuvantibus C. Jourdain et E. Despois (2 vols., Paris 1849–1859). Sic et non, ediderunt E. L. T. Henke et G. S. Lindenkohl (Marburg 1851). Philosophische Schriften zum ersten Male hrg. von Bernhard Geyer, I. Die Logica ingredientibus: 1. Die Glossen zu Porphyrius, 2. Die Glossen zu den Kategorien, 3. Die Glossen zu Peri ermeneias (Beitr. zur Gesch. der Philos. des Mittelalters, Münster 1919, 1921, 1927).

General Criticism—Charles de Rémusat: Abélard (2 vols., Paris 1845). S. M. Deutsch: Abälard. Ein kritischer Theologe (492 p. Leipzig 1883). Luigi Tosti: Storia di Abelardo e de' suoi tempi (Opera completa, vol. 7, Roma 1887). Gabriel Compayré: Abélard and the origin and early history of universities (328 p., New York 1893). Adolf Hausrath: Abälard (320 p., Leipzig 1893). Potthast (910, 1896). Joseph McCabe: Abelard (410 p., London 1901). George Moore: Héloïse and Abélard (2 vols., privately printed, London 1921); a literary interpretation. Pierre Lasserre: Un conflit religieux au XIIe siècle. Abélard contre Saint Bernard (Paris 1930).

Special Criticism—Charles Cuissard: Documents inédits sur Abélard (47 p., Orléans 1880). François Picavet: Abélard et Alexandre de Halès, créateurs de la méthode scolastique (Bibliothèque de l'école des hautes études, sci. relig., vol. 7, 1896). Reiner Danmer: Darstellung der Abälardischen Ethik (Diss., 62 p. Münster 1906). Joseph Schiller: Abälards Ethik im Vergleich zur Ethik seiner Zeit (Diss., 51 p., München 1906). Martin Grabmann: Die Geschichte der scholastischen Methode (1909–1911). Friedrich Schreiter: Abälards Anschauungen über das Verhältnis vom Glauben zum Wissen (56 p., Diss., Leipzig 1912). B. Schmeidler: Der Briefwechsel zwischen Abälard und Heloïse eine Fälschung? (Archiv für Kulturgeschichte, vol. 11, 1–30, 1913). P. Duhem: Système du monde (vol. 3, 39–45, 1915; apropos of the Expositio in hexaëmeron; it is clear that Abaelard's scientific curiosity was exceedingly small). Lynn Thorndike: History of magic (vol. 2, 1–8, 1923).

BERNARD OF CHARTRES

The school of Chartres, founded by Fulbert,[10] became in the first half of the twelfth century an important center of literary and philosophical studies. The first great master was Bernard of Chartres, a Breton, who began his teaching before 1117, was chancellor of the cathedral from 1119, and died about 1126. He was primarily a grammarian. His works are lost, yet such was his influence that he will ever be famous. A fervent pupil of his, John of Salisbury, said of him that he was "the most abounding spring of letters in Gaul in modern times," and also "the most perfect Platonist of his age." The latter statement may seem ridiculous, considering that his knowledge of Plato was of necessity very limited and not any greater than that of his contemporaries, yet it is true in a deeper sense: what little we know of his life has a genuine Platonic ring, and because of his gentleness he reminds us of Plato more than any other mediaeval philosopher.

The views of the school of Chartres were a combination of the extreme realism defended by Anselm (vol. 1, 748), with Platonism; they tried to reconcile Plato and Aristotle, but this attempt was based on a double misunderstanding, for their knowledge of the former was essentially restricted to the Timaeus, and that of the latter to his logic. Imperfect as it is, this philosophy of the school of Chartres is

[10] Fulbert (c. 965–1028), disciple of Gerbert. Bishop of Chartres from 1008 until his death. See Loren C. Mackinney: Fulbert of Chartres, teacher, administrator, humanist (Isis 14, 285–300, 1930).

the most impressive episode in the history of Platonism between the Byzantine renaissance of the second half of the eleventh century and the Florentine revival of the second half of the fifteenth. Unfortunately the school of Chartres attached far more importance to the trivium than to the quadrivium; thus its influence upon scientific thought was relatively small.

One of Bernard's sayings must be quoted: "In comparison with the ancients we stand like dwarfs on the shoulders of giants." (From John of Salisbury, Metalogicon, bk. 3, ch. 4: Dicebat Bernardus Carnotensis nos esse quasi nanos gigantium humeris insidentes, ut possimus plura eis et remotiora videre, non utique proprii visus acumine aut eminentia corporis, sed quia in altum subvehimur et extollimur magnitudine gigantea).[11] A similar saying is ascribed to Newton. It implies some vague understanding of the cumulative nature of science.[12] Bernard of Chartres has been frequently mistaken for Bernard Silvester of Tours.

Criticism—Clemens Bäumker: Der Platonismus im Mittelalter (50 p., München 1916). Sandys: History of classical scholarship (vol. 1^3, 531, 1921). E. Gilson: Le platonisme de Bernard de Chartres (Revue néo-scolastique, 1–19, 1923). C. H. Haskins: Studies in mediaeval science (88–92, 1924). M. de Wulf: History of mediaeval philosophy (vol. 1, 151–153, 1926).

THEODORIC OF CHARTRES

Thierry of Chartres, younger brother of Bernard. French philosopher and educator who lived mainly at Chartres, where he died about 1155. He was one of the most learned men of his time, and as typical a representative as his brother of the humanistic and neo-Platonic tendencies of the school of Chartres. By the time of his death the golden age of that school was already passed. His most important writings are the Heptateuchon, a textbook on the seven arts—that is, the trivium and quadrivium combined, and an hexaëmeron, De sex dierum operibus. The cosmological ideas of the latter mark the earliest appearance in an original Latin work of the Aristotelian physics—De coelo et mundo—which had just been translated by Gundisalvo. But the point of view of this commentary on Genesis is distinctly neo-Platonic and rationalist: God created matter at the beginning, and the work of the six days was, so to say, but an automatic series of consequences of the initial creation.[13] The first Latin translation of Ptolemy's Planisphere from the Arabic was dedicated to Theodoric by Hermann the Dalmatian (1143).

Text—De opere sex dierum, edited as far as extant by Barthélemy Hauréau: Notices et extraits (vol. 32, part 2, 167–186, 1888). Extracts from the Heptateuchon are quoted by Clerval.

Criticism—Alex. Clerval: L'enseignement des arts libéraux à Chartres et à Paris dans la première moitié du XIIe siècle d'après l'Heptateuchon (Congrès scientifique international des Catholiques, Paris 1888; vol. 2, 227–296, 1889); Les écoles de Chartres au moyen âge (Paris 1895). P. Duhem: Thierry de Chartres et Nicolas de Cues (Revue des sciences philosophiques et théologiques, 3e année 525 sq., 1909); showing that large extracts of Theodoric's De opere sex dierum have been

[11] Clemens C. J. Webb's edition (136, Oxford 1929).

[12] See my note on Seneca (vol. I, 247; second half of first century).

[13] Said Duhem (op. cit., 187): "Ni Descartes ni Laplace ne dépasseront l'audacieux rationalisme de Thierry." It is well to take this cum grano salis.

included almost verbatim by Nicolas of Cues in his Docta ignorantia. P. Duhem: Système du monde (vol. 3, 184–193, 1915); on the earliest traces of Peripatetic physics in Latin scholastics. M. de Wulf: History of mediaeval philosophy (vol. 1, 153–154, 1926).

GILBERT DE LA PORRÉE

Gilbertus Porretanus. Born in Poitiers about 1076, studied in Laon and in Chartres, taught in Chartres for more than twelve years, then in Paris; bishop of Poitiers, 1142; died in 1154. French philosopher. Like Abaelard, he tried to compromise between extreme realism and nominalism. His Liber sex principiorum is an endeavor to complete Aristotle's Categories. Aristotle had distinguished ten categories, but had studied in detail only the first four (substance, quantity, quality, relation); Gilbert studied the six others. His work became an inseparable part of the Organon, even as the εἰσαγωγή of Porphyry. He discussed the pseudo-Aristotelian Liber de causis (vol. 1, 404).

Text—See the editions of Aristotle's Categories; for example, Aristotelis Opera nonnulla latine fecit Joannes Argyropulus (Augsburg 1479). Migne's Patrologia latina (vol. 184).

Criticism—P. Duhem: Système du Monde (vol. 3, 194–197, 1915). M. de Wulf: History of mediaeval philosophy (vol. 1, 166–168, 202, 1926).

WILLIAM OF CONCHES

Guilelmus de Conchis. Anglice, William Shelley.[14] French realist philosopher, and man of science. Born at Conches near Evreux, Normandy, about 1080, he was educated at Chartres under Bernard of Chartres, and taught in Paris (?) and Chartres for about twenty years, John of Salisbury being one of his pupils. He then entered the service of Geoffrey the Fair, count of Anjou, and was possibly tutor to Geoffrey's son, the future Henry II. He died c. 1154.

William was one of the most accomplished scholars of his time, and his originality was sufficient to cause his orthodoxy to be questioned. He wrote a commentary on the Timaeus, and one on Boetius' Consolation which was very popular for two centuries and was finally plagiarized by Nicholas Trivet of Norwich (c. 1258–1328). His most important work is a treatise, De philosophia mundi (περὶ διδάξεων sive libri IV de elementis philosophiae) written in his younger years. (It has been wrongly ascribed to Bede, William of Hirsau, and Honorius of Autun).[15] Later in life, about 1144–1150, he published a revised edition of it, entitled Dragmaticon. He got together for Geoffrey's son, before 1150, a collection of moral precepts, extracted from classical authors, chiefly Cicero and Seneca; it is entitled De honesto et utili, also Summa moralium philosophorum. It does not compare with the more scientific ethical treatises of the following century, being simply an unsystematic compilation.

William had learned at Chartres not only Platonism and realism, but also physiology and other sciences, and he was clearly influenced by Abaelard. He had studied Arabic knowledge chiefly in the translations of Constantine the African, and was one of the first Latin philosophers to re-systematize the views of Lucretius, Ḥunain ibn Isḥāq, etc., which had been thus transmitted to him. He attempted

[14] He actually appears under the name of Shelley in various old bibliographies and catalogues.

[15] See my note on Bartholomew of Parma (second half of thirteenth century).

to solve cosmological problems in a purely rational manner. He developed the atomic theory, combining it with the theory of four elements, and with neo-Platonic ideas—for example, with the notion of a world-soul coexisting in every man with his own soul. He continued the Heraclidean tradition, but weakly and badly, and introduced novelties which were partly due to his misunderstanding of Macrobius. He conceived the three orbits of the Sun, Venus, and Mercury, to have nearly the same radius, their centers being at short distances from each other and in a line with the Earth. He remarked that the density and temperature of the air decrease as the altitude increases, and he tried to explain the general circulation of the air and to connect it with the oceanic circulation.

Finally, he distinguished between astronomy, dealing with realities, with laws (quae sunt, sive videantur, sive non) and astrology, dealing with appearances (quae videntur, sive ita sint, sive non). To be sure, this distinction did not work out as nicely as it reads, for William was more of an astrologer than he realized, but this could not be otherwise in his day. Stellar control over nature was then generally considered an established fact. William shared that delusion, yet he cannot be honored too much for having honestly tried to separate astrological fancies from astronomical knowledge.

Text—The first version of William's Philosophia was printed three times, and each time ascribed to another author.

William of Hirsau (second half of the eleventh century): Philosophicarum et astronomicarum institutionum libri tres (Basel 1531).

Bede (first half of the eighth century): Opera (vol. 2, 311–343, 1563). Also in Migne Patrology (vol. 90).

Honorius of Autun (first half of the twelfth century): De philosophia mundi, in Migne's Patrology (vol. 172).

The second version, or Dragmaticon, was published under the title Dialogus de substantiis physicis confectus a Guilelmo aneponymo philosopho (Strassburg 1567).

Meteorological extracts from both versions are included in Gustav Hellmann: Denkmäler mittelalterlicher Meteorologie (Berlin 1904).

A part of the glosses on Timaeus have been printed as the work of Honorius of Autun, by Victor Cousin: Oeuvres inédites d'Abélard (p. 648 sq.).

The De honesto et utili is included in Migne's Patrology (vol. 171, 1007–1056) as the work of Hildebert of Lavardin, bishop of Le Mans, archbishop of Tours, who died in 1134.

Criticism—Histoire littéraire de la France (vol. 12, 455–466, 1763; reprinted 1830). B. Hauréau: Nouvelle biographie générale (vol. 22, 667–673, 1858). Charles Jourdain: Des commentaires inédits de Guillaume de Conches et de Nicolas Triveth sur la Consolation de la philosophie (Paris 1861). Abbé Alexandre Clerval: Les écoles de Chartres du V au XVIe siècle (Paris 1895). Miss Bateson: Dictionary of national biography (vol. 61, 355, 1900). P. Duhem: Système du Monde (vol. 3, 87–125, 1915). Reginald Lane Poole: Illustrations of the history of mediaeval thought (1884; second ed., London 1920). Lynn Thorndike: History of magic (vol. 2, 50–65, 1923; with a list of MSS.). J. K. Wright: Geographical lore (166 and by index, 1924). M. de Wulf: History of mediaeval philosophy (vol. 1, 154–156, 1926).

BERNARD SILVESTER

Also Silvestris, Sylvester. French philosophical poet who lived at Tours about 1145–1153. His chief work is the De mundi universitate (or Cosmographia), dating from about 1145–1153, and dedicated to Theodoric of Chartres. It is written in mixed prose and verse and divided into two parts, Megacosmus and Microcosmus. It is based mainly on the Timaeus and on neo-Platonic writings, and is distinctly pantheistic. He composed an adaptation in prose and verse of an Arabic treatise on geomancy, called Experimentarius, possibly on the basis of a translation by Hermann the Dalmatian. He wrote in verse an astrological romance entitled Mathematicus. He emphasized the influence of the soil upon plant and animal life.

Text—The De mundi universitate was edited by C. S. Barach and Johann Wrobel (93 p., Innsbruck 1876). The astrological treatise is still unpublished.

Criticism—Sandys: History of classical scholarship (vol. 1, 534–536, 1921). Lynn Thorndike: History of magic (vol. 2, 99–123, 1923); with a list of MSS. of the Experimentarius. C. H. Haskins: Studies in mediaeval science (135–137, 1924). J. K. Wright: Geographical lore (231, 1924). M. de Wulf: History of mediaeval philosophy (vol. 1, 191, 1926). Etienne Gilson: La cosmogonie de Bernardus Silvestris (Arch. d'hist. doctrinale et littéraire du Moyen âge, vol. 3, 5–24, 1928; Isis, 13, 421).

PETER THE LOMBARD

See Chapter XVIII, Philosophy.

PEDRO ALFONSO

Petrus Alphonsus (or Alphonsi). A Spanish Jew, originally named Moses Sephardi, born in 1062 at Huesca, Aragon. He became physician to Alfonso VI, king of Castile, and being baptised at Huesca in 1106, he assumed his new name in honor of his patron. He visited England, and was for a time physician to Henry I. He died in 1110. Spanish physician, astronomer, geographer, and theologian. His astronomical treatise on the Dragon (originally written in Hebrew or Arabic ?) was translated in 1120 into Latin by Walcher, prior of Malvern. Petrus compiled (or translated) chronological and astronomical tables, and wrote a letter to the Peripatetics treating of astronomy. He was interested in experimental science and had a critical mind. A sketch map of his (Bibliothèque Nationale, Paris, Suppl. lat. 1218) illustrates the idea of Arim[16] (Aren, Arym), center or navel of the world, and of the seven habitable climates; it is obviously of Muslim origin (south at the top).[17]

However, Petrus' fame rests chiefly upon two other works which are non-scientific. First, a treatise to vindicate Christianity against Judaism, entitled Dialogi cum Judaeo (Dialogi in quibus impiae Judaeorum opiniones confutantur), in the form of a dialogue between Moses and Pedro, his old and new selves. Second, and chiefly, a collection of thirty-three tales, entitled Disciplina clericalis. This collection was exceedingly popular; witness the number of translations in many vernaculars and also in Hebrew. It is very important for the history of folklore, constituting one of the bridges between eastern and western lore; for example, it was one of the sources of Reynard the Fox, and many of the stories told by Chaucer and Shakespeare were derived from it.

[16] The Arabic word arim means a heavy stone (to show the way in the desert), or the summit of the head (or of a mountain); thus a central point.

[17] K. Miller: Mappae arabicae (1926 sq.; Isis, 9, 458).

Text—Dialogi cum Judaeo. First edition, Cologne 1536. Migne's Patrology (vol. 157).

Disciplina clericalis. The first edition was prepared by Méon and published by the abbé J. Labouderie, together with an old version in French verse, Le chastoiement d'un père à son fils (Société des bibliophiles français, Mélanges, vol. 3, 208 p., Paris 1824). This was reprinted by Migne in his Latin patrology (vol. 157, 671-706). The second edition was published independently by Fr. Wilh. Val. Schmidt: Petri Alfonsi Disciplina clericalis. Zum ersten Mal hrg. mit Einleitungen und Anmerkungen (172 p., Berlin 1827).

Michael Roesle: Le castoiement d'un père à son fils (new edition, 60 p., Munich 1899). Jean Ducamin: Disciplines de clergie, traduites en gascon girondin du XIVe et XVe siècles (332 p., Toulouse 1908). J. Stalzer: Stücke der Disciplina in lateinischen Versen der Berliner Handschrift Diez B 28 (Progr., 36 p., Graz 1912). W. H. Hulme: English translation from the fifteenth century Worcester cathedral MS. (71 p., Cleveland, Ohio, 1919).

Alfons Hilka and Werner Söderhjelm: Disciplina; 1. Lateinischer Text; 2. Französicher Prosatext; 3. Französische Versebearbeitungen (3 vols., Acta Societatis scientiarum fennicae; vol. 38, 4, 120 p., 1911; vol. 38, 5, 74 p., 1912; vol. 49, 4, 190 p.; 1922); also small edition of the Disciplina in the Sammlung mittellateinischer Texte (no. 1, 65 p., Heidelberg 1911).

Chapters two and three of the Disciplina, treating of friendship, were anonymously translated into Hebrew, and printed in Constantinople in 1516, and again in Venice in 1544 and 1605. This Hebrew text was edited and translated into French by Aug. Pichard: Le livre d'Hénoch sur l'amitié (Paris 1838).

Criticism—Joseph Jacobs: Jewish ideals (141-143, 1896). C. R. Beazley: Dawn of modern geography (vol. 1, 575, 626, map opposite p. 576, 1897). George Alexandre Kohut: Jewish Encyclopaedia (vol. 1, 377, 1901). Victor Chauvin: Bibliographie des ouvrages arabes (vol. 9, 1-14, Liège 1905). C. H. Haskins: The reception of Arabic science in England (English historical review, Jan. 1915, revised edition in his Studies in mediaeval science, 113-119, 1924). Lynn Thorndike: History of magic (vol. 2, 68-73, 1923).

M. Steinschneider: Hebräische Übersetzungen (933, 985, 1893); Europäische Übersetzungen (59, 1904). Suggesting possible identification with Petrus Anfulsus who translated from Arabic into Latin, or compiled Canones tabularum, a treatise on the chronology of many nations.

For Adelard of Bath, Domingo Gundisalvo, and Hermann the Dalmatian, see Chapter III, Translators.

HONORIUS OF AUTUN

Honorius Augustodunensis. Autun is a town in the department of Saône-et-Loire, Burgundy. Cryptic name of a German writer who lived in the first half of the twelfth century, and died not long after 1150. It is probable that he lived, not in Autun, but in South Germany, in the Danube region, probably in Ratisbon. Would his name mean that he was born or educated in Autun? He wrote many treatises, mainly on theology. The most important is the Elucidarium, formerly ascribed to St. Anselm (second half of the eleventh century), a treatise on dogmatic theology for the use of the clergy and of educated laymen; it enjoyed considerable popularity, as is witnessed by its translations into many vernaculars: French (Lucidaire), Provençal (Lucidari), Italian (Lucidario), Welsh, English, Icelandic, Swedish, Dutch, High and Low German. This Elucidarium should not be confused with the popular German encyclopaedia called Lucidarius (second half of the twelfth century). This treatise is not of special interest to us. My main reason for speaking of Honorius is the ascription to him of another work, far more important, Imago mundi de dispositione orbis (the Image of the world), a cosmographical summary. However, this ascription seems to be wrong. It is more probable that the Imago mundi was written by another Honorius, as mysterious as this one—Honorius Inclusus or Solitarius, an English (?) Benedictine (second half of the eleventh century).

Text—For the Imago mundi, see vol. I, 749, 1927.

The Elucidarium, sive dialogus de summa totius christianiae theologiae, is included in Migne's Latin patrology (vol. 172, 1109–1176, 1854).

Criticism—Barthélemy Hauréau: Notices et extraits (6 vols., passim, 1890–1893). Potthast (620, 1896). Joseph Anton Endres: Honorius. Beitrag zur Geschichte des geistigen Lebens im 12. Jahrh. (170 p., Kempten, 1906; important). Franz Baeumker: Das Inevitabile des Honorius und dessen Lehre über das Zusammenwirken von Wille und Gnade (Beitr. zur Gesch. der Philos. des Mittelalters, vol. 13, 6, 96 p., Münster 1914). M. de Wulf: History of mediaeval philosophy (vol. 1, 198, 1926). Ch. V. Langlois: La vie spirituelle (La vie en France au Moyen âge, vol. 4, 66–122, 1928). Analysis of and extracts from a French paraphrase of the Elucidarium, La lumière as lais, made by Peter of Abernon or Peter Peckham c. 1267 (Abernon and Peckham are in Camberwell, London SE.)

For Otto of Freising, see Chapter XI, Historiography. For Hildegard, see Book II.

IX. VERNACULAR

PHILIP OF THAON

Probably named after the place Thaon (Thaun, Than), near Caen. He lived about 1119–1125, and visited England. He is the earliest Anglo-Norman writer about whom we have definite information, and his poems are the oldest extant monuments of the "langue d'oïl." He wrote in langue d'oïl a compotus, a bestiary, and one or two lapidaries. Li cumpoz, in six-syllabled verse, was probably written between 1113 and 1119. Li bestiaire, being dedicated to Adelaide of Louvain, queen of Henry I, must have been written between 1121 and 1135—perhaps in 1125; it is written in six- and eight-syllabled verse. This is the earliest French version of the Physiologos (vol. 1, 300). The two lapidaries ascribed to him are the so-called "Alphabetical Lapidary" and the "Apocalyptic Lapidary." The ascription of the latter is reasonably certain, that of the former less so. The "Alphabetical Lapidary," the earliest in date, is the most comprehensive of the Anglo-Norman lapidaries. It is based upon the Alexandrian "Damigeron,"[18] Isidore, and an unknown source, quite independently of Marbode's Liber lapidum (second half of the eleventh century, vol. I, 764); but like Marbode, it represents exclusively the scientific and magical traditions, not the Christian. It deals with some 78 stones (1710 verses) in alphabetical order: adamas (lodestone), achates (agate), alectorias (?), etc. The "Apocalyptic Lapidary," written before 1130, treats only of fifteen stones (297 verses).

Text—Both Compotus and Physiologus were edited by Thomas Wright: Popular treatises on science during the Middle Ages (20–131, 1841).

[18] For this lapidary, originally written in Greek, see M. Wellmann in Pauly-Wissowa (vol. 8, 2055, 1901).

E. Mall: Li cumpoz (Strassburg 1873). Fragment of the compotus edited by P. Meyer (Romania, vol. 40, 70–76, 1911).

M. F. Mann: Der Physiologus des P. von Thaun und seine Quellen (Anglia, vol. 7, 420–468, 1884; vol. 9, 391–434, 447–450, 1886). Critical edition with notes and glossary by Emmanuel Walberg (288 p., Lund 1900).

Paul Studer and Joan Evans: Anglo-Norman lapidaries (200–276, Paris 1924; Isis, 9, 123–124).

Criticism—C. L. Kingsford: Dictionary of national biography (vol. 45, 153, 1896). Ch. V. Langlois: La connaissance de la nature et du monde au moyen âge (1–48, Paris, 1911; new edition, 1–43, 1927). C. H. Haskins: Nimrod the astronomer (Romanic review, vol. 5, 203–212, 1914; revised in Studies in mediaeval science, 336–345, 1924).

THE EDDA

When one speaks of the Edda without qualification, one generally means the Younger or Prose Edda, which was edited by Snorri Sturluson (first half of the thirteenth century) about 1222, and is often called after him, Edda Snorra Sturlusonar. This collection of Icelandic writings was probably made almost a century earlier, about 1140–1160. It contains five parts: (1) Formáli (Preface), a Christian history of the world from the time of Adam; (2) Gylfaginning, a summary of Scandinavian mythology, our main source on the subject; (3) Bragaraeður, or sayings of Bragi, a complement to part two; (4) Skládskaparmal, or Skálda, by far the largest part, treats of Icelandic prosody and contains many poems; (5) Háttatal, meaning Number of meters, treats also of prosody.

Another Edda, the Elder or Poetic Edda, was discovered about 1643 by bishop Brynjulf Sveinsson, who published it under the name of Edda Saemundi multiscii; that is, he ascribed its composition to the bishop Saemund Sigfusson, a Norwegian who lived in Iceland (about 1055 to about 1132). There is no doubt that this collection of poems was put together in Iceland, but the ascription to Saemund is now rejected, though he may be the author of individual poems. It is possible that the composition dates only from the middle of the thirteenth century (c. 1240); but at any rate the poems included are much older, some of them dating back to the eleventh century or even to the tenth; hence the name Elder Edda. These poems contain valuable information on Scandinavian mythology and ancient heroic tales, e.g., the Nibelungen (second half of the twelfth century).

Text—For the Prose Edda, see my note on Snorri Sturluson (first half of the thirteenth century).

The original MS. of the Poetic Edda, discovered by Brynjulf, is in the Royal Library, Copenhagen. Edition by Theodor Möbius (320 p., Leipzig 1860). Better edition by Sophus Bugge: Norroen Fornkvaeði (530 p., Christiania 1867).

Translation of the Poetic Edda in English verse by Amos Simon Cottle (Bristol 1797). Better translation by Benjamin Thorpe (London 1866). Edition of the Icelandic text with translation by Olive Bray (Part 1, Viking Club, London 1908). F. Wagner: Les poèmes héroïques de l'Edda, etc., traduction française précédée d'une étude (276 p., Paris 1929).

Bibliography—Halldór Hermannsson: Bibliography of the Eddas (Islandica, vol. 13, Ithaca, N. Y., 1920).

Criticism—Jonas Ramus: Tractatus historico-geographicus, quo Ulyssem et Outinum unum eundemque esse ostenditur, et ex collatis inter se Odyssea Homeri et Edda island. homerizante, Outini fraudes deteguntur, etc., (new ed., Copenhagen 1716); quoted for the sake of curiosity. Johan Gustav Hjalmar Kinberg: Eddas naturhistoria (128 p., Stockholm 1880). Elard Hugo Meyer: Die eddische Kosmogonie (118 p., Freiburg i. B., 1891). Sophus Bugge (1833–1907): Studien über die Entstehung der nordischen Götter- und Heldensagen (590 p., München 1881–1889); The home of the Eddic poems (482 p., London 1899). Potthast (390–392, 1896). Gustav Neckel: Beiträge zur Eddaforschung (520 p., Dortmund 1908). Bertha Surtees Phillpotts: The Elder Edda and ancient Scandinavian drama (Cambridge 1920).

CHAPTER V

MATHEMATICS AND ASTRONOMY

(First Half of Twelfth Century)

I. EASTERN MUSLIM

For 'Umar al-Khayyāmī and for Muḥammad ibn 'Abd al-Bāqī, see volume I, 759–762. For al-Khāzinī, see Chapter VI, Physics.

MUẒAFFAR AL-ASFUZĀRĪ

Abū Ḥātim al-Muẓaffar ibn Ismā'īl al-Asfuzārī (Isfazārī). Asfuzār is a place in Khurāsān, south of Herat, not far from Sijistān. Muslim mathematician and physicist, collaborator of 'Umar al-Khayyāmī. He died before 1122. He wrote a summary of Euclid's Elements, Ikhtiṣār li-uṣūl Uqlīdis, extending to Book XIV composed by Hypsicles (first half of the second century B.C.). According to al-Khāzinī, he made investigations on specific gravity.

Text—Partial French translation of the summary of Book XIV by L. A. Sédillot: Notices et extraits (vol. 13, 146–148, 1838).
Criticism—H. Suter: Mathematiker und Astronomen der Araber (114, 225, 1900).

AL-BADĪ' AL-AṢṬURLĀBĪ

Abū-l-Qāsim Hibatallāh ibn al-Ḥusain ibn Aḥmad (or Yūsuf), Badī' al-zamān, al-Aṣṭurlābī al-Baghdādī al-Iṣfahānī, generally called al-Badī' al-Aṣṭurlābī. Muslim astronomer, the greatest expert of his time in the knowledge and construction of astrolabes. He lived in Ispahan, about 1116; later in Baghdād, where he died in 1139–1140. In 1129–1130 astronomical observations were made under his direction in the palace of the Saljūq sulṭān of 'Irāq, Mughīth al-dīn Maḥmūd (1117–1131). He compiled astronomical tables which were dedicated to that prince and called after him, the Maḥmūdic tables. The praise extravagantly lavished upon him by Muslim biographers—for example, by Ibn al-Qifṭī, proves their lack of appreciation of true mathematical merit.

H. Suter: Die Mathematiker und Astronomen der Araber (117, 1900); Encyclopaedia of Islām (vol. 1, 556, 1911).

MUḤAMMAD IBN AḤMAD AL-KHARAQĪ

Abū Bakr Muḥammad ibn Aḥmad ibn Abū Bishr, Bahā al-dīn (in some manuscripts he is called Abū Muḥammad 'Abd al-Jabbār ibn Muḥammad). The name al-Kharaqī refers probably to the place Kharaq (or Kharak) near great Marv, Khurāsān, for he is also called al-Marwazī. He died in Marv in 1138–1139. Persian mathematician, astronomer, and geographer, writing in Arabic.

He wrote: (1) Muntahā al-idrāk fī taqsīm al-aflāk, the highest understanding on the division of spheres, a development of Ibn al-Haitham's astronomy; (2)

Kitāb al-tabṣira fī 'ilm al-hai'a, a shorter astronomical treatise; (3) Al-risāla al-shāmila, the comprehensive treatise, concerning arithmetic; (4) Al-risāla al-maghribīya (the Maugrabin treatise). The last two are lost.

His most important work is the Muntahā. It is divided into three discourses (maqāla) treating of (1) the arrangement of spheres (tarkīb al-aflāk), their movements, etc.; (2) the shape of the earth, and its subdivision into a part which is inhabited and another which is not, the differences in the ascendents (ṭāli') and ascensions (maṭāli') due to geographical positions; (3) chronology or eras (ta'rīkh, pl. tawārīkh), conjunctions (qirān, pl. qirānāt), chiefly of Saturn and Jupiter, periods of revolution (daur, pl. adwār)—for example, daur al-qirān or 'aud al-qirān (return of the conjunction). The Tabṣira is shorter and covers essentially the same ground; however, it does not contain the elaborate description of the five seas which forms the second chapter of the second part of the Muntahā.

He developed the theory according to which the planets are not supported by imaginary circles, but by massive revolving spheres. That strange theory had been expounded before by Abū Ja'far al-Khāzin (second half of the tenth century), and by Ibn al-Haitham (first half of the eleventh century), to obviate the postulation of a movement through the ether and the difficulties connected with it—a pressure ahead of each planet, and a depression or vacuum behind. It found its way into western Europe through Hebrew and Latin translations of Ibn al-Haitham's treatise, Fī hai'at al-'ālam.

Text—The part of the Muntahā describing the five seas was edited and translated into Latin by C. A. Nallino: Albatenii opus astronomicum (vol. 1, 169–175, Milan 1903).

The introductions to the Muntahā and the Tabṣira are translated in Wiedemann's paper, 1928.

Criticism—A biography of al-Kharaqī is included in the Tarīkh ḥukamā' al-Islām by 'Alī al-Bayhaqī (second half of the twelfth century). E. Wiedemann: Beiträge zur Geschichte der Naturwissenschaften, 20 (Sitzungsber. der phys. med. Sozietät zur Erlangen, vol. 42, 72, 1910).

C. Brockelmann: Arabische Litteratur (vol. 1, 473, 1898). H. Suter: Die Mathematiker und Astronomen der Araber (116, 1900; 173, 1902). C. A. Nallino: Albatenius (vol. 1, xxxii, 17–19, 240, 1903; vol. 2, xxiii, 1907). Karl Kohl: Über den Aufbau der Welt nach Ibn al-Haitham (Sitzungsber. der phys. med. Soz. zur Erlangen, vol. 54, 140–179, 1923). E. Wiedemann: Zur Geschichte des Kompasses und zu dem Inhalt eines Gefässes in verschiedenen Abständen vom Erdmittelpunkt (Zeitschrift für Physik, 24, 166–168, 1924; apropos of a passage of the Muntahā al-idrāk concerning the subject indicated in the second half of the title); Encyclopaedia of Islām (vol. 2, 903, 1926); Einleitung zu Werken von al-Charaqī (Beiträge 70; Sitzungsber. der phys.-med. Soz. zur Erlangen, vol. 58, 203–218, 1928; Isis, 14, 476).

'ADNĀN AL 'AINZARBĪ

See Chapter X, Medicine.

II. WESTERN MUSLIM

For Abū-l-Ṣalt, see Chapter X, Medicine. For Ibn Bājja, see Chapter IV, Philosophic Background.

JĀBIR IBN AFLAḤ

Abū Muḥammad Jābir ibn Aflaḥ. The astronomer Geber of Latin writers, not to be confused with the chemist Geber, Jābir ibn Ḥaiyān (second half of the eighth century). Hispano-Muslim astronomer and mathematician. Born or lived in Seville; died probably about the middle of the thirteenth century. He wrote a treatise on astronomy, Kitāb al-hai'a, also called Correction of the Almagest, Iṣlāḥ al-Majisṭī, which was soon translated into Latin by Gherardo Cremonese, and into Hebrew by Moses ibn Tibbon in 1274, then again by Jacob ben Mahir (second half of the thirteenth century); this second translation was revised by Samuel ben Judah and completed in 1335. He criticized vigorously the Ptolemaic theory of planets but did not propose a better one. The lower planets (Mercury and Venus) at least must have a perceptible parallax; Venus may happen to be exactly on the line joining the sun and the earth.

The most important part of this treatise is the introduction on trigonometry. His spherical trigonometry is based on a rule of four quantities, instead of on the traditional rule of six quantities (regula sex quantitatum, vol. 1, 254). He introduced the equivalent of the formula: $\cos B = \cos a . \sin B$ for a spherical triangle rectangular in C. On the other hand, his plane trigonometry is strangely retrograde (he uses chords instead of sines). A memoir on Menelaos' theorem, shakl al-qaṭṭā', is ascribed to him (extant in Hebrew).

The invention of the astronomical instrument called turquet has also been ascribed to him. See my note on the turquet, apropos of Nāṣir al-dīn al-Ṭūsī (second half of the thirteenth century).

Text—Gebri filii Affla Hispalensis de astronomia libri IX in quibus Ptolemaeum, alioqui doctissimum, emendavit. This is Gherardo's translation published by Peter Apian in Nürnberg in 1534, together with his Instrumentum primi mobilis.

Criticism—M. Steinschneider: Hebräische Übersetzungen (543, 849, 1893). Braunmühl: Geschichte der Trigomometrie (vol. 1, 81–83, 1900). H. Suter: Die Mathematiker und Astronomen der Araber (119, 1900; Nachträge, 174, 1902). J. L. E. Dreyer: History of the planetary systems (261, 267, 1906). Duhem: Système du monde (vol. 2, 172–179, 1914) claims that Jābir's astronomy is simply a translation from the Greek, a plagiarism. Suter: Encyclopaedia of Islām (vol. 1, 987, 1912).

III. HISPANO-JEWISH

ABRAHAM BAR ḤIYYA

Abraham bar Ḥiyya ha-Nasi, often called Savasorda. (This last name is a corruption of the Arabic title ṣāḥib al-shurṭa, meaning governor of a city, chief of police.[1] It does not seem to mean chief of the Jewish community, as the Hebrew title ha-Nasi, the prince, often does. Savasorda was called ha-Nasi for genealogical rather than for political reasons). Abraham Judaeus. Hispano-Jewish philosopher, mathematician, and astronomer, who wrote in Hebrew. He lived in Barcelona and possibly in Provence; he died in or after 1136. He was one of the leaders of the movement which caused the Jews of Provence, Spain, and Italy to become the transmitters of Muslim science to the Christian West. He helped

[1] Very much like the French "préfet de police;" that is, secret and political police is implied—"Scotland Yard." See Ibn Khaldūn's Prolegomena (de Slane, 2, 35–37).

Plato of Tivoli and perhaps others (Rudolf of Bruges?) to translate scientific works from Arabic into Latin. His chief original works are the following:

(1) Yesod ha-tebunah u-migdal ha-emunah (The foundation of understanding and the tower of faith), an encyclopaedia treating of mathematics, astronomy, optics, and music, almost completely lost.

(2) Ḥibbur ha-meshiḥah ve-ha-tishboret, a treatise on practical geometry, written in 1116. This was translated into Latin by Plato of Tivoli in 1145, under the title Liber embadorum. The Ḥibbur contains the complete solution of the quadratic equation $x^2 + b = ax$, Abraham bar Ḥiyya showing that it has two roots.

(3) Ẓurat ha-ereẓ (Form of the earth), a treatise on astronomy. It was translated into Latin and into French.

(4) Ḥeshbon mahlakot ha-kokabim (Calculation of the courses of the stars), may be considered a sequel to the preceding.

(5) Luḥot ha-nasi (Tables of the prince), also called Tables of al-Battānī, which indicates their origin. (See al-Battānī, second half of the ninth century).

(6) Sefer ha-'ibbur (Book of intercalation), also called Ḥeshbon ha-'ibbur (Calculation of intercalation): said to be the oldest Hebrew treatise specifically devoted to the calendar. Written in 1122–23.

(7) Hegyon ha-nefesh (Meditation of the soul). Ethical work written in the spirit of Jewish neo-Platonism. It is largely derived from Ibn Gabirol.

(8) Megillat ha-megalleh (Scroll of the revealer), astrological and Messianic.

The translations from Arabic into Latin which were produced with his assistance have already been mentioned; he is said to have translated also a musical treatise from Arabic into Hebrew; moreover, his lost encyclopaedia treated of music. Abraham may thus have been one of the links through which Muslim music reached the West. In spite of the fact that the Ḥibbur ha-meshiḥah was translated into Latin only in 1145, and was thus anticipated by other Latin writings, it exerted a deep influence upon the development of western mathematics. It was not the earliest channel through which Muslim trigonometry reached the West, yet it was an important one. Abraham was one of the creators of the Hebrew scientific language.

Text—The Ḥibbur was edited by J. M. Guttmann in the publications of the Meqiẓe nirdamim (Berlin 1912).

Ẓurat ha-ereẓ, Forma terrae, with Latin version by Erasmus Oswald Schreckenfuchs, and notes by Sebastian Münster, together with the arithmetical compendium of Elijah Mizraḥi (second half of the fifteenth century), also in Hebrew and Latin (Basel 1546). Another edition, Offenbach 1720.

Sefer ha-'ibbur. Liber de intercalatione seu de chronologia, edited by H. Filipowski (London 1851).

Hegyon ha-nefesh. Edited by E. Freimann with introduction by S. J. L. Rapoport (Leipzig 1860).

Megillat ha-megalleh. Edited by Adolf Poznanski and Julius Guttmann (Meqiẓe nirdamim, Berlin 1924). Translation of the Megillat and of Guttmann's Hebrew introduction to it into Catalan by J. Millàs i Vallicrosa: Llibre revelador (Biblioteca hebraico-catalana; 310 p., Barcelona, 1929; Isis, 14, 476).

Criticism—M. Steinschneider: Die Encyclopädie des Abraham bar Chijja (Hebraeische Bibliographie, vol. 7, 84–95, 1864); Abraham Judaeus. Savasorda und Ibn Esra (Z. für Mathematik und Physik, vol. 12, 1–44, 1867). These important papers are both reprinted in Gesammelte Schriften (vol. 1, 327–406, 1925). P. Tannery: Sur le liber augmenti et diminutionis compilé par Abraham (Bibliotheca Mathematica, vol. 2, 45–47, 1901). This is the work of neither Abraham bar Ḥiyya nor Abraham ibn Ezra; I quote it here to avoid mistakes, for a treatise bearing the same title is ascribed to Abraham bar Ḥiyya; it dates from the twelfth or thirteenth century. Gabriel Schwarz, Jacob Guttmann, and Kaufmann Kohler: Jewish Encyclopaedia (vol. 1, 108–110, 1901). Isaac Husik: History of mediaeval Jewish philosophy (114–124, 1918). B. Cohn: Des mathematische Handbuch des Savasorda (Monatschr. Gesch. u. Wiss. Judent., vol. 62, 186–194, 1918). Henry George Farmer: Clues for the Arabic influence on European musical theory (Journal Royal Asiatic Soc., 71, 1925; Isis, 8, 508–511). Israel Efros: Studies in pre-Tibbonian philosophical terminology (Jewish quarterly review, vol. 17, 129–164, 323–368, 1926–1927; treating also of mathematical, astronomical, and calendrical terms; Isis, 12, 356); More about Abraham ben Ḥiyya's philosophical terminology (Jewish quarterly review, 20, 113–138, 1929). Michael Guttmann: Encyclopaedia judaica (vol. 1, 430–437, 1928).

THE MISHNAT HA-MIDDOT

The Ḥibbur ha-meshiḥah gives me an opportunity of speaking of an earlier Hebrew treatise, the Mishnat ha-middot (study of measurements), the oldest mathematical work in Hebrew. I did not speak of it in volume I, because I did not know where to place it, widely divergent dates having been assigned to it. I was not even sure that it was an original work; it might have been a translation of an unknown Arabic one, as was suggested by comparison with al-Khwārizmī's geometry. The unique manuscript of it (Munich, Cod. Hebr. 36) is only a part of a collection entitled Sefer ha-filosofiya (Book of philosophy), of which many items are explicitly said to have been translated from Arabic into Hebrew by Moses ben Samuel ibn Tibbon of Granada, in 1269–1270.

Thanks to the courtesy of Dr. Solomon Gandz of New York, who kindly communicated to me manuscript fragments of his new edition of the Mishnat ha-middot and his unpublished introduction to it, I have been able to obtain a clearer grasp of the question which I summarize as follows.

To begin with, let us describe this treatise. According to the Munich manuscript, the Mishnat ha-middot is divided into five articles (pereq) and forty-two paragraphs: (1) definitions of quadrangle, triangle, circle, arc, area (nine paragraphs); (2) area of rectangle, triangle, circle, circular segment; volume of prism, cylinder, pyramid, and cone and their frusta (twelve paragraphs); (3) various kinds of quadrangles (five paragraphs); (4) triangle (ten paragraphs); (5) sphere, circle, circular segments (six paragraphs).

The point of view is practical; the definitions and measurements are crude. The treatise reads like a collection of mathematical recipes.

A few peculiarities may be noted. Area of triangle in function of the sides (IV, 9). Suggestion of transformation of ordinary into decimal fractions (I, 8; IV, 7). The circle measurements would correspond to taking π equal to $3\frac{1}{7}$ (V, 3).

Two leaves found in the Bodleian Library contain the text of I, 6 to II, 10, and of V, 3 to 6 plus a new chapter (VI), dealing with the construction and measurements of the Tabernacle. This new chapter is not complete, but what we have of it tallies with the text of the Baraita di mlekhet ha-mishkan (Baraita on the erection of the Tabernacle), or the equivalent text included in the Yalquṭ Shime'oni.[2]

[2] The Baraitot are a series of treatises which were left out of the Mishna when it was finally edited by Judah ha-Nasi (second half of the second century). They are in the same relation to the canonic writings of the Mishna, as the apocryphal books of the Old Testament are to the accepted ones. The Yalquṭ Shime'oni (Simeon's compilation) is a collection of Midrashic material relative to the whole of the Old Testament. The editor and the date are unknown.

It is thus probable that the five chapters previously known were simply meant as a mathematical introduction to that Midrashic text.

This discovery makes the dating of the Mishnat ha-middot more easy. It was believed by Abraham Geiger to date from the post-Talmudic and pre-Arabic period (sixth to the eighth century); by M. Steinschneider, to belong to the beginning of the Arabic period (ninth to tenth century). It would now seem that the older opinion, confirmed by the latest editors, Hermann Schapira and Solomon Gandz, was the true one. The Mishnat ha-middot is a very ancient treatise which must belong to the time of the Mishna. The Bodleian fragment enables us to reach a more definite conclusion. The Mishnat ha-middot and the Baraita di-mlekhet ha-mishkan are probably one and the same book, namely, the Tosefta (addition) to the treatise Middot of the Mishna—that is, the tenth treatise of the Seder qodashim, dealing with the dimensions and arrangement of the Temple. And if so, its author was possibly Rabbi Nehemiah (c. 150).

The Mishnat ha-middot was probably used as a practical guide by land measurers in Syria and Palestine. If so, we can easily conceive how it was gradually transmitted to the Muslims. For example, Syrians may have brought it to that great clearing house, Jundīshāpūr (vol. I, 382, 415, 417, 435, 537). Al-Khwārizmī may have seen a Syriac or Persian version of it; at any rate the geometry (Bāb al-masāḥat) included in his algebra is very similar to it, and might be considered an Arabic version or elaboration of it. Al-Khwārizmī has added a few proofs; there are none in the Hebrew text.

Text—M. Steinschneider: Mishnat ha-middot, die erste geometrische Schrift in hebräischer Sprache, nebst Epilog der Geometrie des Abraham ben Chija. (16 p., Appendix to his Hebraeische Bibliographie, vol. 7, Berlin 1864). Reprint of Steinschneider's text with German translation and notes by Hermann Schapira (Abhandlungen zur Geschichte der Mathematik, 3, 3-56, Leipzig 1880, appended to the Z. für Mathematik und Physik., vol. 25, 1880). For the sake of comparison, Schapira has added to this edition a reprint of the geometry included in al-Khwārizmī's algebra (after Rosen's edition of London 1831). A new Hebrew edition with English translation, notes, and glossary is being prepared by Solomon Gandz, to be published in 1931 by the Kohut Foundation. The introduction to it, which I was privileged to use in MS., has just appeared in the Hebrew Union College Annual (vol. 6, 263-76, Cincinnati 1929; Isis, vol. 15, 396).

ABRAHAM IBN EZRA

See Chapter IV, Philosophic Background.

IV. BYZANTINE

For Prodromos, and for the two brothers Tzetzes, see Chapter IV, Philosophic Background.

V. LATIN

WALCHER OF MALVERN

An English astronomer of Lotharingian origin, he traveled in Italy in 1091, and went to England also about that year; became prior of Malvern; died in 1135. He observed lunar eclipses on October 30, 1091, and on October 18, 1092, made observations of the last one with the astrolabe, and described them. A little later, about 1108, he compiled a set of lunar tables, with explanations, comprising a cycle of 76 years ending in 1112. In 1120 he wrote a Latin adaptation of Pedro Alfonso's treatise on the Dragon. In his tables he used Roman fractions; in the later treatise, however, he used degrees, minutes and seconds.

Walcher's activity is doubly remarkable; first, because he was one of the first Englishmen to make astronomical observations; second, because he was one of the first to establish direct contacts with Arabic culture. It is impossible to say whether he anticipated Adelard of Bath, who flourished about 1116–1142, but the chances are that he did.

C. H. Haskins: Studies in mediaeval science (113–119, 1924). See my note on Pedro Alfonso, in Chapter IV, Philosophic Background.

RAYMOND OF MARSEILLES

French astronomer and philosopher who flourished at Marseilles about 1140. He is known only through an astronomical treatise and astronomical tables, Liber cursuum planetarum, compiled by him about 1140. They represent an adaptation to the meridian of Marseilles and the requirements of Christian chronology, of the so-called Toledan tables—that is, the tables computed by al-Zarqālī (second half of the eleventh century). Raymond was a real astronomer, but his tables do not seem to have exerted any influence until about a century later when another Marseillais, William the Englishman (first half of the thirteenth century), took them up.

Text—The tables exist only in MSS., for which see C. H. Haskins: Studies in mediaeval science.

Criticism—P. Duhem: Système du Monde (vol. 3, 201–216, 1915). C. H. Haskins: Studies in mediaeval science (96–98, 1924).

RALPH OF LAON

Raoul, or Radolf, of Laon. French educator and mathematician who lived at Laon (Aisne) at the beginning of the twelfth century, and died in 1131. He succeeded his brother, the theologian Anselm (1030–1117), as head of the famous cathedral school of Laon. Under the direction of Anselm and Ralph that school became quite famous, but after Ralph's death it relapsed into obscurity. Ralph wrote an important work on the abacus, containing historical information on the subject; he speaks of "divisio aurea" as well as of "divisio ferrea" (common and complementary division). He uses Roman, but also Hindu numerals; thus his work may be considered an abacus or an algorism (see vol. I, 756).

Text—Alfred Nagl: Der arithmetische Tractat des Radulph von Laon (Z. für Mathematik, vol. 34, hist. Abt., 85–133, 1889; e codice Parisiensi latino no. 15120).

Criticism—Moritz Cantor gives an unusually full account of this work in his Vorlesungen (vol. 1, 3rd ed., 890–900, 1907). Reginald L. Poole: The exchequer in the twelfth century (Oxford 1912).

OCREATUS

A mathematician who was probably a pupil of Adelard of Bath,[3] and if so he lived about the middle of the twelfth century. He may be identical with one

[3] This is based upon the assumption that Adelardus Batensis means Adelard of Bath, though the correct form would be Bathoniensis.

Joannes Ocreatus (John O'Creat) mentioned in a manuscript[4] as a translator of Euclid (?). At any rate, the Ocreatus of whom we are speaking is the author of an arithmetical treatise beginning, "Prologus H. (or N.) Ocreati in Helceph ad Adelardum Batensem magistrum suum." The word helceph suggests an Arabic origin; it may be a corruption of al-kāfī, name of an arithmetical treatise by al-Karkhī (first half of the eleventh century); or more probably of the word ḥisāb, meaning calculation, for a little further along occur the words "helceph Sarracenicum," which are nicely translated as Muslim computation. The whole treatise contains about 1800 words; it deals with numbers in general, multiplication and division. Ocreatus' numerals are a very strange mixture; he uses zeros, together with Roman figures and place value; he also uses the Greek letter tau instead of zero. For example:

$$1200 = \text{iccoo or 1. ii } \tau\tau$$

He mentions the so-called rule of Nicomachos (regula Nicomachi):

$$a^2 = (a + b)\,(a - b) + b^2$$

Text—Charles Henry: Prologus N. Ocreati in Helceph ad Adelardum Batensem magistrum suum. Fragment sur la multiplication et la division (Abhandl. zur Geschichte der Mathematik, 3, 129–139, 1880).

Criticism—L. Leclerc: Médecine arabe (vol. 2, 397, 1876). M. Steinschneider: Europäische Übersetzungen (51, 1904). M. Cantor: Vorlesungen (vol. 1^3, 906, 1907). Smith and Karpinski: Hindu-Arabic numerals (119, 1911).

For the translators from the Arabic: Adelard of Bath, John of Seville, Hermann the Dalmatian, Hugh of Santalla, Robert of Chester, Rudolf of Bruges, and Plato of Tivoli; see Chapter III, The translators.

For Theodoric of Chartres, and William of Conches, see Chapter IV, Philosophic Background.

A few anonymous mathematical treatises of the twelfth century

The following references, which could not be used in the sections devoted to specific mathematicians, have been collected here for the convenience of students. No investigation of twelfth century mathematics, nor of the works of a single contemporary mathematician, should be deemed complete, which does not include an examination of these anonymous treatises, and eventually a deeper study of some of them.

A. Nagl: Über eine Algorithmusschrift des XII. Jahrh. und über die Verbreitung der indisch-arabischen Rechenkunst und Zahlzeichen in christlichen Abendlande (Z. für Mathematik, vol. 34, hist. Abt., 129–146, 161–170, 1889).

M. Curtze: Über eine Algorismus-Schrift des zwölften Jahrhunderts (Abhdl. zur Gesch. der Mathematik, 8. Heft, 3–27, 1898). P. Tannery: Sur l'auteur du traité algorithmique publié par Curtze (Bibliotheca Mathematica, vol. 5, 416, 1904; Mémoires, vol. 5, 343–345); Sur la division du temps en instants au Moyen âge (Bibliotheca Mathematica, vol. 6, 111, 1905; Mémoires, vol. 5, 346–347, Isis, 6, 433–434). Suzan Rose Benedict: Comparative study of early arithmetics (1914). Louis C. Karpinski: Two twelfth century algorisms (Isis, 3, 396–413, 1921), from two MSS. in the British Museum. These algorisms are compared with other early algorisms, and a bibliography of the subject is included.

[4] Catal. MSS. Angl. (vol. 2, 247, no. 8639), as quoted by Cantor (vol. 1^3, 907).

M. Curtze: Ein Tractatus de abaco aus der Wende des XII. und XIII. Jahrh. Nach Codex Vindobonensis Palatinus 901 hrg. (Z. für Math., vol. 43, hist. Abt., 122–138, 1898). Some interesting information may be found also in Reginald L. Poole: The exchequer in the twelfth century (206 p., Oxford, 1912, especially ch. 3). C. H. Haskins: The abacus and the exchequer (Studies in mediaeval science, 327–335, 1924).

C. H. Haskins: Some twelfth century writers on astronomy (Studies in mediaeval science, 82–112, 1924). This treats of compotists, the School of Chartres, treatises on the elements, the Marseilles tables, a critic of Macrobius, and translations of Ptolemy. Louis Eugène Lefèvre: Le calendrier zodiaque du portail royal de Chartres et les influences mithriaques (Revue archéologique, vol. 26, 207–232, ill., 1927).

VI. VERNACULAR

PHILIP OF THAON

See Chapter IV, Philosophic Background.

STJÖRNU ODDI

Icelandic mathematician and astronomer who lived in Iceland in the twelfth century. He wrote on the compotus, but is best remembered as the author of two poems which are said to have been created in his sleep, Stjörnu Odda draumr. He is quoted in the Rimbegla as the one who knew the stars best.

Text—Compotus and dream in the Rimbegla, edited by Stephanus Björnonis (Copenhagen 1780). Stjörnu Odda draumr, edited by Guðbrandur Vigfússon (1860). Swedish translation and commentary by Sidenbladh (Uppsala 1866).

Criticism—Eugen Mogk in Hermann Paul's Grundriss der germanischen Philologie (vol. 2, second edition, 707, 773, 899, 1904). Björn Magnússon Ólsen: Stjörnu-Odda (15 p., reprinted from Afmaelisrit til Dr. Kristian Kålund, Copenhagen 1914).

See my notes on Ari Fróði Þorgilsson, in Chapter XI, Historiography; and on Bjarni Bergþorsson in Book II.

VII. HINDU

ŚATĀNANDA

The author of a very popular karaṇa (astronomical calculation) called Bhāsvatī, dealing with the years 1099 and following.

This work ought to have been quoted in the last chapter of my volume I; I quote it here faute de mieux.

Text—Bhāsvatī, edited by S. Dvivedī and Lattara Śarma (Benares 1883).

Criticism—M. Winternitz: Indische Litteratur (vol. 3, 565, 1922).

BHĀSKARA

Or Bhāskarācārya, which might be translated the learned Bhāskara. Hindu mathematician and astronomer, born in 1114, and still living in 1178. He completed in the year 1072 Śaca[5] (about 1150 A.D.) his main work, the Siddhāntaśiromaṇi, one of the Hindu mathematical masterworks; and in 1178 another work called Karaṇakutūhala. The Siddhāntaśiromaṇi is divided into four parts, of which the first two form a mathematical introduction, while the two others

[5] See F. K. Ginzel: Handbuch der Chronologie (vol. 1, 390–391, 1906).

treat of astronomy: (1) Līlāvatī (the beautiful); (2) Vījagaṇita (root-extraction); (3) Grahagaṇitādhyāya; (4) Golādhyāya. The first two parts are by far the most important. At the end of the Vījagaṇita, Bhāskara declares that he has made use of the mathematical works of Brahmagupta (first half of the seventh century), Śrīdhara (first half of the eleventh century), and Padmanābha (the algebra of the two last named are unfortunately lost).

Bhāskara realized the true meaning of division by zero. He explained the method of false position. His work includes the following:

Anticipation of modern theory concerning the convention of signs—that is, our minus by minus makes plus, minus by plus makes minus. Suggestion of the use of letters (of the Devanāgarī alphabet) to represent the unknown quantities.[6] Quadratic equations reduced to a single type and completely solved, except that only positive roots are considered genuine. Solution of a few special types of cubic and biquadratic equations. Dim notion of quadratic and cubic residues. Application of the formula:

$$\sqrt{(a + \sqrt{b})} = \sqrt{[\tfrac{1}{2}(a + \sqrt{(a^2 - b)})]} + \sqrt{[\tfrac{1}{2}(a - \sqrt{(a^2 - b)})]}$$

Solution of indeterminate equations of the first and second degrees. Cyclic method of solving the (Pellian) equations $ax^2 + 1 = y^2$, $ax^2 + c = y^2$ (a and c being non-square integers), "the finest thing achieved in the theory of numbers before Lagrange."[7] Solution of the equation, $ax^2 + bx + c = y^2$. Combinatorial analysis.

Study of right-angled triangles, and of regular polygons up to 384 sides, leading to $\pi = \frac{3927}{1250}$, also $\pi = \frac{754}{240} = 3.141666. \ldots$ Anticipation of Kepler's method for finding the surface and volume of a sphere by a sort of integration.

Elaborate computation of sine tables based upon the value of the sine of the arc unit, 3°45′ or 225′[8] and upon the formula of recurrence used in the Pauliśa Siddhānta (about the first half of the fifth century). Also $\sin 1° = \frac{10}{573}$, $\cos 1° = \frac{6568}{6569}$, etc. Approximate value of the chord c of a given arc a, the diameter and circumference being respectively d and p.

$$c = \frac{4\,da\,(p - a)}{5/4\,p^2 - a(p - a)}$$

The astronomical part of the Siddhāntaśiromaṇi is essentially an elaboration and clearer exposition of the knowledge contained in the Sūryasiddhānta; it shows that Bhāskara had a better understanding of the equation of time. It is not comparable to the mathematical part, for instead of marking any sort of progress it is behind the times, being very inferior to the contemporary Muslim astronomy.

Bhāskara was aware of the extension of oil upon the surface of water. It is true, some empirical use of the surface tension of a film of oil to subdue the waves in a storm seems to have been made by Greek sailors in early times.

In 1206 Caṅgadeva, a grandson of Bhāskara, founded a school for the study of the Siddhāntaśiromaṇi.

[6] A similar suggestion had been made before by Āryabhaṭa.

[7] Thus said Hankel, quoted by G. R. Kaye (Isis, 2, 337).

[8] The twenty-fourth part of a right angle. Sin 225′ ≈ 225′. See my notes on the Sūrya and Pauliśa Siddhānta (vol. I, 387), and on Āryabhaṭa (second half of the fifth century), also G. Sarton: Note on kardaja (Isis, 14, 421–22, 1930).

Text—Sanskrit text of the Siddhāntaśiromaṇi, edited by Lancelot Wilkinson (Calcutta 1842), by Bāpu Deva Śāstrī (Benares 1866), with commentaries by Muralidhar Jhā (Pandit, vols. 30–33). Edition of the Līlāvatī, with notes, by Sudhākara Dvivedī (Benares Sanskrit Series, 153, 1912), and Persian translation by Feizi (Calcutta 1827). Editions of the Vījagaṇita (Benares 1864); of the Gaṇitādhyāya (Calcutta 1881); of the Golādhyāya, with a commentary called Mitāksharā (Calcutta 1882); of the Karaṇakutūhala, by Sudhākara Dvivedī (Benares 1881).

English translations—John Taylor: Lilawati, or a treatise on arithmetic and geometry (161 p., Bombay 1816). Henry Thomas Colebrooke: Algebra with arithmetic and mensuration from the Sanskrit of Brahmagupta and Bhascara (462 p., London 1817). Reprinted with Sanskrit text by Haran Chandra Banerji (324 p., Calcutta 1927). Translation of the Sūrya Siddhānta by Bāpu Deva Śāstri, and of the Siddhāntaśiromaṇi by Lancelot Wilkinson (Bibliotheca indica, Calcutta 1861–1862).

Criticism—H. Hankel: Geschichte der Mathematik im Altertum und Mittelalter (Leipzig 1874). Ed. Lucas: Sur un théorème de l'arithmétique indienne (Boncompagni's Bull., vol. 9, 157–162, 1876). H. Suter: Über die Vielecksformel in Bhāskara (Verhdl. des 3. Mathematikerkongresses in Heidelberg, 556–561, 1904). J. L. E. Dreyer: Planetary systems (242–243, 1906); for Bhāskara's fantastic astronomical ideas. M. Cantor: Geschichte der Mathematik (vol. 1^3, passim, 1907; very elaborate account). George Rusby Kaye: Indian mathematics (Isis, 2, 326–356, 1919; also Calcutta 1915). M. Winternitz: Geschichte der indischen Litteratur (vol. 3, 564, 1922). G. R. Kaye: Hindu astronomy (Calcutta 1924). Sāradākānta Gāṅguli: Bhāskarāchārya and simultaneous indeterminate equations of the first degree (Bull. of the Calcutta mathematical society, vol. 17, 89–98, 1926; Isis, 12, 356); Bhāskarāchārya's references to previous teachers (ibidem, vol. 18, 65–76, 1927; Isis, 12, 356); The source of the Indian solution of the so-called Pellian equation (Bull. Calcutta mathematical society, 19, 151–176, 1928; Isis, 13, 214); Notes on Indian mathematics. A criticism of G. R. Kaye's interpretations (Isis, 12, 132–145, 1929). Sukumar Ranjan Das: The equation of time in Hindu astronomy (American mathematical monthly, vol. 35, 540–543, 1928; Isis, 13, 213). Bibhutibhusan Datta: The Hindu solution of the general Pellian equation (Bull. Calcutta mathematical society, vol. 19, 87–94, 1928; Isis 13, 507).

THE BAKHSHĀLĪ MANUSCRIPT

This Sanskrit mathematical manuscript was discovered in 1881 at Bakhshālī, near Mardān, fifty miles from Peshawar, in the so-called Gandhāra country. It is now in the Bodleian Library, Oxford. The late A. F. Rudolf Hoernlé, who was first to study it, believed that it dated from the third or fourth century. On the other hand, George Rusby Kaye, who has continued Hoernlé's investigations for many years, has reached the conclusion that both the manuscript and the work itself date more probably from the twelfth century—not from an earlier time. This conclusion is largely based upon the examination of script and language.

The language is an irregular Sanskrit; the script is Śāradā, a descendant of the Brāhmī character, in a line distinct from but parallel with the Nāgarī. The Bakhshālī manuscript consists of some seventy leaves of birch bark, of which the original size was probably about 17 by 10.5 cm. Not more than half of the leaves are in a fair condition, and even those are broken at the edges; the other leaves are far more damaged, and eleven are hardly more than scraps. The author was in all probability a Śaivite Brahman, not a Jain or a Buddhist.

The mathematical contents may be summarized as follows: Problems involving systems of linear equations. Indeterminate equations of the second degree. Arithmetical progressions. Quadratic equations. Approximate evaluations of square roots. Complex series. Problems of the type

$$x(1 - a_1)(1 - a_2)\ldots.(1 - a_n) = p.$$

Computation of the fineness of gold. Problems on income and expenditure, and on profit and loss. Miscellaneous problems. Mensuration.

The work is arithmetical in form, but the solutions are so general that it might be considered algebraic. Proofs are given. The author seemed to prefer simple numbers, but some large ones occur, including one of 23 digits. Each problem is explained in the following order: sūtram (rule); udāharanam (example); sthāpanam (statement); karaṇam (solution); pratyayam (verification).

There is no symbol for the unknown quantity. The only symbol used is +, placed *after* the number affected, to indicate a *negative* quantity. Its origin is unknown. It might be connected with Diophantos' use of an inverted psi; or it might be an abbreviation of a Sanskrit word; or something else. The mensuration problems are of special interest because of methods to pass from one kind of unit to another, which are unique in Sanskrit literature.

This work seems to be essentially Hindu and in some details it resembles closely the Gaṇitasārasaṃgraha of Mahāvīra (first half of the ninth century). Yet it also contains western (Muslim) elements—for example, the use of sexagesimal fractions, and of the rule $\sqrt{\ }(A + b) \approx A + b/2A$, to find approximate roots.

Text—George Rusby Kaye: The Bakhshālī manuscript (162 p., 4 tables, 48 pl., 33 x 24.5 cm.; Archaeological Survey of India, New Imperial Series, vol. 43, parts 1 and 2, Calcutta 1927); contains a facsimile of the manuscript; a critical edition of the text in our alphabet, and a very elaborate introduction. A third part, as yet unpublished, will probably contain a translation, additional notes, and glossary (Isis, 12, 157–161). Reviews by Bibhutibhusan Datta (Bull. of the Calcutta mathematical Soc., 21, 1–60; and Bull. Amer. math. Soc., 35, 579–580, 1929).

Criticism—The earliest account of the discovery appeared in the Bombay Gazette of August 13, 1881. First description of the MS. by A. F. Rudolf Hoernlé in Indian Antiquary (vol. 12, 89–90, 1883). Fuller account by Hoernlé in the Verhandlungen des siebenten internationalen Orientalisten Congresses (Wien 1886, Arische Section, 127 sq.), and in Indian Antiquary (vol. 17, 33–48, 275–279, 1888). G. R. Kaye: The Bakhshālī manuscript (Journal and Proc. of the Royal Asiatic Society of Bengal, 8, 349–361, 1912; Isis, 1, 547). Bibhutibhusan Datta: The Bakhshālī mathematics (Bull. Calcutta mathematical Society, vol. 21, 60 p., 1929). Datta claims that the Bakshālī MS. is a copy of a much earlier work which must date back (the work) to the beginning of our era (Isis, 13, 506).

CHAPTER VI

PHYSICS, TECHNOLOGY, AND MUSIC

(First Half of Twelfth Century)

I. PHYSICS

'UMAR AL-KHAYYĀMĪ

See volume 1, 759–761.

AL-KHĀZINĪ

Abū-l-Fatḥ 'Abd al-Raḥmān al-Manṣūr al-Khāzinī (or al-Khāzin). Flourished about 1115–1121. Greek (rūmī) slave whom his master 'Alī al-Khāzin al-Marwazī caused to receive a good scientific and philosophic education in Marw. He compiled astronomical tables called Al-zīj al-mu'tabar al-Sinjarī (The esteemed Sinjaric tables) in honor of Sinjar ibn Malikshāh ibn Alp Arslān, governor and later sulṭān of Khurāsān (1097–1098 to 1157–1158). They give the positions of the stars for the year 1115–1116, and the latitude of Marw. In 1121–1122 he completed the Kitāb mīzān al-ḥikma (Book of the balance of wisdom), one of the most remarkable books on mechanics, hydrostatics and physics of the Middle Ages. It contains tables of specific gravities of many liquids and solids (based upon al-Bīrūnī), and a history of the subject: theory of gravity (universal force directed toward the center of the universe—that is, the center of the earth); gravity of air; observations on capillarity; use of areometer[1] to measure densities and appreciate the temperature of liquids; theory of the lever; application of the balance to levelling, and to the measuring of time.

Text and translation—N. Khanikoff: Analysis and extracts of the Book of the Balance of Wisdom, in Arabic and English (Journal of the American Oriental Society, vol. 6, 1–128, New Haven 1859; with notes by the editor on p. 107–128; discussion of the authorship of this work). Other parts of the Mīzān are translated in the papers of Thomas Ibel and E. Wiedemann quoted below.

Criticism—H. Carrington Bolton: The book of the balance of wisdom. An essay on determination of specific gravity (American Chemist, May 1876; reprint, 20 p.). Comparison of the specific gravities quoted by al-Bīrūnī in Clément-Mullet's memoir (Journal asiatique, 1858), and by al-Khāzinī in Khanikoff's memoir. The former figures are apparently more accurate, the differences being due to the European editors. H. Suter: Mathematiker der Araber (122, 226, 1900). Thomas Ibel: Die Wage im Altertum und Mittelalter (187 p., Erlangen 1908).

Papers by Eilhard Wiedemann: Inhalt eines Gefässes in verschiedenen Abständen vom Erdmittelpunkte nach al-Chāzinī (Wiedemann's Annalen, vol. 39, 319, 1890); Über die Kenntnisse der Mulime auf dem Gebiete der Mechanik und Hydrostatik (Archiv für Geschichte der Naturwiss., vol. 2, 394–398, 1910), apropos of al-Khāzinī and of Fakhr al-Dīn al-Rāzī, second half of the twelfth century; Encyclopaedia of Islām, articles al-qarasṭūn, steelyard (vol. 2, 757–760, 1926), al-Khāzinī (vol. 2, 937, 1926), and mīzān (not yet published).

[1] Vol. 1, 338.

All of the following papers, containing abundant extracts from the Mīzān, appeared in the Sitzungsberichte der Physik. med. Sozietät, Erlangen: Über arabische Auszüge aus der Schrift des Archimedes über die schwimmende Körper (Beitr. 7, vol. 38, 152–162, 1906); Über das Schachspiel und dabei vorkommenden Zahlenprobleme (Beitr. 14, vol. 40, 45–54, 1908); Über die Bestimmung der Zusammensetzung von Legierungen (Beitr. 15, vol. 40, 105–132, 1908); Über die Lehre vom Schwimmen, die Hebelgesetze und die Konstruktion des qarasṭūn (Beitr. 16, vol. 40, 133–159, 1908; contains a list of the parts of the Mīzān already translated); Einige Biographien nach al-Baihaqī (Beitr. 20; vol. 42, 73, 1910; contains al-Khāzinī's biography); Über die Stundenwage (Beitr. 37, vol. 46, 27–38, 1914); Über die Wage des Wechselns von al-Chāzinī, und über die Lehre von den Proportionen nach al-Bīrūnī (Beitr. 48, vol. 48, 1–15, 1918).

For Muẓaffar al-Asfuzārī, see Chapter V, Mathematics and Astronomy. For Abū-l-Ṣalt, see Chapter X, Medicine.

For Bhāskara, see Chapter V, Mathematics and Astronomy.

II. TECHNOLOGY

ARTESIAN WELLS

One calls "Artesian" the wells which are obtained by boring the earth until one reaches a level of water, submitted to hydrostatic pressure; the water is then driven upwards, as in a natural spring, by that pressure. They were called Artesian because they were relatively common in Artois in mediaeval times. The earliest recorded in that country is the one at the Dominican monastery in Lillers (Pas-de-Calais), dating from 1126; this is probably the earliest Artesian well in Europe. But such wells are really far more ancient. There is a reference to them in al-Bīrūnī (first half of the eleventh century), who correctly explains their action by the principle of communicating vessels (vol. I, 708).

In desert or semi-desert countries where springs are uncommon, it is natural to dig for water. It must have happened more than once that an Artesian well was thus accidentally created, for between a natural well and a deep Artesian well there is a whole gamut of transitional stages. The story of Moses obtaining water by smiting the rock in Horeb is conceivably the echo of such a happy accident (Exodus, 17, 6).

III. MUSIC

For Abū-l-Ṣalt, see Chapter X, Medicine. For Ibn Bājja, see Chapter IV, Philosophic Background. For Abraham bar Ḥiyya, see Chapter V, Mathematics and Astronomy.

For Frutolf of Bamberg, see volume 1, 763. For Adelard of Bath, see Chapter III, the Translators.

LEONINUS AND PEROTINUS

Magister Leo, or Leoninus, was a famous organist and precentor at Notre Dame, Paris, about the beginning of the twelfth century. He wrote a Liber organi de graduali, and is said to have been one of the first to indicate the different time values of notes.

His treatise was revised and his musical notation improved by his disciple and successor, Perotinus, or Perotinus Magnus.

Grove: Dictionary of music (third edition, vol. 3, 143, 1927; vol. 4, 122, 1928).

CHAPTER VII

CHEMISTRY

(First Half of Twelfth Century)

I. MUSLIM

AL-ṬUGHRĀ'Ī

Abū Ismā'īl al-Ḥusain ibn 'Alī ibn Muḥammad, surnamed al-'Amīd al-dawla (pillar of the state), Fakhr al-kuttāb (glory of the civil servants), Muwayyid al-dīn (defender of the faith), and generally called al-Ṭughrā'ī.[1] Born in Iṣpahan, he was in Baghdād in 1111–1112; later he became wazīr to the Saljūq sulṭān Mas'ūd ibn Muḥammad in Mūṣul. He was put to death on the pretext of atheism about 1121, when he was over sixty years old. Persian poet and alchemist, who wrote in Arabic. He is chiefly known because of his famous Lāmīyat al 'Ajam (the ode rhyming in *l*, of the Persians or non-Arabs),[2] written in Baghdād in 1111–1112. Various treatises on alchemy are ascribed to him: Kitāb al-jauhar al-naḍīr fī ṣanā'at al-iksīr (Book of the brilliant stone for the preparation of the elixir); Jāmi' al-asrār wa tarākīb al-anwār (Collection of the secrets and composition of lights); Mafātīḥ al-raḥma wa maṣābīḥ al-ḥikma (Keys of mercy and lamps of wisdom); Ḥaqā'iq al-istishhād (fī-l-kīmīyā) (Truths of the evidence submitted with regard to alchemy); etc. He discussed Ibn Sīnā's sceptical views on alchemy.

Text—There are many editions and translations of the Lāmīyat. I quote very briefly only a few of them, as they do not directly concern us. Arabic-Latin edition by Edward Pococke (Oxford 1661), Englished by Leonard Chappelow (Cambridge 1758). Arabic-Latin edition by Jacob Golius (Utrecht 1707; with additional notes, Franeker 1769). Arabic-French edition by A. Raux (Paris 1903).

I know of no edition of the writings on alchemy.

Criticism—Ibn Khaldūn: Prolégomènes (de Slane, 3, 208, 255, 260). F. Wüstenfeld: Arabische Aerzte (87, 1840). Ibn Khallikān (vol. 1, 462–464, 1842; does not speak of alchemy). C. Brockelmann: Arabische Litteratur (vol. 1, 247–248, 1898). Eilhard Wiedemann: Zur Geschichte der Alchemie (Z. für Chemie, 35, 522, 528, 1921); Zur Alchemie bei den Arabern (Abhdl. zur Gesch. der Naturwiss., 5, 1922; Isis, 5, 534). J. Ruska and E. Wiedemann: Alchemistische Decknamen (Beitr. 67, Sitzungsber. der physik. med. Soz., 56, 17–36, Erlangen 1924; Isis, 8, 794). This last paper is a very valuable study of the secret names used by Arabic alchemists; it is partly based upon al-Ṭughrā'ī's Al-jauhar al-naḍīr.

See my note on "Artephius," which follows immediately.

[1] The Persian word ṭughrā means not the royal signature, but the flourish written as elegantly as possible at the beginning of state papers over the Bismillāh, and containing the titles of the ruler issuing the document. Thus al-Ṭughrā'ī means the chancellor, but with the implication, special to the East, of caligraphist.

[2] So called, with reference to the Lāmīyat al-'Arab (the ode rhyming in *l* of the Arabs), by the pre-Islāmic poet Shanfarā.

II. LATIN

"ARTEPHIUS"

Also Artepius, Artesius. An unknown alchemist whom I place here tentatively because he has been identified with the Muslim poet and alchemist al-Ṭughrā'ī. That identification is unproved, but the Latin writings bearing Artephius' name are possibly translations from the Arabic. It is as yet impossible to date the unknown Arabic originals or the Latin translations. All that can be said is that the original author must be placed after Ibn Sīnā (first half of the eleventh century), and before William of Auvergne (first half of the thirteenth century) and Roger Bacon, who quote him. The fact that "Artephius" is reputed to have lived a thousand and twenty-five years, thanks to his elixir, does not make it easier to place him in any single century. The two works generally ascribed to him are treatises on alchemy, entitled Liber secretus, and Clavis majoris sapientiae de transmutatione metallica. King Alfonso el Sabio (second half of the thirteenth century) caused the latter to be translated from the Arabic into Castilian. It treats of the Aristotelian elements or qualities, the generation of minerals, of plants from minerals, and of animals from plants.

Text and translations—The Clavis majoris sapientiae was first printed in Paris in 1609. Then it was printed in Opuscula quaedam chemica (107–146, 1614). Printed in Strasbourg in 1699. German translation, Leipzig 1736, 1748, etc.

The Liber secretus was printed in Amsterdam in 1678; in Frankfurt in 1685. French translation by Pierre Arnaud: Trois Traictez de la philosophie naturelle (Paris 1612). Anonymous German translation (Hamburg 1619). Nicolas Flamel: Exposition of the hieroglyphical figures which he caused to be painted upon an arch in St. Innocent's church-yard in Paris. With the Secret Book of Artephius, and the Epistle of John Pontanus concerning the philosopher's stone. Done into English out of the French and Latin copies by Eirenaeus Orandus (250 p., London 1624).

Criticism—J. C. Poggendorff: Handwörterbuch (vol. 1, 67, 1863). M. E. Chevreul: Examen critique d'un écrit alchimique intitulé Artefii Clavis majoris sapientiae (Comptes Rendus de l'Académie des Sciences, vol. 36, 33–82, 1867; Journal des Savants, 1867, 1868). J. Gildemeister: Alchymie (Zeitschrift der morgenländischen Gesellschaft, vol. 30, 534–538, 1876). M. Steinschneider: Europäische Übersetzungen (8–10, 1905). John Ferguson: Bibliotheca Chemica (vol. 1, 24, 50–51, 1906; with additional bibliography). E. O. v. Lippmann: Alchemie (408, 1919).

THEOPHILE THE PRIEST

Theophilus Presbyter. An unknown craftsman who lived about the end of the eleventh century and the beginning of the twelfth, probably in Germany. I have already devoted a note to him (vol. I, 763), to which the following information may be added. The Diversarum artium schedula contains many chapters devoted to the preparation and use of oil colors. It is thus wrong to speak of the brothers Van Eyck (first half of the fifteenth century) as the inventors of oil colors. Such colors are fully described by Theophilus, and may be earlier still. But the colors used by Theophilus, and until a later period—probably until the fifteenth century—were extremely difficult to dry. Each color had to be dried in the sun before another could be laid upon it; and if there was no sun it was necessary to use a reflecting brazier (like the Roman cauterium). Theophilus used linseed oil together with some kind of resin (amber, copal, or sandarac); the fornis and glassa mentioned by him cannot be identified with certainty, but fornis was probably the same as vernix (hence our word varnish), which was either a generic name for resin, or represented one of them—probably sandarac, which was the best known. Theophilus gives many recipes for the preparation of panels for painting; for making glues, colors, lakes, varnishes, dyes, etc.; also for making ink by means of an infusion of tannin and green vitriol (sulphate of iron); he also explains in detail the manufacture of glass.

Text—Albert Ilg's edition of 1874 was reprinted in 1888.

Criticism—Lessing: Vom Alter der Oelmalerei aus dem Theophilus Presbyter (1774). Charles Dalbon: Les origines de la peinture à l'huile (15–17, 63, 74, 76, 80, 82–83, 100, Paris 1904). A. P. Laurie: Materials of the painter's craft (143–171, 328, 340–341, 387, London 1910) Theobald: Was sagt uns die Schedula diversarum artium (Beitr. zur Gesch. der Technik, vol. 16, 217–222, 321, 1926; Isis, 12, 355). Hermann Degering: Theophilus Presbyter, qui et Rugerus (Westfälische Studien Alois Bömer gewidmet, p. 248–262, 1 pl., Leipzig 1928): an important paper. Degering claims that the text of the Schedula is earlier than the eleventh century; and would trace it back at least to the Ottonian period (second half of the tenth century). He shows the untenability of Ilg's hypothesis identifying Theophilus with Roger of Helmarshausen.

For Adelard of Bath, Hugh of Santalla, and Robert of Chester, see Chapter III, The Translators.

For Bartholomew of Salerno, and for Salernus, see Chapter X, Medicine.

III. CHINESE

CHU I-CHUNG

Chu^{1} I^{4*}-chung^{1} (2544, 5507, 2875). He lived early in the twelfth century. A Chinese chemist who wrote (about 1120) a standard treatise on the distillation of spirits, entitled Pei^{3}-shan^{1} Chiu^{3} ·ching^{1} (8771, 9663, 2260, 2122). "The first part is a general discourse on spirituous liquors, the remainder giving ample details on the compendium of ferments and the various methods of distillation."

Text—The Pei shan chiu ching, in three chüan, is included in the Chih^{1} pu^{1*} tsu^{2*} chai^{1} ts'ung^{1} shu^{1} (1783, 9456, 11840, 234, 12039, 10024), vol. 91 (copy in Library of Congress).

Criticism—A. Wylie: Chinese Literature (150, 1902). L. Wieger: La Chine (429, 515, 1920). See my remarks apropos of Tou-P'ing (first half of the eleventh century, vol. I, 723).

CHAPTER VIII

GEOGRAPHY

(First Half of Twelfth Century)

I. EASTERN MUSLIM

SAHL IBN ABĀN

One of the Muslim authors of nautical instructions mentioned with special admiration by the most famous of them, Aḥmad ibn Mājid (second half of the fifteenth century). The latter called himself the fourth of the "Lions" (of the sea), the first three "Lions" being Muḥammad ibn Shādhān, Sahl ibn Abān, and Laith ibn Kahlān. Sahl lived in the first half of the twelfth century; the two others were possibly contemporaries of his. These three were not mu'allim (masters of navigation), but compilers of sea-voyages and route-books dealing with the eastern seas, chiefly those east of India.

Gabriel Ferrand: Encyclopaedia of Islām (vol. 4, 367, 1926).

IBN AL-BALKHĪ

Unknown Persian geographer. One of his ancestors was born or flourished at Balkh, Khurāsān. At some time during the first decade of the sixth Muslim century, 1106–1116, he compiled in Persian a description of the province of Fārs, corresponding to the southwestern part of modern Persia, along the Persian Gulf; this work is entitled Fārs nāmah. A shortened transcription of it was included by Ḥamdallāh al-Qazwīnī (first half of the fourteenth century) in his Nuzhat al-qulūb, completed in 1340.

G. Le Strange: Description of the province of Fars at the beginning of the twelfth century (Journal of the Royal Asiatic Society, 1–30, Jan., 1912). Complete edition with English translation by G. Le Strange and R. A. Nicholson: Ibnu' l-Balkhī: The Fārsnāma (Gibb Memorial, new series, 1, 231 p., Cambridge 1921; Isis, 7, 188).

AL-ZAMAKHSHARĪ

See Chapter XIII, Philology and Education.

II. WESTERN MUSLIM

MUḤAMMAD AL-ZUHRĪ

Muḥammad ibn abī Bakr al-Zuhrī. Lived in Granada about 1137–1138. Hispano-Muslim geographer. He wrote, after 1139–1140, a general treatise on geography, Kitāb al-jughrāfiyā.

Text—A partial edition by O. Houdas and René Basset: Description du Sous el Aqṣā' (Bulletin de correspondance africaine, 192–198, 1884). This contains also a table of contents of the whole work.
Criticism—C. Brockelmann: Arabische Litteratur (vol. 1, 476, 1898).

For al-Idrisī and al-Māzinī, see the geographical chapter of Book II.

III. LATIN

PEDRO ALFONSO

See Chapter IV, Philosophic Background.

HENRY OF MAYENCE

German geographer. Canon of the Church of St. Mary in Mayence in 1110. He made, in 1110, a compilation of the De imagine mundi, and added to it a map derived from other sources and showing some affinities with the Hereford map (second half of the thirteenth century). For the Imago mundi, see my notes on Honorius Inclusus (second half of the eleventh century) and on Walter of Metz (first half of the thirteenth century).

The "Jerome maps"—so called after St. Jerome (second half of the fourth century, vol. 1, 363), who may have possibly inspired their prototype—are closely related to the Henry map. They belong to the middle of the twelfth century.

Konrad Miller: Mappae mundi. Stuttgart, (vols. 2 and 3, 1895). A small sketch of Henry's map will be found in Isis (vol. 5, 87). C. R. Beazley: Dawn of modern geography (vol. 2, 563–568, 1901, facsimiles of maps). J. K. Wright: Geographical Lore (124, 245, 251, 1925; Isis, 7, 495–498).

GUIDO THE GEOGRAPHER

Flourished about 1119. Italian (?) geographer who compiled in that year an encyclopaedic treatise entitled Geographica. It is based upon Isidore of Seville (first half of the seventh century), the Ravenna Cosmography (second half of the seventh century), Paul the Deacon (second half of the eighth century), etc. Two manuscripts contain a T-O map, a map of the world, and a map of Italy.

Text—M. Pinder and G. Parthey: Ravennatis anonymi Cosmographia et Guidonis Geographica (449–556, Berlin 1860).

Criticism—Cornelius Peter Bock: Lettre sur un MS. de la bibliothèque de Bourgogne intitulé Liber Guidonis (Annuaire de la Bibliothèque royale de Belgique 41–219, 1851). J. K. Wright: Geographical Lore (49, 104, 124, 1925).

LAMBERT OF SAINT OMER

Lambertus canonicus Audomarensis. French cosmographer who was canon of Saint Omer (Pas-de-Calais), early in the twelfth century; his father died in 1077–1078; Lambert is presumably identical with a monk and teacher at the monastery of St. Bertin, in Saint Omer, who became abbot in 1095 and died in 1125. He completed, about 1120, the compilation of an encyclopaedia entitled Liber floridus, similar to the De imagine mundi (vol. 1, 749) but less popular. It is derived from the writings of Macrobius, Martianus Capella, Isidore, Bede, Hrabanus Maurus, etc. Lambert believed in the sphericity of the earth and in the existence of antipodal regions, and had a correct (Eratosthenian) notion of the size of the earth.

The twelfth century manuscripts of the Liber floridus include some maps of great interest for the history of cartography. The oldest manuscript, kept in the Library of Ghent in Flanders, seems to have been written by the author himself, probably about 1120. It contains a portrait of him.

Text—Liber floridus in Migne's Patrology (vol. 163, 1003–1032, summary).

Criticism—Jules de Saint-Genois: Note sur le Liber floridus, in Migne's Patrology (vol. 163). Emile von Arenbergh: Lambert le Chanoine (Biographie nationale de Belgique, vol. 11, 162–166, 1891). Konrad Miller: Mappae mundi (6 vols., Stuttgart 1895–1898). C. R. Beazley: Dawn of modern geography (vol. 2, 570–573, 1901). Léopold Delisle: Notice sur les MSS. du Liber floridus (Notices et extraits, vol. 38, (2), 577–591, 1906). J. K. Wright: Geographical Lore (1925).

For Hermann the Dalmatian, see Chapter III, The Translators. For Bernard Silvester, see Chapter IV, Philosophic Background.

IV. LATIN PILGRIMS

SAEWULF

Born in Worcester (?), lived about 1102, and died, a monk, in the abbey of Malmesbury. English merchant, traveler and pilgrim to the Holy Land and the Near East in 1102–1103. His account in Latin is partly lost; what remains of it describes his journey from July 13, 1102, when he sailed from Monòpoli near Bari delle Puglie, to Sept. 30, 1103, when he reached Rodosto on the sea of Marmora on his way to Constantinople, homeward. This is the earliest pilgrim narrative posterior to the First Crusade.

Text and translations—Armand d'Avezac: Relation des voyages de Saewulf à Jérusalem et en Terre Sainte (Recueil de voyages et de mémoires publié par la Société de Géographie, vol. 4, 42 p., Paris 1839). Th. Wright: Early travels in Palestine (Bohn's library, London 1848; English translation). Saewulf translated by W. R. Brownlow (Palestine Pilgrims' Text Society, 21, London 1892; Latin text and translation; map). William Boulting: Four pilgrims (65–88, London 1921); spirited summary of Saewulf's accounts.

Criticism—R. Röhricht: Bibliotheca geographica Palaestinae (28, 1890). C. R. Beazley: Dawn of modern geography (vol. 2, 139–155, 1901).

BELARDO D'ASCOLI

Belardus de Esculo. Lived about 1112–1120. Author of a Latin description of the Holy Land.

G. A. Neumann: La Descriptio Terrae Sanctae de Belardo (Archives de l'Orient latin, vol. 1, 225–229, 1881). R. Röhricht: Bibliotheca geographica Palaestinae (32, 1890).

ANONYMOUS PILGRIMS TO THE HOLY LAND

Among the few accounts of the pilgrimages which were made at the time of the First Crusade or soon after, two or three are anonymous. These accounts are not important and a brief mention of them will suffice.

The first of these unknown pilgrims went to the Holy Land before the conquest of Jerusalem (1099). He is conventionally called "Innominatus I"; he has left a notebook containing a few observations and extracts from older records; the beginning of it is closely similar to some parts of the Bordeaux Jerusalem itinerary (A. D. 333; see vol. 1, 371).

Another pilgrim, a German, "Innominatus IV," went to Jerusalem some time within the first quarter of the century (Röhricht places him much later, c. 1270).

A third pilgrim, "Innominatus VII," went to Jerusalem probably some time within the fifth decade.

The accounts of these three pilgrims are of little value. Their main interest consists in being the witnesses of a number of inarticulate pilgrims who traveled to the Near East in the first half of the twelfth century.

The narrative ascribed to Fetellus (second half of the twelfth century) may be dated back, in its original and longer form, to soon after 1118. Finally, we may refer to this same period the famous plan of Jerusalem, called Situs Hierusalem which was possibly a section of a larger map.

Text—Innominatus I. "Si quis ab occidentalibus ubi et ipse Abraham filium suum Isaac immolare voluit." Titus Tobler: Theoderici libellus de locis sanctis (St. Gall, 113–118, 1865). Bonnardot et Longnon: Le saint voyage de Jérusalem du seigneur d'Anglure (117–120, Paris 1878).

Innominatus IV. "De Famagusta est proprior via quod hominis caput recipiat." Titus Tobler (ibidem, 134–140).

Innominatus VII. "Si quis vult intrare Jerusalem." Titus Tobler: Descriptiones Terrae sanctae (100–107, Leipzig 1874).

Criticism—R. Röhricht: Bibliotheca geographica Palaestinae (28, 33, 55, 1890). Potthast (651, 1896). C. R. Beazley: Dawn of modern geography (vol. 2, 138, 203, 583, 636–638, 1901).

V. OTHER CHRISTIAN PILGRIMS

DANIEL OF KIEV

Daniil. Russian archimandrite who lived in the province of Chernigov, and made a pilgrimage to Palestine about 1106–1107. His account of the journey is the earliest Russian text of its kind; it is also, with the possible exception of Nestor's chronicle, the earliest important text of Russian literature of any kind. Aside from its purely Russian interest, which is of course considerable, it is very valuable because of its fullness and relative veracity.

Text and translation—First edition, St. Petersburg 1835–1837. Abraham de Noroff: Pélérinage en Terre Sainte de l'igoumène russe Daniel au commencement du XIIe siècle (1113–1115). Traduit pour la première fois; accompagné de notes critiques et suivi du texte russe, collationné à la commission archéologique d'après 30 MSS. (229 p., St. Petersbourg 1864; Russian and French). Mme B. deKhitrowo: Vie et pélérinage de Daniel, hégoumène russe, 1106–1107 (Itinéraires russes en Orient traduits pour la Société de l'Orient latin, 3–83, Genève 1889). Colonel Sir C. W. Wilson: The pilgrimage of the Russian abbot Daniel in the Holy Land, 1106–1107 (Palestine Pilgrims' Text Society, no. 6, 126 p. London 1888).

Criticism—R. Röhricht: Bibliotheca geographica Palaestinae (30–32, 1890). Potthast (363, 1896). C. R. Beazley: Dawn of modern geography (vol. 2, 155–174, 1901).

SIGURD OF NORWAY

Sigurd Jorsalafare, son of Magnus III Barfod (Barefoot), King of Norway, who died in 1103; himself king from 1103 until his death in 1130. Traveler to Palestine (1107–1111). He is often called King Sigurd the Crusader.

Towards the end of Magnus' reign, Skopti Ogmundson sailed with five ships and entered the Mediterranean sea.[1] Skopti died in Rome, but some of his followers brought back home alluring stories of the wonderlands of the south. In 1107

[1] He is sometimes said to be the first Northman to go through the "Norva Sound" (Straits of Gibraltar), but others of his race had certainly preceded him.

Sigurd sailed with sixty ships to England, thence to Galicia, Portugal, the eastern coast of Spain, and the Balearic Islands, fighting the Muslim whenever the opportunity occurred. Sigurd stopped some time at the court of Roger II of Sicily; then proceeded to Palestine, and finally in 1111 sailed off to Cyprus and Constantinople where he was given a royal reception by Alexios I Comnenos (emperor from 1081 to 1118). The Northmen returned home overland by way of Bulgaria, Hungary, Pannonia, Bavaria, Suabia and Schleswig. Sigurd's travels and adventures are told in the Sigurd's Saga.

C. R. Beazley: Dawn of modern geography (vol. 2, 174–182, 1901). Salmonsens konversations Leksikon (Bind 21, 390, 1926).

VI. CHINESE

HSÜ CHING

Hsü[2] Ching[1] (4748, 2173). Lived about 1125. Chinese geographer. He was a member of a Chinese mission sent to Korea in 1125, and wrote a description of that country and of its customs and institutions, entitled Hsüan[1]-ho[2] fêng[4]-shih[3]kao[1]-li[4] t'u[2] ching[1] (4805, 3945, 3574, 9896, 5927, 6911, 12128, 2122).

Text—The manuscript contained maps, but these do not appear in the first printed edition, 1167. The Library of Congress has a copy of the Hsüan-ho in one work of 40 chüan.

Criticism—A. Wylie: Chinese literature (57, 1902).

CHINESE GEOGRAPHY

The two oldest Chinese maps extant were engraved on both sides of a stone slab in the same year, 1137, and probably in the same place, Ch'i[2] (1103), prefecture of Fêng[4]-hsiang[2] (3560, 4278), province of Shensi. They are kept in the museum of Hsi[1]-an[1] fu[3] (4031, 44, 3682). They are both of about the same size (77 x 79 cm.; 77 x 80 cm.), and both are oriented so that the North is at the top. The original maps, however, were made before 1137, and probably at different times. The first, entitled "Map of China and of the foreign countries," was made by a subject of the Liao[2] (7058) empire about 1043; it represents China and a part of Korea, the other foreign countries being simply mentioned in places around the map suggesting their direction. The second map is entitled "Map of the vestiges of Yü[3]" (13618). It is divided into squares, the sides of which are 100 li long.[2] This is not to be considered as a system of cartographic projection, for the earth is supposed to be flat; but it is a scale of reduction—a decimal scale.

These two maps have been excellently described and discussed by Ed. Chavannes: Les deux plus anciens spécimens de la cartographie chinoise (Bulletin de l'école française d'Extrême Orient, vol. 3, 214–247, 1903; with facsimiles); Mémoires concernant l'Asie orientale (vol. 1, footnote on p. 20, 1913). W. E. Soothill: The two oldest maps of China extant (Geographical journal, vol. 69, 532–555, 3 pl., 1927; Isis, 11, 423).

I saw rubbings of these maps in the Field Museum of Chicago, and in all probability such rubbings are available in other museums.

[2] This was not a new thing. (See Chia Tan, second half of the eighth century, vol. I, 536).

CHAPTER IX

NATURAL HISTORY

(First Half of Twelfth Century)

I. MUSLIM

For Serapion the Younger, and for Ibn al Tilmīdh, see Chapter X, Medicine.
For Ibn al-Jawālīqī, see Chapter XIII, Philology and Education.
For Ibn Bājja, see Chapter IV, Philosophic Background.

II. LATIN AND VERNACULAR

For Marbode, see volume I, 764.
For Philip of Thaon, see Chapter IV, Philosophic Background.
For Cistercian husbandry, and for Suger of Saint Denis, see Chapter II, Religious Background.
For Nicholas of Salerno, and for Matthaeus Platearius, see Chapter X, Medicine.

BOTANIC ICONOGRAPHY

The most popular, in mediaeval times, of the classical medical works was the Herbarium or De herbarum virtutibus (medicaminibus) of Apuleius Platonicus (or Barbarus). This work was derived from a Greek model, probably in the fifth century (see vol. I, 296, 392). There are a good many manuscripts of it. It is probable that the earliest manuscripts of the Latin text contained some illustrations of plants, similar to those of the Johnson Papyrus, a Greek manuscript of about 400 A.D.

An Oxford manuscript (Bodleian 130) written at Bury St. Edmunds in western Suffolk about 1120 is of great interest in the history of plant illustration, for it contains a few figures obviously drawn from nature. The unknown artist probably had a herbal of the usual Apuleius-Dioscorides type—that is, a text accompanied by very conventional figures. He probably tried to identify some of these with actual plants of the monastery garden. Then he drew the plants themselves, and thus produced some of the earliest naturalistic drawings that have come down to us—drawings of a blackberry, a labiate, a nightshade, a thistle. The tradition of these illustrations can be traced continuously, down to the time of printing; indeed, the first printed herbal has figures like those of an Anglo-Saxon manuscript herbal.

The Herbal of Apuleius Barbarus, from the early twelfth century manuscript formerly in the abbey of Bury St. Edmunds. Described by Robert T. Gunther, and presented to the members of the Roxburghe Club by Edward George Spencer-Churchill (Oxford 1925). Reviewed in Nature (vol. 117, 617, 1926).

Charles Singer: The herbal in antiquity (Journal of Hellenic studies, vol. 47, 52 p., 10 pl., 46 fig., 1927; Isis, 10, 519–521).

TREATISES ON FALCONRY

Falconry and, more generally, hunting with birds and other animals, was a favorite pastime in mediaeval times, both in the East and in the West. There are a number of treatises on falconry, in many languages, wherein is explained not only the proper way of keeping, handling, and using the birds, but also the means of healing them when they were ill. Unfortunately it is difficult, if not impossible, to identify many of these treatises; in some cases it is hardly possible to date them. A comparative study of the earliest ones, chiefly those in Arabic and Latin, is badly needed.

I have already referred to an Arabic treatise (vol. 1, 731) by Īsā ibn 'Alī ibn Ḥasan al-Asdī, dating from the eleventh century (?). Harting mentions a Persian treatise by Jamāl Muḥammad al-Ganjahī al-Samāni, dated 1145–1146. Ganjah (or Janzah) is the modern Elizabetpol, in the Caucasus, between Bardhā'ah and Tiflīs. I have been unable to identify the author, though I have consulted all the catalogues of Persian manuscripts available to me. However, the existence of an early Persian treatise would not be at all surprising, as falconry, judging from its terminology, owed much to Persian influence. Of course the sport is very old; it can be traced back to ancient Mesopotamia and Egypt.[1] But it was exceptionally popular in Iran, and more generally in the East from the Caucasus to Central Asia and India.

It is impossible to say when falconry was introduced into western Europe. It may have been transmitted there directly from Egypt or from some other ancient source, or it may have been discovered there independently. One of the earliest Latin documents on the subject is a dialogue between a scholar and a falconer in the Colloquium of the English monk and grammarian Aelfric (second half of the tenth century). There are no sufficient grounds for asserting that European falconry was of Muslim origin, but there is no doubt that it did not become truly popular (if this term may be applied to such aristocratic sport) until after the Crusades. The better and wider knowledge of falconry in the twelfth century and after was undoubtedly due to eastern influence. It is noteworthy that the practice and language of falconry are essentially alike east and west.

However, the earliest Latin treatise on the subject which has come down to us is the one by Adelard of Bath, already mentioned. (Adelard refers to an earlier work, the Libri Haroldi regis, which is lost). It seems free from Arabic influence, and deals mainly with old English recipes for the diseases of hawks.

Another early Latin treatise was composed by William, falconer to Roger II of Sicily. The original is lost, but extracts are known through quotations by Frederick II, Albert the Great, etc.

J. von Hammer-Purgstall: Falknerklee (Wien 1840). H. Schlegel and A. H. Verster de Wulverhorst: Traité de fauconnerie (Leiden 1844–1853, with folio atlas). This is the most elaborate treatise ever published. H. Werth: Altfranzösische Jagdlehrbücher, nebst Handschriften-bibliographie der abendländischen Jagdlitteratur überhaupt (Z. für romanische Philologie, vol. 12, 146–191, 381–415; vol. 13, 1–34, 1888–1889). Additional notes by Biedermann (ibidem, vol. 21, 529–540). James Edmund Harting: Bibliotheca accipitraria (197, London 1891); includes a technical glossary in English and in six other languages (p. 219–239). Louis Agassiz Fuertes: Falconry (National geographic magazine, vol. 38, 429–460, Washington 1920, with many illustrations explaining technical details; Isis, 4, 453.) C. H. Haskins: Some early treatises on falconry (Romanic review, vol. 13, 18–27, 1922; Isis, 5, 213).

[1] For Egypt, see note by Jean Capart in Isis (vol. 14, 222, 1930).

For information on Muslim falconry see Sid Mohamed el Mangali: Traité de vénerie traduit de l'arabe par Florian Pharaon, avec une introduction par le marquis G. de Cherville (Paris 1880). This contains the Arabic text, together with a French translation. The treatise is of Syrian origin. The fact that it is undated matters relatively little, for falconry has not changed much throughout the ages. An analysis of it is included in J. E. Harting: Essays on sport (London 1883). See also my note on Frederick II (first half of the thirteenth century) and the index sub voce falconry. Louis Mercier: La chasse et les sports chez les Arabes (256 p., illus., Paris 1927; Isis, 10, 511–513).

III. BYZANTINE

For Michael Glycas, see Chapter XI, Historiography.

For Joannes Tzetzes, see Chapter IV, Philosophic Background.

IV. CHINESE

CH'ÊN-FU

Ch'ên[2]-fu[1] (658, 3638). Lived about 1149. Chinese agriculturist. In 1149 he wrote a short treatise on husbandry, in three parts, called Nung[2] shu[1] (8408, 10024). It treats of agriculture, the breeding of cattle, and sericulture.

Text—Often published usually with an appendix on sericulture, Ts'an[2] shu[1] (11574, 10024), by Ch'in[2] Chan[4] (2093, 313) of the Sung dynasty. The Library of Congress has both the Nung shu and the Ts'an shu in the Chih[1] pu[1]* tsu[2]* chai[1] ts'ung[1] shu[1] (1783, 9456, 11840, 234, 12039, 10024), vol. 69, and also in other ts'ung shu.

Criticism—A. Wylie: Chinese literature (94, 1902). L. Wieger: La Chine (420, 512, 1920).

For the Pên ts'ao, see Chapter X, Medicine.

CHAPTER X

MEDICINE

(First Half of Twelfth Century)

I. SERAPION JUNIOR, OR IBN SARĀBĪ

Ibn Sarābī, or Serapion the Younger. Not to be confused with Serapion the Elder, Yaḥyā ibn Sarāfyūn (second half of the ninth century). A physician who wrote in Arabic, but who is otherwise unknown. He was possibly a Christian. His date is determined only by the facts that he quoted Ibn al-Wāfid (first half of the eleventh century), who lived until about 1074, and is quoted by Ibn al-Baiṭâr (first half of the thirteenth century); he lived probably in the twelfth century; I place him tentatively in the first half of that century.

He wrote a treatise on simples, Kitāb-al-adwiya al-mufrada (Liber de simplici medicina; De medicamentis simplicibus; De temperamentis simplicium), the Latin text of which enjoyed much popularity. It is an elaborate compilation derived from Byzantine and Muslim sources.

It is strange that Ibn Sarābī is not mentioned by Muslim bibliographers. It has been suggested that the Latin text was not a translation from the Arabic, as it pretended to be, but was written originally in Latin, or was translated from the Hebrew. That hypothesis is unproved. The original was translated into Latin by Simon Januensis with the assistance of Abraham ben Shem-ṭob (second half of the thirteenth century). This Latin translation was so popular that it eclipsed the Arabic text. The latter remained practically unknown. Yet a part of it is available in an Arabic manuscript; there is also a Hebrew version, derived from the Arabic, not from the Latin.

Text—Liber Serapionis aggregatus in medicinis simplicibus translatio Simonis Januensis interprete Abraham Judaeo Tortuosiensi de arabico in latinum (185 fol., Milano 1473). This is the first edition. Other editions appeared in Venice in 1479, Strassburg in 1531, and Venice again in 1552. The best edition is that of 1531, prepared by Otto Brunfels and Gerardus Noviomagus. It includes treatises De simplicibus by al-Rāzī and Ibn Rushd, and Galen's De centaurea; and an Arabic-Latin glossary.

Criticism—F. Wüstenfeld: Arabische Aerzte (83, 1840). L. Choulant: Handbuch der Bücherkunde (371, 1841). Ernst Meyer: Geschichte der Botanik (vol. 3, 234–239, 1856). L. Leclerc: Médecine arabe (vol. 2, 152–176, 1876); places Serapion in the thirteenth century. M. Steinschneider: Hebraeische Übersetzungen (737–738, 1893). Pierre Guigues: Les noms arabes dans Sérapion (Journal asiatique, mai-août, 1895. Reprint of 137 p., plus 4 p. of errata); Guigues considers 544 drugs; bibliography, and French and Arabic indices; important.

II. WESTERN MUSLIM

IBN ḤASDAI

Abū Ja'far Yūsuf (Joseph) ibn Aḥmad ibn Ḥasdai. He belonged to the Judaeo-Spanish family Ḥasdai (vol. I, 680), but his father's name, Aḥmad, suggests that the latter was a Muslim. Yūsuf was probably born in Spain, but he lived in Egypt during the caliphate of the tenth Fāṭimid, al-Āmir (1101–1130); he was protected by the wazīr al-Ma'mūn (crucified in 1128). He was a scientific correspondent of Ibn Bājja. He wrote commentaries on Hippocrates and Galen: for example, the Ma'mūnic commentary (thus named in honor of his patron), Al-sharḥ al-Ma'mūnī, on the Hippocratic oath; Sharḥ al-fuṣūl, commentary on the first book of Hippocrates' aphorisms; Fāwā'id, useful remarks, being extracts from 'Alī ibn Riḍwān's commentary on Galen's treatise to Glaucon; Qaul 'ala awwal ṣana'ah al-saghīrah, commentary on the first book of Galen's Ars parva. He also wrote a summary (ijmāl) on logic.

Criticism—F. Wüstenfeld: Arabische Aerzte (88, 1840). M. Steinschneider: Arabische Literatur der Juden (148, 1902). Isaac Broydé: Jewish Encyclopaedia (vol. 7, 256, 1904).

ABŪ-L-ṢALT

Abū-l-Ṣalt Umaiya ibn 'Abd al-'Azīz ibn abī-l-Ṣalt al-Andalusī. Born in 1067–1068 at Denia, and lived in Seville; after 1096 he lived in Cairo, and after 1112 in Mahdīya, Tunis, where he died in 1134. Hispano-Muslim physician, mathematician, and astronomer. About the end of the eleventh century he tried to raise a ship sunk at Alexandria, but failed. He wrote various treatises on medicine, mathematics and astronomy; also letters or essays—Al-rasā'īl al-Miṣrīya—about things and people observed by him in Egypt. His most important works are a treatise on simple drugs, Kitāb al-adwiya al-mufrada; a treatise on logic, Taqwīm al-dhihn (Rectification of the understanding); and a treatise on the astrolabe, Risāla fī-l-'amal bi-l-iṣṭarlāb.

A treatise on music, Risāla fī-l-mūsīqī, is partly extant in Hebrew. This translation is doubly interesting, first because the original is lost, second because there are but very few Hebrew writings on music. The Simplicia were translated into Latin by Arnold of Villanova (second half of the thirteenth century), and into Hebrew by Judah Nathan (second half of the fourteenth century).

Text—The Taqwīm al-dhihn was edited, and translated into Spanish, by Angel González Palencia: Rectificación de la mente (thesis, Madrid 1915).

Criticism—F. Wüstenfeld: Arabische Aerzte (92–93, 1840); Geschichtschreiber (80, no. 237, 1881). M. Steinschneider: Hebräische Übersetzungen (735, 855, 1893). L. Leclerc: Médecine arabe (vol. 2, 74–75, 1876). C. Brockelmann: Arabische Litteratur (vol. I, 486, 1898). H. Suter: Mathematiker (115, 1900; 272, 1902). Henry George Farmer: History of Arabian music (221, 1929; Isis, 13, 375).

IBN BĀJJA

See Chapter IV, Philosophic Background.

ABŪ-L-'ALĀ' ZUHR

Abū-l-'Alā' Zuhr ibn abī Marwān 'Abd al-Malik ibn Muḥammad ibn Marwān, al-Ishbīlī. A Spanish-Muslim physician, the most illustrious representative—except his son Avenzoar—of the Ibn Zuhr family.

That family, originating from the Arabian tribe of 'Adnān, established itself at the beginning of the tenth century at Jafn Shātiba (Játiva) in eastern Andalusia.

The ancestor of the Spanish line was named Zuhr, hence the patronymic Ibn Zuhr. They lived in Játiva until the Christian conquest in 1247–1248. The first prominent member of the family was a jurist, Abū Bakr Muḥammad ibn Marwān, who died at Talavera in 1030–1031, at the age of 86. His son, Abū Marwān 'Abd al-Malik, was a great physician, especially famous as a skilful diagnostician, who practised in Qairawān, Cairo, and finally returning to Spain, settled in Denia where he died in 1077–1078. This Abū Marwān had a son, Abū-l-'Alā', who is the subject of the present note.

Abū-l-'Alā' studied at Cordova and was even more successful as a physician than his father; he was attached to the court of al-Mu'tamid, the last 'Abbādid king of Seville (ruled from 1068 to 1091). After the conquest of Seville by the Berber Murābiṭīn[1] (Almoravides) in 1091, he became wazīr to the conqueror Yūsuf ibn Tāshfīn (who ruled until 1106). His usual name, Al-wazīr Abū-l-'Alā' Zuhr, was corrupted by early Latin translators into Alguazir Albuleizor (and variants). He died in Cordova in 1130–1131, and was buried in Seville. His main title to fame is the fact of being Avenzoar's father, but he deserves to be remembered for his own activity. He wrote a number of medical books: Kitāb al-khawāṣṣ, Book of (medical) properties; Kitāb al-adwiya-l-mufrada, Book of simple drugs; Kitāb al-'īḍāḥ, Book of explanation; Kitāb ḥall shukūk al-Rāzī 'alā kutub Jālīnūs, Solution of al-Rāzī's doubts with regard to Galen's works; Mujarrabāt, Experimental facts (Medical observations); Maqāla fīl-radd 'alā Abū 'Alī ibn Sīnā fī mawāḍi' min kitābihi fī-l-adwiya-l-mufrada, Discourse of refutation of a few points in Ibn Sīnā's book on simple drugs; Maqāla fī basṭhi lirisāla Ya'qūb ibn Isḥāq al-Kindī fī tarkīb al-adwiya, Discourse wherein he develops al-Kindī's letter on the composition of drugs; Kitāb al-nukat al-ṭibbīya, Main principles of medicine. The last named is almost certainly identical with another work of his, the Tadhkira, or Reminder, which he wrote for his son 'Abd al-Malik (Avenzoar) when the latter was traveling in Morocco. It is a practical guide containing special references to climatological and pathological conditions in Marrākush; complementary information on various medical subjects; also deontological advice; the medical philosophy involved is the Galenic. This treatise has sometimes been ascribed, wrongly, to the son.

Text—Gabriel Colin: La Tedkira d'Abu'l-'Alā', publiée et traduite pour la première fois (86 p., Publications de la Faculté des lettres d'Alger, 45; Paris 1911); Arabic and French text with technical glossary.

Abohaly Abenzoar de regimine sanitatis liber continens sanitatis tuendae rationem secundum praecipuas humani corporis partes capitibus triginta duobus (sic) distinctus. (Basel 1618); atrocious translation published by Jo. Georg Schenck.

Criticism—F. Wüstenfeld: Arabische Aerzte (91, 1840). L. Leclerc: Médecine arabe (vol. 1, 83–86, 1876). Ibn abi Uṣaibi'a (vol. 2, 64, 1882). C. Brockelmann: Arabische Litteratur (vol. 1, 486, 1898). Gabriel Colin: Avenzoar (16–22, Paris 1911). Cl. Huart: Journal Asiatique (2, 381–384, 1913).

IBN ZUHR

This patronymic, when used alone, represents without ambiguity the most illustrious member of the greatest medical family of Muslim Spain. His full name

[1] Murābiṭ means one entirely devoted to the service of the faith; hence, French marabout, a holy man.

was Abū Marwān 'Abd al-Malik ibn Abī-l-'Alā' Zuhr, etc. (see his father's name, above). He was often called Abū Marwān Ibn Zuhr, hence the Latin form Abhomeron Avenzoar, or Avenzoar. Among the many distinguished physicians of the Muslim West, he was by far the greatest; he was also the most famous physician of his time, not only among Muslims, but in Christendom. His greatest originality as compared with other Muslim physicians, is that he was content to remain a physician; his works are devoted exclusively to medicine. He was born in Seville about 1091–1094. He served under the Almoravides, and after their defeat by the Almohades (Muwaḥḥid, Unitarians), he became wazīr and physician to 'Abd al-Mu'min (the first Muwaḥḥid, 1130–1163). He died in Seville in 1161–1162. He was perhaps the greatest clinician of Islām, after al-Rāzī. His medical theories were Galenic, of course, but with strong empirical tendencies in sharp contrast to the doctrinairism of the other Muslim physicians. He wrote at least six medical works, but three of these are lost. The three extant works, in chronological order, are as follows:

(1) Kitāb al-iqtiṣād fi iṣlāḥ al-anfus wal-ajsād, Book of the iqtiṣād[2] concerning the reformation of souls and bodies, completed in 1121–1122, for the Murābiṭ prince Ibrāhīm ibn Yūsuf ibn Tāshfīn—the son of the Murābiṭ king of Seville to whom Abū-l-'Alā' Zuhr had been the wazīr. It is a summary of therapeutics and hygiene, composed for the benefit of lay readers. It remained apparently incomplete; it contains fifteen iqtiṣād; it is probable that the author meant to write a second volume; there would then have been thirty iqtiṣād—that is, as many as there are sections in the Qur'ān. As the title indicates, it treats of souls as well as bodies; the beginning of it is a summary of psychology.

(2) Kitāb al-taisīr fi-l-mudāwāt wal-tadbīr, Book of simplification concerning therapeutics and diet. This is Ibn Zuhr's most important work. It was written at the request of Ibn Rushd, who was a great friend and admirer[3] (though not a disciple); this could not have occurred long before the middle of the century. It would seem that they both meant the Taisīr to be the counterpart of the Kullīyāt, the latter dealing with the generalities of medicine, the former with more special topics. If that be true, the task was certainly very well distributed between them, Ibn Rushd being primarily a philosopher, while the older man, Ibn Zuhr, was first of all a clinician or practitioner. After a very long preamble of doubtful value, the Taisīr contains an elaborate study of pathological conditions and relevant therapeutics, the whole being followed by an antidotary or formulary called Jāmi' (meaning Collector— collected recipes), which is sometimes mentioned as a separate work.

(3) Kitāb al-aghdhiya, Book of foodstuffs, composed for the first Muwaḥḥid caliph, 'Abd al-Mu'min, who ruled from 1130 to 1163. This work, much less important than the two others, treats various kinds of food and their use according to the seasons; simple drugs, and hygiene. It also indicates the usefulness of various bezel stones. This, and some other indications in his works—for example, on sympathetic remedies—shows that Ibn Zuhr was not entirely free from superstition; but we could hardly expect him to be so.

His fundamental work is the Taisīr which contains many clinical descriptions

[2] The word iqtiṣād is difficult to translate; it may mean keeping the middle course, but it seems to refer here to the division of the treatise in equal parts, comparable to the Qur'ānic juz.

[3] In the Kitāb al-kullīyāt, Ibn Rushd declares that the author of the Taisīr is the greatest physician since Galen.

(mediastinal tumors, pericarditis, intestinal phthisis, pharyngeal paralysis, inflammation of the middle ear, scabies). He recommended tracheotomy and artificial feeding through the gullet and rectum; he realized the nocuousness of the air coming from marshes; he was a great advocate of venesection; he examined human ossements.

Ibn Zuhr is often credited with the first description of the itch-mite (Acarus scabiei); he would thus be the earliest important parasitologist since Alexander of Tralles (second half of the sixth century). However, he was anticipated in this by Aḥmad al-Ṭabarī (second half of the tenth century), a fact which I did not know when writing the note about the latter in vol. I, p. 677. Since then a few extracts of the Kitāb al-mu'ālaja al-buqrāṭīya have been translated into German by Mohamed Rihab (Archiv für Geschichte der Medizin, 19, 123–168, 1927; the reference to the itch-mite will be found on p. 134; Isis, 10, 119).

Ibn Zuhr was not a Jew. This is sufficiently obvious, and need not be stated but for the fact that some good scholars, beginning with Casiri (Bibliotheca arabico-hispana, 1760), have maintained erroneously the opposite view.

To complete the history of this great medical dynasty, Ibn Zuhr's only son, Abū Bakr Muḥammad ibn 'Abd al-Malik, etc., nicknamed al-Ḥafīd (the grandson), was born in Seville in 1110–1111 (or 1113–1114), and died (poisoned) in Marrākush in 1199. He was a successful physician, but was more famous among his contemporaries as a man of letters and a poet. A treatise on eye diseases is ascribed to him. Ibn Zuhr had also a daughter who became a skilful midwife, as did her own daughter later. The latter was poisoned at the same time as her uncle, in Marrākush in 1199. Abu Bakr Muḥammad left a son, Abū Muḥammad 'Abdallah ibn al-Ḥafīd, born in Seville in 1181–1182, who became also a successful physician in the Muwaḥḥid service. 'Abdallāh died poisoned, as his father had been, in Saleh in 1205–1206; he was buried in Seville. He left two sons who lived in Seville; the youngest, Abū-l-'Alā' Muḥammad, was also a physician; he represented the sixth generation of physicians in direct descent in the Ibn Zuhr family.

Through Hebrew and Latin translations, Ibn Zuhr's influence upon European medicine was maintained until the end of the seventeenth century.

Text—The Taisīr was promptly translated into Hebrew. There were at least two early Hebrew translations, both anonymous, one of which was known in Italy before 1260. M. Steinschneider: Die hebräischen Übersetzungen des Mittelalters (748–752, 1893). Jacob the Hebrew (Magister Jacobus Hebraeus) translated a Hebrew translation into vulgar language (Venitian?), and this version was turned into Latin by Paravici in 1280–1281. This Latin translation, Adjumentum de medela et regimine, was printed in Venice in 1490, 1496, 1497, 1514, 1530; Lyon 1531 (bis); Venice 1554 (?). All of these editions contain both the Taisīr and the Kullīyāt. Outside of these complete editions, there appeared also many separate ones: for example, Libellus Zoar de cura lapidis (Venice 1497); editions of relevant parts included in the collections De balneis (Venice 1553); and De febribus (Venice 1594).

Another Latin translation of the Taisīr was made by John of Capua (second half of the thirteenth century); not from the Arabic as has been claimed, but from the Hebrew. (Illustrated MS., Faculty of Medicine, Paris). This translation seems to be more correct than the one which was so often reprinted; yet both are full of incorrections and obscurities.

A critical edition of the Arabic text, and a good translation based upon it, are badly needed.

Criticism—I must quote first Gabriel Colin: Avenzoar, sa vie et ses oeuvres (200 p., Publications de la faculté des lettres d'Alger, vol. 44; Paris 1911); an elaborate study containing an analysis of the three works above mentioned, with comparison chapter by chapter of the Arabic and Latin texts, a good medical index, a technical glossary and a bibliography. But even this excellent work is only an introduction to a more technical study from the medical point of view. Review by Cl. Huart: Journal Asiatique (vol. 1, 713–716, 1913).

F. Wüstenfeld: Geschichte der arabischen Aerzte (90, 1840). L. Leclerc: Médecine arabe (vol. 2, 86–93, 1876). Ibn abī Uṣaibi'a (vol. 2, 66, 1884). C. Brockelmann: Arabische Litteratur (vol. 1, 487, 489, 1898). Gabriel Colin: Encyclopaedia of Islām (vol. 2, 430–431, 1918). Gesamtkatalog der Wiegendrucke (vol. 3, 213–216, 1928).

III. EASTERN MUSLIM

'ADNĀN AL-'AINZARBĪ

Abū Naṣr 'Adnān ibn Naṣr al-'Ainzarbī. The last name refers to the place 'Ain Zarba, the ancient Anazarbos in southeastern Cilicia, Dioscorides' birthplace. He lived a long time in Baghdād, and later in Cairo at the court of the Fāṭimid caliph al-Ẓāfir, who ruled from 1149 to 1154. He died in 1153–1154. Muslim physician and astrologer. He wrote in 1116–1117(?)a medical compendium Kitāb al-kāfī fī 'ilm al-ṭibb (The sufficient in medicine); and a treatise on the application of astronomy to medicine, Kitāb fī ma yaḥtāj al-ṭabīb min 'ilm al-falak (What the physician needs [to know] of the science of the celestial sphere).

Criticism—F. Wüstenfeld: Arabische Aerzte (95, 1840). L. Leclerc: Médecine arabe (vol. 2, 51, 1876). Ibn abī Uṣaibi'a, in A. Müller's edition (vol. 2, 107, 1884). C. Brockelmann: Arabische Litteratur (vol. 1, 487, 1898). H. Suter: Mathematiker und Astronomen (120, 1900).

IBN AL-TILMĪDH

Abū-l-Ḥasan Hibatallāh ibn Ṣā'id Ibn al-Tilmīdh Amīn al-daula. He traveled in Persia, then established himself at Baghdād where he became finally chief of the medical profession and physician to al-Muqtafī, caliph from 1135–1136 to 1160; he died, very old, in 1164–1165. A Christian physician, who was very famous in his time. He wrote various medical works in Arabic; notably an antidotary, Aqrābādhīn, which threw into the shadow the previous work of Sābūr ibn Sahl (second half of the ninth century); a treatise on bloodletting, Al-maqāla al-Amīnīya fī-l-faṣd; and a collection of observations, Al-mujarrabāt.

Criticism—F. Wüstenfeld: Arabische Aerzte (97, 1840). L. Leclerc: Médecine arabe (vol. 2, 24–27, 1876). C. Brockelmann: Arabische Litteratur (vol. 1, 487, 1898).

ISMĀ'ĪL AL-JURJĀNĪ

Abū-l-Faḍā'il Ismā'īl ibn al-Ḥusain al-Jurjānī, Zain al-dīn. Often called Sayyid Ismā'īl. Persian physician who wrote in Arabic and Persian. He originated in the Jurjān, east of the Caspian, and lived at the court of Khwārizm; he died in 1135–1136. He compiled in Persian an immense medical treatise, Dhakhīra al-Khwārizmshāhī (The treasure of the king of Khwārizm). This work was probably completed soon after 1110, for Quṭb al-dīn Muḥammad, shāh from 1097 to 1127. It was probably the first medical encyclopaedia written in Persian instead of Arabic. It contains about 450,000 words, and is divided into nine books (75 discourses, 1107 chapters); a tenth book, Kitāb qarābādhīn—an antidotary—was added later. For the wazīr of Quṭb al-dīn's successor, Atsīz, shāh from 1127 to 1156, he wrote another treatise (partly based upon the Dhakhīra), the Aghrāḍ al-ṭibb (The aims of medicine); this treatise was thus completed about 1127-1135.

I do not know whether his other works were written in Persian or in Arabic, or in both languages, or in which language they were written first. In 1113 he completed a condensed edition (two volumes) of his Dhakhīra, entitled Khafī 'Alā'ī. He dedicated to 'Alā' al-dīn 'Alī Arslān another medical repertory entitled Tadhkira al-ashrafīya fī-l-ṣinā'a al-ṭibbīya. Among other writings, I may still quote a philosophical one entitled Al-munabbih (The admonisher), wherein he showed the vanity of worldly desires.

The Dhakhīra was translated into Hebrew in a somewhat abbreviated form by an anonymous author. This is very remarkable, because there are practically no other translations of medical writings from Persian into Hebrew.

Text—According to Browne, the Dhakhīra is still unpublished, though he thinks that a lithographed Urdū translation is used in India.

Criticism—F. Wüstenfeld: Arabische Aerzte (95, 1840). L. Leclerc: Médecine arabe (vol. 2, 18-19, 1876). M. Steinschneider: Hebraeische Übersetzungen (754, 1893). C. Brockelmann: Arabische Litteratur (vol. 1, 487, 1898). Karl Sudhoff: Beitrag zur Geschichte der Anatomie im Mittelalter (1908); apropos of the illustrations of a MS. of the Dhakhīra, Bodleian, 1576. Adolf Fonahn: Quellenkunde der persischen Medizin (7-13, 1910); analysis of the Dhakhīra and of the Aghrāḍ. E. G. Browne: Arabian medicine (110-112, 1921); analysis of the Dhakhīra.

IV. JEWISH

IBN BIKLĀRISH

Yūsuf ibn Isḥāq ibn Biklārish al-Isrā'īlī. Hispano-Jewish physician who lived at the court of Aḥmad al-Musta'īn (Hūdid sulṭān of Saragossa from 1085 to 1109). About 1106 he wrote in Arabic a treatise on simple medicines entitled (after his patron) Kitāb al-Musta'īnī. This treatise is arranged in the form of synoptic tables after the model of earlier medical works by Christian physicians of Baghdād, Ibn Buṭlān (first half of the eleventh century), and Ibn Jazla (second half of the eleventh century). These tables are preceded by a long introduction, explaining the whole subject. They include five columns: (1) name of each remedy; (2) nature and grade, according to the four fundamental qualities; (3) translation of name in various languages—Syrian, Persian, Greek, Latin, Spanish; (4) abdāl, succedanea; (5) action, use, preparation.

Ibn abi Uṣaibi'a (Königsberg i. Pr., vol. 2, 52, 1884). C. Brockelmann: Arabische Litteratur (vol. 1, 486, 1898). M. Steinschneider: Arabische Literatur der Juden (147, 1902). J. Renaud: Etude sur Ibn Beklarech (Bull. soc. franç. hist. méd., vol. 21, 345, 1927).

SALĀMA BEN RAḤMŪN

See Chapter IV, Philosophic Background.

V. BYZANTINE

For Joannes Tzetzes, and for Theodoros Prodromos, see Chapter IV, Philosophic Background.

HIEROPHILOS THE SOPHIST

Ἱερόφιλος ὁ σοφιστής. Lived about the middle of the twelfth century (?). Unknown author of a treatise on diet, περὶ τροφῶν κύκλος, ποίᾳ δεῖ χρᾶσθαι ἑκάστῳ μηνὶ καὶ ὁποίοις ἀπέχεσθαι, giving advice with regard to the proper food for each month, together with a few other hygienic rules.

Text—First published by Boissonade in 1827. New edition by J. L. Ideler: Physici et medici graeci minores (vol. 1, 409–417, Berlin 1841). This text might be compared with two others, both anonymous, published by Ideler in the same collection: Περὶ τῶν δώδεκα μηνῶν τοῦ ἐνιαυτοῦ ὁποίαις δεῖ χρῆσθαι τροφαῖς ἐνὶ ἑκάστῳ αὐτῶν καὶ ἀπὸ ποιῶν ἀπέχεσδαι (vol. 1, 423–429, 1841), and περὶ χυμῶν, βρωμάτων καὶ πωμάτων (τῶν τε χερσαίων, ἐναερίων καὶ θαλαττίων, ὅσα τε ἐκ τούτων εἰσὶ τρόφιμα καὶ εὔχυμα καὶ ὅσα δύσπεπτα καὶ κακόχυμα) (vol. 2, 257–281, 1842).

Criticism—Auguste Corlieu: Les médecins grecs depuis la mort de Galien jusqu'à la chute de l'empire d'Orient (163–165, Paris 1885; extract translated). K. Krumbacher does not mention this Hierophilos (1897).

For additional information on contemporary Byzantine medicine, see E. Jeanselme and L. Oeconomos: Les oeuvres d'assistance et les hôpitaux byzantins au siècle des Comnènes (Premier Congrès de l'art de guérir, 20 p., Anvers 1921; Isis, 4, 582). E. Jeanselme: Calcul de la ration alimentaire des malades de l'Hôpital . . . du Pantocrator à Byzance (1136). (Deuxième Congrès d'histoire de la médecine, 10 p., Evreux 1922; Isis, 6, 148).

VI. LATIN

For Joannes Afflacius, *alias* John the Saracen, see vol. I, 769.

STEPHEN OF ANTIOCH

Stephen the Philosopher. Born in Pisa, educated at Salerno. He lived in Antioch about 1127. Italian physician and translator from the Arabic into Latin. About 1127 he finished a complete translation of the Kitāb al-malikī of 'Alī ibn 'Abbās (second half of the tenth century). The Malikī had been translated before, partly, under the title of Pantegni, by Constantine the African, Afflacius, and Rusticus (second half of the eleventh century), but Stephen's version was entirely new. He added to it a glossary (Greek, Arabic, Latin) of the technical terms in Dioscorides, called by later writers "Stephen's Synonyms." He was probably the author of the medical treatise entitled De modo medendi, formerly ascribed to Copho and to Archimatthaeus.

It is said[4] that the terms pia mater and dura mater, to designate the membranes enveloping the brain and spinal cord, first appeared in Stephen's translation of the Malikī. At any rate, they appeared in Latin at about this time; see glossary in Sudhoff's Beiträge (vol. 2, 1918); and they are obviously of Arabic origin (cf. umm al-dimāgh, mother of the brain).

The Liber Mamonis in astronomia a Stephano philosopho translatus, represented by a late twelfth century manuscript, Cambrai no. 930 (829), contains a violent criticism of Macrobius. It reads more like an original treatise than a translation,

[4] However, see below, my note on the Anatomia porci.

but betrays both Arabic and Greek influences. This Stephen was probably a Sicilian or a Syrian. However, his identification with Stephen of Antioch is not sufficiently warranted.

Text—The Liber regalis, or Regalis dispositio, was first printed at Venice in 1492; this was Stephen's translation. A second edition with glossary by Michael of Capella (fecundis synonymis) appeared in Lyon in 1523. Neither edition contains Stephen's glossary. Constantine's Pantegni was printed only in 1539, and this edition only included the first—theoretical—part.

De modo medendi. Cophoni tractatus de arte medendi (Haganoae, 1532). Joh. Caesarius: Tractatus rei medicae tres (Strassburg 1534); included in the Mesuë editions of 1540; Florence 1570, 1582. J. J. Jac. Berthold: Initia doctrinae de ossibus ac ligamentis corporis humanae (Nuremberg 1794). S. de Renzi: Collectio salernitana (vol. 4, 415–438).

Criticism—M. Steinschneider: Europäische Übersetzungen (77, 1904). K. Sudhoff: Beiträge zur Geschichte der Chirurgie im Mittelalter (vol. 2, 95, 99, 1918). C. H. Haskins: Studies in mediaeval science (98–103, 131–135, 1924). R. Ganszyniec: Stephanus de modo medendi (Archiv für Geschichte der Medizin, vol. 14, 110–113, 1923). Identifying the author of the De modo medendi, disciple of Copho, with Stephen of Antioch (Isis, 8, 740).

For John of Seville, and for Plato of Tivoli, see Chapter III, The Translators.

THE FIRST SALERNITAN ANATOMICAL DEMONSTRATION (ANATOMIA PORCI; ANATOMIA COPHONIS)

I have already discussed this text (vol. 1, 770, 742), but it is necessary to go back to it because it dates more probably from the beginning (say, first decade) of the twelfth century than from the end of the eleventh century. The ascription to Copho, which dates only from the sixteenth century, is unwarranted, though one Copho, teacher of Stephen of Antioch, was an exact contemporary. This Anatomia porci is of considerable importance as the earliest Salernitan anatomy showing traces of the new terminology introduced by the translations from the Arabic, published by Constantine the African (second half of the eleventh century). Indeed, it marks a sort of transition, for it also contains traces of the earlier Greco-Latin terminology of Vindicianus (second half of the fourth century), or of Isidore of Seville (first half of the seventh century); for example, we find in it the old word oesophagus, instead of the Constantinian one meri (Ar., marī); and the classical words epiplon (ἐπίπλοον) and omentum, together with the new word zirbus (Ar., tharb); we also find the terms pia mater and dura mater, which would suggest that they were introduced not by Stephen of Antioch but by earlier translators.

The Anatomia porci is a guide describing the public dissection of a pig for teaching purposes. It deals first with the neck, then with the chest and abdomen, finally with the uterus and brain. The bloodvessels and abdominal membranes are treated very rapidly; and nothing is said of the skeleton, except the cranium. Anatomy, physiology, and pathology are all mixed up.

Text—First edition in the Divi Mesuë Vita (Lyon 1531); it is here that the ascription to Copho first occurs. Often reprinted in various editions of Mesuë the Younger (first half of the eleventh century). Also included in Joannes Dryander: Anatomia (Marburg 1537) and in Marco Aurelio Severino: Zootomia democritea (Nuremberg 1645). A slightly different text, with two additional sections on the brain and uterus, entitled Anatomia parva Galeni, was included in the earliest complete editions of Galen; it took its place among the Galenic apocrypha in the editions of Venice 1541, Basel 1542, Florence 1576, etc. Salvatore de Renzi's edition in his Collectio salernitana is a reprint of Severino's. English version of the Dryander text by Le Roy Crummer: Annals of medical history (vol. 9, 180-182, 1927).

Modern editions—Ignaz Schwarz: Die medizinischen Handschriften des Universitäts-Bibliothek zu Würzburg (Würzburg 1907). George W. Corner: Anatomical texts of the earlier Middle Ages, with a revised Latin text and English translation of Anatomia Cophonis (Washington 1927; Isis, 9, 452-456). Karl Sudhoff: Die erste Tieranatomie von Salerno und ein neuer salernitanischer Anatomietext (Archiv für Geschichte der Mathematik, vol. 10, 136-154, 1927; Isis, 11, 172).

Criticism—Vol. I, 770; and the introductions to the modern editions.

THE SECOND SALERNITAN DEMONSTRATION

Another text very similar to the Anatomia porci must be placed a little later, though probably still in the first half of the twelfth century. Its purpose and arrangement are the same, but it is more elaborate—it is more than four times longer—and it denies or corrects four statements made in the earlier text. We know nothing of the author except that he wrote at least three other books, namely, commentaries on the Hippocratic Aphorisms, and on the works of Theophilos Protospatharios and Ḥunain ibn Isḥāq. This would suggest identification with Maurus (second half of the twelfth century); indeed, the second anatomy has many points of contact with the Anatomia Mauri—it obviously belongs to the same family of texts—yet seems somewhat anterior.

The influence of the works upon which the author wrote commentaries can be easily traced in his writings on anatomy; some paragraphs of it are taken almost bodily from the Pantegni, Constantine's translation of the Kitāb al-Malikī of 'Alī ibn 'Abbās (second half of the tenth century). The dissection proper is preceded by an introduction wherein the organs are classified according to their functions; this is largely taken from the Pantegni.

Text—First edition by C. L. Nagel: Commentatio de anatomia salernitana per compendium salernitanum (Breslau 1852). Reprinted by Salvatore de Renzi in his Collectio salernitana (1853). Revised edition by Karl Heinrich Benedict: Die Demonstratio anatomica corporis animalis (Diss., Leipzig 1920). Englished by George W. Corner: Anatomical texts of the earlier Middle Ages (54-66, Washington 1927; Isis, 9, 454).

For the Anatomia Mauri, which might be called the Third Salernitan demonstration, see my note on Maurus (second half of the twelfth century).

ARCHIMATTHAEUS

A Salernitan physician who lived in the first half of the twelfth century. Possibly identical with Matthaeus de Archiepiscopo (Matteo de Vescova). Author of a remarkable treatise on clinical conduct and medical tact, De instructione medici (a slightly different version is entitled De adventu medici ad aegrotum); and of a Practica wherein special emphasis is laid on dietetics. He was possibly the author of De urinis, ascribed to Matthaeus de Archiepiscopo.

Text—Th. E. G. Henschel: De praxi medica salernitana commentatio cui praemissus est anonymi salernitani de adventu medici ad aegrotum (Breslau

1850). S. De Renzi: Collectio salernitana (vol. 2, 74–80, 1853; vol. 5, 333–349, 1859); Practica Archimathaei (ibidem, vol. 5, 350–376); De urinis secundum Mattheum de Archiepiscopo (ibidem, vol. 4, 506–512).

For the De modo medendi, formerly ascribed to Archimatthaeus, see my note on Stephen of Antioch.

Criticism—M. Neuburger: Geschichte der Medizin (vol. 2, 293–295, 1911); with long extracts. Hans Erchenbrecher: Der salernitaner Arzt Archimatthaeus und ein bis heute unbekannter Traktat unter seinen Namen (Diss., Leipzig 1919). Friedrich Hartmann: Die Literatur von Früh- und Hochsalerno (14, 20–24, 1919).

BARTHOLOMEW OF SALERNO

Bartholomaeus Salernitanus. Lived in the first half of the twelfth century. Author of a Practica, a treatise on pathology and therapeutics which, judging from the number of commentaries and the translations into various vernaculars, enjoyed a great popularity in Western Europe. Some of the translations, however, seem to be based not simply on his Practica, but on other texts. Bartholomew may be the real author of the booklet on distilled waters, of which a German translation or adaptation is generally ascribed to Michael Puff (second half of the fifteenth century).

Texts and translations—Practica magistri Bartholomaei Salernitani, edited by S. de Renzi: Collectio salernitana (vol. 4, 321–406, 1856). Other manuscripts of the same work are entitled Introductiones et experimenta in practicam Hippocratis, Galieni, Constantini, graecorum medicorum. Felix von Oefele: Angebliche Practica des Bartholomaeus (Neuenahr 1894). Fragments of an old Danish translation in H. Harpestrengs Danske Lägebog, edited by Chr. Molbech (Copenhagen 1826).

Criticism—Joseph Haupt: Das mitteldeutsche Arzneibuch des Meisters Bartholomaeus (Wiener Sitzungsber., phil. Kl., vol. 71, 542 sq., 1872). August Hirsch: Biographisches Lexikon (6, 455, 1888). K. Sudhoff: Deutsche medizinische Inkunabeln (139, 1908). M. Neuburger: Geschichte der Medizin (vol. 2, 290, 1911) Christian Graeter: Ein Leipziger deutscher Bartholomäus (Diss., Leipzig 1918). F. Hartmann: Die Literatur von Früh- und Hochsalerno (18, 1919). Henri Quentin: Une correspondance médicale de Pierre le Vénérable avec Magister Bartholomaeus (Miscellanea F. Ehrle, 1, 80–86, 1923; Isis, 8, 740).

NICHOLAS OF SALERNO

Nicolaus Salernitanus. A Salernitan physician, of whom nothing is known except what is implied in the phrase Antidotarium Nicolai. Later writers like Platearius and Giles of Corbeil spoke of that work without mentioning any author. Thus in the following pages the words Nicholas of Salerno will be simply a shorter way of saying "the author of the Salernitan antidotary." This author is sometimes called Praepositus, which should be avoided because it introduces a confusion with Nicole Prévost of Tours (second half of the fifteenth century).

The antidotary written by Nicholas of Salerno was often called Antidotarium parvum to distinguish it from the Byzantine antidotary which was called magnum. (See my note on Myrepsos, second half of the thirteenth century). It contains about 140–150 recipes for the preparation of drugs, most of them very complicated, with indications relative to their applications and action. It recommends the use of spongia soporifera to induce anaesthesia. About one-third of these recipes are found in ancient or early mediaeval antidotaries; their greatest divergence from the latter is due to the fact that they show many traces of Arabic influence, from which the early mediaeval antidotaries are almost entirely free. About half of the Salernitan recipes can be traced back to the translations published by Constantine the African (second half of the eleventh century).

It is possible that the Antidotarium Nicolai was simply a revision of an older Salernitan antidotary in the light of the new Arabic knowledge. However, such a hypothesis is hardly necessary to account for the relatively large amount of ancient material which was retained in it. In short, the Salernitan antidotary was a collection of most of the recipes transmitted by Greek and Latin writers, plus a number of additions and modifications obtained from the new Arabic sources. It was largely because of its very eclecticism, of its curious combination of novelty and conservatism, that it enjoyed such immense popularity; witness the number of translations, adaptations, and commentaries appearing in Italian, French, Spanish, Hebrew, and even Arabic. The study of the tradition is thus extremely complicated; for example, there are at least two, possibly four, separate Hebrew translations. The Salernitan antidotary may be said to be the basis of all the later pharmacopoeias.

Text—There are many early editions of the Antidotarium, either independently (Venice 1471, Rome 1476, Naples 1478, Milan 1479, etc.), or together with the works of Mesuë or of Matthaeus Platearius.

The Tractatus quid pro quo (on substitutes), often attached to the antidotarium, may be also Nicholas' work.

The Anatomia magistri Nicolai is the work of another Nicholas who lived towards the end of the century. (See my note on Richard of Salerno, second half of the twelfth century.)

The Antidotarium magnum, or Antidotarium ad aromatarios, is certainly not Nicholas' work, but a Latin translation of Myrepsos' Δυναμερόν (second half of the thirteenth century.)

Translations of Nicholas' antidotarium—Two French translations of the fourteenth and fifteenth centuries, edited by Paul Dorveaux (Paris 1896), with a preface by Antoine Thomas. A Dutch translation of the fourteenth century, edited by W. S. van den Berg, together with the Latin text of the princeps 1471 (314 p., Leyde 1917; Isis, 4, 402). Some of the commentaries will be quoted later when I speak of their authors (see, e.g., Mathaeus Platearius, below; also Saint Amand, second half of the thirteenth century). An early one (twelfth century) has been published by Ehrhard Benndorf: Der Liber de confectione medicinarum im Breslauer Codex (Diss., 25 p. Leipzig 1920).

Criticism—L. Choulant: Handbuch der Bücherkunde (second ed., 282–291, 1841). M. Steinschneider: Hebraeische Übersetzungen (811–816, 1893). John Ferguson: Bibliotheca chemica (vol. 2, 223, 1906). Neuburger: Geschichte der Medizin (vol. 2, 302, 1911). F. H. Held: Nicolaus Salernitanus und Nikolaos Myrepsos (Diss., Leipzig 1916). F. Hartmann: Die Literatur von Früh- und Hochsalerno (24–26, 1919). Henry E. Sigerist: Studien und Texte sur frühmittelalterlichen Rezeptliteratur (228 p., Leipzig 1923; Isis, 6, 429–430).

SALERNUS

A Salernitan physician who lived in Salerno about 1130–1160. He wrote a short medical introduction; a summary of pathology and therapeutics, entitled Catholica; and medical tables which were in all probability inspired by those published by the Christian Baghdādites, Ibn Buṭlān (first half of the eleventh century) and Ibn Jazla (second half of the eleventh century). Salernus' mention of alcoholic distillation is one of the earliest in the Latin West; it is probably one of the earliest in the whole world. The only other mention definitely known to me, which probably antidates Salernus, is that included in the second edition of the Mappae clavicula, ascribed to Adelard of Bath (vol. 1, 534).

Text—Tabulae Magistri Salerni de virtutibus et operationibus medicinarum (sunt tabulae XII quae continent L columnas, edited by S. de Renzi: Collectio salernitana (vol. 5, 233–253, 1859). Shorter text (ibidem, vol. 2, 422–424, 1853). Compendium Magistri Salerni (ibidem, vol. 3, 52–65, 1854). Longer text (ibidem, vol. 5, 201–32).

Catholica Magistri Salerni, edited by Piero Giacosa: Magistri salernitani nondum editi (69–166, 1901).

Criticism—A. Hirsch: Biographisches Lexikon (vol. 4, 96, 1886). Neuburger: Geschichte der Medizin (vol. 2, 303, 1911). F. Hartmann: Die Literatur von Früh- und Hochsalerno (28, 1919).

MATTHAEUS PLATEARIUS

Salernitan physician. Probably the son of Joannes Platearius the Younger (second half of the eleventh century). He died in 1161. He wrote the earliest commentary on Nicholas' Antidotarium, and a treatise on simples, De simplici medicina, which is often called, from its first words, Circa instans. This work was almost as popular as the Antidotarium Nicolai until the sixteenth century; witness the number of manuscripts. There are two traditions of the Circa instans; a larger one containing 432 chapters or articles, and a smaller one containing only 273. These two traditions are intimately connected; it is impossible to subordinate one to the other. (One has tried to connect them with two distinct Platearii, Matthew being the author of the shorter text, and John III, his son, the author of the longer. This is unwarranted.) Each chapter treats of a simple or other drug (sometimes of more than one), and they are arranged in alphabetical order of the Latin names of these drugs. These names are given also in Greek, Italian, and French. Then for each drug we are offered the following information: description, action, mode of application, signs of purity, falsifications, distinctions of various kinds.

The Circa instans is especially important from the botanical point of view. For example, of the 273 chapters of the minor text, 229 treat of medicinal plants. It marked a great progress over Dioscorides and other herbals. During the thirteenth and fourteenth centuries it gradually superseded the Herbarius ascribed to Apuleius, and it became one of the prototypes of our Western pharmacopoeias. Illustrated manuscripts also influenced botanical iconography; of 379 illustrations in the Gart der Gesundheit, 94 can be traced back to the Platearius manuscripts.

The Circa instans was translated into Hebrew by Solomon ben Moses of Melgueil (second half of the thirteenth century), by Solomon ben Elia in 1414. This version containing 279 (281) articles was arranged in the order of the Hebrew alphabet

Text—The Glossae in antidotarium Nicolai are found in the early Venetian editions of Mesuë.

The Liber de simplici medicina secundum Plateariurn dictus Circa instans was printed, together with Joannes Platearius' Practica brevis, in Venice in 1497; it is also found in many editions of the Antidotarium. Fritz Wolfgang Klaus: Die Abschnitte über Milch und Wein aus dem Liber simplicium medicinarum im Breslauer Codex Salernitanus (Diss., 15 p., Leipzig 1920).

Translations—The Circa instans has very often been translated; e.g., into French. The earliest French translation was published by Paul Dorveaux: Le livre des simples médecines (Publications de la Société française d'histoire de la médecine, 1, 280 p., Paris 1913). Additional information on French translations and adaptations will be found in the preface (Isis, 1, 517–518).

Criticism—Giulio Camus: L'opera "Circa instans" ed il testo primitivo del "Grant Herbier en Françoys" secondo due codici del secolo XV conservati nella R. Biblioteca Estense (Mem. d. Acc. di Modena, vol. 4, 49–199, 1886). A. Hirsch: Biographisches Lexikon (vol. 4, 585, 1886). M. Steinschneider: Hebraeische Übersetzungen (821–823, 1893). Neuburger: Geschichte der Medizin (vol. 2, 303, 1911). F. Hartmann: Die Literatur von Früh- und Hochsalerno (26–28, 1919). Max A. Ullmann: Geflügel, Eier, Fische, Früchte und Gemüse im Circa instans des Codex Salernitanus in Breslau (Diss., 28 p., Leipzig 1926). Julius Schuster: Secreta salernitana und Gart der Gesundheit (Mittelalterliche Handschriften, Festgabe zu Hermann Degering, 203–237, Leipzig 1926; 2 pl., 6 fig. in text; Isis, 11, 429); interesting for the study of the Platearian tradition and of its influence. Hermann Fischer: Mittelalterliche Pflanzenkunde (3, 20–24, München 1929; Isis, 15, 367).

PETRUS OF MUSANDA

Petrus Musandinus. Salernitan physician who lived in the middle of the twelfth century. Teacher of Giles of Corbeil. He wrote a short but excellent treatise on diet, Summula de cibis et potibus febricitantium. It is derived from the Hippocratic treatise, De diaeta morborum acutorum. Peter of Musanda shows the medical importance of good cooking.

Text—Tractatulus de cibis et potibus febricitantium, in S. de Renzi: Collectio salernitana (vol. 2, 407–410, 1853). Summula de preparatione ciborum et potuum infirmorum secundum Musandinum (ibidem, vol. 5, 254–268, 1859), is a development of the first text. A treatise printed in the Opera omnia of Arnold of Villanova is the same work or a commentary upon it.

Criticism—Barthélemy Hauréau: Histoire littéraire de la France (vol. 28, 65, 1881). Neuburger: Geschichte der Medizin (vol. 2, 302–303, 1911). F. Hartmann: Die Literatur von Früh- und Hochsalerno (24, 1919).

"TROTULA"

The Trotula (Trotulae curandarum aegritudinum muliebrium ante in et post partum; or De passionibus mulierum) is an obstetrical and gynaecological treatise in 60 chapters dating from the best Salernitan period. It has been ascribed to a woman physician Trotula (or Trotula di Ruggiero), said to be the wife of Joannes Platearius the Elder who lived in the second half of the eleventh century. There were of course women physicians (mulieres salernitanae), that is, midwives who treated also female disorders. It is probable that Trotula was one of them, a famous one, and that this treatise was thus named in her honor. The Trotula is distinctly post-Constantinian. We might place it tentatively in the first half of the twelfth century, toward the middle. (Neuburger considers it a thirteenth century elaboration of Trotula's work).

Text—Editio princeps, in the collection entitled Experimentarius medicinae (Strassburg 1544). Later editions in the Aldine collection, Medici antiqui omnes (fol. 71–80, Venice 1547). Benedictus Victorius: Empirica (Venice 1555). Collectio gynaeciorum (Basel 1566, 1586; Strassburg 1597). First separate edition by Heinrich Kornemann (Leipzig 1778).

Criticism—A. Hirsch: Biographisches Lexikon (vol. 6, 16, 1888). M. Steinschneider: Hebraeische Übersetzungen (811, 1893). Neuburger: Geschichte der Medizin (vol. 2, 286, 1911). Hartmann: Die Literatur von Früh- und Hochsalerno (17–18, 1919). Hermann Rudolf Spitzner: Die salernitanische Gynäkologie und Geburtshilfe unter dem Namen der Trotula (Diss., 43 p., Leipzig 1921; analysis of the Trotula, list of the manuscripts, bibliography; Isis, 5, 499). Conrad Hiersemann: Die Abschnitte aus der Practica des Trottus in der salernitanischen Sammelschrift De aegritudinum curatione (Diss., 36 p., Leipzig 1921).

Kate Campbell Hurd-Mead: Trotula (Isis, 14, 349–367, 1930). This article reached me in manuscript long after my own Trotula note had been written. It is a strong plea for the existence of a woman physician called Trotula, wife of John I Platearius about the middle of the eleventh century. She would be the real author of the gynaecological treatise which has come down to us under her name, and instead of being influenced by Constantine she would have been plagiarized by him. If Mrs. Hurd-Mead's thesis is correct, my Trotula note ought to be entirely rewritten and placed in vol. I, p. 769.

BENEVENUTUS GRASSUS

Also called Grapheus, Graphius, etc.; Benvengut, Benevenuto Graffeo, Bienvenu, etc. Benevenutus of Salerno, or of Jerusalem.

The most famous non-Muslim oculist of mediaeval times. Very little is known about him; we do not even know his time, race, or nationality. The latest author quoted by him is Ḥunain ibn Isḥāq (second half of the ninth century), and the oldest one to quote him is Guy de Chauliac (second half of the fourteenth century). The earliest manuscript of his Practica is a Provençal manuscript of the thirteenth century (in Basel). We shall not be far wrong if we place him in the twelfth century, probably in the second quarter. He was born or lived for a time in Jerusalem; he traveled considerably in Italy and in Languedoc; he lived probably in Salerno and in Montpellier. It is also said that he was a baptized Jew, and a disciple of Nicholas of Salerno.

Whoever he was, whenever and wherever he lived, we think of him as the author of the most popular Latin textbook on eye diseases, the Practica oculorum (or Ars nova, Ars probatissima de egritudinibus oculorum). The popularity is proved by the number of manuscripts, most of them in Latin, but some in Provençal, French, English, and possibly Hebrew. No Hebrew manuscript is known to me, but a Latin manuscript in the Vatican ends with the words "e lingua hebraica in latinam translata;" this may refer to a Hebrew original by another author.

Benevenutus' Practica was derived from Arabic writings, probably through their Latin translations; it was also based to some extent upon his own experience. It contains a description of a collyrium hierosolimitanum, made of tutia (impure zinc oxide) and wine, for use in cases of granular conjunctivitis.

The first printed edition of it, De oculis eorumque egritudinibus et curis, appeared in Ferrara in 1474. This was the first printed book on the subject; the Liber de oculo morali of Peter of Limoges was probably later (Augsburg 1475), and was not an ophthalmological treatise (see my note on Peckham).

Manuscripts, text and translation—Editio princeps (Ferrara, undated, 1474). Later editions: Treviso 1492; Venice 1497, 1500, 1549.

Modern editions: A. M. Berger and T. M. Auracher: Des Benvenutus Grapheus Practica oculorum (2 parts, München 1884–1886; edition of the Latin text, and of the thirteenth century Provençal version). Giuseppe Albertotti: Benvenuti

Grassi Hierosolomitani de oculis eorumque egritudinibus et curis, incunabulo ferrarese (Pavia 1897); I codici Riccardiano, Parigino ed Ashburnhamiano (Modena 1897); I codici Napoletani, Vaticani e Boncompagni, ora Albertotti (Modena 1901–1903). P. Pansier et Ch. Laborde: Le compendil pour la douleur et maladie des yeuls qui a esté ordonné par Bienvenu Graffé. Suivi d'une version provençale éditée par Henri Teuilié (Paris 1901). Casey A. Wood: De oculis. English version of the text of the first printed edition (115 p., 5 pl., Stanford University 1929; Isis, 14, 232–233).

Ch. Laborde: Bienvenu de Jérusalem et son oeuvre. Le manuscrit de Metz (Thèse, 76 p., Montpellier 1901). A. Laurans: Le manuscrit de Bésançon (Thèse, 70 p., Montpellier 1903). Karl Sudhoff: Ein neues MS. des ophthalmologischen Büchleins Ars nova des Benevenutus (Archiv für Geschichte der Medizin, vol. 1, 384–385, 1908).

These texts are very different, suggesting that they are the lecture notes of various pupils. A systematic comparison and critical edition is badly needed.

Criticism—Giulio Bertoni: Sulle redazioni provenzale e francese della Practica oculorum di Benvenuto (Revue des langues romanes, vol. 47, 442–454, Montpellier 1904). Neuburger: Geschichte der Medizin (vol. 2, 315, 513, 1911). Edmund O. von Lippmann: Über Rübenzucker im Mittelalter (Chemiker Zeitung, 67, 1907; also Abhd. u. Vorträge, vol. 2, 255–257); apropos of the phrase "pulvis de zuccaro nabetis," which does not refer to a sort of beetsugar but to sugar candy. Lynn Thorndike: Vatican Latin manuscripts (Isis, 13, 65, 1929).

ZACHARIAS

Latin physician who lived in the twelfth century. He was probably educated in Salerno. It is possible that he resided in Constantinople under Manuel I Comnenos (emperor from 1143 to 1180). He wrote a Latin treatise on eye diseases, in two or three books (the third is possibly apocryphal). I place him in the first half of the century to bring him nearer to Benevenutus Grapheus, for his work does not seem to be posterior to that of Benvenutus.

Text—Magistri Zachariae Tractatus de passionibus oculorum qui vocatur Sisilacera id est secreta secretorum. Edited by Paul Pansier in his Collectio ophthalmologica veterum auctorum (Fasc. 5, 57–94, Paris 1907). Friedrich Alexander Krah: Ein Münchner handschriftliches Augentraktat, betitelt Liber sulse ractini, id est secreta secretorum, ein neuer (6.) Text der Sisilacera angeblich eines Magister Zacharias (Diss., 8 p., Leipzig 1923). According to Krah, this treatise shows more definite traces of Arabic than of Greek knowledge; its Byzantine origin is doubtful; it is more probably Salernitan (K. Sudhoff in Mitt. zur Geschichte der Medizin, 23, 61, 1924).

DAVID THE ARMENIAN

David Armenicus. Lived in South Italy probably in the twelfth century. He wrote a treatise on eye-diseases, Compilatio in libros de oculorum curationibus Accanamosali et diversorum philosophorum de Baldach, which, as the title indicates, is derived from Arabic sources. However, it is not a translation of Canamusali's treatise—that is, the Kitāb al-muntakhab of 'Ammār ibn 'Alī (first half of the eleventh century).

Text—Tractatus de oculis Canamusali (Venice 1497, 1499, 1500). P. Pansier: Magistri David Armenici compilatio in libros de oculorum curationibus Accanamosali et diversorum philosophorum de Baldach (Collectio ophthalmologica veterum auctorum, fasc. 4, 56 p., Paris 1904). Edition based on new manuscripts and on the incunabula editions; containing reproductions of the instruments used, and a glossary of Arabisms.

The following texts, partly derived from Benevenutus and David, are quoted for the sake of comparison. Giuseppe Albertotti: Il libro delle affezioni oculari di Jacopo Palmerio da Cingoli, ed altri scritti di oculistica tratti da un codice del secolo XV di Marco Sinzanogio da Sarnano (Memorie della R. Accad. in Modena, vol. 6, 85 p., 1906). One of the other texts following the Libro delle affezioni is entitled Serie di ricette per malattie oculari seguita dalla indicazione di colliri proposti e provati da David Armenio (p. 61–68).

MEDIAEVAL HOSPITALS

The idea of creating establishments where a collective hospitality could be proffered not only to the sick, but also to the aged, to the lame, dumb, deaf, and blind, to strangers, even to those whose souls were ailing—for example, foolish women—this noble idea is very distinctly Christian. There have been charitable people before Christ, and even charitable institutions, but it was the spirit of Christianity which first inspired the creation of houses of mercy, houses of God (Hôtel Dieu), where hospitality would be the rule, not the exception. The earliest hospitals date back to the time of Constantine the Great (324–337), who was probably guided in this by his mother, Saint Helena (d. 327). Hospitals and hospices of various kinds were established in the Byzantine empire. This example was imitated by the Muslims, and large hospitals existed in Baghdād and Cairo, in Syria, in Moorish Spain, etc. Quite a number were founded also in the Christian West. Many monasteries included infirmaries and asylums. Yet a tremendous impulse was given to these institutions by the Crusades.

Thus hospitals became vastly more important during the twelfth and subsequent centuries. Various religious orders were devoted to the accomplishment of nursing duties. The Order of St. John of Jerusalem, and later the Teutonic Order, considered the building and maintenance of hospitals one of their main obligations. Finally the terrible spread of leprosy, which may have been caused, or at least accelerated by the Crusades, necessitated the organization of a vast number of special asylums or leproseries.

The early history of hospitals is as difficult to determine exactly as the early history of universities, and for the same reason. The greatest institutions are so very small at the beginning that they remain unnoticed, and the very people who start them are not always aware of their own doings; moreover, their beginnings are not necessarily unique, as in the case of living creations; there may be false starts, interruptions, etc. Often their birthdates are established retrospectively. Bearing in mind these restrictions, I may mention the following hospitals among those created during the first half of the twelfth century.

1123. St. Bartholomew, Smithfield, London.

1132. Holy Cross, Winchester.

About 1145. Holy Ghost, Montpellier.

The first English hospital had been established by archbishop Lanfranc at Canterbury about 1084. When St. Bartholomew was founded there were already eighteen hospitals in England. In the first half of the twelfth century, at least 46 hospitals were founded, of which 24 were leper houses; in the following fifty years, at least 120 hospitals, of which 56 were for lepers; in the thirteenth century, no fewer than 240 hospitals, seventy-five being leper houses; in the fourteenth century, 248 hospitals, 62 being leper houses; in the fifteenth century, 91 hospitals, etc.

These figures (after Mercier) relative to England alone, are quoted for the sake of illustration. Note the progression, the climax in the thirteenth and fourteenth centuries, and the decrease in the number of leproseries after the thirteenth century; note also that the total number of hospitals established in England from the twelfth to the fifteenth century was almost 750. It is probable that similar figures could be adduced for other countries of western Europe. Throughout the Middle Ages, the ideal of hospitalization was one of the noblest incentives in Christian Europe.

It is not possible to give more space to this subject, which does not concern the History of Science except indirectly. Of course hospitals influenced medical progress in various ways; yet their influence remained unsystematic and casual almost until modern times.

After having written this note, it occurred to me at the last moment that the earliest conception of hospitals was probably Jewish. The Bet heqdesh la 'aniyim (house consecrated to the needy) existed probably in various Jewish communities before the Christian era, but how near did that institution come to the mediaeval hospital largely devoted to the cure of disease? Was there really a definite house or heqdesh—this Hebrew word for hospital was first used in Cologne in the eleventh century—or was there simply a ḥebra qaddisha arranging for the care of suffering brethren as the opportunity arose? Of course mercifulness was Jewish before being Christian, and the Jewish forms of it coexisted with the Christian throughout the ages.

R. Virchow: Zur Geschichte des Aussatzes und der Spitäler (Archiv für pathologische Anatomie, vols. 18, 19, 20, 1860–1861); Krankenhäuser und Hospitalwesen (Gesammelte Abhdl. a.d. Gebiete der öffentlichen Medizin und der Seuchenlehre, vol. 2, 1–130, 1879). Karl Sudhoff: Aus der Geschichte des Krankenhauswesens im früheren Mittelalter in Morgenland und Abendland (Krankenhausjahrbuch, Jena 1913; reprinted in Archiv für Geschichte der Medizin, vol. 21, 164–203, 1929). Charles A. Mercier: Leper houses and mediaeval hospitals (47 p., London 1915). Dorothy Louise Mackay: Les hôpitaux et la charité à Paris au XIIIe siècle (168 p., 6 pl., Paris 1923; Isis, 14, 478). Percy Flemming: The medical aspects of the mediaeval monastery in England (Proc. R. Soc. of med., hist. sect., 22, 771–782, 6 figs., London 1929; Isis, 14, 516).

Sir Norman Moore: The history of St. Bartholomew's Hospital (2 vols., London, 1918). Thomas McCrae: The octocentenary of St. Bartholomew's Hospital (Annals of medical history, vol. 5, 279–82, illus., 1923). See also Nature (vol. 111, 777, 1923).

For Jewish hospitals, see articles entitled hospitals, and hospitality, respectively by Joseph Jacobs and Julius H. Greenstone, in Jewish Encylopedia (vol. 6, 479–481, 1904).

For Muslim hospitals, see Aḥmad 'Īsā bey: Histoire des bimaristans à l'époque Islamique (Comptes rendus du Congrès international des maladies tropicales, 81–209, Cairo, 1929; Isis, 14, 535). Some of the instruments used in the hospitals of Fusṭāṭ (old Cairo) have been discovered; for a description of them see a study in Arabic by the same author, Al-ālāt al-ṭibb wal-jirāḥa wal-kihāla 'ind al- 'Arab (Cairo 1925; Isis, 8, 597). His first study deals with many hospitals of Egypt, Mesopotamia, Syria, Palestine, and Morocco, but chiefly with the Bīmāristān al-Manṣūrī (p. 121–168), also called the Dār al-shifā' (house of health), or Bīmāristān al-Qalā'ūn, because it was built by that Mamlūk sulṭān, al-Manṣūr Qalā'ūn (ruled from 1279 to 1290). Remains of the original buildings still exist, and it is possible to reconstruct, at least mentally, the whole structure;

the bīmāristān al-Manṣūrī is the oldest Muslim hospital extant. For a longer description of the ruins, see Max Herz pasha (d. 1918): Die Baugruppe des Sultans Qalāūn in Kairo (Abhdl. des Hamburg. Kolonialinst., vol. 42, 62 p., 36 pl., 1919). An early description of the same hospital was given by al-Maqrīzī (d. 1442).

A famous māristān was built in Damascus about 1154, by Nūr al-dīn Maḥmūd ibn Zangī, atābeg of Syria from 1146 to 1173. The monumental gate of it is still extant.

VII. HINDU

Ḍallana

A Hindu physician who lived probably in the twelfth century, and wrote one of the earliest commentaries on the Suśruta-saṃhitā (vol. I, 76), entitled Nibandhasaṃgraha. The only earlier one extant is the Bhānumatī, compiled by the Bengali physician Cakrapāṇidatta in the previous century.

Text—Nibandhasaṃgraha edited by Jibananda Vidyasagara (Calcutta 1891).
Criticism—M. Winternitz: Indische Litteratur (vol. 3, 548, 1922).

VIII. CHINESE

Chinese Materia Medica

An important pên ts'ao dates from the beginning of the twelfth century. It is the Chêng[4] lei[4] pên[3] ts'ao[3] (726, 6853, 8846, 11634), a work dated 1108 and ascribed to one T'ang[2] Shên[4]-wei[1] (10767, 9846, 12586), a physician of Shu[3]* (10057) in Ssŭ-chuan. It is also called Ta[4] kuan[1] pên[3] ts'ao[3] (10470, 6363), because it was completed during the reign of the Sung emperor Hui Tsung (who ruled from 1000 to 1126), a year after he had assumed the title (or era name) Ta Kuan (1107). It is important because it contains fragments of the text of the legendary Shên Nung pên ts'ao ching[5] and embodies what was considered most valuable in later works of the same kind. The substance of this work is classified under the headings, precious stones, metals, herbs, cereals, vegetables, fruits, trees, insects, fishes, birds, quadrupeds, man; 1455 objects are described, and 294 plates of illustrations are added. The edition of 1468 contains 600 illustrations of plants.

Text—The Library of Congress has two editions of the Chêng lei pên ts'ao with the preface date 1468, and three others printed respectively in 1523, 1552, and 1654, all carefully illustrated. All these editions are in 30 chüan, except the last, which is in 31 chüan. It has also a Ming edition entitled Ta kuan pên ts'ao in 31 chüan, with a preface of the Sung period, and an edition in 31 chüan published in Japan in 1775. It has two different editions of the Shên Nung pên ts'ao ching, each published in 1626 in 30 chüan, a Chinese edition published in 1813 in 4 chüan, and a Japanese edition published in 1854 in 3 chüan.

It is perhaps not out of place to add here that the Library of Congress has ten different editions of the Pên[3] ts'ao[3] Kang[2] mu[4]* (8846, 11634, 5900, 8080), variously printed in the following years: 1603, 1640, 1655 (two), 1657, 1714, 1784, 1872, 1892, 1894. Each of these editions is in 52 chüan, except that of 1714 which is in 61 chüan. The illustrated edition included in the recently published Ssu[4] pu[4] ts'ung[1] k'an[1] (10291, 9484, 12039, 5861) is reproduced from a Chin dynasty reprint of 1204. There is a complete copy of that ts'ung shu in the Library of Congress.

Criticism—E. Bretschneider: Botanicon sinicum (Part I, 47, Shanghai 1881).

[5] See my vol. I, 122, 436.

M. Courant: Catalogue des livres chinois de la Bibliothèque Nationale (vol. 2, 127, 1910). Encylopaedia sinica (55, 1917).

K'OU TSUNG-SHIH

K'ou^{4} Tsung^{1}-shih^{4}* (6180, 11976, 10003). I know nothing of him except that he was the author of a new pên ts'ao, the Pên^{3} ts'ao^{3} yen^{3} i^{4} (8846, 11634, 13113, 5454) in twenty books, first printed in 1111, as a supplement to the Ching^{1} shih^{3} chêng^{4} lei^{4} ta^{4} kuan^{1} pên^{3} ts'ao^{3} (2122, 9893, 726, 6853, 10470, 6363, 8846, 11634) of T'ang^{2} Shên^{4}-wei^{1} (10767, 9846, 12586), with which we have just dealt. The previous edition of the Chêng lei pên ts'ao, dated 1107 or 1108, did not contain K'ou's work. The Pên ts'ao yen i is often quoted in Chinese herbals. A commentary was devoted to it by Chu^{1} Tan^{1}-ch'i (2544, 10618, 1009), who died in 1358.

It would seem that the Pên ts'ao yen i was originally called Pên ts'ao kuang i, but that the character kuang^{1} (6389) became taboo in 1195; the present title appeared in the Ch'ing^{2} Yüan^{2} (2211, 13744) edition, so-called after the first nien^{2}-hao^{4} (8301, 3884) of the emperor Ning^{2} Tsung^{1} (8328, 11976), 1195–1201, published by the superintendent of water transportation of Kuangsi; hence this edition is called the Ts'ao^{2} ssŭ^{1} (11640, 10250) or "water transport" edition.

Text—The Library of Congress has a facsimile of the Sung edition of the Pên ts'ao yen i, above mentioned, issued as a supplement to the Ching shih chêng lei ta kuan pên ts'ao, in two volumes and 20 chüan. This reprint was published in 1909. This work is also found in the Shih^{2}* wan^{4} chüan^{4} lou^{2} ts'ung^{1} shu^{1} (9959, 12486, 3146, 7343, 12039, 10024), vols. 16–17, with preface dated 1877.

Criticism—Walter T. Swingle: Chinese books added to the Library of Congress, 1924–1925 (Librarian's Report, Washington 1925, 267–269; Isis, 8, 791). K'ou Tsung-shih is not mentioned in the Sung annals.

CHAPTER XI

HISTORIOGRAPHY

(First Half of Twelfth Century)

I. EASTERN MUSLIM

AL-SHAHRASTĀNĪ

Abū-l-Fatḥ Muḥammad ibn 'Abd al-Karīm al-Shahrastānī. Muslim historian of religion and philosophy. Born in 1076–1077 at Shahrastān, Khurāsān; studied in Jurjānīyah and Nīshāpūr, and made the Pilgrimage in 1116–1117; after three years residence in Baghdād he returned to Khurāsān where he died in 1153. He belonged to the Ash'arite school.

His chief work is the Kitāb al-milal wal-niḥal, the Book of religions and sects, written in 1127–1128. The first part of it contains accounts of the sects of Islām; then of the People of Scripture (ahl al-kitāb)—Jews and Christians; finally, of those of dubious revelation, the Magi and Manichaeans. The second part deals with Sabian, Greek, Muslim, Christian, and Arabic philosophy, especially the system of Ibn Sīnā; finally, with the religions of the Arabs before Islām, and of the people of India. It should be noted that two-thirds of the work concern non-Muslim sects. This is a history of religions, comprehensive, learned, and well arranged; the author does not always succeed in being neutral, but he earnestly tries to. Comparing him with his two predecessors of the first half of the eleventh century, we find that he is far more objective than Ibn Ṭāhir al-Baghhādī, but less so than the great Spaniard, Ibn Ḥazm. The works of Ibn Ḥazm and of al-Shahrastānī may be called the earliest histories of religions in any language.

His other writings include a history of the philosophers, Ta'rīkh al-ḥukamā' (or al-falāsifa); and treatises on metaphysics and theology, Kitāb muṣāra'at al-falāsifa, (Discussions of the philosophers), and Kitāb nihāyat al-iqdām fī 'ilm al-kalām (The limit of diligence in the knowledge of scholastic theology).

Text—The text of Al-milal was edited by W. Cureton (2 vols., London 1846). Other edition, Būlāq, 1261 H. German translation by Theodor Haarbrücker (2 vols., Halle 1850–1851). Edition of the Nihāyat al-iqdām by Alfred Guillaume (2 vols., Oxford 1930).

Criticism—Ibn Khallikān (de Slane, vol. 2, 675–677, 1843). F. Wüstenfeld: Geschichtschreiber der Araber (85, 1881). C. Brockelmann: Arabische Litteratur (vol. 1, 428, 1898). Carra de Vaux: Encyclopaedia of Islām vol. 4, 263, 1926).

II. WESTERN MUSLIM

For Abū Bakr al-Ṭurṭūshī, see Chapter XII, Law and Sociology.
For Abū-l-Ṣalt, see Chapter X, Medicine.

IBN BASHKUWĀL

Abū-l-Qāsim ibn 'Abd al-Malik ibn Mas'ūd Ibn Bashkuwāl al-Qurṭubī. Hispano-Muslim historian, born in 1101, he lived at Seville. He died at Cordova in

1183. He completed in 1139 a collection of biographies of the learned men of Spain, entitled Kitāb al-ṣila fī akhbār a'immat al-Andalus (Supplement to the stories of the leading men of Andalusia). This was a continuation of the Ta'rīkh 'ulamā' al-Andalus of Ibn al-Faraḍī (first half of the eleventh century).

Text—The Ṣila was edited by Fr. Codera, in the Bibliotheca arabico-hispanica (vols. 1 and 2, Madrid 1883).

Duo fragmenta inedita, appended to Ibn al-Faraḍī's Historia vivorum doctorum Andalusiae (Madrid 1890–1892).

Criticism—Ibn Khallikān (de Slane, 1, 491). F. Wüstenfeld: Geschichtschreiber der Araber (1, 94, 1881). C. Brockelmann: Arabische Litteratur (vol. 1, 340, 1898). Moh. ben Cheneb: Encyclopaedia of Islām (2, 368, 1916).

III. WESTERN JEWISH

MOSES IBN EZRA

See Chapter IV, Philosophic Background.

IV. BYZANTINE

NICEPHOROS BRYENNIOS AND ANNA COMNENA

Nicephoros Bryennios. Νικηφόρος ὁ Βρυέννιος. Born at Adrianople about 1062, he lived in Constantinople, where he died in 1137. He began a biography of his father-in-law, Alexios Comnenos, emperor from 1081 to 1118, carrying it to 1079; but as he himself said, this was rather historical material (ὕλη ἱστορίας) than history.

His wife, Anna Comnena, Ἄννα ἡ Κομνηνή (born in 1083, died in 1148), continued his work, and completed it in 1148 at the convent τῆς Κεχαριτωμένης founded by her mother Irene (died about 1120), in Constantinople. Her own work deals with the period 1069–1118. Like most Byzantine princesses, Anna had been very well educated. She knew her geography and meteorology very well, and her knowledge of medicine was far above the ordinary. She discussed with remarkable intelligence the origin and treatment of her father's gout. The Alexiad (Ἀλεξιάς), including fifteen books, is the first great monument of the Byzantine literary renaissance of that time (artificial Atticism); it contains some admirable descriptions.

Text—Edition princeps of both texts, by Petrus Possinus (Paris 1661, 1651; very bad). New edition, with Du Cange's commentary (Venice 1729). Editions in the Bonn corpus: of Bryennios, by August Meineke (1836); of the Alexias, bks. 1–9, by Ludwig J. Schopen (1839); and bks. 10–15, by A. Reifferscheid (1878); with Latin translation, Du Cange's commentary, glossary and indexes. Edition in Migne's Patrology (vol. 127, 131). New edition of the Alexias, by August Reifferscheid (2 vols., Leipzig 1884).

Translations—German translation of the Alexiad, in Fr. Schiller's Sammlung historischer Memoiren (vol. 1, Jena 1790). French translation by L. Cousin (Paris 1655). Italian translation by Giuseppe Rossi (2 vols., Milano 1846–1849). Excellent English translation by Elizabeth A. S. Dawes (448 p., London 1928).

Criticism—Potthast (331, 846, 1896). K. Krumbacher: Byzantinische Litteratur (271–279, 1897). Paul Adam: Princesses byzantines (La très pieuse Irène; Anne Comnène; Paris 1893). Henri Grégoire: Notes sur Anne Comnène (Byzantion, vol. 3, 311–317, 1927). Naomi Mitchison: Anna Comnena (96 p., London 1928). Georgina Buckler: Anna Comnena (558 p., Oxford 1929); an admirable study, one of the best Byzantine monographs; includes many extracts from the Alexias, in English; elaborate and excellent index (Isis, 15, 207).

ZONARAS

Joannes Zonaras, Ἰωάννης ὁ Ζωναρᾶς. Byzantine monk and chronicler. He lived in Constantinople and later in Hagia Glyceria—one of the Princes Islands (Kizil Adalar) in the sea of Marmora—from the end of the eleventh century to some time after 1150. He completed, some time after 1143, an Historical Epitome, Ἐπιτομὴ ἱστοριῶν, in 18 books, from the Creation to 1118. It is far superior to the other Byzantine chronicles, being more substantial and critical and based on better sources. We owe to it our knowledge of the first twenty-one books of Dion Cassios (first half of the third century). Zonaras' Epitome was very popular and was soon translated into Servian and other Slavonic languages, and later into Latin, French, and Italian. The lexicon ascribed to him is apocryphal.

Text—First edition, by Hieronymus Wolf (Greek and Latin, 3 vols. fol., Basel 1557). By Du Cange, in the Paris Byzantine collection (Greek and Latin, 2 vols. fol. 1686–1687). By Maur. Pinder, in the Bonn Byzantine collection (3 vols., 1841, 1844, 1897). By Ludwig Dindorf (6 vols., Leipzig 1868–1875); also in Migne's Patrology (vol. 134–135, 1864).

Translations—French translation by J. Millet de Saint-Amour (Lyon 1560). By Louis Cousin (2 vols., 796 p., Paris 1686). Italian translation by Marco Emilio Fiorentino (Venice 1560). By Ludovico Dolce (Vinegia 1564–1570).

Criticism—Potthast (1126, 1896). K. Krumbacher: Byzantinische Litteratur (370–376, 1897).

GLYCAS

Michael Glycas, Μιχαὴλ ὁ Γλυκᾶς. Byzantine chronicler. Born during the first third of the twelfth century, he lived until towards the end of it. His chief work is a popular world chronicle from the creation to 1118, Βίβλος χρονική, written between 1143 and 1156. It is largely anecdotic. The very full account of creation contains much material derived from the Physiologos, and information on the origin of stones, plants, and animals borrowed from Aelianos (first half of the third century) and other sources. During a stay in prison in 1158 or 1159, he wrote a poem which is one of the earliest texts in vulgar Greek.

Text—First Latin edition, by Joannes Leunclavius, i.e., Löwenklau (Bale 1572). First incomplete Greek edition, by Jan Meurs (Leyde 1618); first complete Greek edition, by Phil. Labbe, with Latin version in Paris corpus (1660). Edition by Im. Bekker in Bonn corpus (vol. 36, 1836); reprinted in Migne's Patrology (vol. 158, 1–624, 1866).

Criticism—Potthast (532, 1896). K. Krumbacher: Byzantinische Litteratur (380–385, 806, 1897).

V. ARMENIAN

MATTHEW OF EDESSA

Matthew of Urfah (i.e., Edessa, or al-Ruhā in Jazīrah). Armenian chronicler, who died in old age at Edessa in 1144, probably when the city was taken and destroyed by 'Imād al-dīn Zangī, Atābeg of Mosul and Aleppo. He composed an Armenian chronicle extending from the rule of the Bagratide King Ashot III the Merciful (953–977) to 1136. He had devoted eight years to the study and verification of the facts. This chronicle was continued to 1162 by one Gregory, who was, like Matthew, a priest or a monk.

Text—F. Martin: Détails historiques de la première expédition des Chrétiens dans la Palestine sous l'empereur Zimiscès (71 p., Magasin encyclopédique, Sept. 1811); French translation with notes by Chahan de Cirbied. Chahan de Cirbied: Notice de deux manuscripts arméniens de la Bibliothèque impériale, nos. 95 et 99, contenant l'histoire écrite par Mathieu Eretz (Notices et extraits, vol. 9, 275–303, 1813); containing analysis and extracts in Armenian and French. Edouard Dulaurier: Récits de la première croisade (108 p., Paris 1850; French translation); Chronique de Matthieu d'Edesse (962–1136) avec la continuation de Grégoire le prêtre jusqu'en 1162 (Bibliothèque historique arménienne; 573 p., Paris 1858).

Criticism—C. F. Neumann: Geschichte der armenischen Litteratur (163, 1836).

VI. FRENCH

GESTA FRANCORUM

Gesta Francorum et aliorum Hierosolimitanorum. This anonymous account of the First Cusade was written by an unimportant knight of South Italy who took part in it. It deals with the period extending from the end of 1096 to the taking of Jerusalem and the victory of Ascalon, August 1099. It was partly written while the events occurred, or it was based upon a diary; it was certainly available in Jerusalem as early as 1101. Some amplifications were probably inserted by a clerk. The descriptive part is one of our best sources for the history of the First Crusáde. The success of this narrative can be measured by the number of times it was plagiarized or used by later chroniclers.

The author had some sense of European, Catholic, unity against the infidels, but he hated the Greeks almost as much as the Muslims.

Among the contemporary writers who obviously used the Gesta Francorum in their own accounts of the Crusade, the most important are Guibert of Nogent, Orderic Vital, and Ekkehard of Aura, all of whom are discussed below. It will suffice to mention a few others, without expanding:

Petrus Tudebodus or Tudebovis (Pierre Tudeboeuf), a priest in Civray, Poitou, who took part in the Crusade, and wrote his account of it between 1102 and 1111. It was long believed that Tudebodus' narrative was the original from which the Gesta had been derived, but it is the other way round.

The "Tudebodus imitatus et continuatus" is an anonymous account written in 1131 or later, and first published by Jean Mabillon in 1687.

Baudri (Baudry, Balderich, Baldricus Andegavensis), born at Meung-sur-Loire in 1046; abbot of Bourgeuil, archbishop of Dol de Bretagne from 1107 to his death in 1130.

Robert of Reims (Robertus Remensis monachus). Account written after 1118.

Ralph (Raoul) of Caen (Radulfus Cadomensis), who died after 1130. He wrote the Gesta Tancredi Siciliae regis (1099–1108).

Hugh (Hugues) of Fleury (Hugo Floriacensis, or de S. Maria), about 1135.

Giles of Paris (Aegidius clericus Parisiensis), a monk in Cluny, later cardinal bishop of Tusculum, died about 1142. Latin poem written about 1118–1121.

Richard the Pilgrim. He wrote at the beginning of the twelfth century a French poem dealing with the Crusade, the so-called Chanson d'Antioche. It was rewritten by Graindor of Douay under Philippe Auguste (king of France from 1180 to 1223). This poem was a true chanson de geste, the first ever to be devoted to a contemporary event.

The accounts of the following are more or less independent of the Gesta Francorum:

Raymond d'Aguilers (Agiles, Arguilliers), canon at Le Puy.

Foucher de Chartres (Fulcherius Carnotensis), about 1127.

Albert of Aachen (Albertus Aquensis, Albert d'Aix-la-Chapelle), after 1121.

I have given this long list, which does not claim to be complete, to show the amount of interest which was very promptly paid to the First Crusade, especially by Frenchmen.

Text—The Gesta Francorum was first published by Jacques Bongars: Gesta Dei per Francos (vol. 1, 1–30, Hanover 1611). New edition, by Philippe Lebas, under the misleading title, Tudebodus abbreviatus, in Recueil des historiens des Croisades (Hist. occid., vol. 3, 121–163, 1866). Better edition, by Heinrich Hagenmeyer: Anonymi Gesta Francorum (Heidelberg 1890); with abundant notes. Briefer but excellent edition, with French translation on opposite pages, by Louis Bréhier (294 p., Paris 1924). Edition by Beatrice A. Lees (187 p., Oxford 1924).

The Chanson d'Antioche was first published by Paulin Paris (2 vols., Paris 1848). Translation in modern French, by the Marquise de Sainte-Aulaire (Paris 1862).

For the other texts, see Potthast.

Criticism—Henri Pigeonneau: Le cycle de la croisade et la famille de Bouillon (274 p., Paris 1877). Potthast (214, 517, 1896). Harold Lamb: The Crusades, iron men and saints (380 p., Garden City, N. Y., 1930); a popular account of the first crusade, derived from the sources.

GUIBERT OF NOGENT

French Benedictine and chronicler, born at Clermont-en-Beauvoisis in 1053, educated at the abbey of St. Germer of Flay; abbot of Notre Dame de Nogent-sous-Coucy from 1104 until his death about 1124. He wrote a history of the First Crusade, Gesta Dei per Francos, based largely upon the Gesta Francorum. The Crusade proper lasted from 1096 to 1099, but Guibert's narrative covers the years 1095 to 1101. It is divided in eight books; book 6 existed already in 1108; the work was completed before 1112; it was revised soon after that year.

After 1112 he wrote a treatise in four books, De sanctis et pignoribus sanctorum, wherein he does not hesitate to express his scepticism with regard to many relics. About 1114 he wrote a biography, De vita sua, sive monodiarum libri III, modeled after St. Augustine's Confessions. This is divided into three books, of which the first is more strictly autobiographical, while the two others deal respectively with the history of his convent and of Laon. It is one of the most important mediaeval autobiographies, and contains valuable information on many subjects—for example, definition of a commune.

Text—Edition of his works, by Dom Luc d'Achery (Paris 1651); reprinted in Migne's Patrology (vol. 156). French translation by Guizot in his Collection des Mémoires (1823, etc.).

Separate edition of the Gesta Dei per Francos, by Jac. Bongars (vol. 1, 467–560 1611).

Edition of the Autobiography, by Georges Bourgin (Coll. de textes pour servir à l'étude, 312 p., Paris 1907). English translation by Charles Cooke Swinton Bland, with introduction by G. G. Coulton (Broadway translations, 226 p., London 1925).

The text of the De sanctis will be found in d'Achery's edition, p. 327 sq.

Criticism—H. von Sybel: Geschichte des ersten Kreuzzuges (Leipzig 1881). Potthast (549, 1896). A. Molinier: Sources de l'histoire de France (vol. 2, 186, 283, 1902). Bernard Monod: Le moine Guibert et son temps (370 p., Paris 1905).

ORDERIC VITAL

Ordericus Vitalis. Anglo-French monk and chronicler. Born in 1075 in England, probably at Shrewsbury where his father lived; in 1085, he became a monk at the monastery of Saint Evroul en Ouche, Normandy; he spent the greatest part of his life in that monastery; he was ordained priest in 1107; he died in or soon after 1143. His chief work is the Historia ecclesiastica, a chronicle from the time of Christ to 1143, divided into 13 books. It is the best historical work produced in France in the twelfth century. It is especially valuable for the period posterior to the Norman conquest of England. The narrative is centered upon Saint Evroul, but contains long digressions on Norman affairs. The account of the First Crusade is derived largely from the Gesta Francorum.

Text—First edition, by Andreas Duchesne in his Historiae Normannorum scriptores (Paris 1619). Edition by Auguste le Prévost (Société de l'histoire de France, 5 vols., Paris 1838–1855); vol. 5 contains critical studies by Léopold Delisle, and an excellent index.

French translation by Louis Dubois (4 vols., Paris 1825–1827); reprinted in Guizot: Collection des mémoires (vols. 25 to 28). English translation by Thomas Forester (Bohn library, 4 vols., London 1853–1856).

Facsimile reproduction of the Vatican MS. (Paris 1902). Jules Lair: Matériaux pour l'édition de Guillaume de Jumièges avec notes par Léopold Delisle. MS. autographe d'Oderic Vital (Paris 1910).

Criticism—Potthast (879, 1896). A. Molinier: Sources de l'histoire de France (vol. 2, 219–220, 1902). Société historique et archéologique de l'Orne: Ordéric Vital et l'abbaye de Saint Evroult. Fêtes du 27 août 1912 (Alençon 1912). Heinrich Göken: Normannische Ortsnamen bei Ordericus (Diss., 64 p., Münster 1913).

THE CODEX CALIXTINUS

Among many other chronicles of the twelfth century I would draw the reader's attention to the Codex Calixtinus, so called because it was written during the pontificate of Calixtus II (1119–1124). It was written by a pilgrim (Aymeric ?) to Santiago of Compostela, for the use of other pilgrims. It is of special interest because it contains (in book IV) the earliest explicit mention of the Basque people, that is, of a strange people living in the Western Pyrenees and speaking a language of their own. Various words of that language (Euskara) are quoted and can be readily identified by Euskualdunak. The pilgrim's itinerary across the Basque country included Ostabat, Saint Jean Pied de Port, Roncevaux, Pamplona, etc.

The material included in this Codex—for example, the chronicle of the pseudo-Turpin—is obviously of French origin. It is a remarkable fruit of the active intercourse between France and Galicia, intercourse almost entirely due to the immense attraction exerted by the shrine of Compostela (see vol. I, 774).

Le Codex de Saint Jacques de Compostelle (Liber de miraculis S. Jacobi). Livre IV, publié pour la première fois en entier par le Père Fidel Fita y Colomé avec le concours de Julien Vinson (67 p., Paris 1882). Joseph Bédier: Légendes épiques (vol. 3, second ed., 1921); important.

For Robert of Torigny, see Chapter XII, Historiography, in Book II.
For Hugh of Saint Victor, see Chapter IV, Philosophic Background.
For Suger of Saint Denis, see Chapter II, Religious Background.

VII. ITALIAN

LEO OF OSTIA AND PETER THE DEACON

Leone Marsicano. Born about 1046, he became a monk at Monte Cassino; later cardinal bishop of Ostia. He died in 1115. He wrote a good chronicle of Monte Cassino from its beginning in 529 (vol. I, 419) to 1075, 1094. Thus Leo belongs rather to the previous period. I quote him here because it is hardly possible to consider his work without the additions and interpolations of Peter the Deacon.

Peter the Deacon, Petrus Diaconus Casinensis. Born about 1107, he became a monk in Monte Cassino. He died about 1140. He continued Leo's chronicle to 1139 and modified it. He compiled a list of the illustrious brethren of his monastery. This Peter was a forger, and his wretched activity was a symbol of the decline of that famous Benedictine house.

Text—Chronica sacri monasterii Casinensis auctore Leone cardinale episcopo Ostiensi (Paris 1668); included in Muratori's Rerum italicarum scriptores (vol. 4 241–602); and in Migne's Patrology (vol. 173).

Liber illustrium virorum casinensis archisterii (Rome 1655); also in Migne's Patrology (vol. 173).

Criticism—August Potthast: Bibliotheca historica medii aevi (718, 919, 1895–1896). Elias Avery Lowe (or Loew): The Beneventan script (Oxford 1914).

VIII. ENGLISH

FLORENCE OF WORCESTER

Florentius Wigorniensis. English chronicler; monk in Worcester; died in 1118. He wrote a Chronicon ex chronicis dealing with the period 450–1117. Up to the year 1082 it is largely derived from Marianus Scottus (second half of the eleventh century). It was continued to 1141 by John of Worcester, who was a contemporary. There are other continuations down to 1295.

Text—Florence's chronicle and John's continuation have been almost always edited together. First edition, by William Howard (London 1592). Edition by Benjamin Thorpe for the English Historical Society (2 vols., 1848–1849). Edition of John's continuation, by J. R. H. Weaver (72 p., Oxford 1908).

English translation by J. Stevenson, in his Church historians of England (vol. 2, London 1853); and by Thomas Forester in the Bohn Library (London 1854).

Criticism—William Hunt: Dictionary of national biography (vol. 19, 335, 1889). Charles Gross: Sources of English history (397, 1915).

WILLIAM OF MALMESBURY

Guilelmus Malmesbiriensis. English Benedictine and chronicler. Born in the south of England about 1180, he lived at Malmesbury Abbey in Wiltshire. He died after 1142. He was the best English chronicler of his time; the first one after Bede who tried not only to chronicle events but to explain their causal relations. About 1120 he wrote the Gesta regum Anglorum in five books (second ed., 1127), treating of the period 449–1127; in 1125, the Gesta pontificum Anglorum in five books (history of the English bishoprics from the beginning to 1120; 1140); the Historia

Novella, annals from 1125 to 1142; about 1129–1139, a monograph (De antiquitatibus Glastoniensis ecclesiae) on the Glastonbury abbey where he resided for some time etc.

Text—Very imperfect edition by Sir Henry Savile, in his Scriptores post Bedam (London 1596). Edition of the Gesta pontificum, for the Rolls series, by N. E. S. A. Hamilton (655 p., London 1870). Edition of the Gesta regum, and of the Historia novella, by Sir Thomas Duffus Hardy, for the English historical society (2 vols. London 1840); also by William Stubbs, in the Rolls series (2 vols., London 1887–1889). Hardy's text was reprinted in Migne's Patrology (vol. 179, 955–1440, 1855). Other works will also be found in Migne.

English translation of the Chronicle of the Kings of England, and of the Historia novella, by J. A. Giles (Bohn Library, 560 p., London 1847, 1911).

Criticism—Potthast (557–558, 1896). Kate Norgate: Dictionary of national biography (vol. 61, 351–354, 1900). Charles Gross: The sources of English history (1915). Claude Jenkins: The monastic chronicler (London 1922). R. L. Poole: Chronicles and annals (Oxford 1926). Clark Harris Slover: William of Malmesbury and the Irish (Speculum, vol. 2, 268–283, 1927; Isis, 11, 172).

IX. WELSH

GEOFFREY OF MONMOUTH

Galfridius or Gaufridus Arturus, Galfridus Monmutensis. Galffrai or Gruffyd ab Arthur. Welsh chronicler, born or educated at Monmouth; he was in Oxford in 1129; from about 1140 until his death in 1154 he resided in Llandaff. He was consecrated bishop of St. Asaph in 1151–1152. He completed in 1136 (revised edition, 1147) a history of Britain (Historia Britonum) which is of no value from the standpoint of political history. It is mythology rather than history, and the chronology is fantastic; but it is of considerable importance from the standpoint of literary and artistic history. It is largely based upon Celtic sources, and contains the germs of the most popular romances of European literature—the Grail, Perceval, Lancelot, Tristram, and the Round Table. (To be sure, it was not alone in transmitting these). While he was writing his greater work, he made a Latin version from the Cymric of the "Prophecies of Merlin" (later incorporated into the Historia), which became another source of inspiration of the Arthurian romances. Our interest in Geoffrey is due to the fact that he introduced Celtic lore into the main stream of occidental tradition.

His History was abridged by Alfred of Beverley (fl. 1143), translated into Anglo-Norman verse by Geoffrey Gaimar (fl. 1140) and by Wace (fl. 1170), and Englished by Layamon (fl. 1200) and Robert of Gloucester (fl. 1260–1300)

Text—Historia Britanniae libri XII (Historia Britonum; Britanniae utriusque regum et principium origo et gesta insigna). First edition, Paris, 1508. Second edition, Paris, 1517. Third, Heidelberg, 1587. First critical edition, by J. A. Giles: Galfredi Monumetensis Historia Britonum (London 1844). Other edition by Albert Schulz (Halle 1854).

Acton Griscom: The Historia regum of Geoffrey of Monmouth. With contributions to the study of its place in early British history; together with a literal translation of the Welsh MS. no. LXI of Jesus College, Oxford, by Robert Ellis Jones (686 p., New York 1929). Reviewed in Amer. histor. rev. (vol. 35, 586–587, 1930). Critical edition based on the 190 known MSS., the 58 Welsh MSS. being also examined. The editor considers it very probable that Geoffrey had access to a "vetustissimus liber" now lost; many of the absurdities ascribed to Geoffrey are due to faulty editions or translations.

English translation by Aaron Thompson (London 1718); revised by J. A. Giles (Bohn Library, 310 p., London 1842); also in the Six old English chronicles, edited by Giles (Bohn Library, London 1848); by Sebastian Evans (London 1903).

Prophetia anglicana Merlini Ambrosii Britanni. First edition, Francfort, 1603; later editions, Francfort 1608, 1649.

De vita et vaticiniis Merlini. Edited by William Henry Black (Roxburghe Club, London 1830). Edition by Francisque Michel and Thomas Wright (Paris 1837).

For the Welsh texts derived from Geoffrey, see Tedder's article quoted below, and Welsh bibliographies. It would seem that the Celtic (Brythonic) dialects spoken respectively in Wales and Britanny were not then as differentiated as they are now.

Criticism—H. R. Tedder, in Dictionary of National Biography (21, 133–135, 1890). Potthast (487–488, 1896). Ferdinand Lot: Les sources de la Vita Merlini (Annales de Bretagne, vol. 15, 325–347, 505–537, 1900). Paul Feuerherd: Geoffrey und das Alte Testament (Diss., Halle 1915). Charles Gross: Sources of English history (248, 1915). Emil Greulich: Die Arthursage in der Historia regum Britanniae (Diss., Halle 1916). Hertha Brandenburg: Galfrid und die frühmittelenglischen Chronisten (Diss., Berlin 1918). Acton Griscom: The date of composition of the Historia (Speculum, 1, 129–156, 1926). Roger Sherman Loomis: Geoffrey of Monmouth and Arthurian origins (Speculum, 3, 16–33, 1928). John J. Parry: The chronology of Geoffrey's Historia, books i and ii (Speculum, vol. 4, 316–322, 1929); The Welsh texts of Geoffrey's Historia (Speculum, Vol. 5, 424–431, 1930).

CARADOG OF LLANCARVAN

Welsh chronicler who died about the middle of the twelfth century. There was a famous monastery in Llancarvan, in the vale of Glamorgan. Caradog was a friend of Geoffrey of Monmouth, whose history he continued. The original text of Caradog's chronicle is lost, but it is included in later Welsh chronicles; it was written more probably in Latin than in Celtic.

T. F. Tout: Dictionary of national biography (vol. 9, 30, 1887). Potthast (187, 1896). Charles Gross: Sources of English history (347, 1915).

X. GERMAN

SIGEBERT OF GEMBLOUX

Sigebertus Gemblacensis. Born about 1030, he lived in Gembloux, and died there in 1112. Belgian Benedictine and chronicler. He defended the imperial cause against Gregory VII (1073–1085) and Paschal II (1099–1118). His most important work is a universal chronicle, Chronographia, from 381 to 1111, which obtained much success; it was continued by many other chroniclers—for example for the years 1148 to 1152, by John of Salisbury (second half of the twelfth century). He wrote a history of the Gembloux abbey to 1048, Gesta abbatum Gemblacensium, and various biographies.

Text—First edition of the Chronographia, Paris, 1513. Excellent edition, with various continuations and germane texts, by L. C. Bethmann, in the Monumenta Germaniae historica (scriptores, 6); reprinted in Migne's Patrology (vol. 160)

Gesta abbatum Gemblacensium, edited in the Mon. Germ. hist. (scriptores, 8), and in Migne's Patrology (vol. 160).

Criticism—S. Hirsch: De vita et scriptis Sigiberti Gemblacensis (Berlin 1841). Potthast (1016, 1896). H. Pirenne: Histoire de Belgique (vol. 1, 3rd ed., 159, 1909); says Pirenne: "L'oeuvre de Sigebert nous apparaît comme l'expression la plus haute du monument intellectuel en Lotharingie."

EKKEHARD OF AURA

Ekkehardus (Eccardus, Eggehardus) Uraugiensis. Died in or after 1125. German historian who lived in the Benedictine monasteries of Bamberg and Corvey; he went on a pilgrimage to Jerusalem in 1101, returning in 1106 via Rome; in 1108 he was appointed abbot of the new monastery of Aura, on the Frankish Saale, not far from Kissingen. From about 1100 to the end of his life he was engaged in writing a universal chronicle, which is one of the best mediaeval chronicles of its kind, being of course especially important for the last half-century it covers. This chronicle has been wrongly ascribed to Conrad of Lichtenau (Conradus abbas Urspergensis, d. 1240); it was continued by Burchard of Ursperg (born in Biberach, d. 1230) for the period 1125–1226, by Conrad of Lichtenau for the years 1226–1229, etc. Ekkehard wrote also, after 1114, an account of the First Crusade, which is essentially derived from the Gesta Francorum.

Text—Chronicon universale ab O. C. a 1125. This was the first German chronicle to be printed, under the title: Chronicon abbatis Urspergen. a Nino rege Assyriorum magno usque ad Fridericum II Romanorum imperatorem (Augsburg 1515). Various subsequent editions, including one in the Monumenta Germaniae historica (scriptores, 6), and another in Migne's Patrology (vol. 154, col. 433–1062, 1853). German translation by W. Pflüger (186 p., Leipzig 1879; reprinted 1893).

Hierosolymita seu Libellus de oppressione, liberatione ac restauratione sanctae Hierosolymitanae ecclesiae. First edition by Edm. Martene and Urs. Durand: Thesaurus novus anecdotorum (vol. 5, 511–535, Paris 1717). Editions by Heinrich Hagenmeyer (Tübingen 1877); and by P. Riant, in Recueil des historiens des Croisades (Hist. occ., vol. 5, 1–40).

Criticism—Wilhelm Wattenbach: Allgemeine Deutsche Biographie (vol. 5, 793, 1877); Deutschlands Geschichtsquellen (vol. 2, 189–198, 1894). Potthast (400, 178, 296, 1896).

OTTO OF FREISING

Otto Frisingensis. German Cistercian and chronicler. Born of a princely and imperial family about 1114; his father was the markgraf Leopold III (IV) of Austria; he was the brother of the Hohenstaufen Conrad III (emperor from 1138–1152), and the uncle of Frederick I Barbarossa (1152–1190). Educated in Paris. He became abbot of the Morimond monastery in Burgundy about 1136; then bishop of Freising in Bavaria. He died at Morimond in 1158.

He was perhaps the most philosophical chronicler of the Christian Middle Ages. He was one of the first to introduce Aristotelianism into Germany, probably by means of Boetius' translation. He took part in one of the Crusades, reaching Jerusalem about 1147. His chief work, Chronica sive Historia de duabus civitatibus—that is, Jerusalem and Babel, the spiritual and material worlds—was modeled after the works of Augustine and Orosius; it contains historical information down to 1146. There is an important continuation of it down to 1209 by Otto, abbot of St. Blasius (d. 1223). Otto of Freising had witnessed many of the events described by him, which occurred in Germany, Italy, and the Near East. He wrote the life of his nephew Frederick Barbarossa, the Gesta Friderici imperatoris, from about 1075 to 1156; this biography was continued down to 1160 by his pupil Rahewin (Rachwin, Ragewin, Reguin). His philosophy of history was to some extent based upon the theological notion, developed by Hugh of Saint Victor, of the westward course of civilization. He was the first historian to mention "Prester John."

Text—First edition by John Cuspinian (Strassburg 1515). First critical edition in the Mon. Germ. hist., by Roger Wilmans (2 vols., Hannover 1867). Separate edition of the Gesta Friderici, by Georg Waitz (Hannover 1884). Chronica sive Historia. New edition by Adolf Hofmeister (691 p., Hannover 1912).

Partial German translations by Horst Kohl (Leipzig 1881, 1894). Complete English translation by Charles Christopher Mierow (536 p., Columbia University, New York 1928; Isis, 13, 422).

Criticism—Potthast (885–887, 1896; for Otto de S. Blasio, 884). W. Wattenbach: Allgemeine deutsche Biographie (vol. 24, 688–690, 1887); Deutschlands Geschichtsquellen (vol. 2, 271–285, 1894). J. Hashagen: Otto als Geschichtsphilosoph und Kirchenpolitiker (Leipzig 1900). J. Schmidlin: Die geschichtsphilosophische und kirchenpolitische Weltanschauung Ottos (Freiburg 1906). Dahlmann-Waitz: Quellenkunde der deutschen Geschichte (8th ed., 352, 1912). Adolf Hofmeister: Studien über Otto von Freising (Neues Archiv der Gesellschaft für ältere deutsche Geschichtskunde, vol. 37, 101–161, 635–768, 1911–1912); important. J. K. Wright: Geographical lore (234, 1924). C. H. Haskins: Renaissance of the twelfth century (241–244, 1927).

ANSELM OF HAVELBERG

See Chapter III, The Translators.

XI. BOHEMIAN

COSMAS OF PRAGUE

Czech historian, the "Herodotos of Bohemia," the father of Bohemian history. Born in or about 1045. Dean of the cathedral of Prague. He died on Oct. 21, 1125. He wrote the earliest chronicles of Bohemia down to the time of his death, Chronicae Bohemorum libri III; this work was begun by him after 1117. Various continuations extend them to the year 1283. In spite of the fact that Cosmas' veracity and impartiality have been impugned, his work is of inestimable value.

Text—First (incomplete) edition, Hanover 1602. First complete edition, Hanover 1607. Editions in Migne's Patrology (166, 55–388); also in the Fontes rerum Bohemicarum (2, 1–370, 1874). George Grandaur: Chronik von Böhmen und Fortsetzungen nach der Ausgabe der Monumenta Germaniae übersetzt (Leipzig 1885).

Criticism—J. Loserth: Studien zu Cosmas (Archiv für österr. Geschichte, 61, 3–32, 1880); Kritische Studien zur älteren Geschichte Böhmens (Mitt. des Instituts für österr. Geschichtsforschung, 4, 177–191, 1883). August Potthast: Bibliotheca historica medii aevi (357–358, 1895). Frantz Lützow: History of Bohemian literature (42–48, 1907). Václav Novotný: Zur böhmischen Quellenkunde (238 p. in 2 parts; Bohemian Academy, Prague 1907–1910).

XII. ICELANDIC

ARI FRÓÐI ÞORGILSSON

Ari Þorgilsson hinn fróði. Born in Iceland in 1067, of royal blood. Died in 1148. Icelandic historian. One of the very greatest historians of his time, the founder of the great historical school of his country. He wrote in Icelandic the Book of the Kings, Konungabók, a history of the kings of Norway down to 1067; this work is lost. Also the Book of Icelanders, Islendingabók, written about 1127, of which only fragments remain; it contained an account of Icelandic history from about 874 to 1120, and of Icelandic institutions; it is partly preserved in an abstract of it made by himself about 1137. A third work ascribed to him, the Landnámabók (or Landnáma), the Book of Settlements, is only known through three later recensions: the Sturlubók, made by Sturla þorðarson about 1250–1280; the Hauksbók, made by Haukr Erlendssor about 1320; and the Melabók made by Borgarfjörðr of the Melar family in the first half of the fourteenth century. Though the original Landnáma was largely based on Ari's writings, or on oral traditions, it can not be considered an original work of his. It contains a history and a very accurate description of the Norwegian discovery and settlement of Iceland, 874–930. (See vol. I, 605.)

The Kristni saga, a brief history of the Icelandic church from the advent of the first missionaries in 981 to 1118, was not written by Ari; it is a later work dating from about 1200. It deals chiefly with the introduction of Christianity into Iceland about the year 1000.

Text—Islendigabók. Schedae Ara Prestz Froda um Island. Edited by Bishop þórður þorláksson (24 p., Skalhollte 1688); this was the first edition. Icelandic text with Latin translation and notes by Andreas Bussaeus (Copenhagen 1733). Icelandic text with German translation by Theodor Möbius (110 p., Leipzig 1869). Icelandic text by Wolfgang Golther (74 p., Halle 1892; revised edition, 76 p., Halle 1923). French translation with commentary by Félix Wagner (105 p., Bruxelles 1898). Icelandic text with English version by G. Vigfusson and F. Y. Powell: Origines islandicae (vol. 1, 279–306, Oxford 1905). Icelandic text with English version by Halldór Hermannsson (Islandica, vol. 20, 95 p., Ithaca, New York, 1930).

Landnámabók—Sagan landnáma, edited by þórður þorláksson (212 p., Skalhollte, 1688). Liber originum Islandiae. Icelandic text with Latin translation by Hannes Finnsson (530 p., Copenhagen 1774). Icelandic text edited by Finnur Jónsson (467 p., Copenhagen 1900); new edition of the text established by Finnur Jónsson (250 p., Copenhagen 1925). The same had published the text of the Melabók (178 p., Copenhagen 1921). Icelandic text with English translation in G. Vigfusson and F. Y. Powell: Origines islandicae (vol. 1, 2–236, 261–74, Oxford 1905).

Kristni saga—Christendoms saga, edited by þórður þorláksson (32 p., Skalhollte 1688). Icelandic text with Latin translation by Hannes Finnsson and B. W. Luxdorph (Copenhagen 1773). Icelandic text by B. Kahle (178 p., Halle 1905). Icelandic text with English translation in G. Vigfusson and F. Y. Powell: Origines islandicae (vol. 1, 370–406, 1905).

Criticism—Oskar Brenner: Über die Kristni-saga (172 p., München, 1878). Halldór Hermannsson: Bibliography of the Icelandic sagas (Islandica, vol. 1, 126 p., Cornell University, Ithaca, N. Y., 1908); very elaborate. Finnur Jónsson: Den oldnorske og oldislandske Literaturs Historie (3 vols., Copenhagen 1894–1902; new edition 1920–1924).

For the Eddas, see Chapter IV, Philosophic Background.

XIII. RUSSIAN

NESTOR OF KIEV

Born about 1056, he became a monk of the Pecherskiy monastery at Kiev in 1073. He died about 1110. The father of Russian history. Reputed author (or editor) of the earliest Russian chronicle extant, The Chronicle of Nestor or The Ancient Chronicle. This chronicle is of national scope, and is based on Byzantine chronicles, chiefly that of Georgios Monachos (first half of the ninth century), and also upon earlier Slavonic chronicles which are lost. It begins with the Deluge, and ends within Nestor's own time (1110). It is of fundamental importance for the early history of Russia, and contains also ethnological information of great value.

A continuation of the Chronicle was edited by Silvester, abbot of the Viebuditski monastery in Kiev, before 1125. According to Kluchevsky (op. cit., p. 18) Silvester is the real editor of the Chronicle, rather than Nestor.

Text and translations—Chronica Nestoris. Textum russico-slovenicum, versionem latinam, glossarium edidit Fr. Miklosich (Vienna 1860). Better edition of the Russian text alone (St. Petersburg 1872).

German translation, together with the original text, by Ludwig Schlözer (5 parts, Göttingen 1802–1809). French translation by Louis Paris (2 vols., Paris 1834–1835); by Louis Léger (Paris 1884).

Criticism—Mikhail Petrovich Pogodin: Nestor, eine historische-kritische Untersuchung, übersetzt von F. Löwe (St. Petersburg 1844). Potthast (843–845, 1896). V. O. Kluchevsky: A History of Russia (vol. 1, 1911). D. S. Mirsky: History of Russian literature (13, 15, 1927).

XIV. KASHMIRIAN

KALHAṆA

Kashmirian historian and poet. His father Caṇpaka was a minister at the court of Harsha, "the Nero of Kashmīr," who ruled from 1089 to 1101. Kalhaṇa was probably born at the beginning of the twelfth century. His Rājataraṅgiṇī, the Stream of Kings, is a history in verse of the kings of Kashmīr from the earliest times down to his own days; it is divided into eight books. It was completed in 1148, and is by far the most important work of its kind in Hindu literature. Kalhaṇa was a Shivaite, yet he speaks of Buddhism with sympathy. He was a very learned man, and his history is unusually critical and impartial as compared with other Hindu works; his sources were not only literary but also archaeological.

It is not enough to say that the Rājataraṅgiṇī is the best early Hindu chronicle; it is practically the only one extant. Earlier Sanskrit works can hardly be called chronicles; they are panegyrical poems (historical kāvya, carita) of little scientific value. However, we have an excellent chronicle of Ceylon, the Mahāvaṃsa, written by Mahānāma in Pāli verse (second half of the fifth century, vol. I, 412). The Rājataraṅgiṇī is a fundamental source for the archaeology of Kashmīr, and it is one of the most important documents for the study of civilization in mediaeval India. For a continuation of it, see my note on Jonarāja (second half of the fifteenth century).

Text—Editio princeps under the auspices of the Asiatic Society of Bengal (Baptist Mission Press, Calcutta 1835); corrupt text of the first six cantos. Sanskrit-French edition by A. Troyer (3 vols., Paris 1840–1852); poor. Critical edition by M. A. Stein (316 p., folio, Bombay 1892).

English translation by Joseph Chunder Dutt (330 p., Calcutta 1879); poor. New translation by M A. Stein (2 vols., Westminster 1900). This is a very important publication containing an exhaustive introduction (145 p.), and (in vol. 2, 347–494) a long memoir on the ancient geography of Kashmīr, with historical maps.

Criticism—M. Winternitz: Indische Litteratur (vol. 3, 86–91, 1922).

XV. CHINESE

TÊNG MING-SHIH

Têng^{4} Ming^{2}-shih^{4} (10870, 7940, 9969). Flourished under the Sung, about 1134. Chinese scholar. He wrote in 1134, with the collaboration of his son Têng^{4} ch'un^{1} (10878, 2856), a treatise on the origin and history of Chinese clans and families, Ku^{3}-chin^{1} hsing^{4}-shih^{4}-shu^{1} pien^{4}-chêng^{4} (6188, 2027, 4599, 9978, 10024, 9207, 726), which has remained the basis of all ulterior investigations.

Text—The Library of Congress has a copy of the Ku-chin, in 40 chüan bound in four volumes, with a preface dated 1808. Another copy is included in the Shou^{3} shan^{1} ko^{2*} ts'ung^{1} shu^{1} (10012, 9663, 6037, 12039, 10024), in 40 chüan bound in six volumes.

Criticism—L. Wieger: La Chine (433, 504, 1920).

HUNG TSUN

Hung^{2} Tsun^{1} (5252, 11955). Chinese archaeologist, born in 1120. He died in 1174. Canonised as Wên^{2} An^{1} (12633, 44). One of three distinguished brothers, called the Three Hungs. The two others were Hung Kua (second half of the twelfth century), and Hung^{2} Mai^{4} (5252, 7620), a literary critic (1124–1203). Hung Tsun published in 1149 the earliest extant work on Chinese coinage, the Ch'üan^{2} chih^{4} (3187, 1918). It is divided into fifteen books and "contains cuts and descriptions of the various coins in use from the earliest period down to the middle of the tenth century, both the legitimate currency and those cast by successive usurpers, with a collection of coins of foreign nations and also of medals" (Wylie). Other works had been written in earlier times (as early as the sixth century, if not earlier), but are lost. Besides, all the dynastic histories from the Han to the Ming devote a special section to currency.

Text—The illustrated text of the Ch'üan chih, in fifteen chüan, is included in at least two ts'ung shu: Hsüeh^{2*} ching^{1} t'ao^{3} yüan^{2} (4839, 2163, 10838, 13700); Ching^{1} tai^{4} pi^{4} shu^{1} (2163, 10562, 8932, 10024). Copies of both are in the Library of Congress.

Criticism—A. Wylie: Chinese literature (146, 1902); with information on modern Chinese publications completing and correcting the Ch'üan chih. H. A. Giles: Chinese biographical dictionary (344, 347–348, 1898). Article on numismatics, in Encyclopaedia sinica (401, 1917). On Chinese numismatics (Isis, 4, 425).

CHINESE ARCHAEOLOGY

The Sung dynasty was the golden age of painting in China, and art was strongly encouraged by the emperors, above all by the emperor Hui^{1} Tsung^{1} (5160, 11976) who ruled from 1100 to 1126, himself a great artist. The love of art treasures such as bronzes and works in jade led to scientific research relative to them, and very important archaeological publications were compiled during the twelfth century. The value of those publications has possibly been overestimated by some innocent enthusiasts, but one should keep their date in mind and remember that nothing in the slightest degree comparable to them was produced in the West at the same time (and for many centuries afterwards), either by Christians or by Muslims.

The two chief works of that kind are the Po^{4*} ku^{3} t'u^{2} lu^{4*} (9372, 6188, 12128, 7386) and the Ku^{3} yü^{4*} t'u^{2} p'u^{3} (6188, 13630, 12128, 9515).

The Po ku t'u lu is a catalogue of the collections of the emperor Hui Tsung, in 30 books. There are two different editions of it in the Library of Congress, both dated 1588. It was written by Wang^{2} Fu^{2*} (12493, 3702) in 1107–1111. Wang Fu also constructed astronomical instruments in 1124 (L. Wieger: La Chine, 457, 1920).

The Ku yü t'u p'u (illustrated description of ancient jades) is a catalogue of the collections of jade belonging to the first emperor of the S. Sung Dynasty, Kao^{1} Tsung^{1} (5927, 11976) (1127–1162) and consisting of over 700 pieces. The editor was Lung^{2} Ta^{4}-yüan^{2} (7479, 10470, 13713), president of the Board of Rites, li^{3} pu^{4} (6949, 9484), who prefaced the work in 1176 but died before its completion. This work really belongs to the next period, second half of the twelfth century, but I speak of it now because it is simpler to deal with the Po ku and the Ku yü at the same time.

It is said that Lung Ta-yüan was assisted by four of the greatest artists of the time: Liu^{2} Sung^{1}-nien^{2} (7270, 10449, 8301) (c. 1190–1230), Li^{3} T'ang^{2} (6884, 10767) (c. 1100–1130), Ma^{3} Yüan^{3} (7576, 13743) (c. 1190–1224), and Hsia^{4} Kuei (4227, 6436) (1180–1230); but it is impossible to accept that statement literally considering the dates of these artists.[1] The Ku yü t'u p'u was published for the first time in 1752, if not before.

The Library of Congress has the edition of 1752, and two other abbreviated editions. For both works, see Friedrich Hirth: The ancient history of China (73, 89–91, 1908). Berthold Laufer: Jade (Chicago 1912). Laufer's introduction contains a critical appreciation of both books, but chiefly of the latter of which he had made a deep study. His work is based to a certain extent upon it, but far more upon the Ku^{3} yü^{4} t'u^{2} k'ao^{3} (6188, 13630, 12128, 5966), Investigations into ancient jades, with illustrations, published by Wu^{2} Ta^{4}-ch'êng^{2} (12748, 10470, 779), in 1889. There is a copy of this work in the Library of Congress.

XVI. JAPANESE

FUJIWARA TAMENARI

Japanese historian who lived during the reign of Sutoku, emperor from 1124 to 1141. He died, a Buddhist monk, on Mt. Ohara near Kyōto. Author of the Great Mirror (Ō-kagami), a history of Japan from 851 to 1036, in 8 volumes. The Ō-kagami is one of the "Three Mirrors" (Mitsu kagami, or San kyō), the two others being the Water Mirror (Mizu-kagami) for the period 660 B.C. to 850 by Nakayama Tadachika (second half of the twelfth century), and the Clear Mirror (Masu-kagami) anonymous chronicle of the period 1184 to 1333. Or, one of the "Four Mirrors" (Yotsu-kagami, or Shi-kyō), if a fourth one be considered, the Mirror of the Present (Ima-kagami, twelfth century). All these "mirrors" (Kagami) are historical works (cf. the Western use of the same metaphor, Speculum, Spiegel, etc.).

[1] The dates are taken from Arthur Waley: Index of Chinese artists (London 1922).

CHAPTER XII

LAW AND SOCIOLOGY

(First Half of Twelfth Century)

I. WESTERN MUSLIM

ABŪ BAKR AL-ṬURṬŪSHĪ

Abū Bakr Muḥammad ibn al-Walīd ibn Muḥammad ibn Khalaf al-Ṭurṭūshī, surnamed Ibn abī Randaqa. Born at Tortosa in 1059–1060; studied in Saragossa and Seville; made the pilgrimage in 1083–1084, and remained in the Near East, settling finally in Alexandria, where he died in 1126 (or 1129). Hispano-Muslim theologian of the Mālikite school. In 1122, at Fusṭāṭ, he completed for the wazīr al-Ma'mūn a treatise of practical politics, Sirāj al-mulūk (Lucerna regum, Lamp of Kings), containing many historical anecdotes.

Text—Printed edition, Cairo, 1289 H. Extracts quoted by R. P. A. Dozy: Recherches sur l'histoire et la littérature de l'Espagne (vol. 2, 2nd ed., 254, Leyde 1860).

Criticism—Ibn Khaldūn (de Slane, vol. 1, 82, 321; vol. 2, 89–90; vol. 3, 19). Ibn Khallikān (de Slane, vol. 2, 665–667). F. Wüstenfeld: Geschichtschreiber der Araber (1, 77, 1881). C. Brockelmann: Arabische Litteratur (1, 459, 1898).

IBN AL-'ARABĪ

Abū Bakr Muḥammad ibn 'Abdallāh, generally called Ibn al-'Arabī. Not to be confused with his great namesake Ibn 'Arabī, Abū Bakr Muḥammad ibn 'Alī (first half of the thirteenth century). Hispano-Muslim traditionist. Born at Seville in 1076, he went to the East with his father, being educated in Syria, Baghdād, Mecca, and Egypt; while in Syria, he studied jurisprudence under Abū Bakr al-Ṭurṭūshī (see above); when his father died, at Alexandria in 1099, Ibn al-'Arabī returned to Seville where he was appointed chief qāḍī; later he moved to Fās where he remained until his death in 1148. He wrote a commentary on the Kitāb al-muwaṭṭa' of Mālik ibn Anas (second half of the eighth century), the fundamental treatise on Mālikite law. According to Ibn Khaldūn, who praises him, he had conceived a very original plan of elementary education: first the study of the Arabic language, then arithmetic, the Qur'ān being a culmination rather than a beginning.

Ibn Khallikān (vol. 3, 12–14). Ibn Khaldūn: Prolégomènes (vol. 1, 442; vol. 3, 289). F. Pons Boigues: Ensayo bio-bibliográfico (216–217, Madrid 1898). C. Brockelmann: Arabische Litteratur (vol. 1, 176, 1898). D. B. Macdonald: Aspects of Islam (317, 1911). Encyclopaedia of Islām (vol. 2, 362, 1916); very short unsigned article.

II. LATIN

MANEGOLD OF LAUTENBACH

Manegaldus de Lutinbach. Augustinian Canon. Alsatian philosopher and sociologist who in 1083 was living in a house of the Regular Canons at Lautenbach near Gebweiler, Alsace; in 1086 he became dean of Raitenbuch, or Rottenbuch, in Upper Bavaria; in 1094 he was at Marbach near Colmar, being provost of a new monastery which he had helped to establish; in 1096 he was in Tours with Urban II (1088–1099). He died after 1103. I ought to have spoken of him in my chapter on the second half of the eleventh century; I speak of him now, faute de mieux, because his work must be taken into account to explain the progress of political thought. He wrote two treatises: (1) in 1083, the Opusculum contra Wolfelmum—that is, Wolfhelm of Cologne—based upon Macrobius' Commentary on the Somnium Scipionis, wherein he tries to show up the errors of philosophers, the superfluity of philosophy (vs. theology or faith); (2) after 1085, a political pamphlet in which he defended papal views against the imperial. This is quite important as it is one of the earliest mediaeval discussions of sovereignty, one of the earliest treatises on the philosophy of the state. The monarchy is an officium, the exercise of which implies moral qualifications and a sort of social contract (pactum) with the people. These views were elaborated in the Polycratus of John of Salisbury (second half of the twelfth century), but Manegold deserves the credit due to a pioneer.

Text—Libellus contra Wolfelmum. Edited by L. A. Muratori: Anecdota (vol. 4, Padoa 163–208, 1713); and in Migne's Patrology (vol. 154, 149–176).

Liber ad Gebehardum archiepiscopum Salisburgensem pro Gregorio VII. This is the political treatise wherein he attacks the views of the schoolman Wenrich of Treves (d. 1082). Edited by Kuno Francke: Monumenta Germaniae historica, Libelli de lite imperatorum et pontificum saeculis XI et XII conscripti (vol. 1, 307–430, 1891).

Criticism—Histoire littéraire de la France (vol. 9, 280–290, 1750). W. Wattenbach: Deutschlands Geschichtsquellen (vol. 2, 52, 1894). Potthast (761, 1896). J. A. Endres: Manegold (Hist. polit. Blätter, vol. 127, 390 sq., 486 sq., 1901). Georg Koch: Manegold und die Lehre von der Volkssouveränität unter Heinrich IV (160 p., Berlin 1902). Cl. Baeumker: Der Anteil des Elsass an den geistigen Bewegungen des Mittelalters (Strassburg 1912). Matthias Baumgartner: Überwegs Grundriss (251, 114*, Berlin 1915). R. W. Carlyle and A. J. Carlyle: History of mediaeval political theory in the West (vol. 3 and 4, passim, Edinburgh 1915–1922). M. De Wulf: History of mediaeval philosophy (vol. 1, 145, 182, 1926).

IRNERIUS

Irnerio of Bologna. Many variants of this name, the first syllable Ir being spelled Hir, Hyr, Ger, Guar, War, Wer. Born in Bologna in the second half of the eleventh century, about 1060. He died some time between 1118 and 1140. Italian legist. Adviser to the countess Matilda of Tuscany (who supported Gregory VII), and after her death (1115), to the emperor Henry V. Though we hear in 1076 of a Bolognese master called Pepo (The Digest was cited in that circumstance; it had dropped out of sight in the West since 603!), Irnerius is generally considered, and rightly so, the restorer of Roman law in Latin Christendom. And though some legal work had been done previously in the schools of Provence, Rome, Pavia,[1] and Ravenna, Bologna was the real cradle of the new study. Roman law attained now for the first time a modicum of independence; hitherto it had been regarded as a branch of rhetoric; it was now a professional subject, distinct from the liberal arts. If Irnerius did not himself found the school of Bologna, he founded

[1] See vol. I, 778.

it indirectly through his disciples. He wrote (1) a large number of glosses on the Corpus Juris, especially on the Digest; (2) a series of Questions on the subtleties of the law; (3) an epitome of Justinian's Novellae. The authenticity of (1) is certain; of (2) probable; of (3) uncertain. His chief purpose was to reestablish as authentic a text of the Corpus juris as possible, then to interpret that text literally.

The importance of Irnerius' work can hardly be overestimated. This is obvious enough from the legal point of view: it was the reintroduction not simply of Roman law, but, what mattered more, of scientific jurisprudence. However valuable the law itself, the method was more valuable still, for its application was universal. This was promptly understood, and the more so in that the age was one of intense political reconstruction. In fact Roman law was revived so exactly when it was most needed that this can hardly be an accident. At any rate its study was carried on with considerable energy. Said Maitland,[2] "in no other age, since the classical days of Roman law, has so large a part of the sum total of intellectual endeavour been devoted to jurisprudence."

From our special point of view, Irnerius' work is hardly less important. Abaelard and Irnerius influenced the scientific thought of the Middle Ages to a considerable degree. That influence was partly an evil one, but it seemed to have been necessary at that particular stage of intellectual progress.

Among Irnerius' first disciples were the so-called "Four Doctors:" Martinus, who died before 1166; Bulgarus, in 1166; Hugo, about 1168; Jacobus, in 1178. The most influential of these was Bulgarus, sometimes called the Chrysostom of glossators; his main work was the De regulis juris. The most remarkable doctor of the following generation was John Bassianus of Cremona (?), pupil of Bulgarus and teacher of Azo; he was a professor in Bologna, and died in 1197 in very old age. He devised the "arbor arborum," a "law tree" whereupon various kinds of actions were arranged like fruits (compare with Ramon Lull's arbor scientiae), a kind of memoria technica for law students.

Text—Part of his Glosses are included in Accorso's collection: Formularium tabellionum saeculo XII ineunte in novam formam redactum (Scripta anecdota glossatorum, 1888–1901). Questiones de juris subtilitatibus, edited, with introduction, by Hermann Fitting (98 p., Festschrift, Universität, Halle; Berlin 1894). Summa codicis edited, with introduction, by the same (Berlin 1894). Enrico Besta: Glosse inedite al Digestum vetus (Torino 1896, forming vol. 2 of the work quoted below).

Criticism—Hermann Fitting: Die Anfänge der Rechtsschule zu Bologna (135 p., Berlin 1888). Gust. Pescatore: Die Glossen des Irnerius (Festschrift, Greifswald 1888); Kritische Studien auf dem Gebiete der civilistischen Litterärgeschichte des Mittelalters (Beitr. zur mittelalterlichen Rechtsgeschichte, 4, Greifswald 1896). Enrico Besta: L'opera d'Irnerio (2 vols., Torino 1896); with bibliography; vol. 1 is biographical and critical, vol. 2 contains original texts. Paul Vinogradoff: Roman law in mediaeval Europe (ch. 2, 1909); containing a summary of the legal work of the eleventh century which prepared Irnerio's task). R. W. Carlyle and A. J. Carlyle: History of mediaeval political theory in the West (vol. 2, Edinburgh 1909). C. H. Haskins: Renaissance of the twelfth century (ch. 7, the revival of jurisprudence, 193–223, with select bibliography; Cambridge, Mass., 1927; Isis, 10, 62–65).

[2] F. Pollock and F. W. Maitland: History of English law (vol. 1, 111, 2nd edition, Cambridge 1898). As quoted by Haskins (loc. cit., 194).

ROMAN LAW IN FRANCE AND ENGLAND

A very clear treatise on Roman law, the Brachylogus juris civilis, dates probably from the first quarter of the twelfth century. Savigny had ascribed it to Irnerio, but it is more probably a French work, possibly a production of the school of Orleans. At any rate it testifies to a genuine acquaintance with Justinian's codification; the author was also acquainted with Alaric's Breviary (first half of the sixth century, vol. I, 438).

Another legal work of considerable interest is the so-called Lo Codi, a summary of Justinian's code, compiled for the use of judges in Provence. It was written about 1149, in south-eastern France, possibly in Arles which was then a part of the Empire. It is the earliest treatise on Roman law written in a vernacular—Provençal. Lo Codi contains far more traces of the influence of Irnerio and the glossators than does the Brachylogus; yet it is original in various ways; it is very clear and practical.

For the introduction of Roman law into England, see my note on Vacarius (second half of the twelfth century). This Italian jurist came to England about 1143, and was teaching civil law in 1149, but his activity falls chiefly within the second half of the twelfth century.

Text—The princeps of the Brachylogus is entitled Corpus legum per modum Institutionium (Lyon 1549). A later edition (Lyon 1557) bears the title Brachylogus, under which it is now generally known. Critical edition by Eduard Böcking (Berlin 1829).

A Latin translation of the Lo Codi, made by Ricardus Pisanus about 1150, was edited by Hermann Fitting (Halle 1906 sq.). An edition of the original Provençal text was prepared by Hermann Suchier.

Criticism—H. Fitting: Über die Heimat und das Alter des sogenannten Brachylogus nebst Untersuchungen über die Geschichte der Rechtwissenschaft in Frankreich am Anfange des Mittelalters (43 p., Berlin 1880). P. Vinogradoff: Roman law in mediaeval Europe (60–66, 1909). R. W. Carlyle and A. J. Carlyle: History of mediaeval political theory in the West (vol. 2, 1909).

Hermann Suchier: Fünf neue Handschriften des Rechtsbuches Lo Codi (Halle 1899); Die Handschriften des castilianischen Übersetzung (Halle 1900). Hermann Fitting: Eine weitere Handschrift der lateinischen Übersetzung des Codi (Progr., 13 p., Halle 1905).

DEVELOPMENT OF FEUDAL LAW

The extraordinary revival of Roman law did not impede the development of feudal law. Indeed the latter was bound to grow as long as feudal conditions obtained, and it continued, if not to grow, at least to exist, in each country as long as these conditions managed to survive. However this hardly concerns us. The history of Roman law may be considered a part of our subject, because it represents to some extent the application of a scientific method to human affairs. The history of feudal or customary law is far more remote from our main interest.

Thus it will suffice to mention very briefly, by way of illustration, the Usages of Barcelona (1068 and following); the beginnings of the Lombard Leges feudorum (end of the eleventh century or beginning of the twelfth); the Assizes of Roger of Sicily, etc.

GRATIAN

Italian Camaldolite and jurist who lived at Bologna in the first half of the twelfth century. Founder of the science of (Christian) canon law. Under the influence of Roman law and of scholastic philosophy—of Irnerio and Abaelard—he compiled a systematic collection of the laws of the church, the decretals of the popes down to 1139, Discordantium canonum concordia, or Decretum. Of course canon law had not ceased to accumulate from the earliest days of papal administration, but it had become very confused. Hence the title of Gratian's work, which defines it quite correctly. It was a "concordance of discordant canons," and by achieving it, Gratian was undoubtedly the founder of canon law.

This work was the first part of what later became the Corpus juris canonici, a counterpart of the Justinian codification in many respects. The three other parts of the Corpus are: the Liber extra (Quinque libri decretalium Gregorii Noni), 1234; the Liber sextus (Liber sextus decretalium), 1294; the Liber septimus, 1313 (1317). To this Corpus were eventually added Extravagantes, corresponding to the Novellae of Justinian; and in 1563 a short treatise by Giovanni Paolo Lancelotti (1511–1591), Institutiones juris canonici, corresponding to the Institutes. To complete this comparison, the Decretum and Decretales may be regarded as counterparts respectively of the Digest and of the Code of Justinian.

Text—Decretum. Strassburg 1471, etc. There are about fifty incunabula editions! An official edition of the Corpus was published in 1582 by order of Gregory XIII. The best edition was prepared by Emil Friedberg (Leipzig 1879–1881). There are a great many other editions with and without glosses.

Criticism—J. F. von Schulte: Geschichte der Quellen und Litteratur des canonischen Rechts von Gratian bis auf die Gegenwart (Stuttgart 1875–1880). Silvio Maria dei Nardi: Graziano (Roma 1894). G. C. Lee: Historical jurisprudence, New York (331–337, 1900). R. W. Carlyle and A. J. Carlyle: History of mediaeval political theory in the West (vols. 2 and 3, 1909–1915). C. P. Sherman: Roman Law (vol. 1, 218–222, Boston 1917). C. H. Haskins: Renaissance of the twelfth century (214–216, 223, Cambridge, Mass., 1927).

ALEXANDER III

Orlando Bandinelli of Siena, Magister Rolandus. Teacher of canon law in Bologna; created cardinal in 1150, papal chancellor in 1153; pope in 1159, when he assumed the name Alexander III; died at Civita Castellana (Viterbo) in 1181. I quote him chiefly because of his activity as a legist which occurred presumably towards the end of the first half of the twelfth century. He composed the earliest commentary on Gratian (or one of the earliest), the Summa Magistri Rolandi.

The Summa is interesting as helping to show the gradual emancipation of canon law from Roman law. This tendency is easier to understand with reference to later events. In 1219 the Pope forbade priests to study Roman law, and he altogether prohibited its teaching at the University of Paris.

A few words must be said of Alexander's political activity. As cardinal, and later as pope, he made himself famous by his protracted struggle against Frederick Barbarossa (emperor from 1152 to 1190). He obliged Henry II (king of England from 1154 to 1189) to purge himself for the murder of St. Thomas Becket (1170). He convoked the Third Lateran Council (1179), which condemned the Albigenses.

Text—Many editions of Alexander's Epistolae. See Potthast (p. 35). Sententiae, first edition by A. M. Gietl (Freiburg i. Br., 1891).

Criticism—Heinrich Kerner: Papst Alexander III (160 p., Freiburg i. Br., 1874). R. W. Carlyle and A. J. Carlyle: History of mediaeval political theory in the West (vols. 2 and 4, 1909–1922). C. H. Haskins: Renaissance of the twelfth century (chapter 7, 1927). Gaines Post: Alexander III, the licentia docendi and the rise of the universities (Haskins anniversary essays, Boston 1929, 255–277; Isis, 15, 210).

III. HINDU

LAKSHMĪDHARA

Hindu legist. Minister to a king called Govindacandra who is in all probability the Gaharwār king of Kanauj, who ruled from 1105 to 1143. He wrote one of the earliest commentaries on dharma, entitled Smṛitikalpataru (also Smṛitikalpadruma or Kṛityakalpataru). It treats of religious dharma, the king's rights and procedure.

M. Winternitz: Indische Litteratur (vol. 3, 502, 1922; quoting other works of the same kind).

GOVINDARĀJA

Hindu legist who lived probably in the twelfth century. He composed a valuable commentary on the Manu-smṛiti (the laws of Manu). The best known commentary, written in Benares in the fifteenth century by Kullūka, is essentially a plagiarism of Govindarāja's work. The latter is thus the most important mediaeval commentary on Manu; it is not the earliest—an earlier one by Medhātithi (of Kashmīr ?) dates probably from the ninth century.

Text—Govindarāja's commentary on Mānadharma śāstra, edited by Vishvanāth Nārāyan Mandlik (Bombay 1886).
Criticism—M. Winternitz: Indische Litteratur (vol. 3, 494, 1927).

CHAPTER XIII

PHILOLOGY AND EDUCATION

(First Half of Twelfth Century)

I. EASTERN MUSLIM

AL-ḤARĪRĪ

Abū Muḥammad al-Qāsim ibn 'Alī ibn Muḥammad al-Ḥarīrī. Born at Baṣra in 1054–1055; died in 1122. Arabian man of letters and grammarian. He wrote a grammatical poem, Mulḥat al-i'rāb; a treatise on the linguistic mistakes made by educated people, Kitāb durrat al-ghawwāṣ fī auhām al-khawāṣṣ (Pearl of the diver or opinions of the educated people); etc. He is chiefly remembered because of his famous stories in rhymed prose, the Maqāmāt, the masterpiece of an Arabic form of "belles lettres" (adab) which had been initiated at the end of the tenth century by al-Hamadhānī.[1] The word maqāma (pl., maqāmāt) means meetings, assemblies, and by extension, conversations held at these meetings. Al-Ḥarīrī's Maqāmāt are a collection of fifty picaresque stories, the adventures of a precious rascal called Abū Zaid of Sarūj, which serve as a pretext for the exhibition of very refined language, elaborate wit, and sophisticated literary culture. They were begun in 1101, and completed in 1110 or later. These Maqāmāt were imitated in Hebrew by Judah al-Ḥarizī (first half of the thirteenth century). Although they are far removed from our subject, they have exerted such a deep influence upon Arabic letters and thought, and to a much smaller extent upon Hebrew letters, that they deserve to arrest our attention if only for a moment.

Text—The Maqāmāt were edited by Silvestre de Sacy: Les séances de Ḥarīrī, with introduction and commentary in Arabic (Paris 1822). New edition by Reinaud and Derenbourg (2 vols., Paris 1847–1853). Thomas Chenery and F. Steingass: The Assemblies, translated, with an introduction and notes (2 vols., Oriental translation fund, London 1867–1898). Many oriental editions.

Léon Pinto: Molhat al irab ou Les récréations grammaticales (French translation, Paris 1885–1889).

Criticism—Johan Willmet: Lexicon linguae arabiae in Coranum, Haririum et Vitem Timuri (840 p., Rotterdam 1784). Ibn Khallikān (de Slane, vol. 2, 490–498). E. Renan: Essais de morale et de critique (2d ed., Paris 1860). M. Steinschneider: Hebräische Übersetzungen (851, 1893). C. Brockelmann: Arabische Litteratur (vol. 1, 93–95, 276–278, 1898). D. S. Margoliouth: Encyclopaedia of Islām (vol. 2, 268, 1916). C. Brockelmann: Maqāma (ibidem, vol. 3, 161–164, 1929).

IBN AL-JAWĀLĪQĪ

Abū Manṣūr Mauhūb ibn abī Ṭāhir Aḥmad ibn Muḥammad ibn al-Khiḍr al-Jawālīqī. The last word means the maker or seller of sacks (jawālīq). Born at

[1] That is, Badī' al-zamān Aḥmad ibn al-Ḥusain al-Hamadhānī. Born in Hamadhān, lived in Jurjān, Nīshāpūr, Ghazna, etc.; died in Herāt in 1007–1008.

Baghdād in 1073–1074; died there in 1134 (or 1114–1145). Arabic grammarian. He wrote a commentary on Ibn Qutaiba's Adab al-kātib (second half of the ninth century), entitled Kitāb al mu'arrab min al-kalām al-'ajamī (The Arabicised, dealing with the foreign words introduced into Arabic); a supplement to al-Ḥarīrī's Durrat al-ghawwāṣ (Pearl of the diver), entitled Kitāb al-takmila fī mā yalḥanu fīhi-l-'āmma (Completion, dealing with the incorrect expressions of the vulgar); a book on the names of horses, Kitāb asmā' khail al-'arab wa fursāniha; and a short treatise on syntax, Kitāb al-mukhtaṣar fī-l-naḥw.

Text—The Mu'arrab has been edited by E. Sachau (Leipzig 1867). The Takmila, by H. Derenbourg: Livre des locutions vicieuses (Morgenländische Forschungen, H. L. Fleischer Festschrift, 107–166, Leipzig 1875).

Criticism—Ibn Khallikān: de Slane's translation (vol. 3, 498–502, 1848). J. T. Reinaud: Géographie d'Aboulféda (vol. 1, 111, 1848). C. Brockelmann: Arabische Litteratur (vol. 1, 280, 1898).

AL-MAIDĀNĪ

Abū-l-Faḍl Aḥmad ibn Muḥammad ibn Aḥmad al-Maidānī. Persian grammarian who was born at Maidān Ziyād, a quarter of Nīshāpūr; he died there in 1124. He completed in 1104 an Arabic dictionary, wherein the words are classified by subjects (fiqh, living, heavenly and earthly things), with Persian explanations, Kitāb al-sāmī fī-l-asāmī (the great book on words); he wrote also a treatise on Arabic syntax with Persian explanations, Kitāb al-hādī li-l-shādī (Guide for him who knows already a little); etc.; but he is best known because of his collection of proverbs, Kitāb majma' al-amthāl.

Text—The Majma' has been printed in Būlāq, 1284 H., Cairo, 1310 H. Latin translation by Georg Wilhelm Freytag: Arabum proverbia (3 vols., Bonn 1838–1843).

Criticism—Ibn Khallikān: de Slane's translation (vol. 1, 130, 1842). C. Brockelmann: Arabische Litteratur (vol. 1, 289, 1898); Encyclopaedia of Islām (vol. 3, 144, 1929).

AL-ZAMAKHSHARĪ

Abū-l-Qāsim Maḥmūd ibn 'Umar al-Zamakhsharī. Mu'tazil[2] theologian and commentator on the Qur'ān, Arabic grammarian and lexicographer. Born in 1075 at Zamakhshar in Khwārizm, he lived so long in Mecca that he was nicknamed Jār Allāh (God's neighbour). He died at Jurjānīyah on the Oxus, in Khwārizm, in 1144. He knew and occasionally used the Persian language, but was thoroughly convinced of the superiority of the Arabic and repressed Shu'ūbiyya tendencies.[3] His chief work is a commentary on the Qur'ān, called Kitāb al-kashshāf 'an ḥaqā'iq al-tanzīl (The revealer of the truths of revelation). Between 1119 and 1121 he wrote an Arabic grammar, Kitāb al-mufaṣṣal. He compiled a number of lexicographical works; Kitāb muqaddimat al-adab, an Arabic-Persian dictionary; Kitāb al-amkina wal-jibāl wal-miyā (the book of places, mountains, and waters), a geographical lexicon; Kitāb al-fā'iq, a lexicon relative to the ḥadīth; Kitāb asās al-balāgha.

[2] Vol. 1, 557.
[3] Vol. 1, 541.

Text—The Kashshāf was edited by W. Nassau Lees (2 large vols. 4°, Calcutta 1856). Cairene editions in 1307, 1308 H. For the super-commentaries see Brockelmann, and also my note on al-Baiḍāwī (second half of the thirteenth century).

The Mufaṣṣal was edited by Jen Peter Broch (1859; 2d ed., Christiania 1879). It has been the subject of many commentaries of which the most important is that by Ibn Ya'īsh (d. 1245–1246), edited by G. Jahn (2 vols., Leipzig 1876–1886).

Johann Gottfried Wetzstein: Lexicon arabicum persicum (Leipzig 1850).

M. Salverda de Grave: Lexicon geographicum (Leyde 1856).

Kitāb nawābigh al-kalim. Anthologia sententiarum arabicarum cum scholiis Zamachsjarii edidit vertit et illustravit H. A. Schultens (Leyde 1772).

Kitāb aṭwāq al-dahab. Les colliers d'or, allocutions morales. Texte arabe et traduction française par C. Barbier de Meynard (Paris 1876).

The Kitāb asās al-balāgha was lithographed in India.

The Kitāb al-fā'iq was printed in Būlāq (2 vols., 1299 H.).

Criticism—Ibn Khaldūn: Prolegomena (de Slane; by index, chiefly vol. 3, 326, 328). Ibn Khallikān: Biographical dictionary (de Slane; vol. 3, 321–328). C. Brockelmann: Arabische Litteratur (vol. 1, 289–293, 1898).

II. WESTERN MUSLIM

IBN AL-'ARABĪ

See Chapter XII, Law and Sociology.

III. WESTERN JEWISH

ISḤĀQ IBN BARŪN

Abū Ibrāhīm Isḥāq ibn Barūn. Hispano-Jewish grammarian of Lucena who lived about the beginning of the twelfth century. Pupil of the grammarian Levi ibn al-Tabbān of Saragossa, about 1100. With the exception of the Maghrabī Judāh ibn Qarīsh (first half of the ninth century, vol. I, 581), he was the first grammarian to explain the essential similarity of Arabic and Hebrew forms. This he did in a treatise entitled Kitāb al-mīzān, or al-mawāzīn (The balance, the agreement between both languages).

Text—Partial edition by Paul v. Kokowzoff (264 p., St. Petersburg 1893; in Hebrew character, with Russian introduction).

Criticism—W. Bacher: Die hebräisch-arabische Sprachvergleichung des Abū Ibrāhīm Ibn Barūn (Z. für die alttestamentliche Wissenschaft, vol. 14, 223–249, 1894). M. Steinschneider: Arabische Literatur der Juden (145, 1902); note on Levi ibn al-Tabbān (ibidem).

For Nathan ben Jehiel, see volume I, 782.

For Ibn Biklārish, see Chapter X, Medicine.

For Abraham Ibn Ezra, and for Jacob ben Meïr. see Chapter IV, Philosophic Background.

IV. EASTERN JEWISH

See my notes on the two Qaraites: 'Alī ibn Sulaimān of Jerusalem, in Appendix to Book I; Judah Hadassi of Constantinople, in Chapter IV, Philosophic Background.

V. BYZANTINE

For Nicephoros Bryennios, Anna Comnena, and Zonaras, see Chapter **XI, Historiography.**

VI. LATIN AND VERNACULAR

A good survey of the revival of the Latin classics and of the Latin language will be found in C. H. Haskins: The renaissance of the twelfth century (93–152, Cambridge 1927; Isis, 10, 62–65).

For Matthaeus Platearius, see Chapter X, Medicine.

For Lo Codi, see Chapter XII, Law and Sociology.

For the Codex Calixtinus, Geoffrey of Monmouth, Caradog of Llancarvan, Ari Fróði þorgilsson, the Eddas, and Nestor of Kiev, see Chapter XI, Historiography.

For Daniel of Kiev, see Chapter VIII, Geography.

For the early translations from Greek into Old Slavonic, see histories of Russian literature—for example, D. S. Mirsky's (London 1927). The version of Josephus' De bello judaico was remarkable for its freedom. It seems to have exerted much influence upon the early Russian chroniclers; but aside from that, it is important because of various interpolations which go back to very early Christian times, some of them perhaps to the author himself. The student of Josephus' text must needs take this Slavonic version into account.

See papers by Robert Eisler, Maurice Goguel, and Paul Louis Couchoud, in Revue de l'histoire des religions (vol. 93, 1–64, 1926; Isis, 11, 159).

VII. HINDU

HEMACANDRA

See Chapter XXVII, Philology.

VIII. MANCHU

MANCHU WRITING

Manchu is a Turanian, Tungusian, language of considerable antiquity, which remained unwritten until the beginning of the tenth century. In 920, T'ai Tsu, the first emperor of the Liao dynasty (Ch'i-tan or Kitan[4] Tartars), ordered the transcription of Manchu by means of Chinese characters. Whether this was actually done or not, not a trace of this early Manchu script has been preserved.

New efforts were made under the Chin dynasty (Nü-chen Tartars) in the first half of the twelfth century. In 1119 their first emperor, also called T'ai Tsu, ordered the use of a new script, derived from the Uighūr (itself inspired by the Syriac alphabet introduced into the East by Nestorian missionaries). Still another attempt was made in 1135 (or 1145) by the third Chin emperor, Hsi Tsung. This second script was used, but not very long. A few books and inscriptions in these Nü-chen characters are still extant. However, this new script was promptly forgotten, for the Manchus were soon driven out by the Mongols (the Yüan dynasty began in 1206).

To complete this story, I may say that a last, and this time successful, attempt to reduce Manchu to a written form was made at the end of the sixteenth century by Nurhachu (the future Ch'ing emperor T'ien Ming, 1616–1627) who proposed to adopt the Mongol script, itself a modification of the Uighūr. This script was improved and finally established in 1632, and was much used for a century to publish Manchu versions of Chinese classics, and dictionaries. The earliest Manchu printed text is dated 1646.

[4] Hence the mediaeval name of China—Cathay! and the Russian name, to these days, Kitai.

Berthold Laufer: Skizze der manjurischen Litteratur (53 p., Revue orientale pour les études ouralo-altaïques, Budapest 1908); not seen. Samuel Couling: Encyclopaedia sinica (323, 1917). J. Deny: Langues tongouzes, in A. Meillet and Marcel Cohen: Les langues du monde (234–243, Paris 1924). J. Dyer Ball and E. Chalmers Werner: Things Chinese (5th ed., 362–364, London 1926).

APPENDIX TO BOOK I

(First Half of Twelfth Century)

The following notes inserted at the eleventh hour have not been considered in my survey of science in the first half of the twelfth century, but if I had been able to consider them, my conclusions would hardly have been affected by them.

Eadmer of Canterbury was a good chronicler who fully deserved to be mentioned together with Florence and John of Worcester, and with William of Malmesbury. The Qaraite, 'Alī ibn Sulaimān, was not by any means as important as his younger contemporary, Judah Hadassi; yet it would have been a pity if his name had been altogether omitted. He was a theologian and grammarian, and his Hebrew grammar (in Arabic) was strangely regressive as compared with the older one of Ḥayyuj.

EADMER

Eadmer, or Edmer. A monk of Canterbury, director to St. Anselm during the latter's archbishopric (1093–1109). In 1120 he was appointed archbishop of St. Andrews, but because of rivalries between the northern and southern primates was never consecrated. Soon afterwards he returned to Canterbury. He died about 1124.

English chronicler. Author of an excellent chronicle of contemporary events, Historia novorum, from about 1066 to 1122, and of various biographies, notably one of St. Anselm. His chronicle deals largely with ecclesiastical matters, but is remarkably rational.

Text—First edition of the Historia novorum, by John Selden (234 p., London 1623). Reprinted in Gabriel Gerberon's edition of St. Anselm's works (Paris 1675). First edition of the Vita Anselmi (Antwerp 1551).

Critical edition by Martin Rule: Historia novorum in Anglia et opuscula duo de vita S. Anselmi et quibusdam miraculis eius (Rolls series, no. 81, 588 p., London 1884).

Other writings are included in Henry Wharton: Anglia sacra (vol. 2, London 1691).

Criticism—G. G. Perry: Dictionary of national biography (vol. 16, 309–310, 1888). Father Ragey: Eadmer (338 p., Paris 1892). Potthast (387, 1896).

'ALĪ IBN SULAIMĀN

Also called the shaikh Abū-l-Ḥasan of Jerusalem. (His Jewish name is unknown). Qaraite theologian and grammarian who lived at the beginning of the twelfth century (about 1103).

He wrote in Arabic commentaries on the Torah, and a Hebrew dictionary (also in Arabic) entitled Agron. The Agron was compiled from the abridgment by Abū Sa'īd (Levi) ben Yefet ha-Levi of the dictionary (also called Agron) of David ben Abraham.[1] He was acquainted with Ḥayyuj,[2] whom he quoted, and knew the

[1] David ben Abraham of Fez (second half of the tenth century, vol. I, 690; Isis, 13, 153).

[2] Judah ben David Ḥayyuj (second half of the tenth century, vol. I, 691; Isis, 13, 154).

latter's theory of triliteral roots, but preferred to follow the biliteral and even uniliteral theory of David ben Abraham. He freely used the Mishnah, Talmud, and Targum in the interpretation of words. Words were generally classified by him under their roots, but rare ones appeared in alphabetical order. He showed similarities between sundry Hebrew, Aramaic, and Arabic roots.

A commentary of his on the Torah was begun in 1103, being compiled from the abridgment by Abū-l-Faraj Hārūn ibn al-Faraj of Jerusalem (lived about 1002–1036) of the commentary by Abū Ya'qūb Joseph ibn Nūḥ (lived in the ninth or tenth century).

Text—Extracts of the Agron were edited with Hebrew translation by Simḥah Pinsker: Liqquṭe qadmoniyot (Vienna 1860). Also in appendix to Adolf Neubauer's edition of the Kitāb al-uṣūl of Ibn Janāḥ (Oxford 1875).

Solomon L. Skoss: The Arabic commentary of 'Alī ben Suleimān the Karaite on the book of Genesis (Jewish quarterly review, vol. 18, 1–35, 153–206, 1927; vol. 18, 267–314, 385–435, 1928). The first two papers contain an elaborate introduction, the other two, the text with variants, in Hebrew script.

Criticism—M. Steinschneider: Arabische Literatur der Juden (241, 1902). I. Markon: Encyclopaedia judaica (vol. 2, 314–316, 1928).

BOOK TWO
The Time of Gerard of Cremona, Ibn Rushd, and Maimonides
(Second Half of Twelfth Century)

It is of great advantage that man should know his station and not erroneously imagine that the whole universe exists only for him.

—*Maimonides*

(Dalālat al-ḥā'irīn, Part iii, chapter xii, c. 1190)

CHAPTER XIV

SURVEY OF SCIENCE AND INTELLECTUAL PROGRESS IN THE SECOND HALF OF THE TWELFTH CENTURY

I. INTRODUCTION

The second half of the twelfth century was essentially identical with the first half in that it was a period of transition. If we consider the three main streams of western civilization—Muslim, Jewish, and Christian—we find that they are of almost equal importance, or rather that none is so obviously superior to the others (as the Muslim stream was before the twelfth century) that its hegemony could not be denied. The Christian efforts were more abundant, yet the main leaders were still a Muslim and a Jew.

The title of this book is particularly fitting: The time of Gerard of Cremona, Ibn Rushd, and Maimonides. The two greatest leaders were the last named; both covered almost completely the period under consideration; Ibn Rushd, born in 1126, died in 1198; Maimonides, born in 1135, died in 1204. The third protagonist, Gerard of Cremona, died somewhat earlier (1114–1187). He represents Christendom—the most progressive part of it, Western Christendom—and he reminds us of the fact that progressiveness consisted to a large extent in a wise gathering of the fruits of Muslim culture. For Gerard was not a creator, but simply a translator from Arabic into Latin. However, as he was perhaps the greatest translator of all times, as no man ever transmitted so large a bulk of alien culture to his own people, he fully deserves to be recorded in our title. He is as symbolic a figure of contemporary Christendom and of its dependence on Arabic sources, as we could wish to find. He is named first, simply because he was the oldest of the trio; the first to come and the first to go.

Gerard was simply a transmitter. On the other hand, Ibn Rushd and Maimonides were creative minds of the first order—and this means trouble makers. For no such mind can function and accomplish its destiny without upsetting the intellectual equilibrium. If the trouble they raised were a correct measure of their eminence, they would be among the very greatest thinkers in the whole history of mankind, for the vicissitudes of Maimonidism and Averroism lasted centuries and have continued to echo until our own days. An influence which is at once so deep and so lasting is a certain proof of their greatness, but it does not enable us to measure it. One would be tempted to conclude that great as they were, they raised far more trouble than they were worth; the splash which they made in the quiet waters of human thought was unduly aggravated by various accidents. However, they were the foremost thinkers of their age, and must be counted among the leading philosophers of all ages.

It is interesting to note that the activities of Ibn Rushd and Maimonides were to a large extent independent, except that they had been nurtured in the same soil; both were Cordovans, but the former resided for many years in Morocco, and the latter in Egypt. This is, I believe, one of the most impressive synchronisms in the whole history of thought.

The Latin revival, symbolized by Gerard of Cremona, was essentially a scientific revival, not a literary one as was the new Latin Renaissance which occurred three centuries later. From the point of view of the history of science, this twelfth century renaissance was fully as important as the later one.

The title of the preceding book (first half of the twelfth century) was two-thirds Spanish and one-third French; the title of this book (second half of the twelfth century) is two-thirds Spanish and one-third Italian. But Gerard of Cremona spent the best part of his life in Toledo. Thus this book is a real glorification of Spain. The three leaders of the age represented three different faiths, and two towns—Cordova and Toledo—but one single country, Spain. Yet as we shall see in the following pages, the twelfth century world was already very complex, and intellectual centers occurred not only in Spain, but in many other countries. Think of the great schools and universities of Salerno, Bologna, Montpellier, Paris, and Oxford! Think of the many Muslim and Christian courts, and of that extraordinary one of Palermo, which was a combination of both. But we must not anticipate. The full complexity and richness of the twelfth century will be analyzed presently.

II. RELIGIOUS BACKGROUND

1. *Christendom*—The spiritual unrest which was already well marked at the beginning of the century, continued to wax throughout its second half. Indeed the same causes continued to act. The Church had become very wealthy and powerful; it was outwardly united; yet it failed to satisfy the deeper aspirations of some fervent souls. There was an ever widening breach between its power and pomp on the one hand, and the poverty, material and spiritual, of the flocks, on the other. The Crusades, the growth of cities, the development of commercial and industrial organization, the appearance of new classes, all these social causes contributed as much as did the crystallization of the Church to the creation of new religious aspirations. Whether these aspirations would remain orthodox or not depended as much on the Church as on the blessed people who experienced them.

Moreover, some parts of Europe which had been controlled in the past by Arians, who denied the divinity of Christ, had kept, so to say, a temperamental bent towards heresy. This was especially true in southern France which had been ruled for some time by Western Goths (Visigothic kingdom of Tolosa, Toulouse, 419–507). In that country Arianism had been leavened with Manichaeism, and lingering tendencies of both had given birth in the course of time to Catharism and other suspicious novelties. The number and power of the Cathari increased considerably during the second half of the twelfth century.

The combination of religious and social motives was well illustrated by the attempt of Lombard workmen—chiefly workers in wool—to create a new brotherhood which was partly a religious order and partly an industrial guild. The Humiliati, as they were called, may also serve to show that such movements were not inherently unorthodox. A social movement is revolutionary or not, according to the degree of opposition it meets, as much as by its way of meeting it. Some of the Humiliati, whom the Church was pleased to consider the True ones, remained obedient; others, the False Humiliati, drifted into heresy.

The Waldensians, who owed their original inspiration to Peter Waldo of Lyons in

1173, were men of a similar type. As in the case of the Humiliati, their main interest was ethical, not theological; their ambition was to live the good life according to the Evangel. They suggest comparison with the brethren of St. Francis. Some of them, the Poor Catholics, were eventually conciliated by Innocent III; a great many, who did not submit, were destroyed at the same time as the Albigensians; still others escaped and carried their "heretical" faith to distant parts of the world where it is still flourishing to-day.

These movements were largely popular, anonymous, and inarticulate; but from time to time a leader would appear who would voice the vague aspirations of a new age and put the stamp of his own personality upon them. Such a leader was Arnold of Brescia, who was hanged for it in Rome in 1155. But the foremost apostle of that religious revival was the Calabrian Cistercian, Joachim of Floris. The meaning and implications of his Eternal Evangel were not fully understood, or exploited, until the middle of the thirteenth century, when they became for a time the main sustenance of the more adventurous souls of Christendom.

Meanwhile large hordes of Christians armed cap-a-pie were trying to inculcate the Evangel by means of the sword. Thus arose those paradoxical organizations, the religious orders of knighthood. To the two orders already discussed must now be added a third, the Order of the Teutonic Knights. Though it owed its origin, like its predecessors, to the Crusades, and was created at Acre (in 1191), its main activity took place on the eastern borders of Germany. The Teutonic Knights were then the champions of German against Slavonic culture. Another fruit of warring Christianity was the founding of the Trinitarians by St. John of Matha and St. Felix of Valois in 1198. The Trinitarians were not monks but canons regular whose life was devoted to the redemption of Christian slaves in Muslim hands.

The genius of western Christendom was also evidenced and immortalized by the development of "Gothic" architecture, and the construction of marvelous cathedrals, each of which was an everlasting source of inspiration and education not only for the people living in its neighborhood, but for the travelers who came and carried away its message of beauty and knowledge to other countries. The transformation of Romanesque architecture into Gothic, and the first Gothic masterpieces, were French achievements. Gothic art originated in the very heart of France, the Ile-de-France. It developed with surprising rapidity during the second half of the twelfth century.

Meanwhile another Christian revival was taking place in an entirely different and far distant country, Armenia—that is, Lesser Armenia, corresponding roughly to ancient Cilicia. The Armenians had been converted to Christianity by Gregory the Illuminator at the beginning of the fourth century, and Armenian culture was solidly established by Mesrop at the beginning of the fifth. After centuries of vicissitudes the Armenian people were enabled to recruit their strength in Cilicia. The main agent of that renaissance was their patriarch, Nerses the Graceful, who did much to promote the culture and to insure the safety of his flock.

2. *Israel*—The Jewish mathematician Samū'īl ibn 'Abbās who embraced Islām in 1163, wrote in Arabic a refutation of Judaism from the Muslim point of view. A Latin translation of this work (1339) was popular among Christians for centuries.

Another Arabic treatise written by the Samaritan Munaja' ben Ṣadaqa, probably at Damascus towards the end of the twelfth century, discussed the differences between the Jews and his own brethren.

Philip Augustus (King of France from 1180 to 1223), after having exacted all the money he could from the Jews residing in the royal domains, drove them out. He canceled all debts owed to them except one-fifth payable to himself, and confiscated their immovable property. Fortunately the royal domains were not very large, and the persecuted Jews found a precarious safety in other parts of France. This incident is mentioned to illustrate the disabilities of the Jews in Christendom and the dark shadows under which Jewish doctors were working. Happily the conditions meted out to them by Muslims were incomparably better. So most of the Jewish work was done by Jews living under the protection of Islām.

3. *Islām*—The sect of the Yazīdī, or Devil-worshippers, which is often considered a Muslim sect—it is in reality a synthesis of all sorts of elements, Muslim and others—originated about this time, probably in the mountain region north of Mūṣul. According to their own traditions, their founder was the Shaikh 'Adī ibn Musāfir.

4. *Buddhism*—The intellectual activity of Chinese Buddhists is represented by the Sanskrit-Chinese dictionary of Buddhist terms compiled by Fa Yün about 1157.

The first original Japanese sect, the Nembutsu-shū, had been founded by Ryōnin in the first half of the twelfth century. A second sect, the Jōdo-shū (the Pure Land sect), was founded by Genkū (also called Hōnen) in 1175. Both these sects were Amidaist, but it is really the second which introduced Amidaism to the mass of the Japanese people, as the first remained comparatively unsuccessful. The famous Zen-shū, the Japanese form of the Ch'an tsung, was introduced by Eisai in 1192; however, it did not really begin before the dawn of the thirteenth century. We shall discuss Zen Buddhism later, but Eisai belongs to the twelfth century and no account of twelfth century thought would be complete which did not pay homage to this great personality.

III. THE TRANSLATORS

1. *From Arabic into Latin*—A large part of the activity of the age was in the form of translations from the Arabic and subsidiarily from the Greek. The foremost translator was Gerard of Cremona—perhaps all considered the greatest translator of all times. A biography of him written by his own pupils tells us that it was the love of the Almagest, then inaccessible to Latin readers, which led him to Toledo. When he arrived there and saw the abundance of writings on every subject available in Arabic, he felt sorry for the penury of books from which the Latin people were suffering, and being possessed by the desire of translating the Arabic ones he studied that language. He then passed in review the whole scientific literature of the Muslims, and selecting the best of every kind, devoted all of his energy to their translation until the very end of his life in 1187.

The whole of this almost unbelievable activity of his and his pupils took place in Toledo, which was not only the best place but perhaps the only one where a Christian could then have accomplished a task as systematic and as gigantic. I have already spoken of the importance assumed by Toledo in the first half of the twelfth century as a center of distribution of Arabic knowledge, but the splendid efforts of John of Seville, Domingo Gundisalvo and others were overshadowed by those of Gerard and his school. To give here even a short list of their main translations would take too much space. It must suffice to state that they include a number of Aristotelian and pseudo-Aristotelian writings, many treatises of the Muslim and Jewish Aristotelians, some of the best works of Greek and Muslim mathematicians, astronomers and physicists, a good part of the Galenic corpus published in Arabic by Ḥunain ibn Isḥāq, plus the main medical works originally written in Arabic; finally a few alchemical writings. In other words, thanks to Gerard's unparalleled activity, the treasures of Greek and Arabic philosophy, mathematics, astronomy, physics, medicine, and alchemy were generously opened to the Latin world. It is very difficult to choose among all these translations, but perhaps the two most important are those of the Almagest (completed in 1175), and of Ibn Sīnā's Qānūn.

Aside from Gerard there was but one other translator from the Arabic, Marc of Toledo; while it is probable that he flourished at the same time as Gerard, this is not established beyond doubt. Marc translated the Qur'ān, and a number of medical treatises.

2. *From Arabic into Hebrew*—Gerard and Marc of Toledo translated from Arabic into Latin; but two other contemporary translators helped to transmit Arabic knowledge to the West in a less direct manner, by means of Hebrew versions. Joseph Qimḥi composed a metrical version of a work of Ibn Gabirol. Judah ibn Tibbon, "the father of Jewish translators," translated a number of grammatical and philosophical treatises by Saadia ben Joseph, Ibn Gabirol, Ibn Janāḥ, Judah ha-Levi, and Baḥya ben Joseph. Judging by his prefaces and by the testament addressed to his famous son Samuel, it is clear that Judah was keenly aware of the difficulties involved in a good translation. Samuel ibn Tibbon will be discussed later; but his earliest dated work, his translation of 'Alī ibn Riḍwān's commentary on Galen's Tegni, belongs to this period, for it was completed at Béziers in 1199. Like Abraham ibn Ezra and Abraham bar Ḥiyya, whose task they were continuing, Joseph Qimḥi and Judah ibn Tibbon were both Spaniards. Both flourished in Provence.

It is interesting to compare the translators from Arabic into Latin with the translators from Arabic into Hebrew. The superiority of the former is considerable, both with regard to the quantity of translations, and to their intrinsic importance. The translations of the latter, be it noted, were restricted to Jewish works. It would be more difficult to compare them with regard to the quality of the translations. It will suffice to observe that the Hebrew translations were made with considerable care; with certainly as much care as the Latin. The Jewish as well as the Christian translators were scientifically minded. Their translations were scientific rather than literary—more likely to be too literal than the opposite. In both cases the translators were often obliged either to create new words or to assimilate Arabic ones. The second alternative was more tempting in Hebrew than in Latin; and for a similar reason it was easier for the Jews than for the Christians to give an exact translation and to reproduce the flavor of the Arabic originals.

3. *From Greek into Latin*—Meanwhile the stream of translations made directly from the Greek, which had been brilliantly inaugurated by James of Venice in the first half of the twelfth century, took on more importance. In fact the translators from the Greek formed by far the largest body—I shall discuss no less than seven of them—and if there had been among them a man endowed with as much genius and energy as was Gerard of Cremona, the history of the tradition of Greek knowledge to the West might have been very different.

Eugene the Amīr, of Palermo, translated in 1154 the Optics ascribed to Ptolemy, and took part in the anonymous translation of the Almagest made in Sicily about 1160. This Eugene, who was a good symbol of the Sicilian cosmopolitism, also helped to transmit the Arabic fables of Kalīla wa-Dimna, and he wrote poems in Greek. Aristippus of Catania brought the Almagest and other Greek manuscripts from the Byzantine court to Sicily; he translated the Meno and Phaedo of Plato about 1156, and the fourth book of Aristotle's Meteorology. Paschal the Roman was probably the author of the translation of the Ciranides made in 1169. William Le Mire, abbot of St. Denis was sent to Constantinople to obtain manuscripts of Dionysios the Areopagite, who was confused with the patron of Le Mire's monastery, St. Denis, martyr and first bishop of Paris (died probably under Decius in the middle of the third century); he translated various Greek texts, none of scientific interest. Pseudo-Dionysios was translated by another contemporary, John Sarrazin. The greatest of these translators was Burgundio of Pisa, to whom we owe versions of Hippocrates' Aphorisms, of nine Galenic treatises, of others by Nemesios of Emesa and John of Damascus, of a part of the Geoponica, etc. Finally Leo Tuscus of Pisa, interpreter to Manuel Comnenos, translated the dream book of Aḥmad ibn Sirin. This otherwise insignificant translation is very interesting because it reversed the usual procedure. Most Greek works reached the West by means of Arabic translations. In this case an Arabic work was transmitted to the Latin world by the intermediary of a Greek version. Such little facts help us to realize the ever growing complexity of cultural exchanges.

Note that with the exception of the Provençal William Le Mire, all these men were Italians. Two Sicilians, Eugene of Palermo and Aristippus of Catania; two Pisans, Burgundio and Leo Tuscus; one Roman (?), Paschal. Of John Sarrazin we know nothing except that he was a correspondent of John of Salisbury.

Some of the texts thus translated from the Greek were very important; notably the Fountain of knowledge of John of Damascus (about 1150), Ptolemy's Optics (1154), the Meno and Phaedo (about 1156), the Almagest (about 1160), nine Galenic treatises (one of them in 1185), the fourth book of Aristotle's Meteorology, Hippocrates' Aphorisms, and extracts from the Digest and the Geoponica. Certainly a fine collection of Greek works, though it does not begin to compare with the immense quantity of Greco-Arabic knowledge which was being poured out at the same time from Arabic vessels. The net result of this inequality was that these translations from the Greek, which were as painfully literal as the other twelfth century translations, were somewhat eclipsed by those made from the Arabic. This may seem paradoxical, as the latter, being indirect, were likely to be inferior; but such was the case. For example, the translation of the Almagest from the Greek original made in Sicily about 1160 was entirely eclipsed by the translation made by Gerard of Cremona from the Arabic in Toledo in 1175. In fact, by that time the translations from the Arabic enjoyed a tremendous prestige, a prestige that was a sort of inertia, a considerable intellectual inertia, which it would be necessary to overcome before the superiority of the direct translations could be admitted.

4. *From Latin into Hebrew*—Berakya ha-Naqdan composed a free Hebrew version of Adelard's natural questions. The interest of that version is somewhat spoiled by the lack of sufficient chronological data. It is probable, but not certain, that this Berakya was identical with one Benoit le Puncteur, a French Jew who flourished in England about the end of the twelfth century. At any rate the translator must have been a Jew of France or England who was out of touch with Arabic culture. This explains the paradox of Arabic knowledge being transmitted to the Jewish world by the intermediary of a Latin textbook!

IV. EDUCATION

Our modern universities are direct descendants of mediaeval institutions of which the earliest examples appeared in the second half of the twelfth century. To be sure, there had been various kinds of schools before that, for as soon as a civilization has become sufficiently complex, it cannot continue (let alone progress) unless some means are found of imparting its principles and methods to the young. Yet the schools of Greece and Rome, of India and the Far East, and those of Israel and Islām were essentially different from our own. The best of them—such as the Museum of Alexandria, and the academies of Baghdād and Cairo—were more comparable to the research institutions of our day than to the teaching ones. Moreover, the ancient and oriental schools were generally centered about a brilliant personality and did not survive it very long. The Academy and the Lyceum are splendid exceptions; the latter lasted six centuries, and the former nine, longer than any of our universities thus far; but this relative impersonality and corporate existence is almost their only point of contact with our modern institutions.

These, I repeat, are connected by an unbroken tradition to some of the larger schools which began to appear in Christendom in the twelfth century. By the end of that century, five of them were in existence, in different stages of development: two in Italy—Salerno and Bologna; two in France—Paris and Montpellier; one in England—Oxford. The oldest, Salerno, was essentially a medical school, and on that account might be ruled out. Bologna was primarily a law school, but it had become a *studium generale* before the end of the century. The greatest of these early universities was Paris, and it was already full-fledged some time before 1200 when it received its first official recognition from the King of France. Montpellier grew around two professional schools, law and medicine. Oxford was an offshoot of Paris, and in 1209 it gave birth to another university, Cambridge, by a new swarming off.

It is vain to try to fix the exact dates of the foundation of these universities. The truth is, they were not deliberately founded. Various acts of incorporation were given to them later, sometimes much later, when each had already grown to a respectable size and shown by its own being what a university was. The fact that not merely one university grew in that manner—somewhat unconsciously, like a living thing—but many, in different countries, proves that these creations answered a definite need of the time. The amount of Greco-Arabic knowledge which had reached the West by the end of the twelfth century was already so large that systematic methods of education became necessary. Meantime the growth of cities had made the application of such methods at once more tempting and more easy. Thus our universities appeared in the second half of the twelfth century, and not before, because there had not been sufficient scope nor opportunity for them until that time, and they appeared then because the need was suddenly urgent. Nothing can better illustrate the intellectual revolution caused in the Christian West by the sudden transmission of Greco-Arabic culture.

Among the contemporary writers who might be called educators, the two outstanding were Gerald the Welshman and John of Salisbury. Gerald wrote a treatise on the education of princes. John's Polycratus, or Ruler's book, and his Metalogicus were very influential each in its sphere. The first was a political treatise; the second a vindication of humanism, which was very timely. Remember what I said above of the extreme literalism of the twelfth century translators.

They appreciated so deeply the substance of the works which they were putting into Latin, that they overlooked the form, or rather that they were afraid of changing the form of the original, be it ever so little. The literary result may be imagined. John, who continued in this the Chartres tradition, was one of the first to defend another point of view, and in doing this he anticipated the humanists of the fifteenth century.

The Chinese philosopher Lu Chiu-yüan developed sane views on education in opposition to the rigid formalism which was then already sterilizing the minds of his countrymen.

V. PHILOSOPHIC BACKGROUND

1. *Western Muslim*—We have seen that the most original Muslim philosophers of the first half of the twelfth century were westerners, and this western superiority was considerably increased during the second half of the century. Indeed Spain produced in this period two of the greatest philosophers of the Middle Ages, Ibn Ṭufail and Ibn Rushd. Both were attached as physicians to the court of the Almohade caliph Abū Ya'qūb Yūsuf in Marrākush; Ibn Ṭufail until 1182, when his younger friend succeeded him. Ibn Ṭufail wrote a philosophical romance, Ḥaiy ibn Yaqẓān, which is one of the most curious mediaeval creations; it is the story of a sort of metaphysical Robinson Crusoe. It obtained considerable success, not only in Arabic and Hebrew but also in Latin and down to modern times—for example, it won the praise of so keen a judge as Leibniz. It includes an account of the development of Muslim philosophy, and a classification of the sciences. Ibn Ṭufail influenced his contemporaries al-Biṭrūjī and Ibn Rushd; he advised the latter in his great undertakings.

It is difficult to speak adequately of so great a man as Ibn Rushd (Averroës)—a man great in his own right, and greater still because of the tremendous stir he made in the minds of men for centuries. A history of Averroism would include all the essential elements of a history of thought from the end of the twelfth century to the end of the sixteenth—a period of four centuries which would perhaps deserve as much as any other to be called the Middle Ages, for it was the real transition between ancient and modern methods. I cannot stop now to prove this statement, but its truth will be gradually revealed in the sequel. The immortal monument to the building of which his life was mainly devoted was a treble series of commentaries on the works of Aristotle. Aside from his medical fame, he is chiefly remembered because of them; Dante spoke of him as "Averrois che'l gran comento feo;" and therefore readers may be led to think of him only as a "commentator"—that is, not as a creative genius, but as a purely reflecting and subordinate one.

To destroy that wrong impression, it is well first of all to bear in mind that a "commentary" was simply a mediaeval form of publishing one's views on a definite subject. To write a commentary on Aristotle was merely to compose a philosophic and scientific encyclopaedia, using Aristotle's writings as a framework and guide. Such a commentary might be original or not; but the fact of its being a commentary does not justify in itself any presumption. In fact Ibn Rushd's paraphrases are a series of treatises bearing the same titles as those of Aristotle. As Renan observed,[1] "It is largely by the titles of his books that Aristotle has dominated the human mind; the labels of his books have remained for two thousand years the divisions

[1] Averroès et l'Averroïsme (p. 60, 3d and ff. editions, 1869, sq.).

of knowledge itself." To put it in still another way, it is clear that every textbook on elementary geometry might be considered a commentary on Euclid; one which is explicitly called so is not necessarily less original than another wherein Euclid is not even mentioned, for we well know that both are essentially derived from Euclid. Indeed, the most original thoughts of mediaeval times are generally found not in treatises assuming an air of independence, but in the commentaries or super-commentaries. The reason for this is that, then as now, truly original minds were far less afraid of stating their indebtedness to their predecessors than were those who, lacking creative power, attempted in various ways to camouflage their mediocrity.

To return to Ibn Rushd; when we speak of his originality this must be understood in a relative sense. There is not much scope for true and obvious originality in philosophy; at any rate much less so than in the purely scientific field, where new experiments may originate at almost any moment streams of thought which are radically new. Thus Ibn Rushd's originality, like that of every philosopher, appeared chiefly in his way of interpreting anew the teachings of the wise men who had come before him. He was primarily an Aristotelian, a realist, a rationalist—all of which designations would need many qualifications. His superiority over Ibn Sīnā and other Muslim philosophers lay partly in his better knowledge of Aristotle. It will be remembered that the early Muslim Aristotelians mistook many apocryphal works—for example, the "Theology of Aristotle"—for genuine ones; and thus their Aristotelianism always contained a variable number of neo-Platonic elements. Ibn Rushd's philosophy was essentially a return to the purer Aristotelianism, a return to positivism or scientific philosophy, which was largely stimulated (as most philosophical systems are) by the opposite tendencies—mystical and pragmatic—of al-Ghazzālī. In fact, the most important of Ibn Rushd's independent treatises, and the one which is individually the most famous, was a refutation of al-Ghazzālī's Destruction of Philosophy—the Destruction of the Destruction. This book obtained considerable success in Islām, but it was mainly a success of scandal. It offended the feelings of the Muslims, even as an immoral book—or rather more so, but it did not influence them. For one thing, Muslim philosophy was then already decaying, and Ibn Rushd was at once the greatest and the last of their philosophers. Hence the history of Averroism treats but very little of the Muslims; it is primarily a history of Hebrew and Latin thought. The strange vicissitudes of Averroism will frequently be referred to in the following chapters. At present it is sufficient to note them in a general way, for they were not inherent in the ideas of Ibn Rushd but were caused by various distortions of those ideas.

The introduction of my third westerner, Abū-l-'Abbās al-Sibtī, after these two giants, is an anticlimax. But it is well to introduce him, if only to prevent the reader from forgetting that Ibn Ṭufail and Ibn Rushd represent but one aspect of the Moorish thought of those days. The noblest aspect, to be sure, but, then even as now, the rarest. The Moroccan ṣūfī, Abū-l-'Abbās, is mentioned here not so much for the sake of his own insignificant personality, but rather as the representative of a large class of astrologers who had a fast hold on the imaginations of the people. But while Ibn Ṭufail and Ibn Rushd, however great, were distinctly men of their time, Abū-l-'Abbās and the likes of him, however small, belong to no time in particular. His magical table of the universe might have been compiled a few centuries earlier, or yesterday—it would have been essentially the same.

For while rational thought is capable of progress, superstition is not; the more it seems to change, the less it varies.

2. *Eastern Muslim*—Though the eastern part of Islām could boast no philosopher at all comparable with Ibn Rushd or even with Ibn Ṭufail, there were more Easterners interested in philosophy, and the spectacle of their activities was far more varied than the one we have just witnessed in the Maghrib.

For example, consider the following: the jurist Ibn al-Dahhān added a logical introduction to his legal summary. 'Abd al-Raḥmān ibn Naṣrallāh, representing the seamy side of eastern thought (as Abū-l-'Abbās al-Sibtī that of the Maugrabins), wrote a treatise on the interpretation of dreams. Al-Marghīnānī wrote juridical treatises which were very popular in Ḥanīfite countries. Two polygraphs, 'Alī al-Bayhaqī and Ibn al-Jauzī, discussed a number of philosophical subjects, and the latter prepared a critical edition of al-Ghazzālī's Iḥyā. Two mystics, both strangely enough of Suhraward (in Jibāl): Yaḥyā al-Suhrawardī, one of the originators of the new illuminism (ḥikmat al-ishrāq), devoted many writings to the subject; and 'Umar al-Suhrawardī wrote books on ethics and on practical mysticism, and against Greek philosophy.

To these Arabic writers may be added two more who wrote mainly in Persian. The courtier Niẓāmī-i-'Arūḍī composed essays which contain evolutionary views, explaining connections between the three kingdoms of nature. It should be said that such intuitive views were almost a commonplace among Muslim intellectuals; and that the creationism of their most advanced philosophers, such as Ibn Rushd, could be easily reconciled with them. Fakhr al-dīn al-Rāzī, the greatest of them all, wrote treatises on many scientific and philosophical questions, notably one on the principles of physics and metaphysics. In spite of his genuine scientific interests he had mystical leanings, and might have been mentioned together with the two al-Suhrawardī, Yaḥyā and 'Umar. He composed two encyclopaedias in Persian.

Considering the abundance and diversity of these efforts, we realize that eastern Islām was still the center of culture, and understand how the Easterners could persist in considering the Moors barbarians. The appearance of two men as great as Ibn Ṭufail and Ibn Rushd was somewhat accidental, and without them the Muslim West would have been a philosophical desert.

Note the religious diversity of these Easterners: al-Marghīnānī was a Ḥanīfite; Ibn al-Jauzī, a Ḥanbalite, 'Umar al-Suhrawardī and Fakhr al-dīn, Shāfi'ītes; Yaḥyā al-Suhrawardī, a Shī'a. No such diversity was then conceivable in the Far West under the iron hand of the Almohades, those Puritans of Islām. The only license which they could allow was a moderate dose of taṣawwuf within the rigid frame of orthodoxy.

Most of these Easterners were Persians. Two of them, al-Marghīnānī and Niẓāmī-i-'Arūḍī, came from Transoxiana; and Fakhr al-dīn, though born in Jibāl, flourished in Herat. Only two were Baghdādites, Ibn al-Dahhān and Ibn al-Jauzī. The point which I wish to make is that Syria and Egypt had hardly any part in this philosophical activity, which was largely restricted to the Muslims who lived east of the Tigris. The public burning of philosophical works at Baghdād in 1192[2] helps us to understand the relative sterility of that city, which had once been one of the cultural centers of the world.

[2] See my note on Joseph ibn 'Aqnīn (second half of the twelfth century, Chapter XVIII).

3. *Western Jewish*—My account of Muslim philosophy in the second half of the twelfth century, brief as it is, shows clearly enough that there was still considerable activity in Islām, yet, as we shall see later, this was the climax. In spite of the gigantic personality of Ibn Rushd, Islām could no longer claim the leadership. The Western Jews could boast a doctor, Maimonides, who was fully Ibn Rushd's equal; besides at least twelve others who were sufficiently distinguished to require consideration in any general survey. The achievements of the Western Jews were equal to those of the Eastern and Western Muslims combined; but the equality was more apparent than real, for the Muslims were already going down while the Jews were going up; they just happened to meet here on the same level.

These Jewish philosophers are so numerous that I have to divide them into four groups. I shall consider successively a group of Talmudists and early Qabbalists; Aristotelian philosophers; ethical writers; and a miscellaneous group of translators, jurists, and grammarians.

The main Talmudist was a south Italian, Isaac ben Melchizedek, who flourished in Salerno. This confirms our impression that Salerno was a Jewish center, and that its intellectual interests were not restricted to medical matters. Isaac's commentaries never obtained the prestige of Rashi's, yet his influence was not restricted to Italy but was felt beyond the Alps.

The two other Talmudists, Abraham ben David of Posquières, and his son Isaac (often called Isaac the Blind), were both children of southern France; they were born there, and spent their whole lives there. Abraham did not hesitate to criticize Maimonides' Yad, and this does not surprise us for his innate tendencies were mystical; that is, he was a natural anti-Maimonidean. He is sometimes called the founder of the Qabbalah; the same title is also given to his son Isaac, and to the latter's chief disciple, Azriel ben Menahem (first half of the thirteenth century). Who is most deserving of it? It is futile to discuss such a question, which is less a matter of fact than of appreciation. And it is especially futile to try to determine the beginning of a mystical syncretism such as the Qabbalah, the roots of which may be traced back to Babylonian and Hellenistic times and even to the earliest days of Israel. One might as well attempt to find the beginning of the rainbow. At any rate one of the earliest Qabbalistic books, the Bāhīr, is generally ascribed to Isaac the Blind or to his school; and the Bāhīr contains a number of ideas which are certainly Qabbalistic, notably the doctrine of emanation. But remember first, that Isaac's authorship and the date of the Bāhīr are uncertain; second, that the Bāhīr is not the earliest work of its kind. It is partly derived from the Sefer yeẓirah, which goes back at least to the Geonic period, for Saadia Gaon (first half of the tenth century) wrote a commentary upon it. One thing is clear, Qabbalism appears (or reappears) about the end of the twelfth century, probably in southern France; it is interesting to note its simultaneity with the revival of rationalism, due to Maimonides. But we shall postpone a fuller discussion of Qabbalism until later, for at least another century of secret growth was needed before it began to make a strong appeal to the people.

Let us turn now to the main group of philosophers, those who are by far the most important from the point of view of this survey—the Jewish Aristotelians. The first was Abraham ben David ha-Levi of Toledo, who wrote in 1168 the Kitāb al-'aqīdah al-rafī'ah, which was the earliest deliberate attempt to reconcile Aristotelianism with the Jewish faith. He has been called the first Jewish Aristotelian; this is true but needs qualification. Saadia Gaon and other Jewish doctors had studied Aristotle before him, but he was one of the first to know the purer Aristotelian doctrine, and not to confuse apocryphal writings with genuine ones; he was the first to prepare the final Aristotelization which was to be completed by Maimonides.

Maimonides! The second Moses! It is almost as embarrassing to define him in a few paragraphs as it was to define his contemporary Ibn Rushd. These two giants not only dominated the thought of their age, they are still alive to-day. Their popularity never was the cheap popularity so often reaped by mediocre teachers—partly because of their very mediocrity; in fact, they never were truly popular; they never were understood and never will be except by a small élite, and among those who took cognizance of them there were always far more enemies than friends. Both were creative minds; which means that they could not traverse the human stage without upsetting things and causing a profound disturbance. How profound it was we shall see by-and-by. Both were engaged in essentially the same undertaking—to reconcile Aristotelian philosophy with the dogmas of their faiths. The fact that their faiths were different mattered much less than one might think, because the problems involved in order either to Islamize Aristotle or to Judaize him were very much the same. Ibn Rushd's task was mainly accomplished by means of masterly commentaries on the Aristotelian canon. Maimonides did not attempt anything as systematic; but he wrote a number of treatises, one of which, the Dalālat al-ḥā'irīn (Moreh nebukim), caused a tremendous furore. Even more than Ibn Rushd's Tahāfut al-tahāfut, its effect on the more conservative and orthodox was as if a bombshell had been thrown among them. Maimonides' rabbinical commentaries were even more influential than his Dalālat, and far less disquieting. By far the most important of these—the only one which is well known, but it is known all over the Jewish world—is the Mishneh Tōrāh, often called Yād ha-ḥazāqāh, or Yād. This "Repetition of the Law" was a codification of all the Mosaic and rabbinical laws. Some Talmudists (like Abraham ibn David of Posquières) objected to it on general principles, or because it was too brief and lacked references, or because the language was too modern, or because nothing good could be expected from the author of the Moreh nebukim; yet in the course of time it became almost a semi-canonical book in Israel. So much so that one of Maimonides' main purposes in writing it was almost defeated, for he had aimed to put an end to endless discussions on legal niceties, and his own work was so revered that it became the subject of further discussions of the same kind!

So far as the diffusion of the purer Aristotelianism is concerned, it is probable that Ibn Rushd's activity was more important than Maimonides'; but in one other respect at least the latter was decidedly superior—in his uncompromising denunciation of astrological nonsense. For this he deserves the everlasting gratitude of men of science.

In spite of the violent antagonism raised by Maimonides' work, he succeeded in his main object, the Aristotelization of Jewish philosophy. To be sure, he did not convince those who rejected every kind of philosophy. But aside from these, the ulterior development of Jewish philosophy was mainly a contest between Aristotelians and neo-Platonicians (most of these Qabbalists), a contest strikingly similar to the one which was waged at the same time in the Latin world. The history of Maimonidism, like that of Averroism, is essentially the history of a continuous battle against fundamentalism on the right, and mysticism (Qabbalism, or its Muslim and Christian equivalents) on the left. And is not this the very battle fought by men of science? For this reason alone, Ibn Rushd and Maimonides would deserve a place of honor in the history of science. But there are many other reasons for honoring them.

Maimonides' chief disciple, the astronomer Joseph ibn 'Aqnīn, wrote a metaphysical treatise, and probably also an ethical one, which contains interesting information on the ordinary course of studies in Jewish Spain.

The three Talmudists of whom I spoke at the beginning were Italian or Provençal, and naturally wrote in Hebrew. The three Aristotelians, on the contrary, were Spaniards. Abraham ben David ha-Levi was a Toledan, Maimonides a Cordovan, and Joseph ibn 'Aqnīn a Moroccan. (I did not make a mistake in calling Ibn 'Aqnīn a Spaniard, for there was but little difference then between the countries on both sides of the Straits of Gibraltar). Moreover, religious persecution drove Maimonides to Egypt in 1165, and Joseph followed him there twenty years later. Thus Jewish learning, which originally came from the East, was now returning there.

These three men wrote mainly in Arabic, the language of positive knowledge; but Abraham ben David's Jewish chronicle was couched in Hebrew, and so was Maimonides' Mishneh Tōrāh. These Arabic works were promptly translated into Hebrew, and it is highly significant that most of them are known only in the Hebrew versions. Some are lost in the original Arabic, or the Arabic texts have remained to this day unpublished. Consider the case of the most famous of them, the Dalālat, one of the few epoch-making books in philosophical literature. It is hardly known under its Arabic title, though the whole world has heard of the Moreh nebukim, or the Guide of the perplexed. The Hebrew version was printed before 1480, the Latin in 1520, the Arabic not until 1856–1866; there are innumerable editions in Hebrew and other languages, but only one in Arabic, and that one in the Hebrew character! Nothing illustrates more vividly the ending of the Arabic supremacy.

The other Jewish thinkers need not detain us very long. There were two moralists: Joseph ibn Zabara, who lived in Barcelona and dedicated his Sefer ha-sha'ashu'im to the Catalan physician Sheshet Benveniste; and that enigmatic Berakya ha-Naqdan, probably a French Jew established in England, who composed an ethical treatise and a collection of animal stories. Joseph's work was also a collection of stories, similar to the Kalīla wa-Dimna. These two collections were the earliest works of their kind in Hebrew literature.

We had spoken of Berakya before as a translator from the Latin into Hebrew. Three other translators must now be mentioned: Joseph Qimḥi translated Ibn Gabirol and Baḥya ben Joseph; Judah ibn Tibbon translated Saadia Gaon, Ibn Gabirol, and other Jewish authors; and Judah's son, Samuel ibn Tibbon, who later became famous as the translator of the Moreh nebukim, published in 1199 his first translation, 'Ali ibn Riḍwān's commentary on Galen's Tegni. All these translations were made from the Arabic into Hebrew (a translation from the Latin was then a very unusual thing), and with one exception they were devoted to Jewish works. Indeed, the singular task of these translators was to make Jewish philosophy available to the Jewish people. They succeeded so completely that in most cases the Arabic originals, sharing the fate of the Arabic culture, fell into oblivion. Joseph Qimḥi and Judah ibn Tibbon were Andalusians, and both flourished in Provence, where Samuel was born.

Two other Provençaux must be mentioned: the jurist, Isaac ben Abba Mari, whose 'Iṭṭur soferim is one of the classics of rabbinical literature; and the grammarian, David Qimḥi, Joseph's son, whose Biblical commentaries influenced Christian as well as Jewish scholars. In fact, their influence can be traced in King James' version.

4. *Eastern Jewish and Samaritan*—Turning from Western Jewry to the Eastern is like passing from the sun into the shade. The contrast is so violent that it is hard to believe that Israel came from the East. I know of but one Eastern Jew of that period who may be called a philosopher, the Baghdādite Hibatallāh ibn Malkā. He wrote various philosophical treatises, one of which, Al-mu'tabar, was of encyclopaedic scope. A contemporary Samaritan, the grammarian Abū-l-Isḥāq Ibrāhīm, was possibly the author of a Hebrew treatise on the Biblical commandments.

However, at this very time Maimonides and Joseph ibn 'Aqnīn were teaching in Egypt and kindling there a new fire. Thus one can never say that scientific activity has ceased here or there; what we take for a stop is generally nothing but an interruption.

5. *Latin*—It will be convenient to divide the Latin-writing philosophers into four national groups: Italian, French, English, and German.

The Italian group is headed by Peter the Lombard, whose Sentences, a theological summary, remained for almost four centuries in spite (or because) of its mediocrity, one of the main textbooks of western Europe. The other Italians were comparatively obscure, yet their contributions were far more important than Peter's. They are the translators of whom I have already spoken. Aristippus of Catania translated Meno and Phaedo from the Greek about 1156. Paschal the Roman compiled a dreambook and was possibly the translator of the Ciranides in 1169; another dreambook was translated from the Greek into Latin by Leo Tuscus. Meanwhile a vast treasure of Greek and Muslim philosophy was translated from the Arabic by Gerard of Cremona. So many were the works put into Latin by Gerard that I cannot name them all; they include the Posterior analytics with commentaries by Themistios and al-Fārābī; Aristotelian treatises, such as the De coelo et mundo and De generatione et corruptione; pseudo-Aristotelian ones, notably the De causis and De elementis; commentaries by Alexander of Aphrodisias; treatises by al-Kindī, al-Fārābī, and Isḥāq al-Isrā'īlī. Try to imagine what this meant—the accumulated wisdom of thirteen centuries suddenly made available to the Latin world. Gerard died in 1187. Thus, if we assume that these translations were made by Gerard or under his personal direction, that philosophical treasure was already available towards the end of the century. All these men were Italians; but Peter spent a part of his life in Paris, and Gerard most of his in Toledo.

The French group is less remarkable, and this is curious considering the climax which French philosophy had reached in the previous period, thanks to the school of Chartres and to Abaelard's genius. It is even more curious if one realizes that Paris was already a beacon of light attracting scholars from many countries. This is but another proof of the well known fact that opportunities, however helpful, do not create men. For the time being, genius had deserted France, or whatever genius there was had to be looked for among the Jews of Provence. Among the Christians I found only Peter the Eater, who was a sort of counterpart of Peter the Lombard; he wrote a Biblical textbook, the Historia scholastica, which was almost as popular as the Libri sententiarum. And two Cistercians: Alcher of Clairvaux, who composed a psychological compendium; and Alan of Lille. Alan was the best of the three; he wrote an encyclopaedic poem, the Anticlaudianus, and other treatises in Latin verse; he was less a philosopher than a humanist, but from the humanistic point of view his was a rare personality suggesting comparison with John of Salisbury. Like John, he had a genuine scientific bent, and even some appreciation of scientific truth.

Aside from the translators, the most impressive group of philosophers in Christendom was the English. It included four men, each of whom was distinguished, and one really great. We might perhaps begin with the latter, John of Salisbury, bishop of Chartres. He was one of the best educated men of his time, and though his knowledge was purely Latin, the number of Latin books available to him was already sufficient to make a modicum of learning possible. To that extent he was a learned man; he could not be in the vanguard of knowledge, but he was a real humanist. Isaac of Stella wrote an original summary of Platonic-Augustinian psychology. Daniel of Morley wrote a treatise on astrological philosophy; and Alexander Neckam compiled a popular encyclopaedia, De naturis rerum. Note that all these men had studied or resided in France. Daniel of Morley had even been to Toledo; irrespective of that, we are not surprised to find traces of Arabic influence in his work; his subject lent itself to it, and he was walking in the footsteps of Adelard of Bath. But what is more remarkable, Isaac, who lived in a Cistercian abbey of Poitou, had also seen the new light, thanks to Gundisalvo. Thus did Arabic learning slowly percolate into the West.

German achievements, though less important than Italian or English, were more original. This age witnessed the birth of the Lucidarius, the earliest encyclopaedia written in German. The Lucidarius had much success, not only in the German world but also in Scandinavia and Bohemia. The leading thinkers of Germany were two women, two nuns: Hildegard of Bingen, and Herrad of Landsberg. All considered, Hildegard was perhaps the most original personality in the whole West. Her theological and scientific treatises were written in Latin but contain German words. Her general vision of the world was mystical, but this did not prevent her from taking a scientific interest in details and explaining these as best she could. Herrad, abbess of Hohenberg on Mt. St. Odile, worked on a lower plane. Yet she produced for the instruction of her nuns a popular encyclopaedia, the Hortus deliciarum, which was especially valuable from the iconographic point of view.

The greatest personalities of the West were Hildegard, John of Salisbury, and Gerard of Cremona. The two who were by far the most popular, Peter the Lombard and Peter the Eater, were mediocre pedagogues. Hildegard, John, and Gerard were towering above their western contemporaries, yet they were like pygmies as compared with Maimonides and Ibn Rushd.

6. *Vernacular*—To complete this account of the philosophical background we must now speak of the popular literature of Europe. Needless to say, no attempt is made to cover the whole field, but simply to select some of the most significant tendencies.

The languages which thus appear in the limelight are French (langue d'oc and langue d'oïl), German (high and low), Spanish, Russian, and Icelandic. To be sure, a deeper study of the literary background would introduce other languages; I speak only of those which force themselves upon our attention by their exceptional vitality or the creation of masterpieces.

One of the most interesting activities was that of the Troubadours in southern France, Italy and Catalonia. These poets continued some of the lyrical and musical traditions of the Muslim singers (mughannī), and thus constituted one of the links between Islām and Christendom. Though the transmission of culture which they achieved was largely anonymous and even unconscious, it was nevertheless very effective. Their task was carried on in northern France by the Trouvères, and in Germany by the Minnesänger. The Latin songs of the Goliards are characteristic of the period which saw the birth of modern universities; for the Bohemian student type, rebellious yet good-humored, is as old as the universities themselves.

Turning to more definite literary creations, we must notice first of all the crystallization of the popular cycle of animal stories, called after its hero, Reynard the Fox. The intention of these stories was largely satirical. Even as the Goliard songs, they help us to remember the complexity of mediaeval life, its intimate resemblance, under the skin, to our own. Then there is the great German epic, the Nibelungenlied, comparable in scope and grandeur with the Chanson de Roland. Its beginnings are impossible to date. Some elements may be traced back to as early a time as the fifth century, and as more were aggregated the story gradually took shape. There were two main traditions, the Icelandic and the Germanic. The latter did not reach anything like its present form until the middle or the end of the twelfth century. The Poema del Cid, the national epic of Christian Spain, dates from about the same time. It will suffice merely to mention the Russian chronicles and the Icelandic sagas. Indeed the earliest literature of each people is an integral part of its philosophy.

7 *Byzantine*—There was but one writer who might be considered a philosopher because of the range of his interests; that was Eustathios, bishop of Thessalonica. He wrote commentaries on the Greek classics, and was primarily a humanist.

8. *Iranian*—The Iranian thought of the age was represented by the Pahlawī encyclopaedia entitled Būndahishn (the ground-giving).

9. *Hindu*—The Hindus were always fascinated by their language, and they had also an innate interest in logic. No wonder they were the inventors of grammar. Indeed the studies of Yāska and Pāṇini on Sanskrit grammar were the earliest elaborate grammatical efforts (see vol. I). These tendencies can be followed throughout the ages. In the period under discussion the Jaina grammarian Hemacandra wrote a treatise on logic. Towards the end of the century a new school of logic, the Navanyāya, was founded by the Bengali philosopher Gaṅgeśa. He wrote a systematic account of the Nyāya system which is the standard work on the subject, and as such has been commented upon ad nauseam.

To illustrate the shadier side of Hindu thought, we may recall the treatise on soothsaying composed by Durlabharāja of Gujarāt (in the Bombay presidency), and the dreambook written by his son Jagaddeva. Needless to say, such abberrations were not peculiar to India; we found them in other places and if we looked closely enough we should probably find them everywhere. Scientific and rationalistic efforts always were (and are) the exception; man's natural tendency is to indulge in superstitious beliefs. There is no shame in producing men like Durlabharāja and Jagaddeva, but a civilization is rightly discredited when it places such men in the foreground and does not allow other types to develop.

10. *Chinese*—One of the most prominent men in the history of Chinese thought, Chu Hsi, flourished at that very time (he died in 1200). He was the last and greatest of the Five Philosophers who originated the movement called Hsing^4-li^3 (the philoso-

[3] See vol. I, 755.

phy of human nature), or neo-Confucianism. This last term is very misleading, for that philosophy was a mixture of Confucianism with Buddhist and Taoist elements, something very remote from the original doctrine of K'ung Fu Tzŭ. A contemporary philosopher, Lu Chiu-yüan, criticized Chu Hsi's philosophy, but the latter remained supreme. Chu Hsi's commentaries on the Classics enjoyed considerable authority. At its best, neo-Confucianism reminds one of Stoicism.

To conclude: the leading philosophers of this period were Ibn Ṭufail, Ibn Rushd, Maimonides, Chu Hsi, John of Salisbury, Hildegard, and—though he was simply a translator, not a creator—Gerard of Cremona, whom we must add because of the exceptional size of his achievement. Seven outstanding persons, but the second and third were by far the greatest. Note that three of the seven came from Spain, one from China, one from England, one from Germany, one from Italy. The intellectual leaders of the world were the Muslims and the Jews of Spain.

VI. MATHEMATICS AND ASTRONOMY

1. *Western Muslim*—The criticism of Ptolemaic astronomy which Ibn Bājja and Jābir ibn Aflaḥ had originated in the first half of the century was continued by the philosopher Ibn Ṭufail and completed under his direction by al-Biṭrūjī. Ibn Ṭufail's illustrious successor at the Almohade court in Marrākush, Ibn Rushd, was also deeply interested in astronomy. He wrote a treatise on celestial motions, and a summary of the Almagest. The latter was soon translated into Hebrew, but strange to say not into Latin.

To return to al-Biṭrūjī (the Latin Alpetragius), Ptolemaic astronomy seemed unsatisfactory to him, so he revived the old theory of the homocentric spheres of Eudoxos, Aristotle, and Autolycos. That theory had reached Muslim philosophers together with Aristotelian physics. Al-Biṭrūjī modified it in various ways, incorporating with it the notion of the trepidation of the equinoxes. In any survey of Arabic astronomy one must pay due attention to that notion, in spite of the fact that it was erroneous, for it was essentially an Arabic one and it influenced the development of astronomy for *seven* centuries. It was introduced by Thābit ibn Qurra (second half of the ninth century), probably to account for some discrepancies already examined by Theon of Alexandria (second half of the fourth century), and by Proclos (second half of the fifth century). Many Muslim astronomers indorsed it, notably the great Spaniard al-Zarqālī. It should be noted however that some others,—for example, al-Battānī and Ibn Yūnus, two Easterners—did not speak of it. It is strange that such an idea should have been so readily accepted in the West, for it was never sufficiently worked out nor submitted to experimental tests. Latin and Hebrew astronomers vied with one another in their adoption of it. It is true that Levi ben Gershon refuted it in 1328, yet it would not die, and two centuries later the great reformer of astronomy, Copernicus, still believed in it!

I said above that this Muslim criticism of Ptolemaic astronomy was completed by al-Biṭrūjī, because his work was really the climax of Muslim efforts in that direction. No Muslim astronomer improved al-Biṭrūjī's arguments. As so often happens, the success of Alpetragian ideas was due far less to their own strength than to the weaknesses of Ptolemaic astronomy, weaknesses which became more and more apparent as observations were multiplied and perfected.

Ibn al-Yāsmīnī composed a poem on algebra, and Muḥammad al-Ḥaṣṣār wrote treatises on arithmetic and algebra. The former was murdered about 1204.

The floruit of the latter is less precise; I place him here tentatively. Treatises on the division of inheritances (Kitāb al-farā'iḍ) offer some arithmetical interest. One of the best known of these was composed by Abū-l-Qāsim al-Ḥaufī.

2. *Eastern Muslim*—The activities of Eastern Muslims were more varied, but there was not among them a man whose powers for good or evil were comparable to al-Biṭrūjī's.

The jurist Ibn al-Dahhān wrote a treatise on the division of inheritances. He was a Shāfi'ite theologian, while his Spanish contemporary Abū-l-Qāsim al-Ḥaufī was a Mālikite. Ibn al-Dahhān was more of a mathematician than Abū-l-Qāsim; he is said to have compiled astronomical tables.

There were two geometers, 'Abd al-Malik al-Shīrāzī, and Muḥammad ibn al-Ḥusain. 'Abd al-Malik wrote summaries of Apollonios' treatise on conics, and of the Almagest. Muḥammad composed a treatise explaining the use of instruments by means of which every conic could be drawn. Thus was the Apollonian tradition continued.

Finally, there was the Persian philosopher Fakhr al-dīn al-Rāzī who wrote astrological treatises, an essay on Euclid's postulates, and two encyclopaedias including mathematical sections. The encyclopaedias and at least one of the astrological works were written in Persian; the Euclidian essay, in Arabic.

3. *Western Jewish*—While the two Hispano-Jewish mathematicians of the first half of the twelfth century, Abraham bar Ḥiyya and Abraham ben Ezra, wrote in Hebrew, those of the second half of the century continued the purely Arabic tradition. I refer to the three Jewish Aristotelians, Abraham ben David ha-Levi, Maimonides, and Joseph ibn 'Aqnīn. It should be noted, however, that the last two were Westerners only in origin; much of their work was done in Egypt. As to the first, there is no reason for mentioning him in this section but that an astronomical treatise was ascribed to him by Isaac Israeli; the treatise itself is otherwise unknown.

Maimonides and Joseph ibn 'Aqnīn introduced the astronomy of Jābir ibn Aflaḥ into the East. It is not surprising that the criticism of Ptolemaic doctrines based on Aristotelian grounds found favor with them. We hear some echo of it in the Moreh nebukim. Maimonides had also made a special study of the mathematical treatise of Yūsuf al-Mutamin, king of Saragossa.

4. *Eastern Jewish*—The record of the Eastern Jews is less remarkable, but the situation would be reversed if we counted Maimonides and Joseph ibn 'Aqnīn as Easterners, which would not be entirely unjustified.

Hibatallāh ibn Malkā discussed the question of the invisibility of stars during the day, and of their nocturnal visibility. Samū'īl ibn 'Abbās, a scientist of Maugrabin origin, wrote a number of treatises on arithmetic and algebra and, in 1165, a denunciation of astrological errors. Both these men embraced Islām late in life; Samū'īl had become a Muslim when he composed his arraignment of the astrologers. It would perhaps be more correct to count them as Muslims, but the essential is to remember the facts. It is interesting to notice that of the four Jewish mathematicians who flourished then in the East, three came from the West, and two completed their orientalization to the point of becoming Muslims.

5. *Syriac*—Simeon Shanqĕlāwī wrote a Syriac treatise on the calendar in the form of a catechism.

6. *Byzantine*—John Camateros wrote two astrological poems which are of a more scientific type than those of his older contemporary Prodromos, but this is not saying very much.

7. *Latin*—The greatest astronomical event in Western Christendom was the publication of the Almagest in Latin. Strange to say, two Latin translations of it appeared within fifteen years. A Greek manuscript of the Almagest had been brought from Constantinople to Sicily by Aristippus of Catania. This Greek text was translated into Latin by unknown scholars; this was the earliest translation; it was completed in Sicily about 1160. The second translation was made from the Arabic by Gerard of Cremona at Toledo in 1175. It speaks volumes for the Arabic prestige that it was chiefly through this second translation, roundabout and inferior, that the Almagest was transmitted to the West. The former translation exerted no detectable influence. Thus for all practical purposes 1175 is the real date of introduction of the Almagest to the Latin astronomers.

Gerard's translation of the Almagest was perhaps his greatest service to astronomers, but by no means the only one. He translated from the Arabic Autolycos' treatise on the sphere, Euclid's Elements and Data, Archimedes' treatise on the measurement of the circle, Apollonios' Conics (?), Hypsicles' Ascensions, and the treatises on spherics of Theodosios, Geminos and Menelaos. In other words, he helped to transmit a whole corpus of Greek geometry and astronomy; he translated not only the "great collection," ἡ μεγάλη σύνταξις (hence Almagest),[4] but the small collection, ὁ μικρὸς ἀστρονομούμενος (τόπος), the "Little Astronomy," which included a number of lesser treatises forming an introduction to Ptolemy. Nor is this all, for he translated also a whole library of original Arabic writings on the same subjects. I can hardly name them except in the briefest manner: the book of the Banū Mūsā, al-Khwārizmī's algebra, al-Farghānī's astronomy, treatises by Aḥmad ibn Yūsuf, al-Nairīzī, Thābit ibn Qurra, the astronomical treatises and tables of Jābir ibn Aflaḥ and al-Zarqālī, etc. And to these should be added—though I would put them on the debit side—at least five astrological treatises.

The original works written in Latin amount to little. FitzNeal's dialogue on the exchequer offers some arithmetical interest. The Practica geometriae Hugonis shows how little was really known of theoretical geometry by the Latin writers who had not yet been reached by the Arabic stream of knowledge. The main difference between this unknown Hugh and the schoolmasters of the eleventh century is that he was at least aware of the existence of theoretical geometry, but this vague awareness was his limit. Roger of Hereford composed a compotus, and treatises on astronomy and astrology. Gerald the Welshman tried to give a comprehensive theory of tides, combining the lunar astrological with other explanations.

8. *Vernacular*—The earliest Icelandic treatise on the calendar was written by Bjarni Bergþórsson, who died in 1173.

9. *Hindu*—Bhāskara, of whom I spoke in the preceding book, ought also to be remembered in this one. His main work, the Siddhāntaśiromaṇi was already completed by the middle of the century; but another work of his, far less important, was written as late as 1178.

10. *Chinese*—A map of stars, probably compiled towards the end of the twelfth century, was engraved in 1247.

11. *Japanese*—Fujiwara Michinori, adviser to the emperor Go-Shirakawa, made a study of keishi-zan (permutations?). It is possible that this was the first germ of a very original Japanese tradition which culminated only in the first half of the seventeenth century.

[4] Vol. 1, 562.

12. *Summary*—This period was on the whole inferior to the preceding one. The outstanding facts were the following:

(1) Al-Biṭrūjī's criticism of Ptolemaic astronomy and his revival of Aristotelian ideas. Al-Biṭrūjī's theory was erroneous, but it was the subject of considerable discussion and may be considered as one of the steps that led indirectly to the astronomical revolution of 1543.

(2) The transmission to the East of the astronomy of Jābir ibn Aflaḥ and of anti-Ptolemaic criticism, by Maimonides and Joseph ibn 'Aqnīn.

(3) The translation of the Almagest into Latin, from the Greek and from the Arabic; the second of these translations (Toledo 1175) was the main agent in the transmission of Ptolemaic astronomy to the Latin world.

(4) The unparalleled activity of Gerard of Cremona, as a translator from the Arabic into Latin. Thanks to him, a whole treasure of Greek and Arabic astronomy and mathematics became available to western scientists.

Gerard thus continued and almost completed the work which had been so brilliantly begun at Toledo in the first half of the twelfth century. He did almost as much singlehanded as the seven translators whom I discussed in Book I. In one important respect his activity was superior to theirs; he did not give so much of his time to the astrological treatises. To be sure, he translated a few of them, but these represented but a small part of his effort. By the middle of the twelfth century the avalanche of Muslim astrology was already over, though unfortunately the evils which it had introduced continued, and will continue as long as fools are born. For a long time the Latin translations of the treatises on astrology were the most popular of the Arabic importations.

Comparison of items (1) and (2) with (3) affords a good illustration of the backwardness of the Latin world. At the very time when Western Christians were finally able to read the Almagest, Jews and Muslims were engaged in criticizing it and showing its weaknesses. The alternative theory which they proposed was not successful, but their criticism was right and useful.

In this summary I have not spoken of treatises on mathematics. Many were published, but none of special merit. However, it should be remembered that astronomy included the whole of trigonometry, and much of spherical geometry, arithmetic and algebra. It is for that very reason that we have to consider astronomy and mathematics at one and the same time.

VII. PHYSICS, TECHNOLOGY, AND MUSIC

1. *Eastern Muslim*—The handbook which the Egyptian 'Abd al-Raḥmān Ibn Naṣr composed for the use of the muḥtasib (the police officer in charge of markets) contained information on weights and measures. Muḥammad al-Sā'ātī constructed a famous clock at the Bāb Ghairūn in Damascus; later this clock was repaired and its movement explained by his son Riḍwān (first half of the thirteenth century).

2. *Eastern Jewish*—Samū'īl ibn 'Abbās wrote a treatise on specific gravity. This was a subject especially dear to Muslim physicists, and Samū'īl had spent all of his life in the East, living with Muslims and finally becoming one of them.

The famous Cairene physician Ibn Jamī' published a general treatise on medicine, the Irshād, the last part of which was devoted to materia medica; the last chapter of that part contains an explanation of weights and measures. I mention this here once for all. Most treatises on materia medica contained such explanation, for correct posology was impossible without it. Thus a student of metrology ought to examine them carefully, as he would find there some of its more reliable information. A discussion of the Talmudic weights and measures was written in Arabic by Joseph ibn 'Aqnīn.

Ibn Jamī' was a genuine Egyptian; Joseph became one in his maturity. Both, as well as Samū'īl ibn 'Abbās, wrote in Arabic.

3. *Latin*—Eugene the Amīr, one of that remarkable group of Sicilian polyglots, translated the Ptolemaic optics from an Arabic version into Latin. That treatise is devoted to a study of refraction, including atmospheric refraction. Whether Ptolemy was the real author or not, it was the most important work of its kind of ancient times, the best example of true experimental physics until the time of Peregrinus (second half of the thirteenth century). Thus Eugene's translation was an important event, or might have been one; it does not seem to have exerted any influence, but it has preserved for posterity the contents of one of the great classics of scientific literature.

Two treatises by Alexander Neckam contain the earliest European mentions of the nautical use of the magnetic needle. Alexander does not speak of it as if it were a novelty. Historians of technology may find other interesting hints in his De utensilibus.

Great engineering works were accomplished in northern Italy. The Naviglio Grande, begun in 1179, brought the Ticino waters to Milan, and with them fertility to the fields of Lombardy and wealth to the burghers. The people of Genoa showed as much initiative as those of Milan; they protected their harbor by means of a gigantic mole, and constructed an aqueduct to bring water to their city.

4. *European music*—The new musical theories which had gradually filtered from Arabic writings into Latin and Hebrew ones, were now for the first time clearly and systematically explained in two Latin treatises, the Ars cantus mensurabilis and the Compendium discantus. The first and earliest was written by Franco of Paris, the second by Franco of Cologne. It is possible that these two names cover the same personality. Franco created a musical notation called after him the Franconian notation, which is not essentially different from our own.

While theories were thus transmitted in their own ungrateful way, Muslim music was crossing the Pyrenees upon the wings of song. Troubadours, trouvères, and minnesingers popularized the new art and improved it. But alas! this does not belong to our own story, and we must stop here and listen to their delightful and merry tunes, like beggars, from the outside.

VIII. CHEMISTRY

1. *Western Muslim*—Ibn Arfa' ra'sahu of Fās compiled a collection of poems on the philosopher's stone.

2. *Latin*—The English astronomer Roger of Hereford wrote a treatise, De rebus metallicis. The treatise on alchemy ascribed to Alan of Lille, Dicta Alani de lapide philosophico, is apocryphal.

As far as we know, alcoholic distillation was invented by Salernitan apothecaries about the middle of the twelfth century. It might have been invented earlier—for example, by Muslim chemists—but we have no proof of it. The oldest mention of distillation occurs in a treatise by magister Salernus who flourished about 1130–1160.

3. *Westward transmission of Chinese porcelain*—The manufacture of porcelain

was invented in China, certainly before the middle of the ninth century and probably at a much earlier date. We first hear of it in the Near East when Ṣalāḥ al-dīn presented forty pieces of it to another ruler. This proves the continuation of cultural exchanges between China and the West.

IX. GEOGRAPHY

1. *Western Muslim*—The greatest geographer and cartographer of the Middle Ages, al-Idrīsī, flourished throughout the first half of the twelfth century, but his chief work was done in the second half. He was a Spaniard, born on the other side of the Straits, in Ceuta, and educated in Cordova, but his life's work was done at Palermo under the patronage of Roger II and William I. The famous Kitāb al-Rujārī (named after the first of these kings), completed about 1154, was the most elaborate description of the world of mediaeval times. Thanks to the fact that the author's patron was a Christian, the Rujārī was not restricted to Islām; it was a description of the whole oikumene. Al-Idrīsī compiled another geography, even larger than the former, for William I; but this is completely lost, unless an anonymous work of 1192, the Rawḍ al-furaj, may be considered an abridgment or a partial copy of it. The Rujārī is a geographical description in the broadest sense; it contains not only geographical facts, but also many others concerning natural history, medicine, etc.

Another great geographer, al-Māzinī, was a contemporary of al-Idrīsī, born before him, and dying three years after him. He was more of a cosmographer in the old Arabic way than a systematic geographer, yet he gives information which is unobtainable anywhere else. For example, he traveled in the Volga region and in Hungary, and while in the former country witnessed the trade in fossil bones (or ivory?). Al-Māzinī came from Granada, and lived more than thirty-five years in Spain; but after many years of travel he settled down in the Near East—as much as a restless person of his type could settle down anywhere—and finally died in Damascus.

Still another geographer, Ibn Jubair of Valencia, wrote a very valuable account of his journey to the East in 1183–1185, one of the best works of its kind in Arabic literature.

2. *Eastern Muslim*—While Spain produced three outstanding geographers, the contributions of eastern Islām were relatively unimportant. Muḥammad ibn Maḥmud al-Ṭūsī composed a cosmography in Persian. 'Alī al-Harawī, another Persian—who, however, wrote in Arabic—was the author of a guide book for pilgrims which treats not only of Syria and Egypt, but also of the Byzantine empire, Mesopotamia, India, Arabia, the Maghrib, and Abyssinia. The most interesting point about him is that he was more than once in contact with Christians. At the time of his visit to Jerusalem in 1173, the Holy City was in Christian hands; moreover, he was presented to Manuel Comnenos in Constantinople. These contacts of Islām with Christendom, exemplified by 'Alī al-Harawī and al-Idrīsī, were something new in the history of Islām, at least outside of Spain; heretofore Muslims had known only such Christians as were disdainfully tolerated in their own midst. That situation was being gradually reversed.

3. *Jewish*—The greatest Jewish traveler of mediaeval times, Benjamin of Tudela, went as far as Baghdād, visiting a number of Jewish communities in southern Europe, the Near East, and Egypt. His account of his travels was the earliest

important Hebrew work of its kind. It is one of our most valuable sources for the understanding of contemporary culture.

Petaḥiah of Ratisbon traveled also to the Near East, but along a northern route across Russia and Armenia. His account is on the whole less valuable than Benjamin's, but it contains unique information—for example, on the Russian Tartars, and on the Jewish college of Baghdād.

A third pilgrim, Jacob ben Nathaniel, is far less important, and the value of his account is further decreased by uncertain chronology; he may have flourished at a later time.

Finally, the Egyptian physician Ibn Jamī' wrote a description of Alexandria and of its climate.

4. *Byzantine*—The Cretan soldier John Phocas visited the Holy Land in 1185 and wrote a description of the road from Antioch to Jerusalem. His account of Palestine was the earliest Byzantine but one.

Eustathios, bishop of Thessalonica, composed a commentary on the geographical poem of Dionysios Peregietes.

5. *Latin*—Before speaking of Latin geographers, it is well to say a few words of a personality wholly mythical but which exerted a very real and very deep influence upon travelers until the end of the fifteenth century. "Prester John" was believed to be a powerful king living somewhere in Central Asia or India, or later, in Abyssinia. Not only were adventurers eager to reach the fabulous court of that potentate, but the popes and the real kings of Christendom became even more anxious to befriend him and to obtain his help against the Saracens.

The Latin geographical works of that period were very different from the cosmographical compilations of the first half of the twelfth century. Three geographical writers must be named. The greatest of the three was undoubtedly Gerald the Welshman. I have already mentioned his observations of tides; he compared their height on various shores of the Irish sea. He wrote descriptions of Ireland and Wales which are among the most remarkable productions of their kind in mediaeval times. They include accounts of the main physical features (rivers, mountains), and of the customs of the people, notes on natural history, and discussions of the climatic factors of human temperaments.

Godfrey of Viterbo, probably a German, may be the author of a geographical poem describing the kingdoms which were constituent parts of the Holy Roman Empire.

The chronicle of England composed by Roger of Howden contains descriptions of routes and coasts—for example, those of Spain—which make us think of portolani, or of manuals of navigation such as were published in Arabic for the benefit of Muslim pilots (see my note on Sahl ibn Abān, first half of the twelfth century).

Some of our best geographical information on Palestine and the Near East is found in the history of William of Tyre.

To these treatises should be added the narratives of many pilgrims. None of these is important in itself, but the mass of them is imposing. We can easily conjure up a vision of these pilgrims suffering innumerable discomforts and jeopardizing their very lives in order to see the Holy Land with their own eyes, to touch it with their hands, to cleanse their souls from sin. How many of them must have died along the land and sea routes, equally insecure! Of those who survived, a few left accounts of their experiences. Much of what they wrote is stereotyped and uncritical, or else too vague to be of any value; yet when all that is trivial or irrelevant has been removed there remains a residue which is truly memorable.

It is not necessary to speak of the individual accounts except in the briefest manner. To begin with, there are six anonymous narratives anterior to the fall of Jerusalem in 1187. The best of these was written about 1150–1170 by an Englishman, the pseudo-Bede. Then there are the accounts of three German pilgrims: John of Würzburg, Theodoric of Hirschau, Burchard of Strassburg. The last named was not an ordinary pilgrim but a diplomatic agent sent by Frederick I Barbarossa to Salāḥ al-dīn. Another exceptional pilgrim was the Calabrian prophet Joachim of Floris, who began the accomplishment of his mission only after his return from the Holy Land. Richard Lionheart was not a pilgrim but a mighty crusader. His anonymous biographer gives an unusually good account of the routes followed; he must have availed himself of one of the manuals of navigation to which I have alluded. Finally, there is the pilgrim narrative associated with the name of Fetellus, a typical guide book, trite and stupid, yet not entirely worthless.

6. *Vernacular*—The two vernacular writings which I have to mention are also pilgrim-narratives, but on the whole far more interesting than the Latin ones. Vernacular writers were bound to be more original, and their works enable us to tap sources of information which are entirely new. On the other hand, the Latin writings are more closely interrelated, and when we read them one after another we have sometimes the impression that we are always tapping the same cask.

Nikulás Saemundarson was an Icelandic Benedictine who wrote in his own language an itinerary to Rome and Jerusalem, together with catalogues of the relics kept in those holy cities. Nikulás would not admit that the northern countries were isolated from the continent. In this he was mistaken; but his was not a foolish error, for one of the grounds of his opinion, opposed to the common one, was the presence in Greenland of continental animals.

Anthony of Novgorod visited Constantinople in 1200 and wrote in Russian a description of it which is of special value, because soon afterwards that Christian metropolis was ignominiously sacked by the Christian barbarians who came from the West under pretense of redeeming the Holy Land!

7. *Chinese*—The Chinese geographers of this time were second only to the Muslims. Fan Ch'êng-ta was a very remarkable man who found time amidst many other occupations, public and private, to write a number of geographical works: a topography of Su-chou in Chiang-nan, a treatise on the geography of southern China, and accounts of his journeys. Another witness to contemporary geographical interest is a map compiled about 1193 for the education of a prince who became the emperor Ning Tsung. Wang Hsiang-chih compiled a description of southern China—in two hundred books—which the Chinese themselves considered the best geographical treatise of the Sung period. It contains abundant archaeological information. Wang has been called a Sung Pausanias, or a Sung Baedeker!

8. *Summary*—The greatest geographical work of the age was the Book of Roger, compiled by a Muslim, al-Idrīsī.

The outstanding personalities were seven in number: four Spaniards, one Welshman, two Chinese. The four Spaniards were al-Idrīsī who flourished in Sicily; al-Māzinī and Ibn Jubair, both of whom died in the East; and Benjamin of Tudela who presumably died in his own country, the only one of the four to do so. Three of these were Muslims, the fourth a Jew. The lonely Welshman and Christian was Gerald. The two Chinese were Fan Ch'êng-ta and Wang Hsiang-chih.

From the geographical point of view, this was an age of achievements, multiple and varied.

X. NATURAL HISTORY

1. *Western Muslim*—We have already observed that the geographical books of al-Idrīsī and al-Māzinī contain much information on natural history. A good example is al-Māzinī's account of the trade in fossil ivory witnessed by him in the Volga region. Ibn Ṭufail's philosophical romance, Ḥaiy ibn Yaqẓān, includes biological views, notably a discussion of spontaneous generation.

The greatest achievements of the Western Muslims were in the field of botany, pure and applied. The Cordovan al-Ghāfiqī collected plants in Spain and Africa, and gave descriptions of them which were reputed for their accuracy; he was often quoted by Ibn Baiṭār. Needless to say, his aims were medical rather than purely botanical. The most important mediaeval work on husbandry was composed somewhat later, towards the end of the century, by Ibn al-'Awwām of Seville. His great work, the Kitāb al-falāḥa, is derived partly from the Greek and Arabic literature on the subject, partly from the experience of the Muslim husbandmen of Andalusia. It treats of 585 plants and explains the cultivation of more than fifty fruit-trees. It contains many new observations on grafting, phytopathology, etc. The development of agriculture was one of the glories of Muslim Spain, and one of their lasting gifts to that country, for many Spanish gardens have preserved to this day a Moorish imprint.

A lost treatise of al-Idrīsī on materia medica has been recently discovered in Constantinople. It contains a description of 360 simples, and seems very important, if not from the medical, at least from the botanical point of view.

2. *Eastern Muslim*—The works of the Damascene Ja'far ibn 'Alī and of the Egyptian 'Abd al-Raḥmān Ibn Naṣr may be consulted to obtain information on various wares such as precious stones, drugs, perfumes. Ja'far's work, written in 1175, was a commercial treatise dealing with falsifications and showing how to detect and avoid them. The treatise of 'Abd al-Raḥmān, unfortunately difficult to date, was written for the benefit of police officers inspecting markets. Its purpose was essentially the same as that of Ja'far's treatise, to avoid frauds and regulate commercial transactions, a task which was apparently very much needed if one may judge by the conditions which obtain to this day in the aswāq.

The historian Ibn Munqidh was a great hunter, and his autobiography relates many of his sporting experiences, including interesting observations on the habits of wild animals.

All the works thus far mentioned were written in Arabic. The two following were written by Persians, and in Persian. Nizāmī-i-'Arūḍī of Samarkand was the author of a literary composition, Chahār maqāla, explaining the duties of royal secretaries, poets, astrologers, and physicians. It contains many anecdotes, and reflections on all sorts of subjects—for example, views on evolution. Muḥammad ibn Maḥmūd of Ṭūs composed a cosmography, 'Ajā'ib al-makhlūqāt (Marvels of creatures), which includes a number of facts which may interest naturalists.

3. *Western Jewish*—The only Jewish work deserving to be quoted in this section is the free Hebrew translation of Adelard's Natural Questions, by Berakya ha-Naqdan. Berakya's animal fables belong only to the history of literature, but he also wrote a lapidary treating of 73 stones. This is the earliest Hebrew lapidary known to me—if one does not take into account the explanations of the twelve

precious stones inserted in Aaron's breastplate, explanations which occurred as a matter of course in every Biblical commentary.

4. *Muslim and Jewish falconry*—I have already set forth the special importance of treatises on falconry. They represented perhaps the best part of zoological knowledge in mediaeval times; knowledge which was not merely bookish and superstitious, like that transmitted in the bestiaries, but experimental. Unfortunately, few of the many Arabic treatises are ascribed to identifiable authors, and fewer still can be dated with any certainty. I found three of them which may be assigned tentatively to the second half of the twelfth century, but a further study of the matter is much needed. One of the authors may possibly be identified with the historian 'Imād al-dīn of Ispahan.

The final part of Ibn Munqidh's Kitāb al-i'tibār is exclusively devoted to falconry and the chase. It contains abundant anecdotes. It is the earliest Arabic work on falconry written by a known author. Ibn Munqidh dictated it in Damascus about 1182.

It is very interesting to record the existence of a Hebrew treatise on falconry dating from about the same period, 1197–1199. We may assume that it was translated from the Arabic, and in all probability it was a Spanish production. As is usually the case, it treats not only of the care of healthy birds, but of their occasional ailments and the means of curing them. It ought to be studied in conjunction with the Arabic treatises.

The popularity of that noble sport in Christendom is witnessed by the code of Sancho el Sabio (1180), which will be discussed later.

5. *Byzantine*—There is nothing in the contemporary Greek literature which may be connected even remotely with natural history, except perhaps a curious little text, the Poricologos, which may be assigned to the twelfth century. A number of fruit-trees are considering the shameful case of the grapevine accused of conspiracy and treason. The intention is ethical and satirical. I quote this faute-de-mieux. This story tells us which fruit trees were then most popular among the Greeks, but little else. Its popularity was astounding, as is witnessed by the Slavonic and Turkish translations from which botanic information of the same kind might be derived.

6. *Latin*—The continued popularity of Pliny's Natural History is attested by the Defloratio compiled by Robert of Cricklade, and by another anthology to which Robert of Torigny contributed a preface.

Alan of Lille wrote a bestiary. The history of Sicily compiled by Hugh Falcandus contains valuable information on the cultivation of sugar cane and other plants. Burgundio of Pisa translated from the Greek the part of the Geoponica treating of vineyards. None of these works was of outstanding importance.

Meanwhile the most distinguished naturalist of the century was flourishing in a convent at Bingen on the Rhine. She was a Benedictine nun, Hildegard—not an abbess, nor a canonized saint, however saintly she may have been. Her main work, the Physica, was a real encyclopaedia of natural history and medicine, special attention being paid to plants. She gives the German names of about a thousand plants and animals.

7. *Vernacular*—The cycle of animal stories which is symbolized by the name of its hero Reynard the Fox, reveals the animals which were then most familiar to men. They also show how well the psychological characteristics of these animals were appreciated.

Sancho VI el Sabio, king of Navarre, promulgated in 1180 a Spanish code of hunting law, Los paramientos de la caza, which was the earliest elaborate code of its kind with the exception of the Forest Laws of Canute the Great. It is of real value for the proper understanding of hunting conditions and may help us to interpret the treatises on falconry.

8. *Hindu*—The great Jaina lexicographer Hemacandra compiled a Sanskrit botanical glossary.

9. *Chinese*—The Chinese contributions were not many but, as we have already learned to expect from them, highly original.

The artist Lou Shou published a collection of forty-five drawings illustrating the cultivation of rice, sericulture, and the silk industry.

Han Ch'an-chih, governor of Wên-chou in Chehkiang, wrote a treatise on oranges, describing twenty-seven varieties and explaining their cultivation. This is the earliest treatise on citrous fruits in the world's literature.

Fan Ch'êng-ta wrote a monograph on chrysanthemums, describing thirty-five varieties cultivated by himself.

10. *Japanese*—Henchiin Seiken wrote in 1156 Japanese treatises derived from the Chinese pên ts'ao; one of them treats of cereals. Seiken's works were illustrated, and as the pên ts'ao from which the illustrations were derived—the Ch'ung kuang of 1061—is lost, Seiken's works are especially valuable.

Tea shrubs were introduced into Japan in 1191 by the famous Buddhist monk Eisai. An earlier introduction had apparently failed, but this one was successful for Eisai organized the cultivation of tea, and doing nothing by halves, he wrote a book explaining its virtues.

11. *Summary*—The chief naturalists of this period were Ibn al-'Awwām, Hildegard, Han Ch'an-chih, and Fan Ch'êng-ta—one Spaniard who was a Muslim, a German nun, and two Chinese.

XI. MEDICINE

1. *Western Muslim*—Let us first consider the enigmatic personality of "Alcoatim," Salome son of Arit, probably a Mudejar or assimilated Muslim who flourished in Toledo and wrote about 1159 a treatise on eye-diseases. His work was probably written in Arabic, but most of it is available in an early Latin version. Or was Alcoatim simply the translator from Arabic into Latin?

Al-Ghāfiqī's work on simples, largely based on his own herborizations in Spain and Africa, was mentioned in the section on natural history. It is interesting to note that al-Ghāfiqī gave the names of simples in Arabic, Latin, and Berber. Al-Idrīsī's geography contains many facts of medical interest, and a treatise of his on materia medica has been recently discovered in Constantinople.

The leading physicians were Ibn Ṭufail and Ibn Rushd, who were both in attendance at the Almohade court in Marrākush; Ibn Ṭufail until 1182 when his old age obliged him to resign (he was then at least 72 years old), then Ibn Rushd from 1182 to 1194. Ibn Ṭufail is said to have written two medical treatises and to have advised his younger colleague. Ibn Rushd wrote before 1162 a medical encyclopaedia, the Kullīyāt (known to Christians under the corrupt Latin name Colliget), which was meant to treat mainly of medical generalities and thus to be a sort of counterpart to the Taisīr of Ibn Zuhr. But it contained other valuable observations; for example, Ibn Rushd seems to have been the first to understand, roughly, the function of the retina[5] (earlier oculists thought that visual perception occurred in the lens); and he realized that an attack of smallpox confers immunity. Aside from the Kullīyāt, he wrote a commentary on Ibn Sīnā's Arjūza. He was unquestionably a great physician, one of the greatest of his time anywhere, but his fame as a philosopher grew to such proportions that the attention paid to the physician was comparatively small. Yet the Kullīyāt was a very important book which was soon translated into Latin and into Hebrew, and was often printed in the fifteenth and sixteenth centuries.

2. *Eastern Muslim*—The principal Eastern physician was perhaps Ibn Hubal, a Baghdādite who practiced at Mūṣul and later at the Armenian court of Akhlāṭ. He wrote a medical treatise, the Mukhtār fī-l-ṭibb.

The erotic books of 'Abd al-Raḥmān ibn Naṣrallāh, of Shīrāz and Aleppo, contain many items of medical interest. Apropos of this, it may be remarked that oriental medical books devote much space to erotic matters—for example, to the consideration of aphrodisiacs and anaphrodisiacs. The other doctors were not physicians in the narrow sense, but literati and philosophers. The last of the Four Discourses of Niẓāmī-i-'Arūḍī deals with physicians; it is essentially a collection of medical anecdotes and miscellaneous thoughts on the subject. The indefatigable polygraph Ibn al-Jauzī wrote books on medical generalities and on spiritual medicine. And the two encyclopaedias compiled by Fakhr al-dīn al-Rāzī included medical sections. These encyclopaedias were written in Persian, and so were Niẓāmī's discourses; the other works were in Arabic.

3. *Western Jewish*—The leading Catalan physician was Sheshet Benveniste. He wrote a treatise on women's diseases.

As the greatest philosopher of Islām in those days was also its greatest physician, even so with the Jews. Maimonides, who was, I will not say their leader, but their strongest and most original mind, was also, and by far, their leading physician. His medical knowledge was derived from the Arabic literature which included almost the whole of the Galenic corpus, and from his own experience which was not inconsiderable. His doctrines might be labeled Arabic Galenism, but they were the doctrines of a man of sense and genius. His most popular (medical) work was the collection of medical maxims commonly called Fuṣūl Mūsā (Moses' Aphorisms), composed about 1188 but possibly revised towards the end of his life. The last chapter, posthumously edited by his nephew, was a very interesting criticism of Galen. He also wrote a commentary on Hippocrates' Aphorisms; a regimen addressed about 1198 to the oldest son of Ṣalāḥ al-dīn; treatises on poisons and antidotes, on asthma, on haemorrhoids, etc. A special physician's prayer is generally ascribed to him; it beautifully completes the Hippocratic oath from the Jewish point of view, and is often found framed in the offices of Jewish doctors. Maimonides' favorite disciple and his companion in Egypt, Joseph ibn 'Aqnīn, was also a distinguished physician. From his Ṭibb al-nufūs we can gather some idea of general and medical education in the Spanish Jewry of his time; that education was, all considered, astonishingly comprehensive, and it helps us to understand the intellectual supremacy of the Jews of Spain.

The great translator Samuel ibn Tibbon, whose Hebrew version of the Dalālat al-ḥā'irīn was to make him famous in the thirteenth century, completed at Béziers

[5] The retina had been known for centuries. Its name is a translation of a Greek word coined by Herophilos (first half of the third century B.C.). The Arabic term reproduces the same metaphor.

in 1199 his first translation, that of 'Alī ibn Riḍwān's commentary on Galen's Tegni.

To these we may add with some hesitation a Hebrew parody of Hippocrates' Aphorisms, which is ascribed to the Catalan poet Joseph ibn Zabara.

With the exception of this parody, and of course of Samuel ibn Tibbon's translation, all the Jewish medical writings here mentioned were in Arabic. However, Sheshet's gynaecological treatise and Maimonides' works were promptly and repeatedly translated into Hebrew, and many of them are far better known in Hebrew than in Arabic. In fact, we are still lacking critical editions of the Arabic texts of some of Maimonides' treatises, even of the Fuṣūl!

I have spoken of all of these men as Western Jews, but it is well to bear in mind that the two leading ones, Maimonides and Joseph ibn 'Aqnīn, flourished in Egypt, and that Maimonides' most important medical works were written in that country. Yet they were Spaniards, not Egyptians.

4. *Eastern Jewish*—Hibatallāh ibn Malkā, who flourished in Baghdād, and died there, blind and deaf, of elephantiasis, composed a summary of Galenic anatomy. He cured a psychopathological case by suggestion; such cures were not uncommonly ascribed to great Muslim physicians, who attached much importance to what they called the medicine of the soul. Samū'īl ibn 'Abbās wrote a treatise on gynaecology and sexual matters, one of those books half-erotic, half-medical, of which there are so many in Arabic. Hibatallāh and Samū'īl might have been counted among the Muslims, for both embraced Islām late in life. Moreover, Samū'īl's erotic work was more typical of Muslim than of Jewish life.

Ibn al-Mudawwar, a Qaraite, compiled a collection of medical observations, and so did the oculist Ibn al-Nāqid. Ibn Jamī' wrote a general treatise on medicine, the Irshād, a commentary on the fifth book of the Qānūn, and two essays on lemons and rhubarb which Ibn al-Baiṭār reproduced in his own work. Abū-l-Ma'ālī wrote various medical works, one of them a collection of medical observations similar to those compiled by Ibn al-Mudawwar and Ibn al-Nāqid. It was probably his son Yūsuf who edited the last chapter of the Fuṣūl Mūsā after Maimonides' death.

These four physicians were all of them Egyptians, and three of them—all, except Ibn al-Nāqid—were in the service of Ṣalāḥ al-dīn. If we add to them Maimonides and Joseph ibn 'Aqnīn, we realize that Egypt was a great medical center in those days, and largely a Jewish center. The foremost of these physicians by far was Ibn Jamī' whose fame equaled that of 'Alī ibn Riḍwān a century before. Needless to say, all of these Egyptian Jews wrote in Arabic.

5. *Salernitan*—The brilliant development of the school of Salerno during the first half of the twelfth century was continued on an even higher scale during the second half. Indeed the twelfth century, and chiefly the second half of it, was the golden age of Salernitan medicine. These splendid efforts, which placed the Christian medical world for the first time on the same level with the Muslim and Jewish, were brutally interrupted by the vicissitudes of war—Salerno, the nursery of European medicine, being destroyed in 1193 by the emperor Henry VI. During the last quarter of the century we witness the beginnings of Salernitan medicine beyond the Alps. It is possible that the emigration was caused as much by unsettled conditions in south Italy as by the attraction of foreign centers, above all of Paris whose university had already become a powerful magnet.

Our knowledge of Salernitan medicine increased considerably after 1837 when a large manuscript including thirty-five separate treatises was discovered in Breslau. Most of these treatises, and of others represented by abundant manuscripts, can be ascribed with sufficient certainty to definite authors. A few are anonymous, and the best known of these is the Regimen sanitatis, a summary of Salernitan medicine and hygiene in rhyming verse, which was perhaps the most popular medical book of the Middle Ages. This attractive vademecum of the layman was widely circulated in Latin editions of various lengths (for such compositions invited interpolations), and it was translated into many vernaculars. Its wise sayings clung in men's memories with the same tenacity as proverbs. In fact, many of the popular maxims which constitute the hygienic knowledge of the average man of to-day are derived, without his knowing it, from that poem. For the sake of illustration I quote a few lines, both in Latin, and in the delightful Tudor adaptation by Sir John Harington in 1607.

Si tibi deficiant medici, medici tibi fiant
Haec tria, mens leta, requies, moderata diaeta.
(Use three Physicions still; first Doctor Quiet,
Next Doctor Merry-man, and Doctor Dyet)

Ex magna coena stomacho fit maxima poena.
Ut sis nocte levis sit tibi coena brevis
(Great suppers do the stomacke much offend,
Sup light if quiet you to sleepe intend)

To be sure, some of these sayings might be traced back to earlier times; but the Regimen sanitatis was such a happy collection of them, and so successful, that it, so to say, crystallized into a definite form all the folklore it contained and impressed its own indelible stamp upon it before transmitting it to posterity. The earliest known editor was Arnold of Villanova, but there is little doubt but that the poem was already old in Arnold's time.

The greatest Salernitan surgeon, Roger, flourished about the middle of the period under consideration. His Practica chirurgiae was the earliest important Latin treatise on the subject. Its appearance was not accidental, for the Crusades had enormously increased the need of good surgeons and at the same time they had enlarged the surgical experience of Christian practitioners. The Practica was based primarily on the Arabic knowledge transmitted by Constantine the African, but also on the author's own experience. It was not restricted to surgery, but included skin-diseases also which were traditionally considered as falling within the surgeon's province. The popularity of the Practica is witnessed by the commentaries devoted to it.

From surgery we pass naturally to anatomy. The two earliest Salernitan anatomies date probably from the first half of the twelfth century. A third was now published by Maurus; it did not differ materially from the two earlier ones, for it was still largely Constantinian, and concerned the pig. However, a fourth text, the Anatomia Ricardi (also called in other editions Anatomia Nicolai), which appeared not long afterwards—say towards the end of the twelfth century—was essentially different. The radical change was not due to the use of new sources, for all these texts had the same literary background, but to the method and the purpose. The treatment was far more systematic, and the aim was to describe human, not porcine, anatomy. The discussion as to whether the author was

Richard of Salerno or Nicholas of Salerno is relatively futile, and we may elude it even as we did a similar discussion with regard to the Salernitan antidotary. The main point is to recognize the appearance towards the end of the twelfth century of the first treatise on human anatomy. Still a fifth (or sixth) anatomical text, somewhat different from all the others, appeared at the end of the twelfth century or the beginning of the thirteenth. It is not a manual of dissection, is more philosophical, and pays more attention to physiology and pathology. The author may possibly be Urso of Calabria, though this ascription is hardly more than a guess.

The anatomist Maurus wrote treatises on urine and on bloodletting, and a commentary on Hippocrates' Aphorisms. Urso, who was more of a philosopher, wrote also a treatise on urine, and others on medical principles. Petronius wrote Curae and a Practica. The historian Peter of Eboli was probably the author of a poem celebrating the mineral waters of Pozzuoli, De balneolis puteolis. Peter died about 1221; thus, even if he was the author of that poem, it may date only from the thirteenth century; but even so it was the earliest Latin balneological writing. Another Salernitan physician whose activities were continued well into the following century was John Ferrarius who wrote treatises on purgation and on fevers.

During the last quarter of the century some Salernitan offshoots began to blossom in other countries. A number of medical writings are ascribed to a mysterious French Salernitan, John of St. Paul. One Bernard, who flourished in Provence, wrote commentaries on the works of Salernus and of Bartholomew of Salerno. Giles of Corbeil carried Salernitan medicine to Montpellier and later to Paris, where he became the chief physician to Philip Augustus (king from 1180 to 1223). He explained the teachings of Salerno in a number of Latin poems; two of these, De urinis and De pulsibus, were used as textbooks for more than three centuries. Apart from their technical interest, Giles' writings give us valuable hints on the medical customs of his time.

One of Giles' poems treated of physiognomy. This was a very old branch of knowledge, vaguely connected with anatomy, physiology, and medicine. It can be traced back to the fourth century B.C. In the course of time it was overgrown with various superstitions. Many Muslim physicians—for example, al-Rāzī—and astrologers took a deep interest in it. The strong astrological revival in the Latin West, itself largely due to Arabic influences, gave a new stimulus to physiognomy, and that pseudo-science (for such it was) enjoyed considerable popularity until the end of the sixteenth century.[6]

6. *Latin (non Salernitan)*—Outside of Salerno the principal Latin contributions to medicine took the form of translations from the Arabic and the Greek. With the exception of Stephen of Antioch, the translators of the first half of the twelfth century were less interested in medicine than in philosophy and astrology. Thus the Salernitan physicians of the twelfth century derived their Arabic knowledge almost exclusively from older translators, Constantine the African and John the Saracen. It is for that reason that Constantine's activity is so important in the history of medicine; it marks a turning point, and one speaks commonly of pre-Constantinian and post-Constantinian medicine. Constantine it was who opened

[6] I do not propose to tell its history in detail. A good introduction to it was contributed by the anatomist Alexander Macalister to the Encyclopaedia Britannica (11th ed., vol. 21, 550–552, 1911).

the sluice-gates to admit the first large stream of Arabic knowledge. But during the second half of the twelfth century a new stream even larger than the first was liberated through the work of a greater man, Gerard of Cremona. Of course Gerard's translations could not be used except by the very few during the twelfth century, and their influence did not begin to tell until the first half of the thirteenth century. Even as we speak of pre- and post-Constantinian medicine, so we may speak of pre- and post-Gerardian medicine. The most characteristic features of the twelfth century Latin medicine are due to its being at once post-Constantinian and pre-Gerardian. The activities of Constantine and Gerard should be the main landmarks in any history of Salernitan medicine, which is thus divided into three periods: the pre-Constantinian, the twelfth century, and the post-Gerardian.

To return to Gerard, who opened the second sluice-gates, his activity was truly gigantic. He translated at least ten Galenic treatises from the canon constituted by Ḥunain ibn Isḥāq (second half of the ninth century); plus a number of Arabic treatises by al-Kindī, Ibn Māsawaih, Yaḥyā ibn Sarāfyūn, al-Rāzī, Abū-l-Qāsim, Ibn Sīnā, Ibn al-Wāfid, and 'Alī ibn Riḍwān. The most important of these Arabic treatises was of course Ibn Sīnā's Qānūn which was in itself a whole encyclopaedia of Greek and Arabic medicine. In other words, while the twelfth century Latin writers had still a very imperfect knowledge of Arabic medicine, after Gerard's time the essential was available in Latin, and the study of Arabic lost its urgency so far as medical purposes were concerned.

Gerard's activity was supplemented by that of Marc of Toledo who translated the Hippocratic treatise on air, waters, and places; and three more Galenic works, one of which on muscular motion, was perhaps the earliest Greek biological treatise, outside of the Aristotelian zoology, to become available to the Christian West.

At about the same time Hippocrates' Aphorisms and ten Galenic treatises were translated directly from the Greek by Burgundio of Pisa. Burgundio also translated the treatise of Nemesios of Emesa on the nature of man. It is noteworthy that with two exceptions (De temperamentis, and De crisibus), the Galenic treatises translated from the Greek were different from those translated from the Arabic.

The only Latin physician apart from the Salernitan school and from the translators was, strangely enough, a woman—the German nun, Hildegard. The Scivias includes curious anatomical views of little scientific interest; but another work of hers, the Physica, contains among other things a medical summary; she also composed a medical treatise, the Causae et curae. Hildegard was deeply versed in herblore, and most of her therapeutical prescriptions were based on the use of simples. She was not only the only physician outside of Salerno; she was also the only one of that time in the whole of Christian Europe who did not despise her own vernacular; she gave the names of simples in German.

The theologian Peter the Eater deserves a brief mention here because of an occasional remark of his on the physiological effects of the rarity of the atmosphere at high altitudes.

7. *Armenian*—In 1184 Mekhitar of Her wrote in Armenian a medical treatise entitled Consolation in case of fever. It was derived from Arabic, Persian, and Armenian sources.

8. *Hindu*—Jagaddeva's book on dreams contains a few observations of medical interest.

9. *Chinese*—The history of Chinese medicine may be symbolized by the development of the pên ts'ao. A new edition compiled by Wang Chi-hsien, Chang Hsiao-chih, Ch'ai Yüan, and Kao Shao-kung was printed in 1159 under the title Shao hsing chiao ting ching shih chêng lei pei chi pên ts'ao. Its illustrations were largely borrowed from an earlier herbal, the T'u ching, published in 1061, and now lost. A treatise on general medicine, and a treatise on obstetrics, were composed by Ch'ên Yen.

10. *Japanese*—The Shao hsing exerted a deep influence upon Japanese medicine, but only much later, at the end of the sixteenth century. Meanwhile a part of the Chinese folklore collected in the pên ts'ao was published in Japanese by Henchiin Seiken. His work was illustrated at the expense of the old T'u ching, already mentioned.

11. *Summary*—The leading personalities of this age were Ibn Rushd, Maimonides, Roger of Salerno, and Gerard of Cremona: one Muslim, one Jew, two Christians—or, two Spaniards and two Italians, and of these Italians one was half Spanish. The most important works were written in Arabic but soon translated into Hebrew. Roger and Gerard wrote in Latin. Other works were composed in Persian, Hebrew, Armenian, Sanskrit, Chinese, and Japanese; and some little use was made of the German and Berber languages.

As far as group activities are concerned, the most impressive occurred in Toledo, in Salerno, and in the Jewish colony of Egypt.

The principal achievements were the translation of Greek and Arabic classics into Latin, the development of Salernitan anatomy, the birth of Latin surgery, and last but not least the encyclopaedic efforts of Ibn Rushd and Maimonides.

XII. HISTORIOGRAPHY

1. *Western Muslim*—Andalusia produced two distinguished historians: Ibn Khair of Seville, and al-Ḍabbī of Cordova and Murcia. The former compiled a very valuable bibliography of the writings published by Spanish Muslims; it contains more than 1400 titles, many of which are not recorded by Eastern bibliographers. Al-Ḍabbī wrote a collection of Hispano-Muslim biographies, and a history of the Muslim conquest of Spain and of the Muslim rule down to 1196.

2. *Eastern Muslim*—As against these two historians, the eastern wing of Islām could muster at least ten; this is not surprising considering the much greater extent and variety of eastern Islām. While Spain and North Africa[7] were united under the Almohades, the eastern countries (including Egypt) were divided between eleven dynasties. Such division would not favor scientific work; but it naturally increased the number of historians, as rival salāṭīn would be anxious to immortalize their deeds, and political differences between states, emulation between cities, would stimulate the composition of historical narratives. However, none of these historians was really important, and a brief enumeration of them will suffice.

Al-Sam'ānī of Marw continued the annals of Baghdād, and compiled the Kitāb al-ansāb, an extensive study of patronymics which is of special value for the history of the easternmost parts of Islām. Ibn Ḥamdūn of Baghdād was the author of a large collection of historical and literary anecdotes. 'Alī al-Bayhaqī wrote a history of Bayhaq (near Nīshāpūr), and compiled a collection of biographies of learned Muslims. 'Umara al-Yamanī composed a history of his native country,

[7] When speaking of Muslim countries, North Africa generally means a region of undetermined size including Morocco, Algeria, Tunis, and perhaps Tripoli, but excluding Egypt.

Yemen, in southwestern Arabia, and an autobiography embodying parts of his literary correspondence with the viziers of Egypt. Ibn 'Asākir compiled an immense history of Damascus; like the history of Baghdād after which it was modeled, this was essentially a collection of biographies. Another Syrian, Ibn Munqidh, has the distinction of having created one of the earliest large autobiographies. 'Imād al-dīn of Ispahan, who died at Damascus in 1201, wrote histories of Ṣalāḥ al-dīn's conquest of Syria, and of the Saljūq rulers, and other memoirs. We owe to Yūsuf ibn Rāfi' a second history of Ṣalāḥ al-dīn and a chronicle of Aleppo. All these men were primarily historians. I must still mention two philosophers or polygraphs, some of whose writings are valuable historical contributions. The Baghdādite Ibn al-Jauzī compiled a history of the world from the creation down to 1180, wrote an autobiography in the form of a letter to his son, and made three lists of his own writings. The Ta'rīkh al-duwal by Fakhr al-dīn al-Rāzī is a political treatise including a history of the first four caliphs; the same author wrote biographies of the Shāfi'ite doctors; his two Persian encyclopaedias also deserve mention.

The chief characteristic of these works is the emphasis on biographies, by that time a well established Muslim tradition. I alluded to two collections of biographies, one devoted to the learned Muslims, the other to the Shāfi'ite doctors; but the local and regional chronicles of which I named five treating respectively of Baghdād, Damascus, Aleppo, Yemen, and Bayhaq, were also primarily collections of biographies. I also named not less than three autobiographies written respectively by 'Umara al-Yamanī, Ibn al-Jauzī (with bibliographies), and Ibn Munqidh, the last being especially valuable. The Kitab al-ansāb of al-Sam'ānī illustrates in another way the immense importance which Muslims attached to lineage. Two independent histories of Salāḥ al-dīn witness his popularity. The interests of these historians were local, regional, or at best Islāmic. The one exception was the philosopher Ibn al-Jauzī who attempted to write a history of the world.

All of them wrote in Arabic, and two used also the Persian language: 'Alī al-Bayhaqī wrote in Persian his chronicle of Bayhaq, and the encyclopaedias of Fakhr al-dīn al-Rāzī were also in Persian.

3. *Western Jewish*—Hebrew historiography was far less abundant than Arabic, and was restricted to the West—Spain and Germany.

The account which Benjamin of Tudela wrote of his journey to Baghdād is as important from the historical as from the geographical point of view.

Abraham ben David ha-Levi, the earliest Jewish Aristotelian, wrote a chronicle covering the period from the creation down to the middle of the twelfth century. Abraham's purpose was mainly to reinforce Jewish orthodoxy, which was imperiled by liberalism and by Qaraism from within, and by Muslim proselytism from without; but his chronicle is valuable for the study of Jewish scholarship from the end of the tenth century down to his own time, and for the understanding of its transmission from the Babylonian geonim to the Spanish rabbis. The religious purpose was further evidenced by the fact that Abraham wrote this chronicle in Hebrew, while his philosophical work was written in Arabic. The latter was meant for the philosophical world, largely Muslim or Arabic speaking; the former was composed for his own brethren.

A third chronicler, Ephraim ben Jacob, was a German Talmudist living in Worms. His account of the persecutions suffered by the Jews in Germany, France, and England, between 1146 and 1196, is invaluable, for it is the testimony of a witness, and in many cases is our chief source of information.

4. *Armenian*—The Armenian chronicle of Matthew of Edessa was continued to 1162 by Gregory the Priest.

Nerses the Graceful composed poems, one of which treated of the history of Armenia, and another of the destruction of Edessa in 1144. His letters are important documents for the history of the Armenian church.

Samuel of Ānī wrote a universal chronicle down to 1177, modeled after Eusebios.

5. *Syriac*—The Jacobite patriarch of Antioch, Michael the Elder, wrote a chronicle from the creation down to 1196. Like Samuel of Ānī and other Christian historians of the East, Michael took Eusebios as his principal model. Much of his work was arranged in tabular form, three parallel accounts being devoted respectively to lay history, church history, and other contemporary events.

Simeon Shanqĕlāwī composed a little treatise on chronology in the form of a catechism.

6. *Byzantine*—The rhymed chronicle of Constantine Manasses (down to 1081) was very popular, not only among Greeks but also among Slavs and even among Rumanians. John Cinnamos wrote a Byzantine chronicle for the period 1118 to 1176, which includes a first-hand account of the Second Crusade (1147–1149). It was essentially different from Constantine's work; it was more pretentious, both as to form and contents, and needless to say, it enjoyed much less popularity; Cinnamos modeled his style after Herodotos and Xenophon.

The humanist Eustathios has given us, among many other things, a history of the conquest of Thessalonica by the Normans in 1185.

7. *Spanish*—It seems best to consider at once Latin and vernacular works, in order not to separate chronicles covering otherwise the same field. The most natural subdivision is the regional; we shall deal successively with Spain, Italy, France, Germany, England, Scandinavia, and Russia.

The outstanding historical work of Spain was the Poema del Cid, written probably towards the end of the twelfth century to celebrate the national hero, Ruy Diaz de Vivar el Cid el Campeador—so typical, even to his name, of the mixed Christian and Muslim civilization of his country. This popular epic was also the first great monument of Spanish literature.

8. *Italian*—Turning to Italy, we first find three Sicilian[8] chroniclers: Romuald of Salerno, who wrote a universal chronicle down to 1178 which is of special value for Sicilian affairs; Hugh Falcandus, who composed a history of the Sicilies under the two Williams (1154–1189), an excellent work containing much information of cultural interest; and Peter of Eboli, who wrote a poem treating of the succeeding period, the crucial years 1189–1195, during which the Norman Kingdom was conquered by the emperor Henry VI.

The fourth Italian historian, Godfrey of Viterbo, was probably of German origin, but he is known after his bishopric, Viterbo, where the end of his life was spent. He wrote the Memoria seculorum, a chronicle of the time from Adam down to 1186, which was very popular.

In this group of four historians, the first two represented the Sicilian point of view; the two others, the imperial.

9. *French*—The French group is more complex; four men, and four different types. First, Wace of Jersey, the Anglo-Norman poet, whose Roman de Brut was an adaptation in French verse of the Historia Britonum of Geoffrey of Monmouth,

[8] Sicilian here refers to the Kingdom of the Two Sicilies.

with sundry interpolations. Another long poem of his, the Roman de Rou, dealt with the history of the Normans. This is a very important chronicle, one of our best sources for the study of the Norman invasion of England. It has the additional distinction of being the earliest important historical work written in a European vernacular.

The second, Peter the Eater, was the type of the successful textbook writer. His manual of sacred history, the Historia scholastica, was immensely popular.

The third, William of Tyre, was a great historian, the greatest historian perhaps of that whole period, East or West. He was himself standing between East and West, being born of French stock in the Latin kingdom of Jerusalem. He wrote in Latin but was well acquainted with Greek and Arabic. He gave the best mediaeval account of the Crusades from 1095 to 1184. Indeed it is very comprehensive and offers a clear picture of the cultural elements involved. His point of view, that of the resident Christian, was at once more steady and more moderate than that of the other chroniclers of the Crusades.

The fourth, Robert of Torigny, though less important than William of Tyre, was yet one of the very best Latin chroniclers. He was for many years abbot of Mount St. Michel, and took advantage of this position at the head of a great pilgrimage center to collect as much and as reliable information as possible. He published it in the form of a continuation to Sigebert's universal chronicle, and in other chronicles. He had much experience as a historian, for in his younger years he had revised the chronicle of Normandy by William of Jumièges.

10. *German*—Other than Godfrey of Viterbo, there was but one German historian of mark, Helmold of Bosau, who gave the first good account of the strife between Germans and Slavs in the eastern marches beyond the Elbe. The life of Anselm of Havelberg, whose bishopric had to be reconquered twice from the Slavs, made us realize the intensity of that strife, but Helmold was the first historian of it. His narrative extended to 1171; it was continued down to 1209 by Arnold of Lübeck.

It is proper at this point to recall the Nibelungenlied, which may be considered a historical work, even as the Chanson de Roland and every other true epic.

11. *English*—The finest group of historians of this period was the English. At least eight deserve remembrance.

Henry of Huntingdon compiled a history of England from the time of Caesar to the midde of the twelfth century. The royal treasurer, Richard FitzNeal, wrote the lost Tricolumnis wherein civil, ecclesiastical, and miscellaneous events were told in three parallel columns. John of Salisbury, the greatest of them all, wrote biographies of his master St. Thomas Becket, and of St. Anselm; and the Historia pontificalis which was a continuation of the chronicle of Sigebert of Gembloux down to 1152. Two other men have already been discussed in the geographical section, because their works are equally important from the geographical and from the historical points of view: Gerald the Welshman and the anonymous author of the life and deeds of Richard Lionheart. Gerald told the story of the conquest of Ireland, a good account in spite of his strong bias against the victims; and he wrote an autobiography, and a list of his writings. William of Newburgh and Roger of Howden wrote chronicles of England extending respectively down to 1198 and 1201. Ralph of Diceto was more ambitious, but his Abbreviationes chronicarum, from the time of Christ down to 1147, have but little value; a second chronicle of his, the Ymagines historiarum, dealing with the contemporary period, 1149–1199, is, as we would expect, far more important.

12. *Scandinavian*—Svend Aagesön wrote in Latin a chronicle of Denmark from the year 300 down to 1187.

13. *Russian*—The school of Kiev continued, and indeed reached its climax during that period, for the best of all the early Russian chronicles was undoubtedly the Chronicle of Kiev (also called Chronicle of Hypatios) covering the years 1116 to 1200.

The beautiful epic, Slovo o polku Igoreve, dates probably from the same period.

14. *Chinese*—The Ku yü t'u p'u, an illustrated description of ancient jades, was edited by Lung Ta-yüan in 1176. Ch'êng Ch'iao wrote a history of China down to the T'ang dynasty; and in a separate treatise had the courage to discredit the high antiquity of the Stone Drums. Hung Kua published a collection of Han inscriptions with facsimile reproductions. This was not the earliest treatise on Chinese epigraphy, for an earlier one had been composed a century before by Ou-yang Hsiu[9], but Hung's treatise was far more elaborate. The leading philosopher of that time, Chu Hsi, revised the annals composed by Ssŭ-ma Kuang. The description of southern China by Wang Hsiang-chih is full of archaeological information; so much so that the author has been called the Chinese Pausanias.

Once more the Chinese achievements are remarkably original, entirely unlike those of the Christians, the Muslims, or the Jews. They give the philosophical historian a means of realizing the possibility of different developments in historiography. The Chinese were born archaeologists, and in addition to the annals they produced archaeological and epigraphical works without equivalents in the West or in the Near East.

15. *Japanese*—Nakayama Tadachika wrote a diary, and a chronicle—the so-called Water mirror (Mizu-kagami)—treating of the history of Japan from its mythical beginning in 660 B.C. down to 850.

16. *Summary*—As I have already observed, the comparative importance of historical writings cannot be determined as there is no common measure between them. For a student of Armenian history, the poorest Armenian chronicle is more valuable than the best English one. The comparison becomes particularly hopeless between historians of the West and those of the Far East. All that we can do is to single out the chief personalities and draw a few conclusions.

The leading historians of the time were William of Tyre, John of Salisbury, and Gerald the Welshman. The most imposing groups were the Muslim, the English, and the French. I leave the Chinese hors concours.

The progress of Latin historiography was considerable. It is to be noted that the majority of Christian historians were influenced mainly by Eusebios, either directly in the East, or indirectly through St. Jerome in the Latin world. The Westerners were also influenced by Augustine, and by Isidore of Seville, but *not* by the great Roman historians. The influence of Eusebios appears strikingly in the tabular form of annals, which we noted was used independently by the Syrian Michael the Elder and by the Englishman Richard FitzNeal. There was thus a deep discontinuity between the old Latin historians and the mediaeval ones, in spite of a common language. I have already said that the two strongest vehicles of human traditions are one's father's religion and one's mother's tongue; in this case religion was the stronger.

All considered, William of Tyre was perhaps the most remarkable historian of the time. At any rate he symbolizes better than any other the meeting of East

[9] See vol. I, 777.

and West. He knew Arabic and Greek; like the Sicilian translators, he stood at the confluence of three civilizations; but unlike them, he took advantage of this exceptional situation to survey human affairs, to discuss the greatest political events of the time, the tragic experience of the Crusades. He accomplished his task very well; indeed his history of Jerusalem was the best mediaeval account of these fateful events. Thus he truly deserves a special share of our gratitude.

XIII. LAW AND SOCIOLOGY

1. *Western Muslim*—Abū-l-Qāsim al-Ḥaufī wrote a treatise on the division of inheritance (al-farā'iḍ) which is said to be the best Mālikite treatise of its kind.

2. *Eastern Muslim*—Ibn al-Dahhān wrote a treatise on comparative law (Taqwīm al-naẓar), wherein the views of the four orthodox schools, and other observations, were disposed in parallel columns.

Two curious commercial treatises were composed, one by a Syrian, Ja'far ibn 'Alī, the other by an Egyptian, 'Abd al-Raḥmān ibn Naṣr. They had much in common, their purpose being to help in the good regulation of market places, the verification of weights and measures, the detection and prevention of falsifications, etc. This is highly interesting, perhaps less so from the legal than from the general cultural point of view. As far as I know, no similar treatises were published in Latin or European vernaculars as early as this.

Ibn Mammātī, who is better known because of his satirical work Qarāqūsh (the ancestor of the oriental Punch), explained the mechanism of the Egyptian government under Ṣalāḥ al-dīn.

Al-Marghīnānī, who came from Transoxiana, wrote treatises on Ḥanīfite law, one of which, the Hidāyat, was extremely popular.

Among the many publications of Fakhr al-dīn al-Rāzī were a treatise on politics, the Ta'rīkh al-duwal, and another on Shāfi'ite law; he was also the author of a collection of Shāfi'ite biographies.

The Spaniard Abū-l-Qāsim al-Ḥaufī, already mentioned, was a Mālikite; Ibn al-Dahhān, 'Abd al-Raḥmān, and Fakhr al-dīn were Shāfi'ites; al-Marghīnānī was a Ḥanīfite; Ibn Mammātī was of Christian origin.

3. *Jewish and Samaritan*—One of the classics of French rabbinical literature, the 'Iṭṭur soferim, was compiled by the Provençal Isaac ben Abba Mari. It is derived from the Halakot of Alfasi, and from many other works, but not slavishly.

A commentary on the laws, Tifṣūr ha-miẓwa, is ascribed to the Samaritan grammarian Abū-l-Isḥāq Ibrāhīm.

4. *Italian*—Peter of Piacenza introduced the teaching of Roman law in France, at the University of Montpellier, but he taught also at Mantua and Bologna. He wrote commentaries on the Code and Institutes.

Burgundio of Pisa translated quotations from the Digest from the original Greek into Latin.

A third Italian, Vacarius, will be mentioned presently.

5. *English*—Vacarius introduced Roman Law in England just before the middle of the century, and his activity continued there almost until the end of it. He composed for the Oxford students a compendium of law, which was familiarly called the Liber pauperum. However, that teaching was soon interrupted by King Stephen.

John of Salisbury's Polycratus, or Ruler's Book, was the earliest Latin treatise on politics; the earliest attempt in Christendom, with the exception of Manegold's pamphlet, to formulate a philosophy of the state.

The financial administration of England was explained by Richard FitzNeal in his dialogue on the exchequer.

Ranulf de Glanville wrote or edited about 1187 the earliest textbook of English law. This work, the Tractatus de legibus et consuetudinibus regni Angliae, is not only of inestimable importance for the English people, and for the English-speaking people all over the earth, who have inherited English institutions; it is also a landmark in the evolution of law, for it was the earliest systematic law treatise to appear after the dissolution of the Roman empire, with the exception of Gratian's Decretum. The astounding feature of Glanville's Tractatus was its thorough Englishness, the borrowings from Roman law being restricted to a few definitions.

This almost simultaneous introduction of Civil Law in England and systematization of Common Law created a curious situation. As the universities favored the Civil Law, in the course of time special schools had to be established (the Inns of Court in London) to teach the laws of England. The latter being thus protected from international influences developed evenly according to their own natural tendencies. This explains, for example, why the English Law was not affected (like the Scotch) by the revival of Roman Law in the sixteenth century.

6. *Spanish*—The hunting code of Sancho VI el Sabio, King of Navarre, has already been mentioned because of its interest for the student of falconry.

7. *Scandinavian*—Svend Aagesön, the Danish historian, translated into Latin the laws of Canute the Great, King of the English, Danes, and Norwegians.

8. *Hindu*—The great lexicographer, Hemacandra, wrote in Prākrit an extensive treatise on Jaina law and politics.

9. *Summary*—According to my account, the most striking creations of the age were the commercial treatises of Ja'far ibn 'Alī and 'Abd al-Raḥmān ibn Naṣr, the Polycratus of John of Salisbury, and the Tractatus of Ranulf de Glanville.

But the reader will bear in mind that my account of this subject is exemplary rather than exhaustive, and thus that one must beware of drawing conclusions from it, the more so because this was a period of intense economic activity and of social reconstruction. That reconstruction, we might almost say revolution, was due to the growth of cities, many of which now began to assume great importance. This growth implied the creation of a new class of people, city burghers, bankers, powerful merchants, etc. The towns developed with special vigor in Flanders, northern Italy, Germany, France, and England. The first legal recognition of the city of London dates from 1191.

The following facts will suffice to illustrate the economic activity and the resulting innovations. Bills of exchange passed between Messina and Constantinople in 1161. Banks were founded in Venice in 1170–1171, the second being the Bank of San Marco. At about the same time, say about 1180–1190, insurance methods were introduced, probably in Italy. According to Villani, marine insurance originated in Lombardy about 1182. The Bank of San Giorgio was founded in Genoa about the end of the century; it was a joint-stock company with transferable shares. The practice of insurance naturally introduced commercial and maritime law, which indeed began to take shape at that time. Again, numerous commercial treaties were made between cities, and thus originated slowly a code of international law. Some of the leading cities organized a consular system abroad. Finally a special jurisdiction protected the dusty-footed merchants, for "piepowder" (pied poudreux) courts were already functioning.

These bare indications are meant to show the complexity of a subject with which I cannot deal more fully. They will serve as a warning to students who wish to reconstruct the cultural background of twelfth century science. A substantial part of that background was economic. This was not equally true of every period of the past, but from this time on it becomes very true.

One more remark. The development of economic activities, and of the new legal institutions which were needed to protect and strengthen these activities, increased enormously the intellectual prestige of law. Jurists became almost the equals of theologians, and in the conduct of political affairs they gradually superseded the latter. This situation was peculiar to Christendom, for in Israel and Islām law and theology were hardly distinguishable, with the unfortunate result that the former partook of the unprogressiveness of the latter, and legal reform became extremely difficult if not impossible.

The Christian separation of law from theology[10] was an essential factor in the development of western civilization. The intellectual damage caused by the obscurantism of theologians was restricted to religion and morality; this was bad enough, of course, but at least the lay world was left enough freedom to move forward and to adjust its laws to the urgent needs of social conditions which were changing more and more rapidly.

XIV. PHILOLOGY

1. *Eastern Muslim*—The treatise on comparative law compiled by Ibn al-Dahhān was preceded by an introduction on grammar. Ibn al-Anbārī wrote a history of Arabic literature and philology and an Arabic grammar. These two eastern grammarians were Baghdādites, but Ibn al-Dahhān flourished in Syria and Egypt, while Ibn al-Anbārī spent the greatest part of his life in Baghdād, and died there.

2. *Western Jewish*—The Jewish scholars of Spain and Provence who were engaged in the translation of Arabic science and philosophy into Hebrew, were naturally obliged to make grammatical studies, for they had in fact to create a new language. This may seem strange if one realizes the great antiquity of some of the Scriptures, but the Biblical language was an old language mixed with Aramaic, and a new language had to be developed to answer the urgent needs of the younger generations which became more and more eager for lay knowledge. The need of a new scientific Hebrew had not been felt before the twelfth century, because the development of Jewish culture had been largely restricted to Spain, North Africa, and the Near East. The learned Jews living in these countries used two languages: they prayed and discussed the Bible and the Talmud in Hebrew, but did their philosophic and scientific writing and thinking in Arabic. But as I have shown in the preceding chapters, in the twelfth century Jewish culture began to move beyond the Pyrenees. The Jews of France and Germany knew no Arabic, and it was necessary to translate for them into Hebrew not only scientific books but even the grammars of their own language.

The wonderful activity of Abraham bar Ḥiyya, and of Abraham ibn Ezra (who died only in 1167), was continued by the Andalusian Joseph Qimḥi. I have already spoken of his translations, but he also wrote a Hebrew grammar in Hebrew. His sons, Moses and David, both educated in Narbonne, distinguished themselves in that noble cause even more than himself. Moses wrote various treatises on

[10] Even canon law was largely independent of theology.

grammar, one of which, the earliest concise textbook of Hebrew grammar, was very popular. The younger brother David was even more important and more influential than either his father or Moses; in fact he was the most influential Jewish doctor of his time, Maimonides being naturally excepted. But we must not forget that David's life extended well into the first half of the thirteenth century; he died only in 1235, and we may assume that his prestige grew with him. Thus his influence belongs rather to the first half of the thirteenth century, even if much of his activity fell within the second half of the twelfth century. His main work, the Miklol, was an extensive grammar followed by a dictionary. It was based largely on the earlier Arabic treatises on Hebrew grammar, yet contained many small improvements and additions. The treatises on grammar by Moses and David influenced most of the later grammarians, Gentiles as well as Jews. They constitute a landmark in the history of Hebrew philology.

Two other great translators and grammarians must be named, Judah ibn Tibbon and his more illustrious son Samuel. Judah, "the father of Jewish translators," wrote a book on rhetoric and grammar, which is lost; but we know some of his views on the technique of translation, from his ethical will addressed to Samuel, and from the preface to his version of Ibn Janāḥ's Kitāb al-luma'. Samuel undertook a double task, the transmission of Maimonidean philosophy to the non-Arabic-speaking Jews, and the consolidation of the Hebrew philosophical language; but neither of these tasks was really completed until the following century.

3. *Samaritan*—Abū-l-Isḥāq Ibrāhīm, a Samaritan who flourished probably at Damascus, wrote a Hebrew grammar in Arabic. His activity is a curious anachronism as compared with that of the Andalusian and Provençal Jews afore-mentioned.

4. *Armenian*—The twelfth century was an age of Armenian revival, a golden age of Armenian literature, which might be compared to the age of Mesrop (first half of the fifth century)—if any ulterior blossoming could ever be compared with the glory of the first. This revival took place not in the old or Greater Armenia (the great Anatolian plateau south of the Caucasus and Black Sea), but in a new country, the so-called Lesser Armenia,[11] the ancient Cilicia, extending from the southern slopes of the Taurus chain down to the sea. The language used in Cilicia was somewhat different from the old one, so much so that one distinguishes two kinds of Armenian, the older or eastern Armenian, and the Cilician or western.[12] The reader will have gathered some idea of that revival from what has been said of it in preceding sections, but it is very strange that it did not include any movement in grammar. At any rate I do not know any treatises of the twelfth century on Armenian grammar.

5. *Byzantine*—The rhymed chronicle of Constantine Manasses offers some linguistic interest because of its influence on Slavonic and even on Rumanian literature.

Gregorios of Corinth wrote treatises on syntax and on Greek dialects, and a commentary on Hermogenes.

6. *Latin*—The most important philological work was the Derivationes, a dic-

[11] This Lesser Armenia should not be confused with the Armenia minor of the ancients, which was situated to the west of the Armenia major, south of Pontus.

[12] The distinction has continued to this day, the eastern language being that of Ararat and Tiflis, the western that which is spoken (or was spoken until yesterday) in Stambul and in Levantine harbors.

tionary composed by Hugutio of Pisa, which enjoyed a long popularity. This was supposed to be an etymological dictionary, yet Hugutio knew no Greek! Hildegard conceived a kind of secret language and script (lingua ignota). Alexander Neckam wrote treatises on grammar, and compiled a vocabulary arranged as a reading book, the De utensilibus. The Carmina burana of the wandering students (goliardi) contributed their share to the vitalization—or should we say disaggregation?—of the Latin language.

Anyone who has realized the extreme poverty of the Derivationes, which was the philological masterpiece of Latin scholarship in those days, cannot help wondering how it was that the translations from the Arabic, which caused a revival of Hebrew grammar, failed to influence the Latin language in any favorable way. Mind you—far more works were translated into Latin than into Hebrew; for more than a century a real torrent of Arabic learning ran through Latin channels.

The reasons for this are many. To begin with, the Latin language existed, and its grammar was standardized, while the new Hebrew language had to be created. We might almost say the Latin language was going down while the Hebrew was going up. The Jews shared the Muslims' genuine interest in grammar, and centuries of Biblical and Talmudic exegesis had sharpened their grammatical wits. Finally, the Hebrew language, being closely akin to the Arabic, was more susceptible of being influenced by the latter's formal perfection. It was possible to translate Arabic literally into Hebrew without distortion. On the contrary, it was almost impossible to avoid distortion when translating from Arabic into Latin; one had to choose between an inaccurate version in tolerable Latin, or an accurate one in intolerable Latin; the translators chose the second alternative, and the language suffered in consequence.

One might ask, would not that situation have been reversed if the great bulk of writings had been translated from the Greek (instead of the Arabic) into Latin and Hebrew? It is idle to try to solve imaginary problems, but I believe that the situation would not have been entirely reversed, and that the grammatical poverty of the Latin people—who allowed their language to run downhill—was not due so much to external conditions as to a real lack of mental vigor.

7. *Vernacular*—Various European languages were kept in a flourishing condition by the efforts of poets—troubadours, trouvères, minnesingers, the editors of the Nibelungenlied; or by the humbler efforts of story tellers—for example, those who scattered all over the continent the delightful tales of Reynard the Fox. Other works in various vernaculars—Spanish, Russian, Scandinavian—have already been mentioned, but none of these languages had yet reached the grammatical stage.

8. *Hindu*—This was the golden age of Hindu grammar. We witness first of all the concurrent efforts of Pāli grammarians in Ceylon and Burma. The Burmese Aggavaṃsa was apparently the first, his Pāli grammar appearing about 1154. At about the same time or a little later, another school of Pāli was flourishing in Ceylon. The foremost Singhalese grammarian was Moggallāna. He compiled a Pāli grammar and probably the earliest Pāli dictionary. The sources of Aggavaṃsa and Moggallāna were the same—that is, Sanskrit grammar, and at least one older Pāli grammatical work of unknown date. Like its Sanskrit models, the Pāli dictionary was in verse.

Meanwhile the greatest Sanskrit scholar of the Middle Ages, Hemacandra, a Jaina, was flourishing in the kingdom of Aṇhilvāḍ in western India. He wrote a Sanskrit grammar—which was the best mediaeval one—and other grammatical treatises. But his work as a lexicographer was even more important; he compiled four dictionaries, three of them in Sanskrit, one in Prākrit.

9. *Chinese*—Fa Yün compiled in 1157 a Sanskrit-Chinese dictionary of Buddhist terms. The geographer Fan Ch'êng-ta published a small collection of rhymes.

XV. CONCLUSIONS

MAIN ACHIEVEMENTS

No one can read this brief survey of the scientific thought of the second half of the twelfth century without realizing how vast and complex our little human world had already become in those days. Indeed it is so complex that it is bewildering, and a further simplification is needed to bring out the main characteristics. Let us first consider which were the outstanding achievements in the various fields.

Above all the translators towers the gigantic personality of Gerard of Cremona, and near him, though much smaller, we recognize Burgundio of Pisa. These two men help us to remember that the chief sources of knowledge were Arabic and Greek. The Arabic was overwhelmingly predominant. Most of the knowledge—Greek or Muslim—available in Arabic came to us straight (translations from Arabic into Latin); some came through the Hebrew detour (translations from Arabic into Hebrew, and from Hebrew into Latin); a little even trickled through Greek versions; and finally some of it reached the Jews through intermediary Latin versions. The complexity of these exchanges may appear more clearly by means of the following symbols, the capitals being the initial letters of the languages mentioned:

(1) $A \rightarrow L$
(2) $G \rightarrow L$
(3) $A \rightarrow H \rightarrow L$
(4) $A \rightarrow G \rightarrow L$
(5) $A \rightarrow L \rightarrow H$

But bear in mind that transmission (1) was far more important in the twelfth century than all the others put together. Remember also that transmission (1) was the third wave of Arabic knowledge reaching the Christian West, the three waves being represented respectively by Constantine the African (second half of the eleventh century), John of Seville (first half of the twelfth century), and Gerard of Cremona (second half of the twelfth century)—each more important and more effective than the preceding one.

During the first half of the twelfth century the philosophical leaders, Abaelard and the teachers of Chartres, were Christians; during the second half the leaders, Ibn Rushd and Maimonides, were Muslim and Jewish. Now the accomplishments of these two last named giants can be stated in the simplest way by saying that they originated an Aristotelian renaissance; they brought the world back to a purer understanding of Aristotle's works. This is obvious enough in the case of Ibn Rushd, "who wrote the great commentary," but it is equally true of Maimonides. Let the latter express his own conviction: "The words of Plato, Aristotle's teacher, are obscure and figurative; they are superfluous to the man of intelligence, inasmuch as Aristotle supplanted all his predecessors. The thorough understanding of

Aristotle is the highest achievement to which man can attain with the sole exception of the understanding of the Prophets."[12a]

This return to Aristotle, away from Plato, was also a return to rationalism, in the theological sense, but both Ibn Rushd and Maimonides managed to reconcile their rationalism with the faith of their fathers; they limited it to the rejection of superstitious ideas and parasitic dogmas. I shall discuss this question later in my note on Maimonides, and what I say of him will apply mutatis mutandis to Ibn Rushd. Moreover, rationalism is always a relative term; nobody is absolutely superstitious or absolutely rational. Ibn Rushd and Maimonides deserve our eternal gratitude for their courageous vindication of reason at a time when most people were afraid of it. Their rationalism and their liberalism may be measured by the odium they reaped; though in this too we must beware of overestimations. Their thought was made to appear much more revolutionary than it really was, because of the violent reactions which it excited. Doctrines which are not revolutionary per se may become so when they are badly understood or hastily applied by untutored minds; it was really such misunderstandings or misapplications which caused the vicissitudes of Averroism and Maimonidism.

The leading thinker in the Latin world was John of Salisbury, who continued the humanistic tradition of the school of Chartres.

In my summary of scientific achievements I shall not speak any more of translations.

In the field of astronomy the influence of Aristotle made itself felt in the increasing criticism of the Ptolemaic hypothesis. This was done by Muslims at a time when Latin astronomers were but beginning to know the Almagest.

The first systematic account of mensural music in Latin and the Franconian notation appeared in the West.

The greatest geographical work of the Middle Ages was completed by al-Idrīsī at the Sicilian court. The earliest geographical work in Hebrew was written by Benjamin of Tudela, the foremost Jewish traveler of mediaeval times. The best geographical works in Latin were the descriptions of Wales and Ireland by Gerald the Welshman.

We owe the earliest treatise on the cultivation of citrous trees to a Chinese, Han Ch'an-chih. But for the best agricultural treatise in general—the best of mediaeval times—we have to turn to Muslim Spain, for it was written by the Andalusian Ibn al-'Awwām.

At least three great physicians flourished in this period: Ibn Rushd in Morocco, Maimonides in Egypt, and Roger in Salerno—a Muslim, a Jew, and a Christian. Roger might be called the father of European surgery.

The leading historians were William of Tyre and Gerald the Welshman. The leaders of political and legal thought were John of Salisbury and Ranulf of Glanville.

The changing economic and social conditions favored the progress of law against theology, and in this way, among others, contributed to the emancipation of scientific thought.

Various languages developed with special vigor during this period, but the development was almost exclusively empirical except for three of them—Arabic, Hebrew, and Sanskrit. The greatest philologist was a Hindu, Hemacandra. The

[12a] Extract from Maimonides' letter to Samuel ibn Tibbon, edited by Abraham Lichtenberg: Qobeẓ teshubot ha-Rambam (p. 28 vb, Leipzig 1859).

work of the Arabic grammarians was hardly progressive; on the other hand, this was a critical age in the creation and consolidation of the new Hebrew language.

COMPARATIVE ACHIEVEMENTS OF VARIOUS GROUPS

Let us start from Japan and travel westward. The outstanding names are italicized throughout.

Japanese (5)

Religious founders (2): Hōnen-shōnin, and Eisai.
Mathematician (?): Fujiwara Michinori.
Physician: Henchiin Seiken.
Historian: Nakayama Tadachika.
Leaving out of account the founders of Buddhist sects, none of these men was important except from the purely Japanese point of view.

Chinese (14)

Philosophers (2): *Chu Hsi*, Lu Chiu-yän.
Naturalists, including geographers (4): Lou Shou, *Fan Ch'êng-ta*, *Han Ch'an-chih*, Wang Hsiang-chih.
Physicians, including compilers of pên-ts'ao (5): Wang Chi-hsien, Kao Shao-kung, Ch'ai Yüan, Chang Hsiao-chih, Ch'ên Yen.
Historians (2) (not counting Chu Hsi): Ch'êng Ch'iao, Hung Kua.
Philologist: Fa Yün.
It is difficult and almost senseless to compare Far Eastern achievements with those of Western peoples. But it is always worthwhile to compare Chinese and Japanese achievements. During this period the Chinese contributions were far superior to the Japanese, in quality as well as in quantity.

Hindu (6)

Philosophers, or soothsayers (3): Gaṅgeśa, Durlabharāja, Jagaddeva.
Philologists (3): *Hemacandra*, Aggavaṃsa, and Moggallāna.

Iranian (1)

The Pahlawī encyclopaedia Būndahishn.

Muslim (44)

A. Eastern Muslim[13] (29)

Philosophers and general writers (5): Niẓāmī-i-'Arūḍī,** Yaḥyā al-Suhrawardī, Ibn al-Jauzī, *Fakhr al-dīn al-Rāzī*,* 'Umar al-Suhrawardī.
Mathematicians (3): Samū'īl ibn 'Abbās, 'Abd al-Malik al-Shīrāzī, Muḥammad ibn al-Ḥusain.
Geographers (2): Muḥammad ibn Maḥmūd al-Ṭūsī,** 'Alī al-Harawī.
Naturalists (3?): Authors of treatises on falconry.
Physicians (2): 'Abd al-Raḥmān ibn Naṣrallāh, Ibn Hubal.

[13] In this section two asterisks following a name mean "wrote exclusively in Persian;" one asterisk means "wrote in Persian and Arabic."

Historians (8): 'Alī al-Bayhaqī,* al-Sam'ānī, Ibn Ḥamdūn, 'Umāra al-Yamanī, Ibn 'Asākir, Ibn Munqidh, 'Imād al-dīn al-Iṣfahānī, Yūsuf ibn Rāfi'.

Jurists and sociologists (5): Ja'far ibn 'Alī, Ibn al-Dahhān, al-Marghīnānī Ibn Mammātī, 'Abd al-Raḥmān Ibn Naṣr.

Philologist: Ibn al-Anbārī.

In all, twenty-nine men, of whom twenty-five wrote in Arabic only, two in Persian only, and two in Persian and Arabic. This was a large crowd, but not a very distinguished one. For example, it did not include any man of outstanding originality. Perhaps the greatest of them was Fakhr al-dīn al-Rāzī.

Distribution of Eastern Muslims: The eastern part of Islām, including Egypt, was so large and so varied that to call a man an Eastern Muslim is a little too vague. How were these eastern Muslims distributed? Let us start again from the east and proceed westward.

Transoxiana (2): Niẓāmī-i-'Arūḍī,** al-Marghīnānī.

Khurāsān (3): Muḥammad ibn Maḥmūd al-Ṭūsī,** al-Sam'ānī, 'Alī al-Bayhaqī.*

Fārs (2): 'Abd al-Raḥmān ibn Naṣrallāh, 'Abd al-Malik, both of Shīrāz.

Jibāl or 'Irāq 'Ajamī (4): Yaḥyā al-Suhrawardī, 'Imād al-dīn al-Iṣfahānī, Fakhr al-dīn al-Rāzī,* 'Umar al-Suhrawardī.

'Irāq and Jazīrah (8): Ibn Ḥamdūn, Ibn al-Anbārī, Ibn al-Dahhān, Ibn al-Jauzī, Ibn Hubal, 'Alī al-Harawī, Yūsuf ibn Rāfi', Muḥammad ibn al-Ḥusain.

Arabia (1): 'Umāra al-Yamanī.

Syria (3): Ja'far ibn 'Alī, Ibn 'Asākir, Ibn Munqidh.

Egypt (2): Ibn Mammātī, 'Abd al-Raḥmān Ibn Naṣr.

Samū'īl ibn 'Abbās was a Jew who embraced Islām late in life. His father was a Moroccan, who died in Mūṣul; Samū'īl died in Adharbāyjān. My classification is somewhat artificial because few men spent their whole life in one district; many could be classified in two or more sections; for example, many of the easternmost Muslims migrated to 'Irāq or even to Egypt. Under the Ayyūbid dynasty (1169–1250), founded by Ṣalāḥ al-dīn, parts of Syria and even of Mesopotamia were gradually added to the Egyptian kingdom, and there was considerable exchange of people, goods, and thoughts between Syria and Egypt. Thus I would have been justified in considering the two last sections as one.

B. Western Muslim (15)

Philosophers (3): *Ibn Ṭufail, Ibn Rushd,* Abū-l-'Abbās al-Sibtī.

Mathematicians (3): *al-Biṭrūjī,* Ibn al-Yāsminī, Muḥammad al-Ḥuṣṣār.

Alchemist: Ibn Arfa' ra'sahu.

Geographers (3): *al-Idrīsī,* al-Māzinī, Ibn Jubair.

Naturalists (2): al-Ghāfiqī, *Ibn al-'Awwām.*

Physician: "Alcoatim."

Historians (2): Ibn Khair, al-Ḍabbī.

Jurist: Abū-l-Qāsim al-Ḥaufī.

All of these men lived in Spain or Morocco, but one of the greatest, al-Idrīsī, lived also at the court of Sicily.

Though the Western Muslim group was much smaller than the Eastern (15 vs.

29), it was incomparably more distinguished. In both cases we noticed but few physicians, but this is due to our classification. Medicine was the most encyclopaedic of the arts, and physicians, especially great physicians, were likely to be many other things besides. For example, one of the greatest, Ibn Rushd, was counted, and rightly so, among the philosophers.

Samaritan (2)

Grammarian: Abū-l-Isḥāq Ibrāhīm.
Theologian: Munaja' ben Ṣadaqa.
Both wrote in Arabic; it would seem that the first wrote also in Hebrew.

Jewish[14] (24)

A. Eastern Jewish (6)

Philosopher: Hibatallāh ben Malka.
Traveler: Jacob ben Nathaniel** (date and origin uncertain).
Physicians (4): Abū-l-Ma'ālī, Ibn al-Mudawwar, Ibn al-Nāqid, Ibn Jamī'.
Leaving out Jacob ben Nathaniel about whom we know practically nothing, all of these men were orthodox except Ibn al-Mudawwar who was a Qaraite; and all were Egyptians except Hibatallāh ben Malkā who flourished in Baghdād. The group of Judaeo-Egyptian physicians was really remarkable, even if Maimonides is not counted with them.

B. Western Jewish (18)

Philosophers (7): Isaac ben Melchizedek,** Abraham ben David of Posquières,** Isaac the Blind,** Abraham ben David ha-Levi,* *Maimonides,** Joseph ibn 'Aqnīn, Joseph ibn Zabara.**
Translators and grammarians (6): Berakya ha-Naqdan,** Joseph Qimḥi** and his two sons Moses Qimḥi** and David Qimḥi,** *Judah ibn Tibbon*** and his son Samuel ibn Tibbon.**
Travelers (2): *Benjamin of Tudela,*** Petaḥiah ben Jacob.**
Physician: Sheshet Benveniste.
Historian: Ephraim ben Jacob.**
Jurist: Isaac ben Abba Mari.**
This western Jewish group compares as favorably with the eastern Jewish, as the western Muslim with the eastern Muslim. It is true, the situation would be greatly modified if we counted Maimonides and Joseph ibn 'Aqnīn as Egyptians. But if we leave Maimonides out of both groups, then the western group is still far superior to the eastern one, except from the purely medical point of view. Moreover, it is largely a Hebrew group instead of an Arabic, as the asterisks show at a glance.
The fact that the western branches of Islām and Israel were both so distinctly superior to the eastern branches is highly significant. It shows that civilization was really passing from East to West.

Distribution of Western Jews: However, while the great achievements of western Muslims were almost entirely to the credit of Spain (the only partial

[14] In this section on asterisk following a name means "wrote in Hebrew and Arabic;" two asterisks mean "wrote in Hebrew only."

exception being al-Idrīsī), the case of western Jewry was very different. For one thing, Spain was already driving her Jews away—witness Maimonides and Joseph ibn 'Aqnīn. Others were moving to Catalonia, Provence, and farther on. Moreover there were a few non-Spanish Jews. Let us examine the Jewish distribution more closely.

Spain (6): Abraham ben David ha-Levi and Benjamin of Tudela, Judah ibn Tibbon and Joseph Qimḥi, Maimonides and Joseph ibn 'Aqnīn; of these three pairs, only the first was entirely Spanish; the second and third became respectively Provençal and Egyptian. Of these six, three wrote exclusively in Hebrew; one (Joseph ibn 'Aqnīn) exclusively in Arabic.

Catalonia and Southern France (9): Isaac ben Abba Mari, Abraham ben David of Posquières, Isaac the Blind, Sheshet Benveniste, Moses and David Qimḥi, Samuel ibn Tibbon, Joseph ibn Zabara. To these might be added the Frenchman (?) Berakya ha-Naqdan who flourished probably in England. All wrote in Hebrew except Sheshet Benveniste of Barcelona, who wrote in Arabic.

Italy: Isaac ben Melchizedek.

Germany (2): Ephraim ben Jacob and Petaḥiah ben Jacob. Needless to say, the Germans and the Italian wrote only in Hebrew.

Christian (80)

A. Eastern Christian (16)

The Eastern Christian section may be conveniently divided into four subsections: Greek, Russian, Syriac, Armenian. This classification is based on the language of the writings, but it cuts much deeper, extending to church and nationality as well.

Greek (7): Philosopher: Eustathios.
Mathematician: John Camateros.
Traveler: John Phocas.
Naturalist: Author of Poricologos.
Historians (2): Constantine Manasses and John Cinnamos.
Philologist: Gregorios of Corinth.

Russian (3): Traveler: Anthony of Novgorod.
Annalists (2 or more): the authors of the Chronicle of Kiev, and of the Campaign of Igor.

Syriac (2): Historians: Michael the Elder, and Simeon Shanqĕlāwī.

Armenian (4): General leader: Nerses the Graceful.
Physician: Mekhitar of Her.
Historians (2): Gregory the Priest, and Samuel of Ānī.

B. Western Christian (64)

The Western Christian section may be subdivided roughly according to nationalities: Italian, French, Spanish, English, German, Scandinavian. All the personalities named here wrote in Latin except the few whose names are followed by an asterisk; these few wrote in their own vernacular.

Italian (23): Religious leaders (2): John de Oldrado of Meda, Joachim de Floris.
Philosopher: Peter the Lombard.

Translators (6): Aristippus of Catania, Eugene the Amīr, Paschal the Roman, Leo Tuscus, *Gerard of Cremona*, *Burgundio of Pisa*.

Physicians (8): *Roger of Salerno*, Peter of Eboli, Petronius, Maurus, John Ferrarius, Nicholas II of Salerno and (or) Richard of Salerno, Urso of Calabria.

Historians (3): Romuald of Salerno, Hugh Falcandus, Godfrey of Viterbo. The last named was probably of German origin.

Jurists (2): Peter of Piacenza, Vacarius.

Philologist: Hugutio of Pisa.

French (13): Religious leaders (3): Peter Waldo, St. John of Matha, St. Felix of Valois.

Philosophers (2): Alcher of Clairvaux, Alan of Lille.

Translator: William Le Mire.

Physicians (3): Bernard of Provence, John of St. Paul (?), Giles of Corbeil.

Historians (4): Wace of Jersey, Robert of Torigny, *William of Tyre*, Peter the Eater.

Of these thirteen men, seven can be assigned to the north of France, and four to the south. Of John of St. Paul we know nothing. The greatest of them all, William of Tyre, was a Frenchman of Palestine.

English (14): Philosophers (3): Isaac of Stella, Daniel of Morley, Alexander Neckam.

Astronomer: Roger of Hereford.

Geographers (2): Author of the life of Richard Lionheart, *Gerald the Welshman*.

Naturalist: Robert of Cricklade.

Historians (4): Henry of Huntingdon, William of Newburgh, Roger of Howden, Ralph of Diceto.

Jurists and sociologists (3): *John of Salisbury*, *Ranulf of Glanville*, Richard FitzNeal.

German (8): Philosophers (3): The author of the Lucidarius*; and two women, *Hildegard** of Bingen, and Herrad of Landsberg.

Musician: *Franco of Cologne*.

Travelers (3): John of Würzburg, Theodoric the Pilgrim, Burchard of Strassburg.

Historian: Helmold.

Spanish (3): Translator: Marc of Toledo.

Historian: Author of the Poema del Cid.*

Jurist: Sancho VI. el Sabio.*

Scandinavian (3): Mathematician: Bjarni Bergþórsson.*

Traveler: Nikulás Saemundarson.*

Historian: Svend Aagesön.

The first two were Icelandic, the third Danish.

To have a complete idea of the intellectual activity of these countries one ought to take into account the contemporary Muslim and Jewish efforts. This applies with particular force to Spain, where the Christian effort was relatively small, while the total effort was immense. Spain was then by far the leading country of Europe.

In the same way our Italian picture ought to include al-Idrīsī in Sicily, and Isaac ben Melchizedek in Apulia. For two other countries, France and Germany, we would not have to consider Muslims, but only Jews. The Jews of Provence played a very important part in the development of their adopted country. Of the twenty-two Frenchmen discussed in this chapter, thirteen were Christians, and nine Jews; if we consider the South of France alone, we find that out of thirteen, nine were Jews, and only four Christians. The proportion of Jewish effort was much smaller in Germany; only two Jews against eight Christians.

Returning now to the Christians of Europe, we find very striking differences when we pass from one country to another.

The three leading countries of Christian Europe were Italy, England, and France. The writings published in these three countries, which I had occasion to quote, were exclusively in Latin. In the three other countries—Germany, Spain, and Scandinavia—we registered a few writings in the vernacular. The Icelanders wrote only in Icelandic; the Spaniards produced the epic of the Cid; the Germans produced a German encyclopaedia, and Hildegard's scientific terminology.

Turning from languages to subjects, the differences are even greater. Most of the translators (6 out of 8), and of the physicians (8 out of 11), were Italians. Thus these two essential features of the second half of the twelfth century—the borrowing of Arabic and Greek elements for the building up of a new culture, and the development of the school of Salerno, the earliest European school of medicine—were largely due to the Italian genius. As we would expect, it was also Italians—Peter of Piacenza, and Vacarius—who transmitted to other nations the Civil Law which their countrymen had brought back to life in the first half of the century. Yet the chief contributions to law and sociology were not due to Italians, but to Englishmen: John of Salisbury, and Ranulf of Glanville.

The most original philosopher was a German nun, Hildegard. The only theorist of music, Franco of Cologne, was also a German.

The greatest geographer of Christendom, and the only astronomer, were respectively a Welshman and an Englishman: Gerald the Welshman, and Roger of Hereford.

Historical work was pretty well divided among the nations, each according to its importance. This is natural enough. But with regard to geography, two of the leading countries, France and Italy, did but little, and the principal travelers were English, German, or Icelandic.

In sharp contrast with the deep interest in philology taken by Muslims and Jews, we met but one grammarian among the Latins—a poor one, Hugutio of Pisa.

Summary[15]

Far East	19 (3)
Japanese	5
Chinese	14 (3)
Hindu	6 (1)
Iranian	1
Muslim	44 (6)
Eastern Muslim	29 (1)
Western Muslim	15 (5)
Samaritan	2
Jewish	24 (3)

[15] The figures between brackets indicate the number of outstanding personalities. See next section.

Eastern Jewish	6	
Western Jewish	18	(3)
Christian	80	(9)
Eastern Christian	16	
Western Christian	64	(9)

The two Christian groups are subdivided as follows:

Eastern		Western		
Greek	7	Italian	23	(3)
Armenian	4	English	14	(3)
Russian	3	French	13	(1)
Syriac	2	German	8	
		Spanish	3	
		Scandinavian	3	

To measure the cultural importance of Spain, one must put together its Christian and non-Christian elements:

Western Muslims	15	(5)
Western Jews	6	(3)
Christians	3	
Total	24	(8)

The total includes al-Idrīsī, educated in Spain; but does not include two Catalans, Sheshet Benveniste and Joseph ibn Zabara, who were counted with the Provençaux.

This summary shows that the most important group was now by far the Christian; it was even more important than the Muslim and Jewish put together, 80 against 44 plus 24 (9 against 6 plus 3). The same relation obtains if one considers only the Western elements, 64 against 15 plus 18 (9 against 5 plus 3).

COMPARATIVE ACHIEVEMENTS OF THESE GROUPS, MEASURED BY THEIR OUTSTANDING PERSONALITIES

A glimpse of the answer has already been given by means of the figures between brackets, in the summary above. Out of a total of about 176 personalities, I have selected 22 outstanding ones. Such selection is always somewhat arbitrary, and I do not claim that mine is perfect, but I have taken pains to establish it as impartially as possible. Here it is. The classification is also more or less arbitrary, as most of these men were many-sided.

Philosophers and Polygraphs (6): Ibn Rushd, Maimonides, Ibn Ṭufail, Hildegard, Fākhr al-dīn al-Ṭūsī, Chu Hsi.

Translators (3): Gerard of Cremona, Judah ibn Tibbon, Burgundio of Pisa.

Astronomer: al-Biṭrūjī.

Theorist of music: Franco of Cologne.

Geographers (4): al-Idrīsī, Gerald the Welshman, Benjamin of Tudela, Fan Ch'êng-ta.

Naturalists (2): Ibn al-'Awwām, Han Ch'an-chih.

Physician: Roger of Salerno.

Historian: William of Tyre.

Jurist and sociologist: John of Salisbury, Ranulf of Glanville.
Philologist: Hemacandra.

Distribution: With regard to the distribution of these twenty-two superior men, it is noteworthy in the first place that three were Chinese and one Hindu. That is, more than one in six was an Asiatic.[16] Six others were Muslims; three were Jews; and nine were Christians. The point of interest is that all of these non-Asiatics but one (Fakhr al-dīn al-Rāzī, perhaps the least important of the whole group) were Westerners. Of the 18 non-Asiatics, not less than 8 were Spaniards, and these included the two who were by far the greatest of the whole group, Ibn Rushd and Maimonides.

To conclude, the twelfth century saw the continued growth of Western Christendom. The relative importance of Western Christians was perhaps smaller in the second half of the century than in the first half, yet it was considerable. On the whole, they were now ahead of the Muslims and Jews, yet the two greatest intellectual leaders were still Muslim and Jewish.

[16] I use the word "Asiatic" here, as I have done in my studies on Asiatic art, in the sense of "belonging to India, Central, and Eastern Asia (or Buddhist Asia)."

CHAPTER XV

RELIGIOUS BACKGROUND

(Second Half of Twelfth Century)

I. CHRISTENDOM

HUMILIATI

Considerable religious and social unrest obtained in Lombardy during the twelfth century. An increasing number of people who suffered oppression and poverty felt that the Church not only did not protect them but even failed to give them the moral consolations which they craved. Thus various attempts were made to satisfy their spiritual needs, and as the Church continued to discourage them they naturally became more and more heterodox.

The most remarkable of these attempts is that of the Humiliati. This brotherhood did not begin in the same way as others. It was a sort of a compromise between a monastic order and an industrial guild. It would seem that what we would call the Third Order was established first. Most of the brethren and sisters belonged to the labouring class, and continued their natural family life. Finally a First or Clerical Order is said to have been established by John de Oldrado of Meda (near Milan), who died in 1159 at the Brera, their oldest monastery.

Some of the Humiliati preached the Evangel, insisting upon evangelical poverty, and got into trouble with the Church. Their community was then gradually divided into two groups, which were later called the "true" and "false" Humiliati. The "true" Humiliati were, from the orthodox point of view, the obedient ones; the "false" Humiliati were the others.

The true Humiliati had a rule inspired by the Benedictine and Augustinian constitutions, which was sanctioned in 1201 by Innocent III. Houses were founded in Florence, in Siena, even in France, but most of them in Lombardy.

Paul D. Alphandéry: Encyclopaedia Britannica (11th ed., vol. 13, 884, 1910). Luigi Zanoni: Gli Umiliati nei loro rapporti con l'eresia, l'industria della lana ed i comuni nei secoli XII e XIII (Milan 1911). Ellen Scott Davison: Forerunners of Saint Francis (168–200, Boston 1927; Isis, 11, 145).

WALDENSIANS

Peter Waldo, a merchant of Lyon, having seen a great light in 1173, began to preach the Evangel. Soon many discontented Christians—Arnoldisti, Humiliati, Albigensians, etc.—gathered around him. They were called the Poor Men of Lyon, or later Vaudois (Waldensians); they were also called Insabbati (unshod). The birth of a new sect in Lyon is not surprising, for Lyon had been from the second century a center of intense religious fervor.[1] In 1179 Waldo attended the Third

[1] For the early Lyonese Christianity, orthodox or heretical, see Ernest Renan: Marc Aurèle et la fin du monde antique (5th ed., 289–344, Paris 1885).

Lateran Council in Rome. The pope Alexander III forgave the Waldensians but forbade their preaching except under the supervision of the local clergy. They continued to preach, and were condemned in 1181 together with the Cathari and other heretics. But even as the Humiliati were finally divided into two groups, one of which was reconciled with the Church, so the more orthodox Waldensians, named Poor Catholics, were conciliated by Innocent III at Pamiers in 1206.

The aims of the Waldensians, like those of the Humiliati, were essentially ethical and practical; their concern was not to solve theological puzzles, but to live in accordance with the Gospel. In spirit and in practice the Waldensians seem to have come nearer to the Franciscans than any other early brotherhood.

After their condemnation some of the Waldensians fled to Dauphiny, Guyenne, and Provence; others, including Waldo himself, are said to have found refuge in Picardy; still others went to Lorraine; it is probable that the Waldensian movement of Piedmont was also originated by Lyonnese refugees. Most of the French Waldensians were destroyed together with the Albigensians, and even the Poor Catholics seemed to have been involved in the general suppression. We may assume that the more conservative joined the new Mendicant orders, whose success was partly prepared for by the efforts of the earlier brotherhood.

The later history of the Waldensians does not concern us, but it is interesting to note that Waldensian churches exist to this day, chiefly in Piedmont and in other parts of Italy, in the Argentine, Uruguay, and the United States.

J. J. I. von Döllinger: Beiträge zur Sektengeschichte des Mittelalters (2 Theil, München 1890). Louis Brunel: Les Vaudois des Alpes françaises (2d ed., 316 p., Paris 1890). Alexandre Bérard: Les Vaudois, leur histoire sur les deux versants des Alpes du IVe siècle au XVIIIe (Lyon 1892). Ludwig Keller: Die Anfänge der Reformation und die Ketzerschulen (65 p., Berlin 1897). Emilio Comba: Histoire des Vaudois (new ed., 224 p., 24 pl., map, Paris 1898). Silvio Pons: Les poèmes vaudois et les mystères provençaux du XVe siècle (17 p., Pinerolo 1909). Teofilo Gay: Histoire des Vaudois (Florence 1912). Antonino de Stefano: I Tedeschi e l'eresia medievale in Italia (Bilychnis, June 1916). Jean Jalla: Histoire des Vaudois des Alpes et de leurs colonies (2d ed., Pignerol 1922). Ellen Scott Davison: Forerunners of St. Francis (237–275, Boston 1927; Isis, 11, 145). C. H. Haskins: The heresy of Echard the Baker of Rheims (Studies in mediaeval culture, 245–255, Oxford 1929; deals with a somewhat later period, c. 1230; Isis, 14,435).

Bulletin de la Société d'histoire vaudoise (Pignerol 1884, etc.). Vol. 15 entitled Società di storia valdese (Torino 1898); vol. 31 entitled Histoire du retour des Vaudois en leur patrie après un exil de trois ans et demi (1913).

JOACHIM OF FLORIS

Gioachimo di Fiore. Joachimus Calaber Florencis. Born of a noble family at Celico near Cosenza, Calabria, about 1145; educated at the court of Duke Roger of Apulia. He visited the holy places in the Near East, and after his return assumed the Cistercian habit in the abbey of Casamari; in 1177 he was abbot of the monastery of Corazzo, near Martirano; some time later he retired into a solitary place, Pietralata; and finally he founded a new abbey, San Giovanni in Fiore (hence his name), at the altitude of 3,445 feet on the slope of Montenero, near Cosenza. He died there in 1202. Italian theologian, mystic, and seer. The abbey of San Giovanni in Fiore represented a new rule and a new order (Ordo Florencis) endorsed by Innocent III in 1204. Joachim wrote a large number of Biblical commentaries, theological treatises, and prophecies, which are important because of their extraordinary influence upon later generations down to the sixteenth century. His tendencies were mystical, ascetic, millennarian, anticlerical, socialistic; their potentialities were not recognized at once by his contemporaries or by the Church, and his orthodoxy was sanctioned as late as 1220 by Honorius III.

However, later the radicals of the Franciscan Order, the so-called Spirituals, found their best nutriment in his writings. In 1254 one of them, Gherardo da Borgo San Donnino, edited some of Joachim's writings, with an introduction and various interpolations, under the title Liber introductorius ad Evangelium aeternum. This work claimed to supply a key to the Scriptures and to reveal their spiritual and eternal meaning. It also contained a mystical interpretation of human history, the recognition of three Ages: the Age of the Father; the Age of the Son introduced by Jesus Christ; and the Age of the Holy Spirit, which would not begin until 1260 and would be an age of contemplation and of complete spiritual freedom (plena spiritus libertas). The Liber introductorius was the main source of the movement called Joachimism, which some have considered an anticipation of the Reformation. And it was, if any revolt of the spirit against the letter, such as must inevitably occur from time to time, may be so considered. But this seems arbitrary. It was in fact a much deeper reaction than the Reformation, one so deep that it could not be safely realized. The Church awoke to the danger and condemned the followers of the "Eternal Evangel" in 1255 and again in 1260. However, a large number of writings spread the new ideals, or else fought them, and some of the best minds of the second half of the thirteenth century and later were influenced by them; for example, Joachimite tendencies can be detected in the thought of Roger Bacon and of Arnold of Villanova; and Dante placed Joachim in Paradise (Paradiso, XII, 140).

Text—There are many early editions of Joachim's Biblical commentaries.

Emmanuel Aegerter: L'évangile éternel (2 vols., 419 p., Paris 1928); the first volume contains a biography of Joachim, the second the first French translation of the Eternal Evangel.

Criticism—Wilhelm Preger: Das Evangelium aeternum und Joachim von Floris (40 p., Abhdl. bayer. Akad., 1874). Ernest Renan: Joachim et l'Evangile éternel (Nouvelles études d'histoire religieuse, Paris 1884). H. C. Lea: History of the Inquisition (vol. 3, ch. 1, 1887). Potthast (653, 1896). Johann Chrysostomus Huck: Ubertin von Casale und dessen Ideenkreis (113 p., Freiburg i.B., 1903). Paul Fournier: Études sur Joachim et ses doctrines (Paris 1909). Paul Alphandéry: Encyclopaedia Britannica (vol. 15, 417, 1910). Herbert Grundmann: Studien über Joachim (218 p., Leipzig 1927; Isis, 11,424).

THE TEUTONIC KNIGHTS

I have already given (Book I) a brief account of the two earliest religious orders of knighthood: the Order of St. John of Jerusalem, founded in 1099; and the Order of the Knights Templars, organized in 1119. A third brotherhood of a similar kind was created in 1191 during the siege of Acre (Third Crusade)—the Teutonic Knights of St. Mary's Hospital in Jerusalem (Der deutsche Orden, Deutsche Ritter), organized by merchants from Bremen and Lübeck. They wore a white mantle with a black cross. This order was not international like the two earlier ones; but national, Teutonic. The charitable purpose was soon smothered by military activity on the eastern frontier of Germany, along the Oder, and later along the Vistula and eastwards. However, the headquarters remained in Acre until 1291 when it was moved for a short time to Venice, and finally in 1309 to Marienburg on the Vistula. The subsequent history of the Teutonic Knights is of purely political interest, largely the history of Teutonic expansion along the eastern marches and of the endless strife between Germans and Slavs.

The histories of these three military religious orders, however dissimilar, are equally tragic. All three failed to accomplish their high ideals. They were semi-monastic orders, the members of which bound themselves to live in chastity, obedience and poverty. Their worldly success soon destroyed their high endeavours. The failure was peculiarly dramatic in the case of the Templars; but it was not less complete, if less obvious, in the two other cases. Their greatest days, days of heroism and devotion, belong to the twelfth century of which they form a conspicuous and noble feature.

See summary by Ernest Barker in Encyclopaedia Britannica (vol. 26, 676–678, 1910). The early history of the order down to 1326 was written by Peter of Duisburg (first half of the fourteenth century). Johannes Bühler: Ordensritter und Kirchenfürsten nach zeitgenössischen Quellen (Leipzig 1928).

TRINITARIANS

St. John of Matha (born in Barcelonnette, Basses-Alpes, about 1160, died in Rome in 1213) and St. Felix of Valois (born in Valois, Isle-de-France, in 1127, died in Cerfroy in 1212) founded in 1198, with the approval of Innocent III, a new religious order for the special purpose of redeeming Christians held captive by Muslims. The Trinitarians (or Mathurins) were not monks but canons regular, and their rule was that of the Augustinian Canons (vol. I, 748) with ascetic restrictions. The mother house was at Cerfroy, near Soissons, Aisne. As the order answered an urgent need of the time, it was very successful for more than five centuries—that is, as long as the need was strongly felt. Captives were redeemed with money, but if necessary the Trinitarians offered themselves in exchange for the slaves or prisoners. There were also sisters, and tertiaries. The order still exists, with headquarters in San Crisogono, Rome, but is of course very small.

Paul Deslandres: L'ordre des Trinitaires (2 vols., Toulouse 1903). E. C. Butler: Encyclopaedia Britannica (vol. 27, 286, 1910); my note is derived from Dom Edward's article.

BEGINNINGS OF GOTHIC ARCHITECTURE

I have indicated in Book I the close connection between architecture and religion, and the tremendous educational importance of the efforts of the Romanesque architects. These were largely patronized by the order of Cluny. But before the middle of the twelfth century a new type of architecture was originated, probably in the Isle-de-France, and it spread rapidly during the second half of the century. Romanesque architecture, which may be said to have reached its climax and its maximal diversity by 1125, was gradually replaced by the new architecture, each Romanesque school (of which there were many, at least in France) being continued in the new manner. This new architecture was called "Gothic" in the first half of the sixteenth century, by Raphael, Vasari, and other artists who meant to deride it; and this name has prevailed, in spite of its obvious incorrectness, because of the lack of a proper one. The term "ogival architecture"—referring to one of its most striking characteristics, the use of pointed arches—is somewhat misleading, because the Gothic architects did not invent the pointed arches (nor the ribbed vaulting) used many centuries before by Muslims, but they used them with more emphasis and boldness.

Further developments of these and related questions do not belong to our subject. It will suffice to remember that the Gothic cathedrals, like the Romanesque, remained for a long time the main centers of popular education in the Christian West. The decorated cathedral was like an illustrated Bible, an education in itself.

NERSES THE GRACEFUL

St. Nerses, Nerses IV, called Shnorhali, or the Graceful, because of his beautiful writing. In 1166, being then an old man, he succeeded his elder brother Gregory III Pahlavuni as catholicos of Armenia. He resided in Rūm qal'a.[2] He died in 1173. Armenian poet, theologian, and grammarian; one of the fathers of the Armenian church. He wrote a long poem (8000 lines) containing the essentials of the Old and New Testaments; another poem (2090 lines) deals with the destruction of Edessa by 'Imād al-dīn al Zangī in 1144; still another, with the history of Armenia. This last one was continued by Vahram of Edessa (second half of the thirteenth century). St. Nerses' official and private letters are of great historical interest. In one of them addressed to a correspondent in Samosata, he explains under what conditions Parsi-Christians (?) can be accepted into the Armenian fold. Five letters addressed to Michael Comnenos and to Byzantine dignitaries discuss the possibility of union of the Greek and Armenian churches.

Text—An edition of St. Nerses' collected poems was published by the Mekhitarists of Venice in 1830.

J. Zohrab: Elégie sur la prise d'Edesse par Nerses Klajetsi (Armenian ed., Paris 1828).

Preces S. Niersis Clajensis Armeniorum patriarchae viginti quatuor linguis editae (345 p., Venetiis, in insula S. Lazari, 1823, 1837). New edition in 33 languages (570 p., Venice 1862); in 36 languages (602 p., Venice 1871).

Armenian edition of the history of Armenia (Constantinople 1824). Many other editions.

His encyclic letter of 1166 was published in St. Petersburg in 1788, Constantinople in 1825, and Venice in 1830. This third edition includes a Latin version by Joseph Cappelletti. The Mekhitarists claim that the Russian and Turkish editions have been adulterated.

Criticism—C. D. Neumann: Geschichte der armenischen Litteratur (151–160, 1836).

II. ISRAEL

SAMŪ'ĪL IBN 'ABBĀS

See Chapter XIX, Mathematics and Astronomy.

[2] Rūm qal'a in Cilicia was the see of the Armenian patriarchate until 1292; the see was then transferred to Sīs, 65 km. N.E. from Ādana.

MUNAJA' BEN ṢADAQA

Abū-l-Faraj Munaja' ben Ṣadaqa, Shams al-dīn. Samaritan theologian who flourished in Damascus about the end of the twelfth century; his son Ṣadaqa died after 1223. He wrote in Arabic a treatise entitled Masā'il al-khilāf, concerning the difference between Samaritans and Jews. He was apparently well acquainted with the works of Saadia Gaon (first half of the tenth century). Biblical commentaries are ascribed to him.

Moses Gaster: The Samaritan literature (Encyclopaedia of Islām, vol. 4, Supplement, p. 7, 1925).

III. ISLĀM

YAZĪDĪ

Yazīdī (or Yezīdī) is the name of a religion which developed among Kurdish tribes possibly as early as the twelfth century. It is a syncretism, of which the original nucleus was possibly Zoroastrian; at any rate it includes Zoroastrian elements together with many others—Assyrian, Nestorian, Manichaean, Muslim, etc.; it is sometimes considered a Muslim heresy, which is not entirely incorrect but is confusing. The Yazīdī tribes flourish in Kurdistān, in Armenia, in the Caucasus. They are often called devil worshippers, but this is misleading; they are devil propitiators. They avoid mentioning the devil's name, and represent him by the peacock angel (Malāk ṭāwus). They believe in the immortality of the soul, and practise both circumcision and baptism. They have a sacred book called Al-yalvah.

Their national saint is the Shaikh 'Adī ('Adī ibn Musāfir ibn Ismā'īl al-Umawī al-Sha'mī al-Hakkārī), a Muslim ṣūfī who was born near Baalbek. He founded a religious order called al-'Adawīya after him, and established himself at Hakkār, near Baadri, in the mountain region north of Mūṣul; he died there about 1162, at the age of 90. The holy city of the Yazīdī has grown around 'Adī's sepulcher, and is called Shaikh 'Adī after him. It is reached by mountain paths from Mūṣul.

George Percy Badger: The Nestorians (vol. 1, London 1852). Joachim Menant: Les Yézidiz (240 p., Paris 1892). C. Brockelmann: Arabische Litteratur (vol. 1, 434, 1898). Cl. Huart: Encyclopaedia of Islām (vol. 1, 136, 1908). W. B. Seabrook: Adventures in Arabia (289–334, New York 1927); entertaining account of a visit to the Yazīdī. R. H. W. Empson: The cult of the peacock angel. A short account of the Yezīdī tribes of Kurdistan, with a commentary by Sir Richard Temple (235 p., 6 pl., London 1928).

IV. BUDDHISM

CHINESE

See my note on Fa Yün in Chapter XXVII, Philology.

JAPANESE

The earliest autochthonous Japanese sect, the Nembutsu shū, was founded by Ryōnin in the first half of the twelfth century. The second sect, the Jōdo-shū (Pure Land or Paradise sect), was established in 1175 by the bonze Genkū. Both sects were Amidaist; but one may say that it is the second which really introduced

Amidaism into Japan, because it was immensely successful while the former remained relatively unimportant. The meaning of Amidaism is that everything depends primarily upon the grace of God (Amida), and thus that the root of salvation is faith in Him.

Genkū, or Hōnen-Shōnin, was born in the province of Mimasaka in 1133, and educated in a Tendai monastery at Hiei-zan. He died in 1212 at the temple Chion-in, Kyōto, which he had founded. He received the posthumous title Enkō-daishi.

The Jōdo sect was represented in Japan about 1917 by 8371 temples out of a total of 72191.

A biography of Hōnen was written at the beginning of the fourteenth century by Shunjō Hōin. An English translation, with abundant notes and Sanskrit-Chinese-Japanese glossary, was published by Harper Havelock Coates, and Ryugaku Ishizuka (1050 p., many plates, Chion-in, Kyōto 1925; Isis, 9, 365–367).

EISAI

Japanese Buddhist. Born in the province of Bitchū in 1141, he was a monk at the Hiei-zan from 1155; he traveled to China in 1168, and again from 1187 to 1191. He died in 1215. His family name was Kaya. In 1203 he was given the title Dai-sōjō, and later the posthumous name Zenkō-kokushi. After his second Chinese journey, he introduced into Japan the Ch'an tsung,[3] or Contemplative school of Buddhism. In 1192 he built the Shōfuku-ji in Hakata (Chikuzen). The date 1192 is sometimes quoted as the birthdate of this new sect, Zen-shū. However, Zen Buddhism was not completely established until 1202, when the Kennin-ji was built in Kyōto and Eisai was placed at its head. (See my note on Japanese Buddhism in the first half of the thirteenth century).

He introduced the cultivation of tea into Japan, and in order to overcome popular prejudices against it, he wrote a book, Kissa-yōjō-ki, wherein he explained its hygienic value.

E. Papinot: Historical dictionary (79, 1909).

[3] Vol. I, 420, 552.

CHAPTER XVI

THE TRANSLATORS

(Second Half of Twelfth Century)

I. FROM ARABIC INTO LATIN

GERARD OF CREMONA

Gherardo Cremonese. Gerardus Cremonensis (not Carmonensis). Italian translator from Arabic into Latin; perhaps the greatest of all translators. Born about 1114 in Cremona, Lombardy (not in Carmona, Andalusia); died in 1187 in Toledo. Being anxious to read the Almagest, which was not yet available in Latin, he went to Toledo, where he studied Arabic and carried on an almost unbelievable activity as a translator until the time of his death.

A biography appended by his pupils to his translation of Galen's Tegni contains a list of seventy-one works translated by him, some of them of immense size—for example, Ibn Sīnā's Qānūn; and that list is far from being complete, for we know of various other translations credited to him. A complete list is included here, but in order to give a general view of his activity I shall name rapidly the main authors or works translated: the Posterior Analytics with commentaries by Themistios and al-Fārābī; various Aristotelian and pseudo-Aristotelian writings, and other philosophical treatises by al-Kindī, al-Fārābī, Isḥaq al-Isrā'īlī; mathematical treatises by Autolycos, Euclid, Archimedes, Apollonios, Hypsicles, Theodosios, Menelaos, Ptolemy, the Banū Mūsā, al-Khwārizmī, al-Farghānī, Aḥmād ibn Yūsuf, al-Nairizī, Thābit ibn Qurra, Abū Kāmil (?), Jābir ibn Aflaḥ, al-Zarqālī; physical treatises by Diocles, al-Kindī, Thābit, and Ibn al-Haitham; medical treatises by Galen (a good part of the Galenic corpus published in Arabic by Ḥunain ibn Isḥāq), al-Kindī, Ibn Māsawaih, Yaḥyā ibn Sarāfyūn, al-Rāzī, Abū-l-Qāsim, Ibn Sīnā, Ibn al-Wāfid, 'Alī ibn Riḍwān; and a few alchemical writings difficult to identify but which may represent the teachings of Jābir ibn Ḥaiyān and al-Rāzī. This is a formidable enumeration!

The immense bulk of these translations cannot fail to raise doubts with regard to their genuineness. Gerard himself, unassisted, could not possibly have made all the translations ascribed to him. It is probable that he himself was tremendously active and that he actually completed many translations alone, but that many others were made under his direction and corrected by him; it is probable that others still, though inspired by him, were almost independent of him. We may assume—as we have done for Constantine the African and John of Seville—that he was the head of a school of translators, and that many of the translations credited to him were made partly or completely by collaborators or pupils. It is possible also that later translations were ascribed to him because he was considered the translator par excellence. Finally, some ascriptions to him may be accidental and erroneous: for example, the Italian astrologer Gherardo da Sabbioneta (second half of the thirteenth century) was mistaken for him; there is also a Gerardus Salernitanus[1] who attended Henry VI (emperor from 1190 to 1197). It is noteworthy that many of the early printed editions of translations ascribed to Gerard of Cremona do not bear his name. In short, ascriptions to Gerard should not be taken too literally.

Gerard's Euclid was a literal translation of a revised edition of the Arabic version of Thābit ibn Qurra (second half of the ninth century); it was independent of Adelard's translation (first half of the twelfth century) and much clearer. Gerard used Greek words such as rombus, romboides, where Adelard kept the Arabic terms. It would seem that Gerard, like Adelard, had before him an earlier Euclid translated from the Greek.

The translation of the Almagest was completed at Toledo in 1175; it is the only Gerardian translation to be dated. It was inferior to the anonymous Sicilian translation made from the Greek about 1160, but far better known. Indeed it was through Gerard's translation from the Arabic that the Almagest was first transmitted to the West.

Gerard's medical translations were even more important, if possible, than his mathematical and astronomical ones. Incidentally they introduced into the European languages a number of new technical terms. For example, his translation of the Qānūn introduced the words (vena) basilica (al-bāsilīq), retina, saphena, cephalica, clavicula, true and false ribs, etc.; and his translation of al-Rāzī introduced the words albugo and albugineus (albugo, or leucoma, is a white opacity in the cornea; cf. Ar. bayāḍ al-'ain—white of the eye) and iris [?].

List of Gerard's Translations

The number of translations ascribed to Gerard of Cremona is so large that for the sake of clearness it is necessary to divide them into groups as follows: 1. Logic; 2. Philosophy; 3. Greek mathematics and astronomy; 4. Arabic mathematics and astronomy; 5. Physics and mechanics; 6. Greek medicine; 7. Arabic medicine; 8. Arabic astrology; 9. Arabic alchemy and geomancy. (As usual, this classification is more or less artificial; moreover I have left all the works of Aristotle in groups 1 and 2, and all those of Galen in group 6, though some of them might have been placed in other groups.) Within each group the works translated are arranged in chronological order. After the mention of each Greek text, I name when possible the Arabic translator whose version was probably used by Gerard. When the Latin texts were printed, I have cited as far as possible the first printed editions. Finally I have added to each item various other remarks as the occasion suggested. It should be noted that these remarks do not by any means exhaust the subject, but are hardly more than indications. Indeed each of these translations raises endless problems: Which text was actually used by Gerard? And in the case of Greek texts, which Arabic translation was used by him? Was Gerard the real translator? How does the tradition represented by Gerard compare with the Hebrew tradition? And so on.

1. *Logic*—(1) Aristotle: Posterior Analytics, two books, from the Arabic version by Mattā ibn Yūnus (first half of the tenth century).

(2) Themistios (second half of the fourth century): Commentary on the Posterior Analytics, one book, probably from the same Arabic version.

(3) al-Fārābī (first half of the tenth century): De syllogismo. A part of his elaboration of Aristotle's Organon.

[1] See De Renzi: Collectio salernitana (vol. 1, 282, 1852).

2. *Philosophy*—Nos. 4 to 10 are Aristotelian or pseudo-Aristotelian writings.

(4) De coelo et mundo, 4 books.

(5) De naturali auditu, 8 books.

(6) De generatione et corruptione.

(7) Liber meteororum, books 1 to 3, from the Arabic version by Yaḥyā ibn Baṭrīq (first half of the ninth century). Book 4 had been translated before.

(8) Liber lapidum. A work quoted by the German encyclopaedist Arnold of Saxony (first half of the thirteenth century).

(9) De expositione bonitatis purae—the famous neo-Platonic Liber de causis—a work which cannot be anterior to Proclos (second half of the fifth century).

(10) De elementis, or De proprietatibus elementorum. In all probability a Muslim work (see vol. I, 135).

Nos. 11 to 15 are Aristotelian commentaries by Alexander of Aphrodisias (first half of the third century).

(11) De motu et tempore.

(12) De sensu.

(13) De eo quod augmentum et incrementum fiunt in forma et non in yle, from the Arabic version of Abū 'Uthmān Sa'īd al-Dimishqī (first half of the tenth century).

(14) De intellectu et intellecto from the Arabic version of Ḥunain ibn Isḥāq (second half of the ninth century). Printed 1501.

(15) De unitate.

Nos. 16 to 18 are writings by al-Kindī (first half of the ninth century). The Latin versions have been edited by Albino Nagy (Münster 1897), who would ascribe 16 and 17 to John of Seville.

(16) De quinque essentiis (or substantiis).

(17) De somno et visione.

(18) De ratione (or Verbum de intentione antiquorum in ratione).

(19) al-Fārābī (first half of the tenth century): Distinctio super librum Aristotelis de naturali auditu.

(20) al-Fārābī: De scientiis. There is an earlier translation or adaptation by Gundisalvo (first half of the twelfth century). Gerard's version was published by Guilelmus Camerarius (Paris 1638); Gundisalvo's by Clemens Baeumker (Münster 1916; Isis, 4, 135). A Hebrew version was edited by Mich. Rosenstein (Breslau 1858).

(21) Isḥāq al-Isrā'īlī (first half of the tenth century): De elementis. Printed in the Omnia Opera Ysaac (Lyon 1515). This text had not been translated by Constantine the African.

(22) Isḥāq al-Isrā'īlī: De descriptione rerum et diffinitionibus earum et de differentia inter descriptionem et diffinitionem. Also included in the Opera (1515).

3. *Greek Mathematics and Astronomy*—(23) Autolycos (second half of the fourth century B.C.): De sphaera mota. Arabic version by Isḥāq ibn Ḥunain and Qusṭā ibn Lūqā.

(24) Euclid: Elements, XV Books. Long believed to be lost, but A. A. Björnbo discovered various MSS. in 1904 which he identified with Gerard's version.

(25) Euclid: Data. Arabic version by Isḥāq ibn Ḥunain; revised by Thābit ibn Qurra.

(26) Archimedes: De mensura circuli. Arabic version as for 25.

(27) Apollonios: Conics. The ascription of the Latin version to Gerard of Cremona was made by Heiberg; it is uncertain.

(28) Hypsicles (first half of the second century B.C.): Ἀναφορικός, De ascensionibus. Arabic version by Isḥāq ibn Ḥunain and Qusṭā ibn Lūqā.

(29) Theodosios (first half of the first century B.C.): De sphaeris.

(30) Theodosios: De locis habitabilibus. Arabic version by Qusṭā ibn Lūqā.

(31) Geminos (first half of the first century B.C.): Liber introductorius ad artem sphaericam.

(32) Menelaos (second half of the first century): De figuris sphaericis.

(33) Ptolemy (first half of the second century): Liber almagesti. This translation was completed by Gerard at Toledo in 1175. Printed in Venice in 1515.

4. *Arabic Mathematics and Astronomy*—(34) Banū Mūsā (first half of the ninth century): Liber trium fratrum. Edited by Max. Curtze (Halle 1885).

(35) al-Khwārizmī (first half of the ninth century): De jebra et almucabala. Edited by Guillaume Libri: Histoire des sciences mathématiques (vol. 1, 253–297, 1838).

(36) al-Farghānī (first half of the ninth century): De aggregationibus scientiae stellarum et de principiis coelestium motuum. An earlier translation by John of Seville was printed in Ferrara in 1493. The Latin text (probably Gerard's) was translated into French, and from French into Italian by Zucchero Bencivenni in 1313. Gerard's translation was paraphrased in Hebrew by Jacob Anaṭoli about 1232; and Anaṭoli's Hebrew version was retranslated into Latin by Jacob Christmann (Francfort 1590).

(37) Aḥmad ibn Yūsuf (second half of the ninth century): De arcubus similibus. Edited by Max. Curtze (Mitt. des Copernikus Vereins, 48–50, 1887).

(38) Aḥmad ibn Yūsuf: De proportione et proportionalitate.

(39) al-Nairīzī (second half of the ninth century): Commentary on Euclid's Elements, Books I to X. Edited by M. Curtze, as supplement to Heiberg and Menge's edition of Euclid (420 p., Leipzig 1899).

(40) Thābit ibn Qurra (second half of the ninth century): De figura alchata.

(41) Thābit ibn Qurra: De expositione nominum Almagesti.

(42) Thābit ibn Qurra: De motu accessionis et recessionis. Printed under the title De motu octavae sphaerae (1480, 1509, 1518).

(43) (?) Abū Kāmil (first half of the tenth century): Liber qui secundum Arabes vocatur algebra et almucabala.

(44) Abū 'Uthmān (first half of the tenth century) or Muḥammad ibn 'Abd al-Bāqī (second half of the eleventh century): Liber Judaei super decimum Euclidis. Edited under the title De numeris et lineis by B. Boncompagni (66 p , 1863?) and by M. Curtze (Leipzig 1899).

(45) 'Arīb ibn Sa'd (second half of the tenth century): Liber anohe (anwā'), a Christian calendar containing astronomical and agricultural information. Edited by G. Libri, Liber anoe, in his Histoire des sciences mathématiques (vol. 1, 293–458, 1838). To the references given in my vol. I, 680, add M. Steinschneider: Der Kalender von Cordova (Zeitschrift für Mathematik, 1874).

(46) Jābir ibn Aflaḥ (first half of the twelfth century): Gebri de astrononomia libri IX in quibus Ptolemaeum emendavit. (Nuremberg 1534).

(47) De practica geometrie. Unknown date and authorship.

(48) Algorismus in integris et minutiis. Unidentified arithmetic; the translator is called Gernandus.

(49) Liber coaequationis planetarum.

The three following items are astronomical tables.

(50) Liber tabularum iahen cum regulis suis. Tabulae Jaén (?) (Jaén is an important town or district in Andalusia); Tabulae Gebri (?) al-Jaihānī (?) (which means of Jaén). Supposing this al-Jaihānī to be the author of the tables, it is not easy to identify him. He may be the Abū 'Abdallāh Muḥammad ibn Yūsuf ibn Aḥmad ibn Mu'ādh al-Juhānī (or Jaihānī) of Cordova, born in 989–990, who spent five years in Egypt, 1012–1017; or he may be the wazīr and qāḍī Abū 'Abdallāh Muḥammad ibn Mu'ādh of Seville who wrote treatises on the dawn, and on the total solar eclipse of July 3, 1079. The matter requires investigation. See F. Wüstenfeld: Die Übersetzungen arabischer Werke (no. 31, 66, 1877); M. Steinschneider: Hebraeische Übersetzungen (574, 1893); Europäische Übersetzungen (no. 64, 24, 1904). H. Suter: Die Mathematiker und Astronomen der Araber (96, 214, 1900; 170, 1902).

(51) al-Zarqālī (second half of the eleventh century): Canones Arzachelis. There are many MSS. of the Latin version of these very popular tables, but some of them which do not bear Gerard's name may represent other versions.

(52) Liber omnium sphaerarum coeli et compositionis tabularum.

5. *Physics and Mechanics*—(53) Diocles (first half of the second century B.C.): De speculis comburentibus (Liber Tidei de speculo). As transmitted by a commentary of Eutocios (first half of the sixth century) on Archimedes.

(54) al-Kindī (first half of the ninth century): De aspectibus; followed by De umbris et de diversitate aspectuum. Very well edited by A. A. Björnbo and Seb. Vogl (Leipzig 1912).

(55) Thābit ibn Qurra (second half of the ninth century): Liber charastonis. F. Buchner: Die Schrift über den Qarasṭūn (Sitzungsber. der phys. med. Soz., vol. 52, 141–188, Erlangen 1922; Isis, 5, 494).

(56) Ibn al-Haitham (first half of the eleventh century): De crepusculis et nubium ascensionibus. Printed in Lisbon in 1542, and in Basle in 1572.

6. *Greek Medicine*—(57) Liber veritatis Hippocratis de istis qui laborant in agone mortis. Also called Liber sapientiae and Capsula eburnea (see my vol. I, 100). There are various Arabic versions of this pseudo-Hippocratic treatise, one by Yaḥyā ibn Baṭrīq, another by Ḥunain ibn Isḥāq. Printed together with Rāzī's Liber ad Almansorem (1497, 1500).

All of the following numbers (58 to 67) of this section are Galenic or pseudo-Galenic writings, all of which were probably translated into Arabic by Ḥunain. No. 64 may have been translated by Yaḥyā ibn Baṭrīq.

(58) Commentary on Hippocrates' Regimen acutarum egritudinum.

(59) Commentary on Hippocrates' Prognostica. Same text previously translated by Constantine the African.

(60) De elementis.

(61) De secretis ad Monteum (apocryphal).

(62) De complexionibus. That is, the περὶ κράσεων de temperamentis.

(63) De malicia complexionis diverse. That is, περὶ ἀνωμάλου δυσκρασίας, de inaequali intemperentie.

(64) De simplici medicina, or De simplicibus medicamentis.

(65) De creticis diebus. That is, περὶ κρισίμων ἡμερῶν.

(66) De crisi. That is, περὶ κρίσεων.

(67) Tegni (τέχνη ἰατρική). See the next section, under 'Alī ibn Riḍwān.

7. *Arabic Medicine*—(68) al-Kindī (first half of the ninth century): De gradibus medicinarum, or De medicinarum compositarum gradibus investigandis. Printed

with the Latin translation of Ibn Buṭlān's Tacuinum (Strassburg 1531). Also in Opusculum . . . de dosibus (Venice 1556). The same text was also translated by Arnold of Villanova.

(69) Ibn Māsawaih (first half of the ninth century): Aphorisms.

(70) Yaḥyā ibn Sarāfyūn (second half of the ninth century): Breviarium. Practica Joannis Serapionis dicta breviarium (Venice 1497).

(71) al-Rāzī (second half of the ninth century): Liber Albubatri Rasis qui dicitur Almansorius.

(72) al-Rāzī: Liber divisionum continens CLIIII capitula cum quibusdam confectionibus ejusdem.

(73) al-Rāzī: Liber introductorius in medicina parvus.

(74) al-Rāzī: De juncturarum aegritudinibus. Nos. 71 to 74 are included in Rāzī's Opera (Venice 1500), together with a few other texts.

(75) Abū-l-Qāsim (second half of the tenth century): Liber Azaragui de cirurgia. First printed, together with Chauliac's Latin surgery (Venice 1498, etc.)

(76) Ibn Sīnā (first half of the eleventh century): Canon Avicennae libri quinque. Often printed: Milano 1473, Padua 1476, etc. (at least fifteen incunabula editions).

(77) Ibn al-Wāfid (first half of the eleventh century): De medicinis et cibis simplicibus, or De simplicium medicinarum virtutibus. Printed with Ibn Buṭlān's Tacuinum (Strassburg, 1531).

(78) 'Alī ibn Riḍwān (first half of the eleventh century): Commentary on Galen's Tegni. Haly Eben Rodan s. Rodoham Aegyptius: Commentarius in artem parvam (Venice 1496).

8. *Arabic Astrology*—(79) Liber alfadhol i. est arab de bachi. The author was possibly al-Faḍl ibn Naubakht (second half of the eighth century) or al-Faḍl ibn Sahl al-Sarakhsī[2] (first half of the ninth century).

(80) Māshāllāh (second half of the eighth century): De orbe, also De scientia motus orbis, De elementis et orbibus coelestibus, De ratione circuli coelestis, De natura orbium. Printed in Nuremberg in 1504 and 1549.

(81) "Alchandrus," "Alcandrinus" (second half of the tenth century). Arcandam de veritatibus et praedictionibus astrologiae (Paris 1542). (See vol. I, 671).

(82) Liber in quo terrarum corporumque continentur mensurationes Abhabuchri, qui dicebatur Heus. Author unidentified.

(83) Liber de accidentibus alfel. Alfel is a corruption of al-fāl; the word fāl means augury, necromancy, anything taken as an omen (cf. Latin sors).

9. *Arabic Alchemy and Geomancy*—(84) Jābir ibn Ḥaiyān (second half of the eighth century): Liber divinitatis de LXX.

(85) al-Rāzī (second half of the ninth century): De aluminibus et salibus. The ascription to al-Rāzī occurs in one MS., but another contains the phrase "apud nos in Yspania." Extract entitled Praeparatio salis armoniaci secundum Rasim quoted in Theatrum chemicum (vol. 3, 179–180, Strassburg 1659). Robert Steele: Practical chemistry in the twelfth century. Rasis de aluminibus et salibus (Isis, 12, 10–46, 1929; 13, 426); Latin text, with English summary of contents, discussion, glossary. (See also Isis, 13, 358, 1930).

[2] Of Sarakhs in Khurāsān. I did not speak of this second al-Faḍl in my vol. I. He was murdered at Sarakhs in 818 at the age of 48 or 60. See Ibn Khallikān (de Slane, vol. 2, 472–476, 1843). M. Steinschneider: Arabische Mathematiker (Orientalistische Litteratur-Zeitung, 4, 345, 1901). H. Suter: Die Mathematiker und Astronomen der Araber (7, 1900; 158, 1902).

(86) Liber luminis luminum; Liber qui dicitur lumen luminum et perfecti magisterii. Also ascribed to al-Rāzī, but according to F. Wüstenfeld (no. 67, 1877) this does not seem to be a translation from the Arabic.

(87) Liber geomantie de artibus divinatoriis.

Criticism—B. Boncompagni: Della vita e delle opere di Gherardo Cremonese traduttore del secolo duodecimo e di Gherardo da Sabbionetta astronomo del secolo decimoterzo. (Atti d. Accad. d. N. Lincei, Roma 1851). F. Wüstenfeld: Übersetzungen arabischer Werke (55–81, Göttingen 1877). J. L. Heiberg: Liber Archimenidis de comparatione figurarum circularium ad rectilineas (Z. f. Mathematik, hist. Abt., vol. 35, 41–48, 1890). M. Steinschneider: Hebraeische Übersetzungen (792–794, 1893). H. Suter: Über einige noch nicht sicher gestellte Autorennamen in den Übersetzungen des Gerhard von Cremona (Bibliotheca Mathematica, vol. 4, 19–27, 1903). A. A. Björnbo: Gerhard von Cremona's Übersetzung von Alkwarizmis Algebra und von Euklids Elementen (Bibliotheca mathematica, vol. 6, 239–348, 1905). M. Steinschneider: Die europäischen Übersetzungen aus dem Arabischen (16–32, Wien 1904; 76, 1905). Karl Sudhoff: Die kurze Vita und das Verzeichnis der Arbeiten Gerhards von Cremona von seinen Schülern und Studiengenossen kurz nach 1187 verabfasst. (Archiv für Geschichte der Medizin, 8, 73–82, 1914; Isis, 3, 324). P. Duhem: Système du Monde (vol. 3, 216–223, 1915); apropos of his translation of the Almagest. Axel Björnbo: Thabits Werk über den Transversalensatz (Abhdl. zur Gesch. der Naturw., 7, Erlangen 1924; Isis, 8, 737).

MARC OF TOLEDO

Marcus Toledanus. Spanish physician and translator from Arabic into Latin. Canon of Toledo. The exact time of his activity is unknown; it was probably towards the end of the twelfth century.

He translated the following: 1. The Qur'ān. 2. Hippocrates: De aëre aquis locis. 3–6. Galenic treatises which Marc translated from the Arabic version of Ḥunain ibn Isḥāq (second half of the ninth century). 3. De tactu pulsus. 4. De utilitate pulsus. 5. De motu membrorum (s. musculorum). 6. De motibus liquidis. 7. Ḥunain ibn Isḥāq: Isagoge ad Tegni Galeni.

No. 5, *περὶ μυῶν κινήσεως*, was one of the earliest Greek treatises on a biological subject to be made available in the Christian West; that is, on the assumption that Marc flourished in the twelfth century.

F. Wüstenfeld: Übersetzungen Arabischer Werke (116, Göttingen 1877). M. Steinschneider: Europäische Übersetzungen (54, Wien 1904).

II. FROM ARABIC INTO HEBREW

JOSEPH QIMḤI

Joseph ben Isaac Qimḥi. Also called Riqam, and Maistre Petit. Hispano-Jewish grammarian, theologian, and translator from Arabic into Hebrew. Born in southern Spain about 1105; flourished at Narbonne, Provence; died about 1170. He continued the activity of Abraham ibn Ezra and Abraham bar Ḥiyya as transmitter of Judeo-Arabic thought to the Jews of Christian Europe. He wrote in Hebrew a Hebrew grammar called Sefer zikkaron. He translated into Hebrew the Kitāb al-hidayat ilā farā'iḍ al-qulūb of Baḥya ben Joseph (first half of the twelfth century). He wrote the Sheqel ha-qodesh (The holy shekel), which is a metrical version of Ibn Gabirol's Mukhtār al-jāwāhir (Choice of jewels); this metrical version was derived from a Hebrew translation entitled Mibḥar ha-peninim; and also the Yesod ha-yirah (Foundation of religious fear). Both these works are collections of religious and philosophical sayings of the same kind.

Text—Wilhelm Bacher: Sepher zikkaron, Grammatik der hebräischen Sprache (Berlin 1888). H. J. Mathews: Sefer ha-galuj (Meqiẓe nirdamim, Berlin 1887). Hermann Gollancz: Shekel hakodesh and Yesod hayirah (Hebrew and English, Oxford 1919).

Qimḥi's translation of Baḥya's Hidayat was gradually superseded by one made at about the same time by Judah ibn Tibbon; only a small part of it has been preserved (see below, Judah ibn Tibbon).

Criticism—Caspar Levias: Jewish Encyclopaedia (vol. 7, 495–497, 1904). Louis I. Newman: Joseph Kimchi as a religious controversialist (Jewish studies in memory of Israel Abrahams, 365–372, New York 1927).

JUDAH IBN TIBBON

Judah ben Saul ibn Tibbon. Hispano-Jewish translator from Arabic into Hebrew. Born at Granada in 1120, flourished there until about 1150; then at Lunel, Provence. He died after 1190. He has been called "the father of Jewish translators," a title of honor which he might share with his patron Meshullam ben Jacob, who died at Lunel in 1170. Between 1161 and 1190 he translated a number of works from the Arabic, and in order to do so was obliged to introduce new words into the Hebrew language. That he was fully conscious of the difficulties of his task is shown in his prefaces and in his ẓawwā'āh. One original work of his, the Sod ẓaḥut ha-lashon, on rhetoric and grammar, is lost; but we have his most interesting ẓawwā'āh (or testament) addressed about 1090 to his son, the great Samuel ibn Tibbon (first half of the thirteenth century). This will contains not only moral advice, but special admonition with regard to methods of study and translation. He recommended his son to read as much Arabic as possible, to keep in good order the large Hebrew and Arabic library he was bequeathing to him, to begin by translating as literally as possible, but then to revise one's translation as though it were an original work. He translated the following texts:

(1) Saadia ben Joseph (first half of the tenth century): Kitāb al-amānāt wal-i'tiqādāt (Faiths and dogmas) under the title Sefer ha-emunot weha-de'ot, about 1186. Printed in Constantinople in 1562.

(2) Ibn Gabirol (first half of the eleventh century): Kitāb iṣlāḥ al-akhlāq (Correction of manners), under the title Tiqqun middot ha-nefesh. Printed in Constantinople in 1550. A translation of the Mukhtār al-jāwāhir is also ascribed to him, but without sufficient grounds.

(3) Ibn Janāḥ (first half of the eleventh century): Kitāb al-luma', a grammar, under the title Sefer hariqmah, about 1171. Edited by B. Goldberg, with notes by R. Kirchheim (Francfort 1856). New edition by Michael Wilensky: Sefer hariqma, ad quattuor versionis codicum fidem collato ipso auctoris libro edidit praefatione notis indicibus auxit (Scripta Academiae literarum Judaicarum, Corpus grammaticorum et exegetarum Judaeorum; 212 p., 4 pl., Berlin 1928). The preface to this translation contains Judah's views on the art of translating.

(4) Ibn Janāḥ: Kitāb al-uṣūl, a dictionary, under the title, Sefer ha-shorashim. This translation was begun by two other scholars, Isaac of Barcelona and Isaac ha-Levi; it was completed by Judah in 1171. Edited by Wilhelm Bacher (Berlin 1896).

(5) Judah ha-Levi (first half of the twelfth century): Kitāb al-ḥujjah, under the title Sefer ha-Kuzari, 1167. Printed in Fano in 1506, etc.

(6) Baḥya ben Joseph (first half of the twelfth century): Kitāb al-hidayat ilā farā'iḍ al-qulūb, under the title Torat ḥobot ha-lebabot, begun in 1161. This superseded the translation by Joseph Qimḥi. Baḥya's version and what remains of Joseph's were edited by Isaac Benjacob and Ad. Jellinek (Leipzig 1846).

Apropos of Judah's ẓawwā'āh, διαθήκη, I may add that such documents—ethical wills, we might call them—were quite common among Jews, and constitute a very characteristic form of mediaeval Hebrew literature. The earliest one extant dates from the middle of the eleventh century.

Text—Editions of the translations have already been cited.

Judah's Ẓawwā'āh was edited by M. Steinschneider, with a German introduction (Berlin 1852). New editions by Ẓ. H. Edelmann with English version by M. H. Bresslau: Derek ṭobim (London 1852).

Criticism—Max Schloessinger: Jewish Encyclopaedia (vol. 6, 544–545, 1904). On ẓawwā'āh, see Lewis N. Dembitz (ibidem, vol. 12, 522–524, 1906).

III. FROM GREEK INTO LATIN

EUGENE THE AMĪR

Eugenios of Palermo, Eugenios of Sicily. He flourished under Roger II and William I, kings of Sicily, and was a member of the latter's administration (William I ruled from 1154 to 1166). Mathematician, astronomer, and translator from Greek and Arabic into Latin. He was a Greek-speaking Sicilian who knew Arabic as well as Latin. In 1154 he translated from an Arabic version into Latin the Optics ascribed to Ptolemy (the Greek text is lost). He collaborated in the anonymous translation of the Almagest from the Greek into Latin, made in Sicily about 1160. He helped to transmit to the West the fables[3] of Kalīla wa-Dimna, and wrote poems in Greek.

Text—Gilberto Govi. L'ottica di Claudio Tolomeo da Eugenio, ammiraglio di Sicilia, ridotta in Latino sovra la traduzione araba di un testo greco imperfetto (220 p., Torino 1885).

Criticism—K. Krumbacher: Byzantinische Litteratur (768, 1897). Apropos of Eugenios' poems, one of which is devoted to the elaborate description of a flower, νύμφερον, growing in Palermo; Eugenios is called ἄρχων κῦρος Εὐγένιος. Another poem, ascribed to the philosopher Eugenios, nephew of Basilios the Amīr (?), and dedicated to King William, is also mentioned. This might be the same Eugenios (?) M. Steinschneider: Europäische Übersetzungen (13, 1904). C. H. Haskins and Dean Putnam Lockwood: The Sicilian translators of the twelfth century (Harvard studies in classical philology, 21, 75–102, 1910; 23, 155–166, 1912). Revised edition, C. H. Haskins: Studies in the history of mediaeval science (155–193, Cambridge, Mass., 1924; see also p. xiii in 2d ed. 1927).

ARISTIPPUS OF CATANIA

Henricus Aristippus. Archdeacon of Catania, on the eastern coast of Sicily, in 1156; principal officer of the Sicilian court in 1160–1162. He died probably in 1162 or soon afterward. He brought Greek manuscripts from the library of Manuel I Comnenos to Sicily; among them the Almagest which was translated

[3] For the history of these fables, see vol. i, 449, 540, 771.

into Latin about 1160 by an unknown author. He himself translated directly from Greek into Latin (and his were the first translations) the Meno and Phaedo of Plato, about 1156, and the fourth book of Aristotle's Meteorology. He investigated an eruption of Etna.

C. H. Haskins and Dean Putnam Lockwood: The Sicilian translators of the twelfth century (Harvard studies in classical philology, vol. 21, 1910); reprinted in Studies in mediaeval science, (155–193, 1924). F. H. Fobes: Mediaeval versions of Aristotle's Meteorology (Classical philology, vol. 10, 297–314, 1915). See also Fobes's edition of the Greek text of the Meteorology (Harvard Press, Cambridge, 1919; Isis, 3, 278).

According to Karl Sapper: Katalog der geschichtlichen Vulkanausbrücke (32, Strassburg, 1917; Isis, 4, 196), eruptions of Etna occurred in 1157, 1158, and 1160.

PASCHAL THE ROMAN

Pascalis Romanus. Pascal or Paschal. Italian occultist who flourished in Constantinople about 1158–1169. In 1158 or 1163 he translated from Greek into Latin a dialogue between a Jew and a Christian; this dialogue has been ascribed to Anastasios, abbot of the Sinai monastery. At Constantinople in 1165 he compiled from Latin, Greek and Oriental sources, a dreambook called Liber thesauri occulti. It is most probably this same Paschal who in 1169 translated from the Greek the Ciranides (or Cyranides), a compendium of ancient lore on the virtues of animals, stones and plants.

Text—Greek text of the Ciranides, with translation in F. de Mély: Les lapidaires de l'antiquité et du moyen âge (vols. 2 and 3, Paris 1898–1902).

Criticism—Lynn Thorndike: History of magic (vol. 2, 229–235, 1923). C. H. Haskins: Studies in mediaeval science (218–221, 1924); Studies in mediaeval culture (165–169, 1929).

For the Ciranides, see Thorndike (ibidem, vol. 2, 229–235); also the Catalogue des manuscrits alchimiques grecs; for example, Marie Delcourt: Libri Koeranidum, Codices parisini (vol. 1, 135–228, 1924; Isis, 7, 507). C. O. Zuretti: Libri Koeranidum, Codices veneti, ambrosiani, bononienses, laurentiani (vol. 2, 263–331, 1927; Isis, 11, 244).

WILLIAM LE MIRE

William the Physician, from Gap in Provence. Abbot of Saint Denis, Paris, from 1172 to 1186. In 1167 he brought back Greek manuscripts from Constantinople to Saint Denis. Indeed he had been sent to the East by the abbot mainly to obtain manuscripts of Dionysios the Areopagite (vol. I, 406) whom they confused with their own patron saint. He translated various texts from Greek into Latin—for example, summaries of the letters of St. Paul. I quote him further to illustrate the state of Greek studies in Western Europe in his time.

Léopold Delisle: Traductions de textes grecs faites par des religieux de Saint-Denis au XIIe siècle (Journal des Savants, 725–732, 1900).

SARRAZIN

John Sarrazin. Correspondent of John of Salisbury, who died in 1180. Translator from Greek into Latin. He visited the Near East in search of Greek manuscripts, and translated some of the works of the pseudo-Dionysios. His translations are painfully literal; they are made word for word, as indeed were most of the translations of that time. He is not to be confused with John the Saracen, alias Afflacius (second half of the eleventh century, vol. I, 769).

John E. Sandys: History of classical scholarship (1^3, 540, 556, 1921). C. H. Haskins: Studies in the history of mediaeval science (147, 151, 1924).

BURGUNDIO OF PISA

Italian translator from Greek into Latin; jurist, physician. Born in Pisa about 1110; died there in 1193. He went three times to Constantinople, the first in 1136, the third in 1171–1172; he was in Ragusa in 1169, in Rome in 1179, etc. But most of his life was spent in his native city. In spite of abundant activities as advocate, judge, and diplomat, he made a large number of literal translations from Greek into Latin, namely the following:

(1) Hippocrates: Aphorisms. This translation was quoted in the thirteenth century as superior to that from the Arabic.

(2) to (11), Galen: De sectis medicorum, in 1185. De temperamentis. De virtutibus naturalibus. De sanitate tuenda. De differentiis febrium. De locis affectis. De compendiositate pulsus. De differentiis pulsuum. De crisibus. Therapeutica (Methodus medendi).

(12) Nemesios of Emesa (second half of the fourth century): De natura hominis, in 1155. Edited by C. I. Burkhard (134 p., Wien 1891–1902).

(13) Various homilies by St. John Chrysostom and St. Basil (second half of the fourth century); translations dated from 1151 to 1173, perhaps to 1179.

(14) John of Damascus (first half of the eighth century): De orthodoxa fide, in 1148–1150. This translation of the main part of the Fountain of knowledge is very important, because it influenced the development of western scholasticism, chiefly through Peter the Lombard and St. Thomas.

(15) Greek quotations in the Digest.

(16) The part of the Geoponica dealing with vineyards.

Burgundio justified his method of translation, de verbo ad verbum, in the preface to his version of Chrysostom's homily on St. John.

Francesco Buonamici: Burgundio Pisano (Annali delle università toscane, vol. 28, 1908). D. Barduzzi: Di Burgundio Pisano nella cultura medica del medioevo. (Riv. di storia critica delle sci. med., 145–146, 1912). J. de Ghellinck: L'entrée de Jean de Damas dans le monde littéraire occidental (Byzantinische Z., vol. 21, 448–457, 1912). C. H. Haskins: Studies in mediaeval science (151, 206–209, 1924).

LEO TUSCUS

Leo the Pisan. A member of the Pisan colony in Constantinople. Interpreter to Manuel I Comnenos (emperor from 1143 to 1180). In 1176 (not 1160) he translated the dreambook of Aḥmad ibn Sirin (first half of the ninth century, vol. I, 558) from a Greek version, Ὀνειροκριτικόν, into Latin.

Aḥmad's Oneirocriticon has been edited by F. X. Drexl (Leipzig 1925).

C. H. Haskins: Leo Tuscus (English Historical Review, 25, 492–496, 1918; also Byzantinische Zeitschrift, 24, 43–47, 1923); Studies in the history of mediaeval science (chiefly p. 215–218, Cambridge, Mass., 1924; and p. xiii of revised edition, 1927).

IV. FROM LATIN INTO HEBREW

BERAKYA HA-NAQDAN

Berakya ben Naṭronai ha-Naqdan.[4] Jewish moralist, and translator from Latin (or French?) into Hebrew. There has been considerable discussion with regard to his nationality and time, and no certain solution has yet been reached. He is probably identical with Benoît le Puncteur (Benedictus Punctuator), a French Jew who flourished in England towards the end of the twelfth century—for example, in Oxford in 1194. He is also called (in one of his fables) R. Qrespia (or Qrispia) ha-Naqdan. Qresbia ha-Naqdan, a scribe who flourished in 1243, was probably another person; and so was the Berakya ben Isaac (?) who translated a long extract of the Kitāb al-īmānāt wal-i'tiqādāt (Emunot we-de'ot) of Saadia ben Joseph from the Arabic. The Berakya whom we are now discussing was probably a Frenchman; witness the number of French words appearing in his Hebrew translation—for example, grêle, foudre, gésier, jaune—and there is no evidence that he knew Arabic.

Berakya is best known because of a collection of 107 (or 113) fables in rhymed prose, Mishle shu'alim, animal stories, many of which are identical with those of "Aesop" and "Romulus;" some others are comparable to those of Mary of France, a French poetess who flourished in England in the second half of the twelfth century. It is possible that both his collection and hers were derived indirectly from the same Arabic prototype. He also wrote an ethical treatise, Sefer maẓref, divided into thirteen chapters. He composed a very free translation of the Quaestiones naturales of Adelard of Bath, under the title Dodi-we-nekdi (Uncle and nephew); and a lapidary setting forth the virtues of 73 stones, called Koaḥ ha-abanim (power of stones), which includes a reference to the compass.

Text—The Mishle shu'alim were first printed in Mantua in 1557 (copies are dated 1559). Second edition, Parabolae vulpium Rabbi Barachiae Nikdani, translatae ex hebraica in linguam latinam opera R. P. Melchioris Hanel (Prague 1661, with vocalized Hebrew text). Many later editions: Berlin 1756, Prague 1767 (with Yiddish version), Grodno 1818, Warsaw 1844, Baghdād 1874, etc. Hebrew illustrated edition, with German introduction and table of contents by Lazarus Goldschmidt (Berlin 1921). There are other Yiddish editions of which I shall cite only the one included in the Sefer meshalim, the cookbook composed by Moses ben Eliezer Wallich of Worms (Francfort 1697). Facsimile reproduction of that Sefer meshalim with transliteration and an introduction by A. Freimann (Soncino Gesellschaft, no. 1, Berlin 1926).

Hermann Gollancz: Sefer maẓref (London 1902); Dodi venechdi, with English translations of the Hebrew text and of Adelard's questions (242 p., Oxford 1920; Isis, 4, 581).

Criticism—E. Renan: Rabbins français (490–499, 1877). M. Steinschneider: Hebraeische Übersetzungen (963, 1893). Joseph Jacobs: Jewish Encyclopaedia (vol. 3, 53–55, 1902); includes a table of corresponding fables in Berakya, Mary and Romulus. Henry Malter: Saadia Gaon, his life and works (Philadelphia 1921). M. Zobel: Encyclopaedia judaica (vol. 4, 182–187, 1929).

For later Hebrew lapidaries, see Joseph Jacobs: Jewish Encyclopaedia (vol. 7, 619, 1904).

[4] Naqad means to prick or mark, to put diacritical and vocal signs in a MS.; hence naqdan, punctator.

CHAPTER XVII

EDUCATION

(Second Half of Twelfth Century)

THE BIRTH OF EUROPEAN UNIVERSITIES

In ancient times, and in early mediaeval times, there have been many institutions which might have been called universities, if we mean thereby schools of higher learning. Such schools would naturally gather around any great man who was sufficiently interested in imparting his knowledge and wisdom. Thus the Academy and the Lyceum of Athens, the Museum of Alexandria, the Bayt al-ḥikma of Baghdād, the Dār al-ḥikma of Cairo, the palace and cathedral schools in Christendom, madārus in Islām, bate midrashot and yeshibot in Israel, and many other schools in India, China, and Japan, might properly be called universities, because their educational aims were sufficiently high and broad.

But if we are thinking of universities in the modern sense—as organized bodies of students and teachers, independent of and superior to any special personality, having definite statutes, pursuing definite courses of studies, keeping careful records of their memberships, and conferring degrees and diplomas—then we must recognize that all of these ancient institutions were essentially different. Indeed some of them, chiefly the Lyceum, the Museum, and the academies of Baghdād and Cairo, might be compared more adequately to the modern institutions devoted to scientific research rather than to teaching. Our universities and colleges are the modern representatives of a tradition which began in western Christendom in the twelfth century.

To quote Haskins' Renaissance of the twelfth century, (368, 1927): "In 1100 'the school followed the teacher,' by 1200 the teacher followed the school. At the same time these intervening years created a more advanced type of school by the very fact of the revival of learning. At the close of the eleventh century learning was almost entirely confined to the seven liberal arts of the traditional curriculum; the twelfth century filled out the trivium and quadrivium with the new logic, the new mathematics, and the new astronomy, while it brought into existence the professional faculties of law, medicine, and theology. Universities had not existed hitherto because there was not enough learning in Western Europe to justify their existence; they came into being naturally with the expansion of knowledge in this period. The intellectual revolution and the institutional revolution went hand in hand."

This new institution, the university, was essentially a society, a guild, of masters and pupils (universitas societas magistrorum discipulorumque). The word universitas is taken from Roman law and means corporation. It appears for the first time with its new acceptation in a letter of Innocent III in 1208–1209, and again in a charter of cardinal Robert of Courçon in 1215; but as usual the thing was much older than the word. Early universities were often called studium generale, a term emphasizing their encyclopaedic outlook. The earliest form of academic degree was simply the promotion of a scholar to mastership, the licentia docendi; this origin of our degrees is witnessed by the words doctor and master, both of which refer to teaching.

The earliest universities were those of Salerno, Bologna, Paris, Montpellier, and Oxford. They date back at least to the twelfth century, but it is impossible to say exactly when they began. The dates of foundation are necessarily arbitrary, because it was only later when people had learned by experiment what constitutes a university, that it became possible for any individual or authority to establish one deliberately. The earliest organizations of that kind grew unconsciously, and the retrospective determination of a birthdate depends on our conception of the degree of growth and organization necessary to constitute a university. It is significant that no university statutes are anterior to the thirteenth century.

The best way to illustrate these general remarks is to consider briefly the cases of the five universities above-mentioned.

SALERNO

The oldest was Salerno. It is true it was not a studium generale, but a medical college. It goes back at least to the first half of the eleventh century, but the earliest official document concerning it dates only back to 1231.

BOLOGNA

Bologna was primarily a law school. Other such schools had functioned before, in the eleventh century, in Rome, in Pavia, and in Ravenna; but thanks to the genius of Irnerio (first half of the twelfth century) and others, Bologna was the first which grew up into a studium generale. It is worthwhile noting that in Bologna it was the guild of students rather than the guild of masters which at first constituted the university; but this difference does not cut deep for it could not affect the essential relation between teacher and student. The eight hundredth anniversary of the university having been celebrated with considerable pomp in 1888, many people will conclude that it must have been founded in 1088. However, this is purely arbitrary. It is impossible to say when the University was founded, for there never was a charter of foundation. All that we know is that Bologna was already an important center of study in the first quarter of the twelfth century, that by the middle of the century its school of law was already famous, and that the university was completely organized before the end of the century.

PARIS

The university of Paris was the earliest which did not develop from a professional school, but from institutions somewhat similar to itself, though smaller and less organized. There were three great schools in Paris at the beginning of the twelfth century: that of the cathedral of Notre Dame, that of the canons regular of St. Victor, and that of the abbey of St. Geneviève across the river. All contributed to making Paris the leading intellectual center of Christendom, "a city of teachers," but it is chiefly from the cathedral school that the University sprang. The transformation was gradual and imperceptible. By 1170 the University was taking shape; the earliest college was established about 1180 by an Englishman, Josce of London. Little by little, masters and students grouped themselves in four faculties: arts, theology, law, medicine. The faculty of arts continued the tradition of the mediaeval trivium and quadrivium; the three other faculties were largely novel organizations answering the growing needs of the time. The faculty of arts was the "facultas inferior;" the three others the "facultates superiores;" the faculty of theology was of course supreme.

Though we know that the University was full-fledged before the end of the twelfth century, the earliest official document concerning it—a charter of Philip Augustus, king of France from 1180 to 1223—dates only from the year 1200. This charter did not found the University, but recognized it. The earliest statutes, and the papal recognition, date from 1208-1209; by 1231 the formal organization was complete, and indeed complaints of excessive organization were already heard!

MONTPELLIER

This case is a combination of those of Salerno and Bologna, for Montpellier developed primarily as a school of medicine and as a school of law. The former, which was perhaps as old as Salerno, was already famous in the time of St. Bernard; the latter was an offshoot of the school of Bologna. Peter of Piacenza brought the study of Roman law from Bologna to Montpellier sometime after 1160. He died in Montpellier in 1192.

The earliest statutes of the medical school date only from 1220, and the organization was completed in 1240 and recognized by a papal bull in 1289. By that time Montpellier had already blossomed into a studium generale. After the heyday of Salerno was over, Montpellier was for a short time the leading medical school. This school was partly a Jewish creation, and it is said that the earliest teaching was in Arabic and Hebrew; at any rate, Latin was the language used in the twelfth century. After the thirteenth century, Jewish doctors were expelled, or remained only on sufferance.

OXFORD

The birthdate of Oxford is equally uncertain. When English students were recalled from Paris about 1167, most of them settled in Oxford. By 1180 a considerable number of scholars were already gathered there. At the end of the century Oxford was incomparably less organized than either Paris or Bologna, yet it must have been a body of respectable size, as it was able a few years later, in 1209, to produce another university, Cambridge, by division. The first official document concerning Oxford is a legatine ordinance of 1214.

General bibliography—Heinrich Denifle: Die Universitäten des Mittelalters bis 1400 (vol. 1, Berlin 1885). Hastings Rashdall: The universities of Europe in the Middle Ages (2 vols., Oxford 1895). A new edition of this standard work is being prepared by H. H. E. Craster and F. M. Powicke. C. H. Haskins: The rise of universities (144 p., New York 1923; excellent brief account; Isis, 6, 203); Renaissance of the twelfth century (368-397, Cambridge, Mass., 1927; Isis, 10, 62-65); Studies in mediaeval culture (Oxford, 1929; Isis, 14, 433-436). Gaines Post: Alexander III, the licentia docendi and the rise of the universities (Haskins anniversary essays, 255-277, Boston 1929; Isis, 15, 210).

Special bibliography—*Salerno*—See vol. I, 683, 725.

Bologna—Chartularium studii bononiensis. Documenti per la storia dell'Università di Bologna delle origini fine al secolo XV. (8 vols., Bologna 1907-1927). Studi e memorie per la storia dell'Università (8 vols., Bologna 1907-1924).

Paris—Charles Jourdain: Index chronologicus chartarum pertinentium ad historiam Universitatis Parisiensis ab ejus originibus ad finem decimi sexti saeculi adjectis insuper pluribus instrumentis quae nondum in lucem edita erant (500 p. folio, Paris 1862; first document dated 1200). Heinrich Denifle and Emile Chatelain: Chartularium Universitatis Parisiensis (Paris 1889–1897); begins about 1160. L. Liard: L'Université de Paris (Paris 1909). Jean Bonnerot: L'ancienne Université de Paris, centre international d'études (Bulletin of the international committee of historical studies, vol. 1, 661–682, 1928).

Montpellier—Cartulaire de l'Université (2 vols., Montpellier 1890–1912); begins about 1181. Includes a history of the university by Alexandre Germain (vol. 1, 1–176). Ernest Wickersheimer: La question du judéo-arabisme à Montpellier (Janus, vol. 31, 463–473, 1927; Isis, 12, 401).

Oxford—Early documents are collected in the Oxford Collectanea (vol. 2, 137–192, 1890). Sir Charles Edward Mallet: History of the University of Oxford (3 vols., London 1924–1927). Vol. 1 contains nothing new with regard to origins.

Islām—Julián Ribera y Tarragó: La enseñanza entre los musulmanes españoles (Zaragoza 1893; reprinted in Cordoba 1925; Isis, 11, 516; and in Disertaciones y opúsculos, vol. 1, 229–359, Madrid 1928; elaborate study including a number of Arabic documents; Isis, 12, 161–163); Origen del colegio Nidamí de Bagdad (Homenaje a D. Francisco Codera, Zaragoza 1914; reprinted in Disertaciones, vol. 1, 361–83).

The Niẓāmī madrasa in Baghdād was named after Niẓām al-mulk, wazīr to Alp Arslān, Saljūq shāh from 1063 to 1072; according to Ribera it was the model of all later colleges, east and west, but it was not by any means the earliest madrasa. Granted that Muslim colleges of the university type preceded the Christian ones, and may have been, however indirectly, one of the causes leading to the creation of the latter, the fact remains that our modern universities originated towards the end of the twelfth century. From then on the growth was continuous.

Israel—Judah David Eisenstein: Yeshibah (Jewish encyclopaedia, vol. 12, 595–600, 1906).

For John of Salisbury, see Chapter XXVI, Law and Sociology.
For Gerald the Welshman, see Chapter XXII, Geography.
For Lu Chiu-ÿan, see Chapter XVIII, Philosophic Background.

CHAPTER XVIII

PHILOSOPHIC BACKGROUND

(Second Half of Twelfth Century)

I. WESTERN MUSLIM

IBN ṬUFAIL

Abū Bakr Muḥammad ibn 'Abd al-Malik ibn Muḥammad ibn Muḥammad ibn Ṭufail al-Qaisī. Hispano-Muslim philosopher and physician. Al-Qaisī refers to his ethnical origin, the Arab tribe of Qais. From Abū Bakr was derived his Latin name Abubacer. He was also called Abū Ja'far, al-Andalusī, al-Qurṭubī, al-Ishbīlī (the Andalusian, Cordovan, Sevillan). He was born about 1100–1110 in Wādī Āsh, modern Guadix, northeast of Granada. A physician in Granada; later secretary to the governor of the province; in 1154–1155 secretary to the governor of Ceuta and Tangier; finally physician to the Almohade Abū Ya'qūb Yūsuf I (sulṭān 1163–1184); old age obliged him to resign in 1182–1183 to be succeeded by his friend Ibn Rushd. He died in Marrākush in 1185–1186.

Ibn Ṭufail wrote one of the most original books of the Middle Ages, a philosophical romance called after its hero, Ḥaiy ibn Yaqẓān,[1] with the subtitle Asrār al-ḥikma al-ishrāqīya (Secrets of illuminative philosophy). It is the history of a sort of metaphysical Robinson Crusoe proving the identity of revealed religion and philosophy, this philosophy being the extreme Muslim neo-Platonism. And as very few people are able to understand philosophy, it justifies the doctrine of the twofold truth. The introduction contains an account of the development of Muslim philosophy. The story itself includes a sketch of a natural classification of the sciences, a discussion of spontaneous generation, and miscellaneous scientific information. It was translated into Hebrew, and Moses ibn Joshua of Narbonne (second half of the fourteenth century) wrote a commentary upon it in 1349.

It should be noted that the idea of this romance was not entirely new. Ibn Sīnā had written an allegoric risālat bearing the same title. But the comparison ends there. Ibn Ṭufail borrowed the name of his heroes from Ibn Sīnā, nothing more. It is said that a similar story was translated from the Greek by Ḥunain ibn Isḥāq. One can conceive its genesis in Hellenistic neo-Platonic circles, yet the endless discussions of Muslim theologians could not but increase its significance. The romantic frame of the story is certainly old; it is found in an ancient Arabic tale of the Alexander cycle. But Ibn Ṭufail was the first to exploit it with sufficient completeness and to develop the philosophical side of it, which after all, was the essential thing. He was the real creator of it, and he it was who drew the world's attention to it.

Ibn Ṭufail wrote two medical treatises (lost?), and gave advice to Ibn Rushd with regard to the latter's Aristotelian commentaries and to his Kullīyāt. He

[1] This proper name is symbolic. It means the Living One, son of the Vigilant; the Vigilant is God: i.e., the intellect of man derives from the Divine Intellect.

wrote a commentary on Aristotle's Meteorologica. He it was who suggested to al-Biṭrūjī the latter's modification of the theory of homocentric spheres.

Text—Ḥaiy ibn Yaqẓān was first published by Edward Pococke, Sr. (1604–1691), together with a Latin translation by Edward Pococke, Jr. (1648–1727): Philosophus autodidactus sive Epistola Abi Jaafar ebn Tophail de Hai ebn Yokdhan, in qua ostenditur, quomodo ex inferiorum contemplatione ad superiorum notitiam ratio humana ascendere possit (200 p., Oxford 1671; 2d ed. identical with first, Oxford 1700). Oriental editions published in 1299 H. (= 1881–1882), at least 4 in Cairo and 2 in Constantinople. Latest edition based on a new MS. and reexamination of the others by Léon Gauthier, with French translation (Alger 1900).

Other Translations—English translations by Ashwell; by George Keith; by Simon Ockley (London 1708, reprinted 1731; Cairo 1905; London 1929); by Paul Brönnle (Wisdom of the East, 86 p., 4th impression, London 1910; Isis, 1, 514). Dutch translation by A. M. (Amsterdam 1672, reprinted 1701). German translations by J. Georg Pritius (Francfort 1726); by J. G. Eichhorn (Berlin 1782, 1783). Spanish translation by Francesco Pons y Boigues (Zaragoza 1900, with a translation of Avicenna's risāla under same title). Russian translation by J. Kuzmin(Leningrad 1920).

Criticism—The principal study is by Léon Gauthier: Ibn Thofail. Sa vie, ses oeuvres (Publications de l'école des lettres d'Alger, vol. 42, 130 p., Paris 1909).

F. Wüstenfeld: Geschichte der arabischen Aerzte (108, 1840). S. Munk: Mélanges de philosophie juive (410–418, 1859). L. Leclerc: Médecine arabe (vol. 2, 113–114, 1876). F. Wüstenfeld: Geschichtschreiber der Araber (95, 1881). M. Steinschneider: Hebraeische Uebersetzungen (363–368, 1893). C. Brockelmann: Arabische Litteratur (vol. 1, 460, 1898). H. Suter: Die Mathematiker und Astronomen der Araber (125, 218, 1900). De Boer: Geschichte der Philosophie im Islam (160–165, 1901). D. B. Macdonald: Muslim theology (252–255, 1903). P. Duhem: Système du Monde (vol. 2, 132, 1914). Carra de Vaux: Encyclopaedia of Islām (vol. 2, 424–425, 1918); Penseurs de l'Islam (vol. 4, 56–65, 1923). D. K. Petrof: Un problème hispano-arabe (Zapiski; Mémoires du comité des orientalistes, vol. 2, Leningrad 1926); concludes that Ibn Ṭufail did not influence the Spanish writer, Baltasar Gracian (1601–1658) in the latter's Criticón (Saragossa 1651). Emilio García Gómez: Un cuento árabe fuente común de Abentofáil y de Gracián (Revista de archivos, bibliotecas y museos, año 30, 100 p., Madrid 1926; Isis, 15, 404); contains the Arabic text of the old Arabic tale to which I referred, and a Spanish translation; shows that that tale was known to Ibn Ṭufail and to Gracian. See analysis of García's memoir by Ign. Kratchkovsky (Litteris, vol. 4, 28–33, 1927).

IBN RUSHD

Averroës. Abū-l-Walīd Muḥammad ibn Aḥmad ibn Muḥammad ibn Rushd, born in Cordova in 1126. He belonged to an illustrious Cordovan family. His grandfather and namesake Abū-l-Walīd Muḥammad ibn Aḥmad ibn Rushd, who was born in 1058–1059 and died at Cordova in 1126, was a distinguished Mālikite theologian, qāḍī and imām of the great mosque of Cordova.[2] His father, less important, was also a qāḍī. The younger Abū-l-Walīd studied law and medicine in his native city; in 1153–1154 he was in Marrākush, Morocco; in 1169–1170 he was qāḍī of Seville, and two years later qāḍī of Cordova. In 1182–1183 the Almohade caliph Abū Ya'qūb Yūsuf (1163–1184) called him to Marrākush to replace

[2] He wrote a number of juridical treatises for which see C. Brockelmann: Arabische Litteratur (vol. 1, 384, 1898).

Ibn Ṭufail as his physician. The succeeding caliph, Ya'qūb al-Manṣūr (1184–1199), patronized him for awhile, then banished him to Lucena near Cordova, ordering all his books except the strictly scientific ones to be burnt (1194–1195). In 1198 Ibn Rushd was forgiven and recalled to Marrākush, where he died soon afterward, Dec. 10, 1198. He was the greatest Muslim philosopher of the West, and one of the greatest of mediaeval times. Commentator on Aristotle ("The Commentator," "Averrois che'l gran comento feo," Dante, Inferno, IV, 144); physician, astronomer.

He wrote three commentaries on the works of Aristotle as he knew them through Arabic translations (he had no knowledge of Greek): the short (jāmi', meaning summa or σύνοψις; it is rather a summary than a commentary); the intermediate (talkhīṣ); and the long (sharḥ or tafsīr). These three commentaries corresponded to different stages in education, the short one being studied first, then the intermediate, finally the long one. (This general method is still followed in the madārus.) The long commentary was an innovation, probably inspired by Qur'ānic exegesis, the original texts upon which it was based being fully quoted and carefully separated from the glosses. Most of these commentaries are preserved in Hebrew translations, or in Latin translations from the Hebrew, and a few in the original Arabic (generally in Hebrew script); the commentary on the Zoology is entirely lost. Ibn Rushd wrote also commentaries on Plato's Republic, Galen's treatise on fevers, al-Fārābī's logic, Ibn Sīnā, etc.

He wrote a medical encyclopaedia called Kitāb al-kullīyāt fī-l-ṭibb (hence the Latin name Colliget,[3] which has no relation to colligo; it is simply a corruption of the Arabic word kullīyāt, meaning here generalities—that is, generalities on medicine), Liber universalis de medicina, written before 1162, in seven books treating respectively of anatomy, health (physiology), general pathology, diagnosis, materia medica, hygiene, and general therapeutics (see my note on Ibn Zuhr, first half of the twelfth century). He recognized that no one is taken twice with the smallpox. He understood the function of the retina. The Kullīyāt is far inferior to the Qānūn, and its scope is much smaller, corresponding only to the first book of the Qānūn. He also wrote a commentary on Ibn Sīnā's medical poem, or Canticum, Arjūza (or manẓūma) fī-l-ṭibb (see my note on Armangaud, son of Blaise, second half of the thirteenth century). Ibn Rushd's fame as a physician was entirely eclipsed by his fame as a philosopher and commentator.

He wrote also a treatise on the motion of the sphere (Kitāb fī ḥarakat al-falak), and a summary of the Almagest. The latter is divided into two parts: description of the spheres, and movement of the spheres (Is this equivalent to the treatise on the motion of the sphere?). The summary of the Almagest was translated from Arabic into Hebrew by Jacob Anaṭoli in 1231; it was never translated into Latin.

The dated writings of Ibn Rushd may be classified chronologically as follows:

1159. Commentary on the smaller physical writings of Aristotle.

Before 1162. Kullīyāt.

1169. Jāmi' of the Parts and Generation of animals (Seville).

1170. Talkhīṣ on the Physics and on the Posterior analytics (Seville).

1171. Commentary on the De coelo et mundo (Seville).

1174. Jāmi' of the Rhetoric and Poetry. Talkhīṣ on Metaphysics (Cordova).

1176. Talkhīṣ on the Nicomachean Ethics.

[3] The intercalary *g* in colliget would suggest that the Latin translation was made in Spain (Leclerc).

1178. Part of the commentary on the De substantia orbis (Morocco).
1179. Kitāb al-kashf 'an manāhij al-adilla fī 'aqā'id al-milla (Seville).
1181. Talkhīṣ on the De anima.
1186. Tafsīr on Physics.
1193. Commentary on Galen's De febribus.
1195. Questions on logic (written while in disgrace).

(It should be kept in mind that these dated writings are only a few as compared with Ibn Rushd's total production. Nor have I tried to mention elsewhere all of his writings; I have named only the most important, and those about which I had something to say.)

His philosophy was not at all as original as various distortions of it have led us to believe. It continued the tradition of Muslim scholasticism, and in a sense might be said to represent the culmination of Muslim effort in one essential direction, the understanding of Aristotle's thought. From al-Kindī on every Muslim philosopher had done his best to understand that thought, but most of them had failed because they mistook various neo-Platonic works for genuine peripatetic ones. These had gradually reached them, and by the time of Ibn Rushd the Aristotelian works were entirely available in Arabic and the spuriousness of many pseudo-Aristotelian works was recognized. The main difference between Ibn Rushd and his great predecessor Ibn Sīnā lies in the fact that the former was a more thorough Aristotelian than the latter. It is a strange paradox that Ibn Rushd should have obtained a reputation for heterodoxy, for he was far more anxious than any of his predecessors to discover the true meaning of Aristotle's views; that is, he did just what they did, but more thoroughly. His intellectual effort was essentially a reaction against the mysticism and pragmatism of al-Ghazzālī, a return to what one might call Aristotelian positivism, as much as this could be reconciled with Muslim theology. For example, he tried to reconcile the Aristotelian notion of the eternity of the world, which seems to imply a denial of creation, with Muslim creationism. God is eternal, and His creative effort is perpetual; He creates time (or duration) as well as the world, and He may have created it from all eternity, inasmuch as He is Himself without cause. Note that it is easy to reconcile this notion with that of evolution, though in this case it is not so much the creature as the creating power which evolves, the final result remaining the same. For further elucidation of these views see Macdonald's paper of 1927 quoted below; his discussion is mainly based upon Maimonides, but it applies equally well to Ibn Rushd.

Ibn Rushd's chief philosophical work (other than the commentaries) was his reply to al-Ghazzālī's attack on rationalism; it was entitled The destruction of the destruction (Tahāfut al-tahāfut); al-Ghazzālī's work was entitled The destruction (or vanity) of philosophy, Tahāfut al-falāsifa. To complete the history of that famous philosophic and literary battle, I may add that the 'Uthmānlī sulṭān Muḥammad II (ruled 1451-1481) commissioned one of his mullahs, Muṣṭafā ibn Yūsuf al-Bursawī, Muṣliḥ al-dīn, commonly called Khwāja (or Khoja) Zāda (d. 1487-1488), to write a third destruction, The destruction of the destruction of the destruction, in order to vindicate once more the weakness of human understanding and the strength of faith (see Ḥājī Khalīfa, Lexicon bibliographicum, vol. 2, 475, 1837). Strangely enough, Ibn Rushd was best known in Islām for his Tahāfut al tahāfut, while his commentaries made considerably more stir in the Jewish and Christian worlds than in the Muslim.

The much discussed theory of twofold truth—the one more esoteric for the philosophers, the other more concrete and more literal for the masses; or, the one philosophical, the other theological—attributed to Ibn Rushd by Christian schoolmen, exists potentially if not explicitly in his writings. Indeed a doctrine of twofold (or manifold) truth was fundamental with all Muslim thinkers. It is really an economy of teaching, "Teach the people as they can understand."[4] Indeed it is not peculiarly Muslim, but universal; for example, see the Gospel according to St. Matthew (chapter 13, verses 10–11). One can neither teach the same things to all people, nor teach all people in the same words. Moreover, anyone attempting to reconcile religion with philosophy, or faith with reason, without being aware of the impossibility of the task, was irresistibly led to an implicit, if not explicit, acknowledgment of twofold truth, but somehow the odium of such "duplicity" was thrown chiefly upon Ibn Rushd, even as his personality became gradually more obnoxious to the defenders of Muslim, Jewish, or Christian orthodoxy. Ibn Rushd was not by any means less honest and sincere, nor was he necessarily less pious, than the other schoolmen; but he was more intelligent, and his deeper vision enabled him to reconcile statements which seemed irreconcilable to others. The more narrow and evil interpretation of the theory of twofold truth was expressly refuted by him (Miguel Asín, 1904).

Though I shall have many opportunities to refer to the vicissitudes of Averroism in the following chapters, it is useful to give here a brief outline of them. Ibn Rushd did not influence Muslim philosophy considerably for the simple reason that it was approaching the end of its vitality; Ibn Rushd was the last of the great Arabic-writing philosophers. But he deeply influenced Jewish philosophy through many translators and disciples; Jewish Averroism reached its zenith under Levi ben Gershon (first half of the fourteenth century), and it continued to prosper until the end of the fifteenth century. The Christian schoolmen were influenced as deeply as the Jewish, and in various ways. To begin with, the success of Ibn Rushd's commentaries had caused orthodox revulsions everywhere—first among the Muslims of Spain, soon afterward among the Talmudists, and finally in Christendom. Aristotle and Ibn Rushd reached the Christian schoolmen at about the same time, and during the first period of reaction they were treated as a single evil: in 1210, they were both forbidden by a provincial council at Paris; in 1215 the prohibition was confirmed with special reference to the Metaphysics; in 1231 a papal injunction interdicted the reading of their works until their complete expurgation. Meanwhile Averroism, being ostracized, became necessarily more subversive. Thomas Aquinas' immense effort was essentially a part of the general reaction against the heterodox doctrines which had gradually gathered under the Averroistic banner of revolt. By the year 1277 the bishop of Paris was able to condemn specifically 219 errors in the teachings of these troublemakers. Thus Ibn Rushd came to be regarded as the arch-infidel, and the greatest enemy of the faith. This was absolutely wrong; he was neither better nor worse than St. Thomas himself; his creed was different, but his intellectual purpose was essentially the same, and his honesty and good-will not inferior. As shown by Renan, the history of Averroism is nothing but a series of misunderstandings.

Text—An elaborate list of Ibn Rushd's writings was given by Renan in his Averroës (3d. ed., p. 58–79, 1869, and later editions); this list includes writings which we know only indirectly (e.g., through Ibn abī Uṣaibi'a), and is divided

[4] D. B. Macdonald: Life of al-Ghazzālī (Journal Am. Oriental Soc., 20, 125 ff., 1899).

as follows: (1) Philosophy, 28 items; (2) Theology, 5 items; (3) Law, 8 items; (4) Astronomy, 4 items; (5) Grammar, 2 items; (6) Medicine, 20 items.

Philosophical Writings and Commentaries

The Latin editio princeps of Aristotle with Ibn Rushd's commentaries appeared in Padua in 1472, 1473, and 1474. A large number of editions followed within the same century; more than 50 in Venice alone, of which 14 or 15 were almost complete. The best Latin editions are those of Niphus (Agostino Nifo, 1453–1538), 1495–1497, and of the Juntas, 1553, etc. Even these editions are barbaric enough, which is not surprising when one realizes that the texts published are generally a Latin translation of a Hebrew translation of an Arabic commentary based upon an Arabic translation of a Syriac translation of the original Greek!

In meteorologica Aristotelis, Latinized by Elias Cretensis Hebraeus (Venice 1488).

The commentaries were translated into Hebrew by Samuel ibn Tibbon, first half of the thirteenth century; by Jacob Anaṭoli in Naples in 1232; by Judah ben Solomon Cohen of Toledo in 1247; by Moses ibn Tibbon in 1260, etc.; by Qalonymos ben Qalonymos in 1314, etc. Michael Scott and Hermann the German began Latin translations about 1220 and 1240, respectively. These translations were improved towards the end of the fifteenth century by Agostino Nifo and by Abraham de Balmès of Padua, and in the first half of the sixteenth century by Jacob Mantino of Tortosa, and Giovanni Francesco Burana of Verona.

The first Arabic edition of a text of Ibn Rushd, at least in the West, did not appear until 1859. That was M. J. Müller's edition of two or three treatises on the relations of philosophy and theology, Kitāb faṣl al-maqāl and supplement, and Kitāb al-kashf 'an manāhij (Munich 1859; reprinted in Cairo in 1894–1895). German translation by the same, Philosophie und Theologie des Averroës (Munich 1875). English translation by Mohammad Jamil ur-Rehman (Baroda 1921; Isis, 8, 538).

Jacob Freudenthal and Siegmund Fränkel: Die durch Averroes erhaltenen Fragmente Alexanders zur Metaphysik (134 p., Abhdl. d. Akad. der Wiss., Berlin 1884). Max Horten: Die Metaphysik des Averroes nach dem Arabischen übersetzt und erläutert (Abhdl. zur Philosophie und ihrer Geschichte, no. 36, 252 p., Halle 1912); German translation of the jāmi' of the Metaphysics. Carlos Quirós Rodríguez: Compendio de metafísica (524 p., Madrid 1919); Arabic text of the same jāmi', with Spanish translation, introduction, and glossary. S. Van den Bergh: Die Epitome der Metaphysik übersetzt (375 p., Leiden 1924).

Tahāfut al-tahāfut. Printed edition, Cairo, 1303 H. M. Horten: Die Hauptlehren von Averroes nach seiner Schrift, Die Wiederlegung des Gazali, aus dem Arabischen Originale übersetzt und erläutert (Bonn 1913). The Jesuit fathers of Beirut are preparing a critical edition (Isis, 10, 497). Latin text with commentary by Augustinus Niffus (Venice 1497).

Fausto Lasinio: Il commento medio di Averroe alla Poetica di Aristotile (Pisa 1872; Arabic and Italian). Friedrich Heidenhain: Averrois paraphrasis in librum poeticae, Iacob Mantino interprete ex libris qui Venetiis apud Iunctas 1562 prodiit (Jahrbücher für classische Philologie, Suppl., 17, 351–382, 1890).

Fausto Lasinio: Il commento medio alla Retorica (100 p., Florence 1877; Arabic).

J. Hercz: Drei Abhandlungen über die Conjunction des separaten Intellektes mit dem Menschen (Berlin 1869; Hebrew version by Samuel ibn Tibbon; German version, and notes). L. Hannes: Des Averroes Abhandlungen "Ueber die Möglichkeit der Conjunction" und "Ueber den materiellen Intellect" (Halle 1892; Hebrew and German).

Medical writings

The Kullīyāt was translated from Arabic into Latin, not by Armengaud, son of Blaise (second half of the thirteenth century), but by the Jew Bonacosa (second half of the thirteenth century), in Padua 1255. The Latin translation completed by Symphorien Champier (1472-1539) about 1537, included in vol. 10 of the Aristotle-Averroes, was not made from the Hebrew, but was simply a revision of Bonacosa's version. The Kullīyāt was twice translated into Hebrew; by an anonymous writer, and by Solomon ben Abraham ben David of unknown time.

The Colliget was often printed together with the works of Yaḥyā ibn Sarāfyūn and al-Rāzī (e.g., Strassburg 1531, edited by Otto Brunfels), and of Ibn Zuhr (Venice 1490, 1496, 1497, 1514, 1530, 1531, 1533). It was printed separately in Ferrara and in Venice in 1482, this being the Latin princeps.

Ibn Sīnā's Arjūza (Canticum) and Ibn Rushd's commentary were translated into Hebrew prose by Moses ibn Tibbon in 1260; a translation into Hebrew verse by Solomon ben Ayyub ben Joseph of Granada was completed at Béziers in 1261. The same texts were translated into Latin by Armengaud, son of Blaise, in 1280 or 1284, and printed in Venice in 1484, etc. This translation was revised by Andrea Alpago (second half of the fifteenth century), whose notes appear in the Aristotle-Averroes (vol. 10, p. 242 ff.).

De venenis, edited by Baptista de Avolio (Bologna, c. 1497–1500).

General criticism—Ernest Renan: Averroës et l'averroisme (379 p., Paris 1852; 2d ed., 502 p., 1861; 3d ed., 1869, often reprinted). This admirable work has justly become a classic; it is a penetrating study which every student of mediaeval philosophy ought to read, but it must be used with caution. A revised edition would be very desirable. It contains in the appendix a number of Arabic and Latin documents on Ibn Rushd, his works, and influence. M. Steinschneider: Hebraeische Uebersetzungen (276–279, 546–549, 671–677, 1893). C. Brockelmann: Arabische Litteratur (vol. 1, 461–462, 1898). A. Löwenthal and I. Broydé: Jewish Encyclopaedia (vol. 2, 346–348, 1902). Carra de Vaux: Encyclopaedia of Islām (vol. 2, 410–413, 1918); Penseurs de l'Islam (vol. 4, 1923). Giuseppe Gabrieli: Averroè (Archivio di storia della scienza, vol. 5, 156–162, 1924). Maurice Bouyges: Inventaire des textes arabes d'Averroes (Mélanges de l'Université St. Joseph, vol. 8, 54 p.; vol. 9, 43–48, Beirut 1922–1924). Gesamtkatalog der Wiegendrucke (vol. 3, 216–219, 1928). B. Suler: Encyclopaedia judaica (vol. 3, 766–775, 1929).

Philosophic criticism—S. Munk: Mélanges de philosophie juive (418–458, 1859). Auguste Fernand van Mehren: Etudes sur la philosophie d'Averrhoës concernant son rapport avec celle d'Avicenne et Gazzali (Muséum, vol. 7, 613–627; vol. 8, 5–20; Louvain 1888–1889). De Boer: Die Widerspruche der Philosophie nach al-Gazzalī und ihr Ausgleich durch Ibn Rosd (Strassburg 1894); Geschichte der Philosophie im Islam (165–176, 1901). M. Worms: Die Lehre von der Anfangslosigkeit der Welt bei den mittelalterlichen arabischen Philosophen. (Beitr. zur Gesch. der Philos. des Mittelalters, vol. 3, no. 4, 78 p., Münster 1900); contains in the appendix the Hebrew version of a short tract, 4 p., of Ibn Rushd on the problem of creation. Anṭūn Fārah: Ibn Rushd wa-falsafatuhu (Alexandria

1903). D. B. Macdonald: Development of Muslim theology (255, 1903). Miguel Asín: El averroismo teológico de Santo Tomás de Aquino (Homenaje a D. Francisco Codera, 271–331, Zaragosa 1904). Hartwig Derenbourg: Le commentaire d'Averroës sur quelques petits écrits physiques d'Aristotle (Archiv für Geschichte der Philosophie, vol. 18, 250, 1905; commentary on Φυσικὴ ἀκρόασις, Περὶ οὐρανοῦ καὶ κόσμου, Περὶ γενέσεως καὶ φθορᾶς, Μετεωρολογικά, Περὶ ψυχῆς, Μεταφυσικά). Léon Gauthier: La théorie d'Ibn Rochd sur les rapports de la religion et de la philosophie (Paris 1909). D. B. Macdonald: Religious attitude and life in Islām (124, 227, Chicago 1909; on twofold truth). Pierre de Mandonnet: Siger de Brabant et l'averroïsme latin au XIIIe siècle (Fribourg 1899; 2d ed., Louvain 1911–1908; including unpublished documents). Maurice Bouyges: Notes sur les philosophes arabes connus des Latins au Moyen âge (Mélanges de l'Université St. Joseph, vol. 7, 397–406, 1921). D. B. Macdonald: Continuous re-creation and atomic time in Muslim scholastic theology (important; Isis, 9, 326–344, 1927).

Scientific criticism—H. Suter: Die Mathematiker und Astronomen der Araber (127, 1900; Nachträge, 174, 1902). Léon Gauthier: Une réforme du système astronomique de Ptolémée. (Journal Asiatique, vol. 14, 483–510, 1909; important). P. Duhem: Système du monde (vol. 1, 234–239, 1913), on the plurality of worlds, and gravity, comparing Ibn Rushd's interpretation of Aristotle with that of Simplicios; (vol. 2, 133–139, 1914), Ibn Rushd's peripatetic criticism of Ptolemy; (386–389) on tides; (vol. 4, 511–520, 532–575, 1916), mainly philosophic. E. Wiedemann: Ueber die angebliche Beobachtung eines Planetendurganges durch Averroës und andere (Das Weltall, 20. J., 180–181, 1920). H. G. Farmer: History of Arabian music (225, 1929; Isis, 13, 375).

Medical criticism—F. Wüstenfeld: Geschichte der arabischen Aerzte (104–108, 1840); with long bibliography. L. Leclerc: Médecine arabe (vol. 2, 97–109, 1876). V. Fukala: Averroes war der erste, welche die Netzhaut als den lichtempfindlichen Teil des Auges erkannte (Archiv für Augenheilkunde, vol. 42, 203 sq., Wiesbaden 1900).

ABŪ-L-'ABBĀS AL-SIBTĪ

Born in Ceuta (hence the name Sibtī), he flourished in the city of Marrākush under the Almohade Ya'qūb al-Manṣūr (ruled 1184–1199); he died there in the odor of sanctity after having distributed all his belongings to the poor. Moroccan ṣūfī and astrologer. I mention him because Ibn Khaldūn devotes considerable space in his Prolegomena (de Slane; vol. 1, 245–247; vol. 3, 199–206) to the description of his zā'irja-l-'ālam, a magical table of the universe, which was used in conjunction with astrological data for the purpose of divination.

II. EASTERN MUSLIM

For Ibn al-Dahhān and al-Marghīnānī, see Chapter XXVI, Law and Sociology.
For 'Alī al-Bayhaqī, see Chapter XXV, Historiography.
For 'Abd al-Raḥmān al-Shīrāzī, see Chapter XXIV, Medicine.

YAḤYĀ AL-SUHRAWARDĪ

Abū-l-Futūḥ Yaḥyā (or Aḥmad) ibn Ḥabash ibn Amīrak, Shihāb al-dīn. He was born at Suhraward near Sulṭānīyah, Jibāl, about 1154; studied in Marāghah; flourished probably in Ḥiṣn Kayfā, and later in Baghdād and Aleppo during the rule of al-Ẓāhir (1186–1216), son of Ṣalāḥ al-dīn; he was put to death, at al-Ẓāhir's advice, in Aleppo in 1191. (Hence his popular name, al-shaikh al-maqtūl, the murdered sheikh; maqtūl is here used in opposition to shahīd, martyr). A Muslim ṣūfī who was one of the originators (at least in the East) of a new doctrine or method called ḥikmat al-ishrāq (illuminism), his followers being named ishrāqīyūn. He dedicated to the Urtuqid of Kayfā, Qarā Arslān (ruled from about 1148 to 1174) the Kitāb al-alwāḥ al-'Imādīya, dealing with infinity, the absolute, etc. His chief work, Kitāb ḥikmat al-ishrāq, was completed in 1186; it was largely an attack on Peripatetic philosophy. He wrote various other works on philosophy and mysticism: Kitāb al-talwīḥāt (Elucidations); Kitāb al-mashāri' wal-muṭāraḥāt (Crosswords and conversations); Kitāb al-lumaḥāt fī-l-ḥaqāi'q (Glimpses of the truth); Kitāb hayākil al-nūr (Temples of light); etc.

The Ḥikmat al-ishrāq was a combination of old Iranian elements with neo-Platonism, Gnosticism, and other Hellenistic dreams, Muslim theology, and Shī'ite occultism. Al-Suhrawardī was well acquainted with sīmiyā' (natural magic). It would seem that this syncretism originated in the Far West as early as the tenth century, Ibn Masarra of Cordova being the real founder (see my note on Ibn 'Arabī, first half of the thirteenth century). It is probable that al-Suhrawardī was not even the first in the East, for such tendencies as his were very old in Islām. Ibn Sīnā had written a book entitled Kitāb al-ḥikmat al-mashriqīya, but this, be it noted, was not a book on ishrāq but simply on eastern philosophy.

Text—Lithographic edition of the Ḥikmat al-ishrāq (Teheran 1898). Max Horten: Die Philosophie der Erleuchtung nach Suhrawardi (94 p., Halle 1912: annotated translation).

Criticism—Ibn Khallikān: de Slane's translation (vol. 4, 153–159, 1871). C. Brockelmann: Arabische Litteratur (vol. 1, 437–438, 1898). Carra de Vaux: La philosophie illuminative d'après Suhrawerdi Meqtoul (Journal asiatique, vol. 19, 63–94, 1902); Muḥammad Iqbal: The development of metaphysics in Persia (121–150, London 1908). C. A. Nallino: Filosofia "orientale" od "illuminativa" d'Avicenna (Rivista degli studi orientali, vol. 10, 433–467, 1925). S. Van den Bergh: De tempels van het licht (Tijdschift voor wijsbegeerte, vol. 10, 30–59, 1916); Encyclopaedia of Islām (vol. 4, 506, 1927).

For the definition of ishrāq, see Ibn Khaldūn: Prolégomènes (de Slane's translation, vol. 3, 167, 1868); and the brief articles by Cl. Huart and T. J. de Boer in the Encyclopaedia of Islām (vol. 2, 305, 533, 1916–1921). For the definition of sīmiyā', see D. B. Macdonald's elaborate article in the Encyclopaedia of Islām (vol. 4, 425–426, 1927).

IBN AL-JAUZĪ

Abū-l-Faraj (or Faḍā'il) 'Abd al-Raḥmān ibn 'Alī ibn Muḥammad, Jamāl al-dīn. Muslim (Ḥanbalite) encyclopaedist, born in Baghdād about 1115, flourished in Baghdād and in Mecca; he died in Baghdād in 1201. He was one of the most learned men of his time, and his immense literary activity was equalled in Islām only by al-Suyūṭī's (second half of the fifteenth century). His almost innumerable writings treat of history, philology, biography, ḥadīth, fiqh, the Qur'ān, ethics, medicine, geography, etc. His most important work seems to be a history of the world from the creation to 1180, entitled Kitāb al-muntaẓam wa multaqaṭ-al-multazam. He prepared a critical edition of al-Ghazzālī's Iḥyā. He wrote a treatise on medical generalities called Luqāṭ al-manāfi' fī-l-ṭibb, and another on spiritual medicine, Kitāb al-ṭibb al-rūḥānī. Also a sort of autobiography in the form of a letter to his son, Liftat al-kabid, followed by a list of his writings; he compiled two other lists of these.

Text—Apparently there is no critical edition of any of his works.
Criticism—Ibn Khallikān: de Slane's translation (vol. 2, 96–98, 1843). L. Leclerc: Médecine arabe (vol. 2, 36, 1876). F. Wüstenfeld: Geschichtschreiber der Araber (102–104, 1881). C. Brockelmann: Arabische Litteratur (vol. 1, 499–506, 1898); Encyclopaedia of Islām (vol. 2, 372, 1916).

'UMAR AL-SUHRAWARDĪ

Abū Ḥafṣ 'Umar ibn 'Abdallāh al-Suhrawardī (not to be confused with Abū-l-Futūḥ Yaḥyā al-Suhrawardī; both received the same title of honor, Shihāb al-dīn). Born in Suhraward, Jibāl, in 1144–1145, flourished in Baṣra, and later in Baghdād where he died in 1234–1235. Shāfi'ite doctor and Ṣūfī, who wrote a number of books on philosophy and mysticism; e.g., Kitāb 'awārif al-ma'ārif (Benefits of knowledge), and the Kashf al-faḍā'iḥ al-Yūnānīya (Exposition of Greek shame), a criticism of Greek philosophy, dedicated to the 'Abbāsid caliph al-Nāṣir (ruled 1180–1224); the second treatise is also entitled Kashf al-naṣā'iḥ al-īmānīya. The 'Awārif treats primarily of ethics and practical mysticism, but it contains also some historical notes; it is one of the most popular Ṣūfī treatises. The famous Persian poet Sa'dī studied under 'Umar al-Suhrawardī in Baghdād.

Text—The 'Awārif was published in Cairo on the margins of al-Ghazzālī's Iḥyā; it was translated into Persian by Maḥmūd ibn 'Alī al-Kāshānī, and this Persian translation was Englished by Henry Wilberforce Clarke (174 p., Calcutta 1891).
Criticism—C. Brockelmann: Arabische Litteratur (vol. 1, 440, 1898). S. Van Den Bergh: Encyclopaedia of Islām (vol. 4, 506, 1927).

NIẒĀMĪ-I-'ARŪḌĪ

Aḥmad ibn 'Umar ibn 'Alī al-Samarqandī al-Niẓāmī al-'Arūḍī. Persian courtier and writer, born towards the end of the eleventh century, he was still alive in 1152; flourished in Samarkand and in Khurāsān. He wrote in Persian, sometime between 1150 and 1160, his chief work, the Four Discourses (Chahār[5] maqāla) dealing respectively with the four classes of men indispensable for the service of kings: secretaries, poets, astrologers and physicians. It contains general reflections and anecdotes relative to medicine and astrology. Evolutionary views with a suggestion of transitional elements between the three kingdoms: the coral being an intermediate between mineral and plant, the date-palm[6] between plant and animal, and the nasnās (ape or wild man?) between animal and man.

Text and translations—The text of the Four Discourses has been edited, with introduction, notes and indices by Mīrzā Muḥammad ibn 'Abdu'l-Wahhāb of Qazwīn (Gibb Memorial Series, vol. 11, 1, Leyden 1910). E. G. Browne translated it into English in the Journal of the Royal Asiatic Society (July and October 1899; reprint 140 p.). Revised edition of this translation (Gibb Mem. Ser., vol. 11, 2, 184 p., Leyden 1921); this includes an abridged translation of Mīrzā Muḥammad's notes on the Persian text.
Criticism—E. G. Browne: Literary history of Persia (vol. 2, 336–340, passim, 1906); Arabian medicine (Cambridge 1921).

[5] The letters *ch* in this word stand for the Persian letter *che*, the seventh letter of the Persian alphabet.

[6] The sexual reproduction of the date-palm had been known for many centuries and even acilitated by the husbandman's efforts.

FAKHR AL-DĪN AL-RĀZĪ

Abū 'Abdallāh Muḥammad ibn 'Umar ibn al-Ḥusain ibn al-Khaṭīb Fakhr al-dīn al-Rāzī. Often called the Imām Rāzī. Persian philosopher, historian, mathematician, astronomer, physician, Shāfi'ite theologian, encyclopaedist, writing in Arabic and in Persian. Born at Ray, Jibāl, in 1149, he traveled in Khwārizm and Mā-warā-l-nahr (Transoxiana), and finally settled in Herāt where he died in 1210.

His activity was prodigious, and he left so many writings, few of which have been studied, that it is very difficult to choose between them and to judge them and him correctly. The most important seem to be the following: (1) a treatise on Euclid's postulates; (2) an astrological treatise, originally composed in Persian, which was dedicated to 'Alā al-dīn Muḥammad (Shāh of Khwārizm 1199–1220) and called after him Al-ikhtiyārāt al-'Alā'īya; (3) another called Sirr al-maktūm (the hidden secret); (4) the Ta'rīkh al-duwal, treating of politics and of the history of the first four caliphs; (5) a history of Shāfi'ite doctors, Manāqib al-imām al-Shāfi'ī; (6) a treatise on jurisprudence, Maḥsūl fī uṣūl al-fiqh; (7) a very important commentary on the Qur'ān, Mafātīḥ al-ghaib (Keys of mystery) or Tafsīr al-kabir; (8) a treatise on the principles of physics and metaphysics, Kitāb al-mabāḥith al-sharqīya, Oriental (or illuminating) questions.[7] He wrote two encyclopaedias in Persian: (9) the Jawāmi' al-'ulūm (Totality of the sciences), treating of forty branches of knowledge, and (10) the Ḥadā'iq al-anwār (Garden of lights) fī ḥaqā'iq al-asrār (on the truths of the secrets) treating of sixty of them. The mathematical and medical parts of the Ḥadā'iq are extant. One of these encyclopaedias was composed in 1178–1179 for the Khwārizmshāh 'Alā al-dīn.[8]

Text—D. R. Henzius: Fragmenta arabica (second part of the Ta'rīkh, Petrograd 1828).

Editions of the Mafātīḥ: Būlāq 1289, Cairo 1307–1309, Stambul 1307. Turkish translation by the Cretan Sirry Giridy (Constantinople 1302).

For the Kitāb al-Fakhrī which was long ascribed to Fakhr al-dīn, see my note on Ibn al-Ṭiqṭaqā (first half of the fourteenth century).

Criticism—Ibn Khaldūn: Prolegomena (de Slane's translation, by index). Ibn Khallikān (de Slane, vol. 2, 652–656, 1843). F. Wüstenfeld: Arabische Aerzte (111–116, 1840); Geschichtschreiber der Araber (106, 1881). L. Leclerc: Médecine arabe (vol. 2, 20–22, 1876). C. Brockelmann: Arabische Litteratur (vol. 1, 506–508, 1898). H. Suter: Die Mathematiker und Astronomen der Araber (132, 1900). E. G. Browne: Literary history of Persia (vol. 2, 484, 1906). Adolf Fonahn: Quellenkunde der persischen Medizin (45–50, 56, 117, 1910); apropos of a Persian treatise entitled Ḥifẓ al-badan, Preservation of the body, and of a Persian translation of the Continens, both ascribed to Fakhr al-dīn. Eilhard Wiedemann: Ueber optische Täuschungen nach Fakhr al-dīn und Nāṣir al-dīn al-Ṭūsī (Beitr. 33, Sitzungsber., vol. 45, 154–167, Erlangen 1913–1914). Giuseppe Gabrieli: Fakhr al-dīn al Rāzī (Isis, 7, 9–13, 1925); biography based on Arabic sources. Martin Plessner: Der οἰκονομικός des Neupythagoreers Bryson (35–38, Heidelberg, 1928); for the part of the Ḥadā'iq al-anwār concerning domestic economy according to the Greek-Arabic tradition (Isis, 13, 529). H. G. Farmer: History of Arabian music (200, 1929; Isis, 13, 375).

[7] See de Slane's translation of Ibn Khaldūn's Muqaddama (vol. 3, 167, note 4).

[8] The date 1178–1179 given by E. G. Browne (484, 1906) does not tally with the dates of 'Alā al-dīn's rule, 1199–1220 (?).

ABŪ BAKR IBN AL-MUẒHIR[9]

Another encyclopaedic treatise in Persian, of the end of the twelfth century (or beginning of the thirteenth century?), was the Faraḥ-nāma-i-Jamālī composed in 1163 or 1184 or 1201 by Abū Bakr ibn al-Muẓhir (or Abū Bakr al-Muṭahhar) ibn Muḥammad al-Jamāl al-Yazdī. It was a sort of supplement to the Nuzhat-nāma-i-'Alā'ī, compiled by Shāhmardān ibn abī-l-Khayr, who dedicated it to a prince of the Banū Kākūya family (Kākwayhid dynasty), 'Alā al-dawla Abū Kālinjār Garshāsp ibn 'Alī ibn Farāmurz, who ruled from 1095 to 1119. The Nuzhat-nāma is fully described by Wilhelm Pertsch in the Gotha Persian catalogue (p. 30–36) and more briefly by Hermann Ethé in the Bodleian Persian catalogue (col. 906–908). The Faraḥ-nāma is described by Charles Rieu in the British Museum Catalogue of Persian manuscripts (vol. 2, 465–466).

Both works, the Nuzhat-nāma and the Faraḥ-nāma may be discussed together, as they complete each other. They are encyclopaedias treating of every form of the organic and inorganic world, but always in a very superstitious manner. From the scientific point of view these books are worthless, but they constitute an excellent compendium of the superstitions which obtained in Persia in the twelfth century. Many of these superstitions are certainly pre-Islāmic.

W. Ivanow: Faraḥ-nāma-i-jamālī (Journal R. Asiatic Soc., 863–868, 1929; Isis, 14, 477).

III. WESTERN JEWISH

ISAAC BEN MELCHIZEDEK

Born about 1110 in Siponto, a seaport in Apulia near modern Manfredonia. He was educated there but later moved to Salerno where Benjamin of Tudela met him. He died about 1170. One of the earliest Talmudists of southern Italy. He wrote in Hebrew many commentaries full of Greek, Arabic and Latin learning. His influence upon rabbinical studies in Italy was comparable to, though smaller than, that of Rashi (second half of the eleventh century) in France and Germany; it was even felt outside of Italy.

Max Schloessinger: Jewish Encyclopaedia (vol. 6, 625, 1904).

ABRAHAM BEN DAVID OF POSQUIÈRES

Abraham ben David. Called for short Rabad III. Rabad stands for Rabbi Abraham ben David; the number III distinguishes him from two contemporaries, Abraham ben David ha-Levi (Rabad I) and Abraham ben Isaac of Narbonne (Rabad II)[10], his father-in-law. French Talmudist, born in Provence about 1125; flourished mainly at Posquières (near Lunel, arr. de Montpellier), where he died in 1199. He wrote a commentary on the whole Talmud, most of which is lost; his point of view was that of the most conservative rabbinic tradition. He naturally criticized the Yad ha-ḥazaqah of Maimonides, not simply because of the latter's philosophizing tendencies, but also because any such attempt at codification was necessarily

[9] This note was inserted when the rest of the work was complete. It is not referred to in the summaries.

[10] Abraham ben Isaac (1110–1179) was called Rabad from the initials of his office ab bet din, chief judge. See appendix to Book ii.

distasteful to him. He encouraged the translation into Hebrew of Baḥya's Kitāb al-hidāyat (first half of the twelfth century). He is sometimes considered the founder of the Qabbalah; this claim is even less justified than the similar one made in favor of his son, Isaac the Blind.

Text—Sefer ba'ale ha-nefesh (Book of the conscientious), a treatise on the laws concerning women (Venice 1602). Commentary on Torah kohanim (Vienna 1862). Etc.

Criticism—E. Renan: Les rabbins français (Histoire littéraire de la France, vol. 27, 518–520, 1877). Louis Ginzberg: Jewish Encyclopaedia (vol. 1, 103–105, 1901). S. Bialoblocki: Encyclopaedia judaica (vol. 1, 450–459, 1928).

ISAAC THE BLIND

Isaac ben Abraham. Son of Abraham ben David of Posquières. Judeo-Languedocian philosopher. He is cited here because he is often called the founder of the Qabbalah. Whether this title really belongs to him, or should be reserved for his chief pupil 'Azrī'ēl ben Menaḥēm (first half of the thirteenth century), is a moot question. Isaac's relation to his pupil reminds one of that of Ammonios Saccas to Plotinos; if we call Ammonios the founder of neo-Platonism, then Isaac is the founder of the Qabbalah.

The authorship of one of the earliest Qabbalistic books, the Bahir, is now generally credited either to Isaac or to his school. The Bahir (or Sefer ha-bahir, the luminous book) is self-ascribed to Neḥunya ben ha-Qanah (first century)—it is called Midrash R. Neḥunya ben ha-Qanah—but it is obviously a much later production, to which no reference is found in Hebrew literature before the thirteenth century. It is a mystical and exceedingly obscure commentary on the first chapters of Genesis, divided into sixty short paragraphs in the form of a dialogue between master and disciples. It is closely related to the Sefer yeẓirah, and is in its turn a sort of outline of the Zohar, for which see my note on Moses of Leon (second half of the thirteenth century). Note that the titles Bahir and Zohar are almost equivalent. Among the views discussed in the Bahir are the existence of the world, as of God, from all eternity; metempschychosis; and the celestial trinity. It also contains the doctrine of the ten Sefirot—three primary ones, original light, wisdom, and reason (hence, the idea of the trinity); and seven secondary ones. This is the beginning of the Qabbalistic theory of emanation. If we could be sure that the Bahir was composed by Isaac the Blind, he would undoubtedly be the founder of the Qabbalah; but the most that can be done is to ascribe it to him or to his disciples.

Text—First edition of the Bahir, Liber splendoris seu illustris (Amsterdam 1650–1651; new edition (Berlin 1706)). Etc. A critical edition is being prepared presumably by Gerhard Scholem of Jerusalem. G. Scholem: Das Buch Bahir auf Grund der kritischen Neuausgabe (Quellen und Forschungen zur Geschichte der jüdischen Mystik, vol. 1, Leipzig 1923); a German version with commentary.

Criticism—I. Broydé: Jewish Encyclopaedia (vol. 2, 442, 1902). Max Seligsohn: Jewish Encyclopaedia (vol. 6, 620, 1904). For a discussion of the Qabbalah, see my note on Moses of Leon (second half of the thirteenth century). G. Scholem: Bahir (Encyclopaedia judaica, vol. 3, 969–979, 1929). M. Zobel: Chamai gaon (ibidem, vol. 5, 229, 1930); apropos of Ḥammai gaon, unknown author of two qabbalistic treatises belonging probably to Isaac's school.

A BELATED NOTE ON THE SEFER YEẒIRAH

I did not speak of the Sefer yeẓirah (Book of creation) in vol. I (excepting two brief references, p. 627, 683), because I did not know where to place it. Yet some account of it must be given for a proper understanding of the Qabbalah.

This book is sometimes ascribed to R. Akiba (end of the first century), to Abraham the Patriarch, and even to Adam! These ascriptions are meaningless, except in so far as they show the importance attached to it. It is undoubtedly an ancient compilation built with materials still more ancient. It dates probably from the Geonic period; at any rate it is anterior to Saadia Gaon (first half of the tenth century), who wrote a commentary on it.

The Sefer yeẓirah is very important intrinsically, because it may be considered the earliest qabbalistic writing, or to put it in another way, the most significant transition between the old Jewish mysticism and the Qabbalah of the Bahir, Zohar, etc.; extrinsically, because of its immense influence upon Jewish thought. Innumerable commentaries have been devoted to it. A complete history of the Sefer yeẓirah would be in fact a main cross section of Jewish literature down to the nineteenth century

The Sefer yeẓirah contains germs of the fundamental Qabbalistic ideas; for example, the theory of sefirot (clearly an elaboration of the oriental and Greek doctrine of emanation), and the magical power ascribed to letters of the Hebrew alphabet. This latter idea and its development (gematria) implies a mystical philosophy of language in general, and of the language par excellence, God's own language, Hebrew. Some parts of the Sefer yeẓirah are of special interest to the student of Hebrew phonetics. These two fundamental ideas, emanations and magical alphabet, are so to say correlative and complementary. The sefirot represents the substance of things; the letters, the forms through which these substances become cognizable; they help to constitute the bridge which enables our minds to pass from the infinite to the finite, from the immaterial to the material.

The critical study of a text as heterogeneous as the Sefer yeẓirah would always be difficult, but the difficulty is increased by the coexistence of two traditions. The princeps (Mantua 1562) contains both; a shorter text (Mantua I), and a longer one (Mantua II). The shorter text was commented upon by Dunash ibn Tamim or by Jacob ben Nissim (both of the second half of the tenth century), and was used by most of the later commentators; yet the commentaries of Saadia ben Gaon and Donnolo were based upon the longer text. The longer text not only contains material not found in the shorter, but its arrangement is different.

Text—Editio princeps, together with commentaries by Saadia Gaon, Abraham ben David (Joseph Aruc?), Moses ben Naḥman, Eleazar ben Judah, and Moses Botarel (Mantua 1562). Liber Jezirah, qui Abraham Patriarchae adscribitur una cum commentario R. Abraham F. Dior. Translatus e notis illustratus a J. S. Rittangelio (Amsterdam 1642). Many later editions, generally with one commentary or more: Amsterdam 1713?, Constantinople 1719, Zolkiew 1745, Korzec 1779, Grodno 1797 and 1806, Salonica 1831; etc. Lazarus Goldschmidt: Das Buch der Schöpfung (Francfort a.M., 1894); attempt at a critical edition, with vocalized text, German translation, notes.

Latin translations by Guillaume Postel (Paris 1552), Athanasius Kircher (Rome 1653), J. Pistor (Ars cabalistica, vol. 1, Basel 1587), and J. S. Rittangel (Amsterdam 1642, mentioned above). Note that one of these Latin versions is anterior to the princeps.

German translations by Johann Fr. von Meyer (Leipzig 1830, Hebrew and German), L. Goldschmidt (1894, mentioned above), and Erich Bischoff: Die Elemente der Kabbalah (2 vols., Berlin 1913-1914).

English translations by Isidor Kalisch: A sketch of the Talmud (New York 1877), and W. W. Westcott (Bath 1887, London 1893).

French translation by S. Karppe: Etude sur les origmes et la nature du Zohar (Paris 1901).

Commentaries—Of the many commentaries I shall cite only two, of which we have critical editions. David Castelli: Il commento di Sabbatai Donnolo sul libro della creazione (Publ. d. R. Istituto di studi superiori, 166 p., Florence 1880); Hebrew text with notes and introduction. Mayer Lambert: Commentaire sur le Séfer yeṣira par le gaon Saadya de Fayyoum, publié et traduit (Bibliothèque de l'Ecole des hautes études, sci. philol., 85, 250 p., Paris 1891).

Criticism—A. Epstein: Recherches sur le Séfer yeçira (Revue des études juives, vol. 28, 95-108; vol. 29, 61-78, 1894). Louis Ginzberg: Jewish encyclopaedia (vol. 12, 602-606, 1906). Gerhard Scholem: Bibliographia kabbalistica (248 p., Leipzig 1927; Isis, 11, 514).

ABRAHAM BEN DAVID HA-LEVI

Ibrāhīm ibn Da'ūd. Often called Ben Da'ūd or Rabad from the initials of his name (Rabbi A.b.D.), also Rabad I to distinguish him from two other rabbis. Hispano-Jewish philosopher, historian, and astronomer, writing both in Hebrew and Arabic. Born at Cordova about 1110. He died a martyr in Toledo, between 1170 and 1180.

He wrote in Hebrew, in Toledo, 1161, a short chronicle called Sefer ha-qabbalah (The book of tradition), establishing the chain of Jewish tradition from the creation down to his own time (about 1150). His point of view was strongly opposed to that of the Qaraites, and his main purpose was to show the unbroken tradition connecting the rabbinic Judaism of his day, especially in Spain, with the teachings of the Geonim and of earlier doctors. This chronicle contains valuable historical information; for example, on the Geonim and on the Spanish Jews. In fact it is the earliest source for the study of Jewish scholarship in the period posterior to Sherira Gaon (about 980).

He wrote in Arabic, in 1168, a philosophical treatise entitled Kitāb al-'aqīdah al-rafī'ah (The sublime faith). It is divided into three parts: (1) principles of physics and metaphysics; (2) principles of law and religion; (3) "medicine of the soul," that is, practical philosophy, ethics, economics, politics. It is preserved in two Hebrew versions; one by Samuel Moṭoṭ (second half of the fourteenth century) (1392); the other, more elaborate, Emunah ramah, by Solomon ben Labi who lived toward the end of the fourteenth century in Ixar, Aragon. This was the first Jewish attempt at a compromise between religion and Aristotelianism; and Abraham ibn David might be called the first Jewish Peripatetic, but he was soon overshadowed by Maimonides. His point of view implied a strong antagonism to Ibn Gabirol's neo-Platonism. He insisted that positive knowledge strengthens one's religion. According to Isaac Israeli (first half of the fourteenth century), he wrote an astronomical treatise otherwise unknown.

The Sefer ha-qabbalah was continued down to 1525 by Abraham ben Solomon of Torrutiel, who had witnessed the expulsion of the Jews from Spain in 1492. Down to 1467, Abraham ben Solomon copied almost verbatim the chronicle appended by Joseph ben Ẓaddiq of Arévalo (Ávila, Old Castile) to his ritual book Zeker ẓaddīq.

Text—First edition of the Sefer ha-qabbalah, Mantua 1514. Edition with Latin translation by G. Génébrard (Mantua 1519, Paris 1572, Cracow 1820). Edition with Latin translation by Sebastian Münster (1527). Many other editions. I cite only Adolf Neubauer: Mediaeval Jewish chronicles (vol. 1, 47–84, Oxford 1887). The chronicles by Abraham ben Solomon and by Joseph ben Ẓaddiq are also edited by Neubauer (ibidem, 85–114).

Münster's Latin version was Englished by Peter Morvyng (1530?–1573?): A compendious and most marveylous history of the latter times of the Jewes communeweale (London 1561, 1575, 1608, etc.).

F. Cantera Burgos: El Libro de la cabala de Abraham ben Salomon de Torrutiel y un fragmento histórico de José ben Zaddic de Arévalo. Traducción española, prólogo y notas (71 p., Salamanca 1928).

Simson Weil: Emunah ramah (Francfort 1852; Solomon ben Labi's Hebrew text and German translation).

Criticism—Jacob Guttmann: Die Religionsphilosophie des Abraham ibn Daud (248 p., Göttingen 1879); Jewish encyclopaedia (vol. 1, 101–103, 1901); Die Beziehungen der maimonidischen Religionsphilosophie zu der des Abraham ibn Daud (Festschrift Hermann Cohen, 135–144, Berlin, 1912). M. Steinschneider: Hebräische Uebersetzungen (368–372, 1893); Die Mathematik bei den Juden (Bibliotheca mathematica, 97, 1895; 73, footnote, 1897); Arabische Litteratur der Juden (154, 1902). Isaac Husik: Mediaeval Jewish philosophy (197–235, 1918). I. Elbogen and Julius Guttmann: Encyclopaedia judaica (vol. 1, 438–449, 1928).

MAIMONIDES

In Arabic: Abū 'Imrān Mūsā ibn Maimūn ibn 'Abdallāh al-Qurṭubī (or al-Andalusī, the Cordovan or the Andalusian) al-Isrā'īlī. In Hebrew: Moses ben Maimon, or Rabbi M.b.M., hence Rambam. Often called The second Moses, or the Moses of his time (Moses ha-zeman). Moses Maimunī, Moses Aegyptius.

Hispano-Jewish philosopher, theologian, physician, astronomer, born in Cordova, March 30, 1135. He died in Cairo, December 13, 1204, and was buried in Tiberias, Palestine, where his tomb may still be seen. His family lived in Cordova until the Almohade conquest in 1148–1149, when they had to choose between Islām or exile; they left, and for a dozen years lived in various places in Spain; in 1160 they settled in Fez but were soon obliged to move again, reaching Fusṭāṭ (old Cairo) in 1165; Moses' father died in the same year and Moses practised medicine to support the family. He spent the rest of his life in Cairo, becoming a famous physician. He was patronized by Ṣalāḥ al-dīn's wazīr, al-Qāḍī al-Fāḍil al-Baisānī;[11] later he became physician to Ṣalāḥ al-dīn and to the latter's son. From 1177 he was the head of the Jewish community of Egypt; that is, Rā's al-umma (or al-milla), nāgīd.

Maimonides and Ibn Rushd were the greatest philosophers of their time. They developed to a large extent independently but used the same philosophical and scientific sources. Neither knew Greek and their knowledge of Greek philosophy and science was derived from Arabic translations. When Maimonides became acquainted with some of Ibn Rushd's writings, most of his own writings were completed and at any rate his thought was already set. When he quoted Ibn Rushd it was generally to state his dissent. All of his works except one (the Mishneh Torah) were written in Arabic, but they were promptly translated into Hebrew and exerted far more influence in their Hebrew (and sometimes Latin) translations than in the original text.

[11] See Brockelmann (vol. 1, 316).

I discuss Maimonides' thought in the following order: Philosophical and general writings, Medicine, Astronomy, Rabbinical commentaries (Halaka), Rationalism, Influence. And I add an appendix treating of (A) Maimonides' alleged apostasy, and (B) his family.

Philosophical and General Writings

1. Maimonides' most famous work was the Dalālat al-ḥā'irīn, or Guide of the perplexed (Moreh nebukim, Doctor perplexorum), completed in 1187–1190. "The design of this work," said the author, "is to promote the true understanding of the real spirit of the Law, to guide those religious persons who, adhering to the Tōrāh, have studied philosophy and are embarrassed by the contradictions between the teachings of philosophy and the literal sense of the Tōrāh." That is, Maimonides' purpose was to reconcile Jewish theology with Muslim Aristotelianism, or faith with reason. To do this he gave an allegorical interpretation of Biblical anthropomorphism and concreteness, keeping clear at once of mysticism and of religious scepticism; for example, he explained prophetic visions as psychical experiences; and Jewish laws and customs from the point of view of comparative ethnology. He insisted that human perfection is inseparable from knowledge, and that the acquisition of knowledge is one of the highest forms of religion. To that extent Maimonides was the champion of science against Biblical "fundamentalism." In spite of its moderation, the Dalālat scandalized the more conservative theologians—they called it Ḍalālat, error, perdition! It gave a tremendous stimulus to philosophical studies, either directly, or indirectly because of the passionate controversies which it started (see Influence, below). It helped to check Qabbalistic extravagances as well as theological obscurantism. It was translated into Hebrew by Samuel ibn Tibbon at Arles in 1204; this translation made with the benefit of the author's advice, has almost the value of the original. It was translated into Latin in the first half of the thirteenth century.

2. Maqāla fī ṣinā'at al-manṭiq, a treatise on the art of logic, in fourteen chapters, written about 1151. This was probably Maimonides' earliest work. It is partly lost in Arabic. Translated into Hebrew, Millot ha-higgayon, by Moses ibn Tibbon in 1254; then again by Aḥiṭub ben Isaac, rabbi and physician in Palermo (second half of thirteenth century); and finally by Joseph ibn Vives of Lorca (second half of fourteenth century). In spite of its imperfection the earliest translation by Moses ibn Tibbon was not superseded by the later ones, and it was almost exclusively through it that this work was known in Jewish circles where it remained for a considerable time the standard textbook on logic.

3. Maqāla fī-l-tawḥīd, on the unity of God. Translated into Hebrew, Ma'amar ha-yiḥud, by Isaac ben Nathan, in Majorca, about the middle of the fourteenth century.

4. Maqāla fī-l-sa'ādat, on happiness; two chapters. Translated into Hebrew, Peraqim be-haẓlaḥah.

5. Treatise on forced conversions, translated into Hebrew, Iggeret ha-shemad, or Ma'amar qiddush ha-shem (!). Justifying to some extent the Jews who professed Islām under duress.

6. Letter addressed to R. Jacob ben Nathaniel al-Fayyumī about 1172, concerning the Jews of Yemen. Translated three times into Hebrew, Iggeret teman, by Samuel ibn Tibbon about 1210, by Abraham ibn Ḥasdai, and by Naḥum ha-Ma'arabī about 1240?.

7. Essay on resurrection, translated into Hebrew by Samuel ibn Tibbon, Ma'amar teḥiyyot ha-metim.

Medicine

Maimonides' medical knowledge was derived mainly from al-Rāzī, Ibn Sīnā, Ibn Wāfid, and Ibn Zuhr; it was the standard Arabic Galenism of his time, but tempered with rational criticism based on direct observation. He improved the method of circumcision. His medical writings have deeply influenced not only Muslim and Jewish, but also Christian doctors; for example, Henry of Mondeville and Guy of Chauliac. Many are undated, but all were probably written between 1167 and 1200.

8. The most popular of the medical writings is the Kitāl al-fuṣūl fī-l-ṭibb (Medical principles), more often called Fuṣūl Mūsā (Moses' Aphorisms), composed probably about 1187–1190, to diffuse a sounder knowledge of Galen's thought. It is a collection of 1500 aphorisms extracted from Galen's writings, together with 42 critical remarks. Maimonides mentions four Arabic-writing physicians: al-Rāzī, al-Tamīmī, 'Alī ibn Riḍwān, and Ibn Zuhr. Galen's thoughts are classified in 24 chapters devoted respectively to (1–3) anatomy, physiology, general pathology, (4–6) symptomatology and diagnosis, with special reference to pulse and urine, (7) aetiology, (8–9) general and special therapeutics, (10–11) fevers and crises, (12–14) bloodletting, cathartics, emetics, (15) surgery, (16) gynaecology, (17) hygiene, (18) gymnastics, massage, etc., (19) bathing, (20) dietetics, (21–22) drugs, (23) Galenic ideas which are often misunderstood, (24) rare cases. In a final chapter (25) the author outlines a general criticism of Galenic medicine and philosophy, indicating some forty topics about which the master contradicted himself; it ends with a discussion of Galen's teleological ideas from the Biblical standpoint. This last chapter, the most important of the work, was apparently unfinished at the time of Maimonides' death; it was edited by the latter's nephew Yūsuf ibn 'Abdallāh Abū-l-Ma'ālī, in 1204–1205. This would suggest that Maimonides rewrote the Fuṣūl toward the end of his life, or else that he wrote chapter 25 at that time.

The Fuṣūl was translated into Hebrew, Pirqe Mosheh, by Zeraḥya ben Isaac ben Shealtiel Ḥen (or Gracian), in Rome in 1277; and again by Nathan ha-Me'ati in Rome in 1279–1283.

8a. Mukhtaṣarāt (Abridgments, digest). Compendium of the Sixteen Books of Galen, and of five other Galenic books; it is really a collection of extracts from the Galenic writings. Lost in Arabic, but available in Hebrew translations.

9. Commentary on Hippocrates' Aphorisms, as transmitted in Galen's commentary translated by Ḥunain ibn Isḥāq. Translated into Hebrew by Moses ibn Tibbon in 1257 or 1267.

10. Second in popularity only to the Fuṣūl was the Maqāla fī-tadbīr al-ṣiḥḥa, four books on diet addressed about 1198 to al-Malik al-Afḍal Nūr-al-dīn 'Alī, Ṣalāḥ al-dīn's eldest son. This prince suffered from fits of melancholia, and having appointed Maimonides his chief physician, asked him for a regimen. The Tadbīr al-ṣiḥḥa is largely derived from the writings of ancient and Arabic physicians. It is divided as follows: (1) explanation of the case, and general hygienic and dietetic rules, with frequent references to Hippocrates and Galen; (2) easy remedies for use while traveling, or when no physician is available; (3) hygiene of the soul; psychotherapeutic rules, partly derived from Aristotle and from al-Fārābī; (4) summary of hygiene and dietetics in the form of seventeen aphorisms.

This work was translated into Hebrew by Moses ibn Tibbon in 1244. Early Latin translations were made from the Arabic in 1290 by Armengaud, son of Blaise, and from the Hebrew by John of Capua (second half of the thirteenth century).

11. Maqāla fī-l-bayān al-a'rāḍ (Discourse on the explanation of accidents). Composed about 1200 for the same prince al-Afḍal, who apparently was then residing at Riqqa in Upper Egypt. This written consultation, divided into 22 chapters, was Maimonides' last medical effort. It was considered by the early Latin editors as the fifth part of no. 10. Maimonides confirms the prescriptions made by other physicians, with few exceptions gently expressed. His own prescriptions are remarkable because of their moderation and wisdom.

Hebrew translation, Teshubot 'al-she'elot peraṭiyyot. Latin translation, probably from the Hebrew, De causis accidentium apparentium.

12. Kitāb al-sumūm wal-mutaḥarriz min al-adwiya al-qitālah (on poisons, and antidotes against mortal drugs), written in 1199 for his patron the wazīr al-Qāḍī al-Fāḍil, and called after him Risālat al-fāḍilīya. It was twice translated into Hebrew, one of these translations being made by Moses ibn Tibbon, Ha ma'amar ha-nikbad (or Ha-ma'amar be ter'iaq). Latin translation by Armengaud, son of Blaise, De venenis, a text much used by fourteenth century physicians.

The Kitāb al-sumūm is divided into two sections preceded by an introduction. In the latter he explains al-Fāḍil's efforts to obtain from many distant countries all the ingredients needed to prepare the great theriaca. Section 1 deals with the venomous stings of insects, the biting of mad dogs, the treatment of the wounds thus caused. He insists on the great length of incubation of rabies. Section 2 deals with other poisons (verdigris, arsenic, litharge, opium, henbane, and other solanaceous herbs, mushrooms, etc.), and their antidotes—chiefly bezoars and theriacas. This is partly derived from Ibn Zuhr. The best part of this work is the clinical description of some cases of poisoning; for example, by belladonna or by cantharides.

13. Maqāla fī-l-rabw (on asthma). Translated into Latin by Armengaud in 1302, and into Hebrew (from the Latin?) by the Spanish Jew Samuel ben Benveniste about 1320?; another Hebrew translation was made from the Arabic by Joshua Shatibi (of Xativa) about the end of the fourteenth century.

Consultation written about 1190 for an unknown patient in Alexandria. An introduction describes the clinical case. The consultation itself is divided into 13 chapters dealing with diet and climate in general, then with the best diet and climate for asthmatics. Discussion of the climate and food of different countries, particularly of Egypt.

14. Maqāla fī-l-bawāṣīr (on haemorrhoids). Hebrew translation, Ha-ma'amar bi refu'at ha-ṭeḥorim. Also translated into Spanish.

Regimen composed for an unknown patient at an unknown time. Derived partly from al-Rāzī, Ibn Sīnā, Ibn al-Wāfid, but largely from his own experience. Divided into 7 chapters. He ascribed haemorrhoids to bad digestion, mainly to constipation, and prescribed a light diet, predominantly vegetarian. He showed the danger of bloodletting and of surgical intervention, which should be reserved for extreme cases.

15. Maqāla fī-l-jimā', on sexual intercourse. Dedicated to al-Muẓaffar I, Ayyūbid sulṭān of Ḥamāh (1178–1191), nephew of Ṣalāḥ al-dīn. A shorter text on the same subject may be an abridgement of this maqāla. Hebrew translation by Zeraḥya ben Isaac ben Shealtiel, (Rome 1277?), Ma'amar 'al ribbui ha-tashmish. Another Hebrew translation, anonymous, is entitled Ma'amar ha-mishgal.

The longer text is divided into 19 chapters and deals with differences in sexual temperament, the use and danger of sexual intercourse, abstinence, aphrodisiacs and anaphrodisiacs, narcotics, etc. Ibn Sīnā and Ibn Zuhr are quoted.

16. The physician's prayer ascribed to Maimonides is a valuable contribution to medical deontology. It is Maimonidean in tone and spirit, yet its genuineness is not proved.

16a. Other apocryphal writings. Various other medical writings have been ascribed to him, most of them in Hebrew. The best known of these are the Sefer refu'ot (Book of medicines) in Hebrew, and the Kitāb al-asbāb wal-'alāmāt[12] (Causes and symptoms) in Arabic.

Though Maimonides' works are but little known in Egypt, his memory as a great healer has been perpetuated by a curious superstition. Sick people from among the poorest Jews of Cairo are carried to the synagogue of Rabbi Mūsā ibn Maimūn to spend the night in an underground chamber. This is certainly a survival of the Egyptian and Greek rite of incubation.

Astronomy

Together with his favorite disciple Joseph ben Judah ibn 'Aqnīn, Maimonides commented on the astronomy of Jābir ibn Aflaḥ (first half of the twelfth century), and on the Istikmāl of King Yūsuf al-Mutamin (second half of the eleventh century). We know some of his astronomical views through the Dalālat, which contains, for example, a discussion of Ibn Bājja's criticism of Ptolemy. Maimonides rejected epicycles and excentric movements as contrary to Aristotelian physics. Like Jābir, he doubted that Mercury and Venus were nearer than the sun.

17. He wrote in 1158 a treatise on the Jewish calendar, called in the Hebrew translation Ma'amar ha-'ibbur, divided into two parts, on the molad (age of the moon), and on the tequfa (seasons of the year). A discussion of the calendar is also included in the Yad (qiddush ha-ḥodesh).

18. In 1194 he addressed a letter to the rabbis of Marseilles, wherein he did not hesitate to condemn astrology in the most uncompromising manner. According to him, astrology is not a genuine science but a system of superstitions.

Rabbinical commentaries

This is hardly the place to discuss these writings, yet we must speak of them, for they form such an enormous part of Maimonides' activity, that without some consideration of them, we could understand neither his personality nor his influence.

19. Kitāb al-sirāj (Book of the lamp), a commentary on the Mishnah, which Maimonides began in Spain about 1158 and completed in Cairo in 1168. During his lifetime it was partly translated into Hebrew by Judah al-Ḥarizī (1194–1197) and Samuel ibn Tibbon; but the greatest part was not translated until a century later, in 1298, at Huesca and Saragossa, by various people. Among the earliest parts to be translated were the "Eight chapters" (Shemonah peraqim) on ethics; and the commentary on Sanhedrin, chapter 10, which contains a Jewish creed in thirteen articles (now included in the prayer books).

[12] Treatises bearing that title were composed by a disciple of Ibn Sīnā, Muḥammad ibn 'Alī al-Īlāqī, and by Najīb al-dīn al-Samarqandī (first half of the thirteenth century). See Brockelmann (vol. 1, 485, 490, 491).

20. Kitāb al-farā'iḍ (Book on the divine precepts). A list of the 248 mandatory commandments and of the 365 prohibitive commandments (613 in all) contained in the Torah. This was translated into Hebrew, Sefer ha-miẓwot, by Abraham ben Ḥasdai at the beginning of the thirteenth century; by Moses ibn Tibbon about 1240; and by Solomon ibn Ayyub at about the same time.

21. Commentaries on various parts of the Talmud.

22. The Mishneh Torah (Repetition of the Law, Deuteronomy), the first complete classification and codification of all the Mosaic and rabbinical laws. It contains material derived not only from the Torah and from both Talmuds, but also from the Geonim, the whole being classified in fourteen groups, each of which forms a book, as follows: (1) Madda' (Knowledge), unity of God and theological principles; (2) Ahabah (love), religious principles; (3) Zemannim (times), sabbath; festivals; (4) Nashim (women), marriage laws; (5) Qedushshah (holiness), forbidden food and forbidden sexual relations; (6) Hafla'ah (separation), vows and oaths; (7) Zera'im (seeds), agriculture; (8) 'Abodah (religious worship); (9) Qorbanot (offerings); (10) Ṭohorah (cleanliness), clean and unclean things; (11) Neziqim (injuries), criminal law; (12) Qinyan (acquisition), commercial law; (13) Mishpaṭim (rights), civil law; (14) Shofeṭim (judges), government. The Mishneh Torah is often called Sefer ha-yad (Book of the hand) or Yad ha-ḥazaqah (The strong hand).[13] The Yad was written in new Hebrew, not in the Hebrew-Aramaic language of the Talmud. (It was translated into Arabic, and there is an Arabic commentary on the Sefer ha-madda'). Maimonides had tried to simplify the subject; for example, he had suppressed some Talmudic regulations relative to health, which he as a physician knew to be futile. For the sake of brevity he quoted his sources only in a general way. The Mishneh Torah was a masterful work which soon obtained a semi-canonical status in Israel in spite of the antagonism which it raised in many quarters.

Rationalism

A discussion of Maimonides' rationalism is the more necessary because the subject has been obscured by many misunderstandings. This rationalism has been exaggerated by certain writers (for example, Renan) and minimized by others. To see it in its true perspective one must remember that Maimonides was an ardent Aristotelian, and yet an orthodox and pious Jew. Reason, he thought, being a gift of God, cannot be irreconcilable with religion. It must be possible to give a rational account of the universe without traversing religious dogmas, for both the world and the faith are from God. The main stumbling block was the Aristotelian theory of the eternity of matter. How could this be reconciled with the idea of creation? Maimonides' common sense revolted against the artificial doctrines of the Muslim atomists. He saw that one could not accept at once the eternity of matter and the account of Genesis; it was necessary to make a choice; he chose Genesis. This gives us a measure of his rationalism; he was ready to carry it to any extent compatible with his creed, but not further. Being a physician, his philosophy was largely Galenic. What we would call natural law was for him design; all the regularities of nature are contingent upon the existence of a rational God. The world is one individual whole, rational through and through;

[13] The letters of the word Yad, considered as numerals, mean 14, i.e., the 14 books of the Mishneh Torah.

for without rationality, there could not be any knowledge, or morality, or religion. He denounced vigorously the absurdities of superstition and was ever ready to uphold the supremacy of reason. In common with every other philosopher who was more inclined to rationalism than to mysticism, he emphasized the ethical side of religion; man must be good before he can be wise.

Misunderstandings on the subject are largely due to the fact that while Maimonides' rationalism was innocent enough, yet it was an opening wedge. The more conservative who considered the Dalālat with horror were instinctively right. Maimonides himself could not realize the revolutionary import of his views, but it is clear enough to us. All of which amounts to saying that Maimonides had a truly creative mind.

Influence

Maimonides' influence was tremendous and far-reaching in space and time. It affected not only the Jews, but also the Christians, chiefly the Dominicans (while Ibn Gabirol inspired the Franciscans). This influence was important in itself, and also because until the eighteenth century Maimonides was the main channel through which Jewish thought reached the Gentiles. It can be strongly detected in Spinoza, and even in Kant. So much for generalities. Let us now consider separate cases.

Maimonides' denunciation of superstition, and especially of astrology, was too far ahead of his time to be understood. Such views were shared only by men as great as himself, and it is not necessary to assume that each of these was deeply influenced by the others.

The Moreh nebukim raised bitter controversies among the Jews, and for a century at least every Jewish doctor of note was either an ardent opponent or an equally ardent defender of Maimonides. This will be illustrated often in the following chapters. For the present it suffices to remark that the enmity between both parties was heated to such a point that the dispute was referred by them in 1234 to a Christian authority, the papal legate at Montpellier, who ordered Maimonides' works to be destroyed. Later, when the controversy quieted down, the Moreh remained for centuries the guide of the most enlightened Jews.

The Mishneh Torah was also a bone of contention. It was naturally obnoxious to the many rabbis who objected to the codification of the laws. It was quickly known to them; for example, Abraham ben David of Posquières, who died in 1198, had already had ample opportunities of attacking it. Maimonides' enemies disliked the Yad also because of its brevity and lack of references, and because its language, new Hebrew, was too different from the learned language of the Talmud.

The Yad's influence can be appreciated in another way. Maimonides' codification and simplification of the laws was continued by Jacob ben Asher (first half of the fourteenth century) in the Arba' ṭurim; and again by Joseph Caro in the Shulḥan 'arūk, 1564, which has remained to this day the standard code of Jewish life. But if Maimonides hoped to put an end to hair-splitting casuistical discussions (pilpul), he failed for they continued unabated, and the Yad, after having reached the status of a semi-canonical work, became itself the basis of new commentaries and of more pilpul.

Appendix

A. Maimonides' apostasy. Maimonides was accused, not by his Jewish enemies, but by Muslims who envied his position in Cairo, of having confessed Islām in

Spain, then later recanted. If so, his Iggeret ha-shemad (no. 5 above) would have been a special pleading pro domo sua. The accusation is unproved and the double apostasy is hardly plausible.

D. S. Margoliouth: The legend of apostasy of Maimonides (Jewish quarterly review, vol. 13, 539–541, 1901). A. Berliner: Zur Ehrenrettung des Maimonides (Israel. Monatschr., July 1901).

B. His family. Maimonides belonged to a family of doctors which his father had already made prominent, and of which distinguished members can be followed for seven generations. His father Maimon ben Joseph was a judge (dayyan) in Cordova, which he left in 1148–1149, as told above; he died soon after their arrival in the East in 1165.

Maimonides' son, Abraham ben Moses (about 1186– Cairo 1237) was, like his father, a court physician and nagid of Egypt. He succeeded his father in the negiduth in 1205. He was well acquainted with Aristotelian science and with medicine, a famous practitioner. He was very pious, but not superstitious. He wrote in Arabic many responsa in defense of his father. His chief work, the Kitāb al-kifāyat al-'ibdān, The sufficient book for the servants (of God), is a treatise on theology, philosophy, ethics. The ninth part of it (out of ten) was edited by Samuel Rosenblatt.

Samuel Rosenblatt: The high ways to perfection (213 p., Columbia Press, New York 1927). Arabic text in Hebrew script, English translation, and long introduction (Isis, 14, 478). J. N. Simchoni: Encyclopaedia judaica (vol. 1, 515–520, 1928).

Abraham had two distinguished sons; David ben Abraham (1223–1300)[14] who succeeded him as nagid and head of the yeshiva; and Obadiah ben Abraham (1228–1265). David had two sons; Abraham II who died about 1313;[15] and Solomon who became nagid of Egypt. Joshua ben Abraham ben David (1310–1355), a son of Abraham II, had a son David ben Joshua who lived in Damascus about 1375–1386. All of these men wrote chiefly in Arabic; the writings ascribed to them are most of them Biblical or Talmudic commentaries; however, the short-lived Obadiah made a philosophical compilation, and the last-named David ben Joshua wrote an essay on weights and measures.

Maimonides' sister's son, Yūsuf ibn 'Abdallāh Abū-l-Ma'ālī (not Ma'ānī), edited the last chapter of the Fuṣūl Mūsā in 1204–1205.

David Kaufmann: Un neveu de Maimonide (Revue des études juives, vol. 7, 152, 1883). For the other members of Maimonides' family, see M. Steinschneider: Arabische Litteratur der Juden (197–225, 1902). Max Meyerhof: Notes sur quelques médecins juifs égyptiens (Isis, 12, 129, 1929).

Text—The numbers of each separate work correspond to those given above. 1. Dalālat al-ḥā'irīn. The original Arabic text was edited, unfortunately in Hebrew character, by Salomon Munk, together with a French translation, Guide des égarés (3 vols., Paris 1856, 1861, 1866). The Hebrew translation, Moreh nebukim, had been printed many centuries earlier, the Hebrew princeps appearing in Rome (?) before 1480. This was Samuel ibn Tibbon's translation. Another Hebrew version by al-Ḥarizī (first half of the thirteenth century) was edited by Leon Schlossberg

[14] S. A. Horodezky: Encyclopaedia judaica (vol. 5, 835, 1930).
[15] J. N. Simchoni: Encyclopaedia judaica (vol. 1, 449, 1928).

(vol. 1, London 1851; vols. 2 and 3, Vienna 1876–1879). The Hebrew text (apparently Ḥarizī's) was very soon translated into Latin, and this early Latin version, revised by Agostino Giustiniani, was printed in Paris in 1520. Samuel's Hebrew version was translated into Latin by Johann Buxtorf, Jr., and printed in Basel in 1629. Thus the Dalālat was published first in Hebrew (before 1480), then in Latin (1520), while the real princeps, the original Arabic text, appeared only in 1856–1866.

There are innumerable Hebrew editions, with or without commentaries. One of the latest is that printed in 2 vols., Berlin 1925, with many commentaries (Isis, 10, 125).

Italian translations by Jedidiah ben Moses of Recanati (1580), and by D. J. Maroni (1870). German translations of part 1 by J. R. Fürstenthal (Krotoshin 1839); of part 2 by M. E. Stern (Vienna 1864); of part 3 by S. Scheyer (Francfort 1838); of the whole work by Adolf Weiss (Leipzig 1923–1924; Isis, 10, 125). English translation of part 3 by J. Townley (London 1827); of the whole work by M. Friedländer (3 vols., London 1881–1885; new edition in one vol. without the abundant notes, 474 p., London 1904). S. Munk's French translation (1856–1866) has already been mentioned. This list is by no means complete, but is sufficient to prove the popularity of that great work.

2. Maqāla fī ṣinā'at al-manṭiq. Moses ibn Tibbon's Hebrew translation, Millot ha-higgayon, was often printed. Poor Hebrew edition with Latin translation, Logica Simonis, by Sebastian Münster (Basel 1527). Hebrew edition with two anonymous commentaries (Venice 1550). There are a number of Hebrew commentaries, of the fourteenth and fifteenth centuries and of later times. Moses Mendelssohn published the Hebrew text with his own commentary in 1761–1765. German translation by Moses Samuel Neumann (Venice 1822), and by S. L. Heilberg (Breslau 1828). M. Chamizer: R. Achitubs aus Palermo hebräische Übersetzung der Logica Maimunis (Festschrift Cohen, p. 423–456, Berlin 1912; Isis, 13, 423).

3. Maqāla fī-l-tawḥīd. The Hebrew version mentioned above was edited by M. Steinschneider (Berlin 1847), with a German summary and notes.

4. Maqāla fī-l-sa'ādat. First edition, in Hebrew (1567).

5. Iggeret ha-shemad. Arabic text lost. Hebrew translation edited by A. Geiger in his Maimonides (Breslau 1850), and by H. Edelmann (1851, and 1859).

6. Letter to R. Jacob al-Fayyumī. Samuel ibn Tibbon: Iggeret teman, edited by David Holub (Vienna, 1875). Naḥūm ha Ma'arabī: Petaḥ tiqwah (Door of hope) included in a collection edited by Samuel Ashkenasi (Basel 1629), etc. On the addressee, see Irene Chanoch: Encyclopaedia judaica (vol. 2, 260, 1928).

7. Ma'amar teḥiyyot ha-metim, included in the same collection (1629).

8. Fuṣūl Mūsā. The Arabic text of this very important work is still unpublished. Nathan ha-Me'ati's version, the second Hebrew version, was badly printed in Lemberg in 1834–1835 (wrongly dated 1804). Latin translation, probably from the Arabic, with Christian interpolations, Aphorismi medici (Bologna 1489; Venice 1497, 1500), etc. The Latin edition (Basel 1579) is an arbitrary elaboration. Chapter 19 on bathing was included in the Collectio de balneis (Venice 1553). A critical edition of the Arabic text is being prepared by Max Meyerhof under the patronage of the Jewish Theological Seminary of America (priv. comm., July 20, 1930).

9. Moritz Steinschneider: Die Vorrede des Maimonides zu seinem Commentar über die Aphorismen des Hippokrates, zum grössten Theil im arabischen Original, vollständig in zwei hebräischen Übersetzungen, nebst einer deutschen Übersetzung (Z. der deutschen morgenländischen Gesellschaft, vol. 48, 218–234, 1894).

10. Maqāla fi-tadbīr al-ṣiḥḥa. H. Kroner: First edition of the Arabic text, with German translation, notes on the Arabic and Hebrew texts, and medical criticism (Janus, vol. 27–29, passim, 1923–1925).

Hebrew version edited by Sam. J. L. Goldenberg in Kerem ḥemed (vol. 3, 9–31,

Prague 1838), and by Jacob Saphir ha-Levi (Jerusalem 1885). Latin translation, De regimine sanitatis ad Soldanum Saladinum Babylonice (Florence c. 1477; Pavia 1501; Venice 1514, 1518, 1521; Augsburg 1518; etc.). The edition of Pavia 1501 includes also Villanova's Regimen and the Tabula consiliorum of Gianmatteo Ferrari da Gradi. This Latin text is probably the one translated from the Arabic by Armengaud, son of Blaise. A Latin version from the Hebrew was edited by L. S. Kirschbaum (Berlin 1822).

German translation from the Hebrew by D. Winternitz (Wien 1843); very imperfect. H. Kroner: Die Seelenhygiene des Maimonides (Partial German version, Francfort c. 1915); Zur Terminologie der arabischen Medizin und zu ihrem zeitgenössischen hebräischen Ausdrucke (Berlin 1921). Berth. Baneth: Die Macrobiotik des Maimonides (Fortschnitte der Medizin, vol. 29, 153–157, 1911); is this a partial version of the same work?

11. Maqāla fī-l-bayān al-a'rāḍ. First Arabic edition, with German translation and notes by H. Kroner: Der medicinische Schwanengesang des Maimonides (Janus, vol. 32, 12–116, 1928; Isis, 13, 423). The early Latin editions (c. 1477, etc.) of no. 10 contain the translation of no. 11, which is generally considered the fifth part of no. 10. However this is not the case with the edition of Pavia 1501, which does not establish a wrong connection between no. 10 and 11 (a fine set of these early editions, and of Maimonidean editions in general, is kept in the Jewish Theological Seminary of America, New York).

12. Risālat al-fāḍilīya fī 'ilāj al-sumūm wa dhikr al-adwiya 'an nāfi'a minhā wa min al-nuhūsh. French translation from the Hebrew and Arabic by I. M. Rabbinowicz: Traité des poisons (70 p., Paris 1865); with pharmaceutical glossary. German translation by M. Steinschneider: Gifte und ihre Heilung (Virchows Archiv, vol. 52, 73 p., Berlin 1873).

12–13. H. Kroner was preparing an edition and translation of both treatises at the time of his death.

14. Maqāla fī-l-bawāṣīr. H. Kroner: Die Haemorrhoiden in der Medizin des XII. und XIII. Jahrhunderts an der Hand einer medizinischen Abhandlung des Maimonides under Zuziehung eines gleichnamigen Abhandlung des Salomo bar Yussuf ibn Ajjub (Janus, vol. 16, 441–456, 645–718, 1911); Arabic text in Hebrew script, with German translation and notes.

15. Maqāla fī-l-jimā'. H. Kroner: Ein Beitrag zur Geschichte der Medizin des XII Jahrhunderts an der Hand zweier medizinischer Abhandlungen des Maimonides (144 p., Oberdorf-Bopfingen 1906); Arabic, Hebrew and German texts with notes on the Arabic literature devoted to the same subject. H. Kroner: Eine medizinische Maimonides Handschrift aus Granada (Janus, vol. 21, 203–247, 1916); Arabic and German; this is the shorter Arabic text; its edition has been severely criticized by Ernst Seidel (Mitt. zur Gesch. der Med., vol. 17, 49–54, 1918).

16. The physician's prayer has often been published; by Kayserling (Allg. Zeitung des Judentums, 49, 1863, in Hebrew and German); and by P. Toeplitz (Israel.Familienblatt, vol. 5, Hamburg 1902); etc. Wall edition distributed by Paul Haupt: Morgengebet des Arztes. Wandspruch in kunstlerischer Umrahmung (Bern c. 1913).

16a. Reuben Levy: The Tractatus de causis et indiciis morborum attributed to Maimonides (Studies in the history and method of science, vol. 1, 225–234, Oxford 1917; Isis, 3, 97). Levy concludes that it is apocryphal. This treatise was supposed to have been written originally in Hebrew, and translated into Arabic by one Sulaimān ibn Ḥubaish al-Tamīmī, in Jerusalem.

Menasseh Grossberg: Sepher rephuoth. The book of medicine by Maimonides, and a letter of the physician "Ali Hajishmaeli" from a hitherto unpublished MS. (London 1900).

As shown above we are indebted for the edition of Maimonides' medical works to one man above all others, H. Kroner (d. 1930); and this is the more remarkable in that this scholar was not connected with any university or center of research, but was a rabbi in Oberdorf-Bopfingen, a small town in Württemberg (Isis 15, 338).

17. Ma'amar ha-'ibbur. Hebrew text edited by Eliezer Ashkenasi of Tunis (Dibre ḥakamim, Metz 1849). Another Hebrew text, with many variants, was edited by A. Lichtenberg: Qobeẓ teshubot Rambam (Leipzig 1859). Lasar Dünher: Die aelteste astronomische Schrift des Maimonides (Diss., Erlangen; 55 p., Würzburg 1902); German translation based on a new text.

18. Letter to the rabbis of Marseilles. Hebrew version with Latin translation by John Isaac Levi (1555). Alexander Marx: The correspondence between the rabbis of southern France and Maimonides about astrology (Hebrew Union College Annual, vol. 3, 311–358, 1926; reprint of 52 p. plus 2 p. of addenda; Isis, 11, 172); important paper containing the Hebrew text of Maimonides' immortal letter of 1194.

19. Kitāb al-sirāj. The Hebrew translation, completed by many scholars, was first printed at Naples in 1492, and often afterwards. It is frequently included in editions of the Talmud. There is no complete edition of the Arabic original, but various fragmentary ones, the earliest by Pococke: Porta Mosis (Oxford 1654); Arabic in Hebrew character, and Latin. Edition of the Shemonah peraqim by M. Wolf (Leipzig 1863); with German translation; etc. The Shemonah peraqim were edited and translated into English by Joseph J. Gorfinkle (172 p., New York 1912).

20. Kitāb al-farā'iḍ. Partial Arabic edition with German translation by M. Peritz (Breslau 1882). Complete Arabic edition in Hebrew character, with French translation by Moïse Bloch: Le livre des préceptes (366 p., Paris 1888). Moses ibn Tibbon's Hebrew version was first printed in Italy, later in Lisbon (1497), etc. Edition by Ḥayyim Heller: Sefer ha-miẓwot (Piotrkov 1914).

22. Mishneh Torah. First edition, Rome, before 1480; second, Soncino, 1490; third, Constantinople, 1509, etc. Best edition, Leipzig 1862. Partial translations into English by H. H. Bernard (1832), J. W. Peppercorne (1840), and E. Soloweyczik (London 1863). Hebrew text with Rabd's criticism, and with English translation by Simon Glazer (vol. 1, New York 1927).

Letters and responsa (Iggerot and teshubot)—Various collections have been published. Teshubot she'elot we-iggerot (Constantinople 1520). Mordechai Tama: Pe'er ha-dor, Ornaments of the age (Amsterdam 1765). Abraham Lichtenberg: Qobeẓ teshubot Rambam (Leipzig 1859); including some of Maimonides' minor works. (See also nos. 6 and 18). Israel Friedlaender: Ein Gratulationsbrief an Maimonides (Festschrift Cohen, p. 257–264, 1912). D. Simonsen: Vier arabische Gutachten des R. Mose ben Maimon, mit hebräischer Übersetzung versehen von B. Halper (Livre d'hommage à Samuel Poznański, p. 175–181, Warsaw 1927).

Anthology—A. Cohen: The teachings of Maimonides (354 p., London 1927; Isis, 11, 424).

General Criticism—M. Steinschneider: Hebräische Uebersetzungen (40–42, 413–438, 599, 762–774, 922–932, 1893); Die arabische Literatur der Juden (197–225, Frankfurt 1902). David Yellin and Israel Abrahams: Maimonides (London 1903). Isaac Broydé and J. Z. Lauterbach: Jewish Encyclopaedia (vol. 9, 73–86, 1905). Louis Germain Levy: Maimonide (Les grands philosophes; 285 p., Paris 1911). I. Münz: Moses ben Maimon. Sein Leben und seine Werken (Frankfurt 1912). W. Bacher, M. Brann, D. Simonsen, J. Guttmann, etc.: Moses ben Maimon. Sein Leben, seine Werken und sein Einfluss (2 vols., Leipzig 1908–1914); to celebrate the 700th anniversary of his death; the medical chapter was contributed by J. Pagel (vol. 1, 231–247). E. Mittwoch: Encyclopaedia of Islām (vol. 2, 400, 1918). Lynn Thorndike: History of magic (vol. 2, 205–213, 1923). Giuseppe Gabrieli: Maimonide (Archivio di storia della scienza, 5, 12–15, 1924).

Scientific Criticism—H. Suter: Mathematiker der Araber (131, 1900; 174, 1902). J. L. E. Dreyer: Planetary systems (263, Cambridge 1906). P. Duhem: Système du monde (vol. 2, 139–146, 1914, cosmology; 386–390, tides; vol. 5, 170–232, 1917, philosophy).

Medical Criticism—F. Wüstenfeld: Arabische Aerzte (109–111, 1840). L. Choulant: Handbuch (378–380, 1841). L. Leclerc: Médecine arabe (vol. 2, 57–64, 1876). J. Pagel: Maimuni als medizinischer Schriftsteller (Moses ben Maimon, vol. 1, 231–247, 1908). Walter Mendelson: Maimonides (Annals of medical history, vol. 5, 250–262, 1923; Isis, 7, 188). H. Kroner: Der Mediziner Maimonides im Kampfe mit dem Theologen (15 p., Oberdorf-Bopfingen 1924). Louis J. Bragman: Maimonides on physical hygiene (Annals of medical history, vol. 7, 140–143, 1925). H. Kroner: Die Sexualhygiene in der Medizin des Maimonides (Monatschrift für Harnkrankheiten und sexuelle Hygiene, vol. 2, 133–137, 1928). Max Meyerhof: Notes sur quelques médecins juifs égyptiens (Isis, 12, 113–131, 1929); L'oeuvre médicale de Maimonide (Archeion, 11, 136–155, 1929); Zwei hygienisch-diätetische Abhandlungen des Maimonides (Der Morgen, 4, 620–624, 1929).

Philosophic Criticism—M. Joël: Die Religions-philosophie des Moses ben Maimon (Breslau 1876). David Rosin: Die Ethik des Maimonides (Breslau 1876). Israel Finkelscherer: Moses Maimunis Stellung zum Aberglauben und zur Mystik (Diss., 96 p., Jena 1894). Isaac Husik: History of mediaeval Jewish philosophy (236–311, 1918). Israel Isaac Efros: Philosophical terms in the Moreh nebukim (169 p., New York 1924). D. B. Macdonald: Continuous re-creation and atomic time in Muslim scholastic theology (Isis, 9, 326–344, 1927); following mainly Maimonides' account of these atomistic views which he did not share but explained very clearly. Z. Diesendruck: Maimonides' Lehre von der Prophetie (Jewish studies in memory of Israel Abrahams, 74–134, New York 1927).

Maimonides' Influence—M. Joël: Verhältnis Albert des Grossen zu Maimonides (Breslau 1876). David Kaufmann: Der Führer Maimūni's in der Weltliteratur (Archiv für Geschichte der Philosophie, vol. 11, 335–376, 1898); also in his Gesammelte Schriften (vol. 2, 152–189, Frankfurt 1910). J. Guttmann: Der Einfluss der maimonidischen Philosophie auf das christliche Abendland (Moses ben Maimon, 134–230, Leipzig 1908). Isaac Husik: An anonymous medieval Christian critic of Maimonides (Jewish quarterly, vol. 2, 159–190, 1911). J. P. W. Crawford: The vision delectable of Alfonso de la Torre and Maimonides' Guide of the Perplexed (Publications of the modern language association of America, vol. 28, 188–212, 1913). A. Rohner: Das Schöpfungsproblem bei Moses Maimonides, Albertus Magnus und Thomas von Aquin (Beiträge zur Gesch. der Philosophie des Mittelalters, vol. 11, 5; 152 p., Münster 1913). Artur Schneider: Die abendländische Spekulation des 12. Jahrhunderts in ihrem Verhältnis zur aristotelischen und jüdischarabischen Philosophie (ibidem, vol. 17, 4; 82 p., 1915). Leon Roth: Spinoza, Descartes, and Maimonides (148 p., Oxford 1924; important; Isis, 7, 324). Jewish thought in the modern world (Legacy of Israel, 433–472, Oxford 1927).

JOSEPH IBN 'AQNĪN

Joseph ben Judah ben Isaac ibn 'Aqnīn (or 'Aknīn). In Arabic: Abū-l-Ḥajjāj Yūsuf ibn Yaḥyā ibn Isḥāq al-Sibtī al Fāsī al-Maghrabī al-Isrā'īlī. Jewish philosopher, astronomer, and physician, writing in Arabic. Born about 1160. Flourished in Ceuta and in Fās until about 1185, then at Cairo, and finally at Aleppo, where he died in 1226. He was Maimonides' favorite disciple. He took with him in his eastward wanderings the astronomy of Jābir ibn Aflaḥ and discussed it under Maimonides' guidance. Among his writings, we may single out treatises on the absolute, and on creatio ex nihilo, and one on Talmudic weights and measures (these treatises are extant in Hebrew).

An ethical work, Kitāb ṭibb al-nufūs (Medicine of the soul) is also ascribed to him. It contains very valuable information on the ordinary course of studies in Jewish Spain; for example, a list of the medical and mathematical works to be used. For a similar work, see my note on Judah ibn 'Abbas.

In 1192–1193 he witnessed in Baghdād a public burning of the works of the philosopher Al-Rukn 'Abd al-Salām, and of the astronomy of Ibn al-Haitham, by the preacher 'Ubaidallāh al-Taimīya, called Ibn al-Mārastāniya. Al-Rukn was thrown into prison where he remained until the following year.

Text—Moritz Löwy: Drei Abhandlungen (Berlin 1879); Hebrew translation of the treatise on the absolute.

Arabic and Hebrew fragments of the Ṭibb published by M. Güdemann (Das Jüdische Unterrichtswesen, Wien 1873).

J. L. Magnes: A treatise as to necessary existence, the procedure of things from the necessary existence, the creation of the world (Hebrew and English, 46 p., Berlin 1904).

Criticism—Moritz Steinschneider: Review of Munk's memoir of 1842 cited below (Zeitschrift für die religiösen Interessen des Judenthums, vol. 2, 76–80, 108–120, 1845); Ersch und Grubers Allgemeine Encyclopaedie (vol. 31, 45–58, 1855); Hebräische Bibliographie (vol. 13, 38–43, 1873); Analekten (Magazin für d. Wissenschaft d. Judentums, vol. 15, 105–112, 1888); Hebraeische Uebersetzungen (33–35, 406–407, 920, 1893); Arabische Litteratur der Juden (228–233, 1902). The first three are reprinted in Gesammelte Schriften (vol. 1, 35–89, 1925).

S. Munk: Notice sur Joseph ben Jehouda (Journal asiatique, vol. 14, 5–70, 1842). Ibn abī Uṣaibi'a (vol. 2, 213, 1884). Israel Abrahams: Jewish life in the Middle Ages (365–366, 1896). H. Suter: Mathematiker der Araber (136, 1900). Michael Friedländer: Jewish encyclopaedia (vol. 7, 267, 1904). Josef Heller: Encyclopaedia judaica (vol. 2, 33–38, 1928).

JOSEPH IBN ZABARA

Joseph ben Meïr (Ibn) Zabara. Catalan Jewish physician and poet. Born at Barcelona, studied under Joseph Qimḥi at Narbonne, and spent the rest of his life in Barcelona. His chief work (the only one of certain authorship) is the Sefer ha-sha'ashu'im (Book of delight), dedicated to Sheshet Benveniste (second half of the twelfth century). It is a collection of stories in rhymed prose, somewhat after the model of the Kalīla wa Dimna, and is of special interest as the earliest work of its kind in Hebrew literature (unless Berakya's be earlier, which is not impossible). Otherwise it is of greater value to the folklorist than to the historian of science. Ibn Zabara may be the author of the Momeri ha-rofe'im Sayings of physicians), a satyrical parody of the Aphorisms of Hippocrates.

Text—The Sha'ashu'im was first edited by Isaac 'Aqrish (Constantinople 1577). Reprinted in Ha-Lebanon (1865) and again by Senior Sachs (Yen Lebanon, Paris 1866). Critical edition by Israel Davidson (Texts and studies of the Jewish Seminary of America, vol. 4, New York 1914), with English introduction. Reprinted with the same introduction in Hebrew (Berlin 1925). English extracts quoted by Israel Abrahams in his essay on the Sefer ha-sha 'ashu 'im (Jewish quarterly review (vol. 6, 502–532).

The Momeri and two other small texts are included in the Constantinople edition.

Criticism—M. Steinschneider: Ersch und Grubers Allgemeine Encyklopädie (section 2, part 31, 93–96, 1855; reprinted in Gesammelte Schriften, vol. 1, 162–171, 1925). Joseph Jacobs: Jewish Encyclopaedia (vol. 7, 273, 1904).

For Berakya ha-Naqdan, Joseph Qimḥi, and Judah ibn Tibbon, see Chapter XVI, The Translators.

For Isaac ben Abba Mari, see Chapter XXVI, Law and Sociology.

For David Qimḥi, see Chapter XXVII, Philology.

IV. EASTERN JEWISH AND SAMARITAN

HIBATALLĀH IBN MALKĀ

Abū-l-Barakāt Hibatallāh ibn 'Alī ibn Malkā al-Baladī, Awḥad al-zamān. Jewish philosopher, physician, and astronomer, who wrote in Arabic and embraced Islām late in life. He was physician to the 'Abbāsid al-Mustanjid (caliph 1160–1170). Flourished in Baghdād, and died there, of elephantiasis, about 1174–1175, at the age of 80. At the time of his death he was blind and deaf. He wrote various treatises on philosophical and scientific subjects. His chief work, at any rate in his own estimation, was a treatise on logic, physics, and metaphysics, Al-mu'tabar fī-l-ḥikma; he was already blind when he composed it; he dictated it to various disciples. He wrote a summary of Galen's anatomy, Ikhtiṣār al-tashrīḥ. A remarkable cure of a psychopathological case by suggestion is ascribed to him.

He wrote a curious treatise on the reason why stars are visible in the night and not in the day time (Risāla fi sabab ẓuhūr al-kawākib lailan wa khafā'ihā nahāran). A table of stars, ascribed to one Zain al-dīn Abū-l-Barakāt, is probably also a work of his.

Text—E. Wiedemann: Ueber den Grund aus dem die Sterne bei Nacht sichtbar und bei Tage verborgen sind von Hibbat Allāh ibn Malkā al-Jehūdī al-Bagdādī (Jahrbuch für Photographie und Reproduktionstechnik für 1909, 49–54); abridged translation with commentary, and comparison with Ibn Sīnā's views on the same subject.

Criticism—F. Wüstenfeld: Arabische Aerzte (98–99, 1840). L. Leclerc: Médecine arabe (vol. 2, 29–31, 1876). Ibn abī Uṣaibi'a (vol. 1, 278–280, 1884). C. Brockelmann: Arabische Litteratur (vol. 1, 460, 1898). H. Suter: Die Mathematiker der Araber (123, 1900). M. Steinschneider: Arabische Litteratur der Juden (182–186, 1902). Max Schloessinger: Jewish Encyclopaedia (vol. 6, 384, 1904). Max Meyerhof: Notes sur quelques médecins juifs égyptiens (Isis, 12, 124, 1929).

For the Samaritan, Abū-l-Isḥāq Ibrāhīm, see Chapter XXVII, Philology.

V. LATIN

PETER THE LOMBARD

Petrus Lombardus, "Magister sententiarum." Italian theologian, born near Novara, Lombardy, about 1100. He was educated in Paris, and taught there (1139–1140) and in Rome. He was bishop of Paris from 1159 to the time of his death in 1160. Though his work was principally theological—and mediocre at that—it exerted such lasting, if superficial, influence on mediaeval thought that we must take it into account. He wrote many commentaries; but his fame rests upon the four books of Sentences, Sententiarum libri IV, a textbook of theology which was immensely popular in western Europe, as is witnessed by the number of editions, commentaries, etc. Books 1 to 3 deal with things, res (God, creatures, virtues); book 4, with symbols, signa (the sacraments). Peter's knowledge was largely of the patristic type, but he borrowed from many other sources; for example, from John of Damascus who had just been translated by Burgundio of Pisa (1148–1150). The form of his writings was distinctly more modern than the substance and helped to hide the mediocrity of the latter; it clearly reveals Abaelard's and Gratian's influence. While Abaelard enjoyed exposing contradictions and difficulties, Peter was essentially conservative and conciliatory and utterly devoid of originality; hence his success. The Books of Sentences were completed in 1150 or 1152; they were approved by the Fourth Lateran Council in 1215; they remained for about four centuries one of the fundamental textbooks of western universities.

Text—Sententiae: Strassbourg, 1468 (?) not after 1471; Venice 1477; Nuremberg 1481; Basel 1486; Venice 1486; Basel 1490 (?). Libri IV sententiarum studio et cura PP. collegii S. Bonaventurae in lucem editi (2d ed., Ad Aquas Claras, 1916–1917).

Complete works in Migne's Patrologia latina (vol. 1, 191–92).

Criticism—F. Protois: Pierre Lombard, son époque, sa vie, ses écrits, son influence (Paris 1881). Julius Kögel: Petrus Lombardus in seiner Stellung zur Philosophie des Mittelalters (39 p., Greifswald 1897). Michele da Carbonara (or Carbone): Dante e Pier Lombardo (Studi Danteschi, Tortona 1890; reprinted in the Collez. di opuscoli danteschi, 44–45. Città di Castello 1897). Joh. Nep. Espenberger: Die Philosophie des Petrus Lombardus und ihre Stellung im 12. Jahrhundert (150 p.; Beitr. zur Gesch. der Philosophie des Mittelalters, vol. 3, 5, Münster 1901). Martin Grabmann: Geschichte der scholastischen Methode (1909–1911). P. Duhem: Système du monde (vol. 3, 37–43, 1915). Constantin Michalski: Die vielfachen Redaktionen einiger Kommentare zu Petrus Lombardus (Miscellanea F. Ehrle, 1, 219–264, Roma 1923). M. de Wulf: History of mediaeval philosophy (vol. 1, 204–205, 1926).

For Aristippus of Catania, Paschal the Roman, Leo of Pisa, and Gerard of Cremona, see Chapter XVI, The Translators.

For Alcher of Clairvaux, see the note on Isaac of Stella, in this chapter.

For Peter the Eater, see Chapter XXV, Historiography.

Respecting the arrival of the Aristotelian physics in the West, see C. H. Haskins: Studies in the history of mediaeval science, 1924; for example, the section discussing Latin treatises on the elements (p. 92–96).

ALAN OF LILLE

Alanus de Insulis. Alain de Lille. "Doctor universalis." French humanist and moralist, born in Lille, Flanders, about 1128. He assumed the Cistercian habit in Clairvaux, taught in Paris, and became bishop of Auxerre. He died at the monastery of Cîteaux in 1202. His chief work, and the most famous, is an encyclopaedic poem in nine books, entitled Anticlaudianus sive De officio viri boni et perfecti. He also wrote an ethical story, De planctu naturae ad Deum (or, Enchiridion de rebus naturae); a bestiary (De naturis quorumdam animalium); and a treatise against the Albingenses, about 1203 (see my note on the Cathari, Chapter II, Christendom), etc. None of these works has any philosophical importance; the form is poetic and modern, but the substance is out-of-date—Augustinian, Boetian. He knew Aristotle only through Boetius, and Arabic philosophy through Gundisalvo's De unitate; he knew also the Liber de causis. He was anti-realist or at least opposed to extreme realism in the same manner as John of Salisbury, whom he resembled in other respects. He deserves our attention because of the popularity of his Anticlaudianus, and because in spite of the shallowness of his culture he had reached some very remarkable conclusions: physical truth can be attained only by reason controlled by prudence; theological truth, though based on faith, should be accounted for in a rational way.

Text—The Anticlaudianus was printed in Basel 1536, Venice 1582, Antwerp 1625; also in Migne's Latin patrology (vol. 210). Douglas M. Moffat: The complaint of nature (English translation, 95 p., Yale studies in English, New York 1908).

The ascription to him of an alchemical treatise, the Dicta Alani philosophi de lapide philosophico, is gratuitous. Printed six times in German, and once in Latin, in the Theatrum chemicum (vol. 3, 721, 1659).

Criticism—Brial: Histoire littéraire de la France (vol. 16, 396–425, 1824). Eugène Bossard: Alani Anticlaudianus cum Divina Dantis Alighieri Comoedia collatus (Angers 1885). Matthias Baumgartner: Die Philosophie des Alanus im Zusammenhange mit den Anschauungen des 12. Jahrhundert. (Beitr. zur Gesch. der Phil. des Mittelalters, vol. 2, 4; Münster 1896). John Ferguson: Bibliotheca chemica (vol. 1, 14, 1906). P. Duhem: Système du monde (vol. 3, 223–230, 1915). M. De Wulf: History of mediaeval philosophy (vol. 1, 185–188, 1926).

ISAAC OF STELLA

Isaac of Etoile. English psychologist. A monk in Cîteaux; abbot of the Cistercian monastery of Etoile, in Poitou, from 1147 to the time of his death in 1169. In 1162 he wrote an Epistola ad quendam familiarem suum de anima, which is a summary of Platonic-Augustinian psychology, with original developments. This contains the earliest trace or one of the earliest traces of Gundisalvo's influence outside of Spain. Isaac remarks that things can be divided into three groups: bodies, souls, and God. We do not know the very essence of any, but we have a clearer knowledge of God than of souls, and of souls than of bodies.

The friend to whom this letter was addressed was a brother Cistercian, Alcher of Clairvaux, who is probably the author of an answer to it entitled De spiritu et anima. This treatise is also a psychological compendium, more elaborate and more learned than Isaac's, but less original.

Text—Both works edited by Bertrand Tissier: Bibliotheca Patrum Cisterciensium (vol. 6, 1664). The Epistola is included in Migne's Patrology (vol. 194, 1875–1890, 1855). The De spiritu et anima is also included in Migne's Patrology, together with the works of St. Augustine (vol. 40, 779–832).

Criticism—Franz Bliemetzrieder: Isaak von Stella (Jahrbuch für Philosophie und spekulative Theologie, vol. 18, 1–35, 1904); Eine unbekannte Schrift Isaaks (Studien und Mitteilungen aus dem Benediktiner und Zisterzienserorden, vol. 29, 433, 1908; apropos of a commentary on the Book of Ruth). Matthias Baumgartner: Ueberweg Grundriss der Geschichte der Philosophie der patristischen und scholastischen Zeit (10th ed., 329, 334–336, 130*, 1915). M. De Wulf: History of mediaeval philosophy (vol. 1, 184, 1926).

JOHN OF SALISBURY

See Chapter XXVI, Law and Sociology.

DANIEL OF MORLEY

Daniel de Merlac (Merlai, Marlach). English philosopher, born probably in Morley, Norfolk. Educated at Oxford, later in Paris and in Toledo. While in Toledo, one Galippus interpreted for him the Almagest from the Arabic. Daniel returned to England and flourished there in the last quarter of the twelfth century. He wrote a treatise on astrological philosophy, called Liber de naturis inferiorum et superiorum, dedicated to John of Oxford, bishop of Norwich from 1175 to 1200. It is divided into two books treating respectively of the superior and the inferior parts of the world. It quotes Arabian as well as Greek sources, and states the superiority of the former. Daniel was closely dependent upon Adelard of Bath. While in Paris he was deeply influenced by William of Conches. His principal Muslim authorities were al-Farghānī, Abū Ma'shar, and al-Fārābī.

Text—Karl Sudhoff: Daniels von Morley Liber de naturis inferiorum et superiorum (Archiv für Geschichte der Naturwissenschaften, vol. 8, 40 p., 1 pl., 1917).
Criticism—A. F. Pollard: Dictionary of national biography (vol. 39, 74, 1894). M. Steinschneider: Europäische Uebersetzungen (12, 15, 1904). C. Singer: Daniel of Morley (Isis, vol. 3, 263–269, 1920). Alexander Birkenmajer: Eine neue Handschrift des Liber de naturis inferiorum et superiorum (Archiv für Geschichte der Naturwissenschaften, vol. 9, 45–51, 1920; Isis, 5, 498). Lynn Thorndike: History of magic (vol. 2, 171–187, 1923); with a note on MSS. C. H. Haskins: Studies in mediaeval science (126–128, 1924). Franz Bliemetzrieder: Ueber literarische Vorlagen des Liber de naturis inferiorum et superiorum (Archiv für Geschichte der Mathematik, vol. 10, 338–344, 1927; Isis, 11, 172). Martin Müller: Die Stellung des Daniel von Morley in der Wissenschaft des Mittelalters (Philosophisches Jahrbuch, 301–337, 1928).

ALEXANDER NECKAM

Alexander Necham; also, jocularly, Nequam (meaning good for nothing). Alexander de Sancto Albano. English grammarian and encyclopaedist, born in 1157 at St. Albans, Hertfordshire. (His mother suckled him and the future Richard I at the same time). Educated at St. Albans, and later at the school of Petit Pons in Paris. He returned to England in 1186, assumed the habit of an Augustinian Canon, and in 1213 became abbot of Cirencester. He died at Kempsey, Worcestershire, in 1217, and was buried in Worcester. He wrote the De naturis rerum, which includes a popular encyclopaedia of scientific knowledge; De laudibus divinae sapientiae, a poetic paraphrase of the first work; and treatises on grammar. The De naturis rerum is divided into five books, of which the first two treat of moralized science; the three others contain a commentary on Ecclesiastes. He compiled a vocabulary arranged as a reading book, the De utensilibus, which is of some interest to the historian of technology.

Both the De utensilibus and the De naturis rerum contain the earliest European mention of the nautical use of the magnetic needle. It should be noted that Alexander does not speak of the compass as of a novelty. An earlier mention, but a doubtful one, may be found in the Poema de rebus Normannorum of William of Apulia (about 1099). Other mentions, by Guiot of Provins and by James of Vitry (first half of the thirteenth century) may be as early (or almost) as Alexander's. The De naturis rerum is undated but was well known at the end of the twelfth century.

One of the earliest accounts of the barnacle myth (goose-bearing tree, bernicle goose) occurs in the De naturis rerum. The myth itself is far more ancient; it has been traced back to Mycenaean times, but one does not know how it was transmitted from, say, the ninth century B.C. to the eleventh century after Christ when it reappears.

Text—De naturis rerum and De laudibus divinae sapientiae, edited by Thomas Wright (Rerum britannicarum medii aevi scriptores, London 1863); preface, 78 p.; text of De naturis, 354 p.; for the compass, see p. 181–184, chiefly 183.

Thomas Wright: A volume of vocabularies (Joseph Mayer's Library of national antiquities, 1; London 1857, reprinted 1882). De utensilibus, p. 96–119; for the compass, see p. 114.

Criticism—William Hunt: Dictionary of national biography (vol. 40, 154, 1894). C. R. Beazley: Dawn of modern geography (vol. 3, 508, 1906). C. H. Haskins: A list of textbooks from the close of the twelfth century (Harvard studies in classical philology, vol. 20, 75–94, 1909; revised in Studies in mediaeval science, 356–376, 1924). P. Dorveaux: Notes sur quelques drogues mentionnées dans le De nominibus utensilium (Seventeenth Congress of Medicine, section 23, 225–229, 1914). M. Esposito: On some unpublished poems attributed to Neckam (English Historical Rev., vol. 30, 450–471, 1915). Edward Heron-Allen: Barnacles in nature and in myth (Oxford 1928; Isis, 12, 340).

THE LUCIDARIUS

The Lucidarius is a small encyclopaedia of theology and general knowledge written in German about the end of the twelfth century; the earliest encyclopaedia written in German. It was translated into Danish, Dutch, and Bohemian.

It should not be confused with the Elucidarium composed about half a century earlier by Honorius of Autun (first half of the twelfth century). The Elucidarium was a theological treatise written in Latin for clerks; the Lucidarius was written in German for the laity.

Text—Felix Heidlauf: Lucidarius aus der Berliner Hds. (Deutsche Texte des Mittelalters, hrg. von der Preuss. Akademie, Bd. 28, 114 p., Berlin 1915).

Criticism—Karl Schorbach: Studien über das deutsche Volksbuch Lucidarius und seine Bearbeitungen in fremden Sprachen (Quellen und Forschungen zur Sprach- und Culturgeschichte der germanischen Völker, 74, 285 p., Strassburg 1894). Important memoir dealing with both Lucidarii, and with their translations. All these texts have been studied chiefly from the philological point of view; a comparative study of them with the view of determining the diffusion of positive knowledge in Western Europe would be very desirable.

Gustav Hellmann: Meteorologische Volksbücher (53 p., Berlin 1891; enlarged ed., 68 p., 1895).

HILDEGARD

Hildegardis de Pinguia (Bingen). German theologian, scientist, and physician. Born in 1098 at Böckelheim on the Nahe, near Sponheim, flourished in Disibodenberg and Rupertsberg, Bingen, where she died in 1179. Often called Saint Hildegard, though she has not been canonized. She was a Benedictine nun (not abbess), and founded the Rupertsberg convent in 1147. She was a woman of great learning and vision; an encyclopaedic mind of the mystical type; the earliest medical writer of Germany, and one of the leading scientists and of the most influential personalities among the Christians of her time. She carried on an extensive correspondence with St. Bernard of Clairvaux, with four popes, five emperors and kings, and with many prelates.

Her principal writings are of two kinds: first, books of visions; the Scivias (1141–1150), and the Liber divinorum operum simplicis hominis (1163–1170), which contain curious cosmological and anatomical views dominated and amalgamated by the theory of the macrocosm and microcosm[16] (very much elaborated in the second work); second, scientific works based on Benedictine and popular traditions, and also on personal observation; the Physica (Subtilitatum diversarumque creaturarum libri IX) is an encyclopaedia of natural history and cloister medicine, the botanical part being especially important, with almost a thousand animals and plants named in German; the Causae et curae (Liber compositae medicinae de aegritudinum causis, signis atque curis) is a compendium of pathology and therapeutics, the remedies being chiefly of popular origin and derived from plants. It describes under the name of leprosy cases which certainly are not leprosy, but something else, maybe syphilis? (general paralysis of the insane); however this may be an interpolation. She conceived a kind of secret language and script (lingua ignota).

There has been considerable discussion regarding the authenticity of the scientific writings. Some scholars would deny it altogether. It is more probable that they are genuine, but that they contain later interpolations; there are certainly such interpolations in the Causae et curae. The main argument against their genuineness (as developed by Singer, 1917) is the disparity of thought between the mystical and scientific writings; but this is not convincing, for we find the same disparity in the life and works of many mystics. It involves necessarily a disparity of language.[17] The use of German words to designate local animals and plants is natural enough, since Hildegard had plenty of opportunities to become acquainted with them and fewer to know their Latin equivalents. The subject deserves deeper study.

Text and translations—Migne: Patrologia latina (vol. 197, Paris 1855); containing the Epistolae, Scivias, Liber divinorum operum simplicis hominis, Physica, etc., in all 1383 col. of which the Physica cover 250. J. B. Pitra: Analecta S. Hildegardis (614 p., Monte Cassino 1882); containing Liber vitae meritorum; novae epistolae; carmina; opuscula varia; etc. Maura Böckeler: Wissen die Wege, Scivias. Ins Deutsche übertragen und bearbeitet mit einem Geleitwort von Ildefons Herwegen (508 p., 35 pl. reproducing miniatures of the famous Scivias MS. of Wiesbaden; Berlin 1928).

Physica—First edition. Physica elementorum, fluminum aliquot Germaniae, metallorum, leguminum, fructuum et herbarum, arborum et arbustorum, piscium denique, volatilium et animantium terrae . . . . (Strassburg 1533). Reprinted in Experimentarius medicinae continens Trotulae curandarum aegritudinum muliebrium . . . . item quattuor Hildegardis de elementorum . . . . naturis et operationibus. Edited by G. Kraut (Strassburg 1544). Migne's edition (1855). F. A. Reuss: Liber beatae Hildegardis subtilitatum diversarum naturarum, etc. (Paris 1856). Partial German translation with analysis by J. Berendes (Pharmazeutische Post, 1896–1897; reprint, 110 p.).

[16] She does not use these terms.

[17] Moreover it should be noted that people living in bilingual countries do not generally command a double vocabulary. Large parts of their vocabulary exist only in one language. That is especially true when one of the languages is a learned one (like Latin or Arabic in mediaeval times, or even like French in Flanders today) and the other a vernacular.

Causae et curae—Partial edition by Pitra in 1882 (op. cit., 468–482). First complete edition by Paul Kaiser (254 p., Leipzig 1903). Partial translation into German by Paul Kaiser: Die Schrift der Aebtissin Hildegard über Ursachen und Behandlung der Krankheiten (Therapeutische Monatshefte, vol. 16, 1902, passim).

Justus Blanckwalt: Epistolarum liber; scripta alia, vita (Cologne 1566).

Criticism—F. A. Reuss: De libris physicis S. Hildegardis (Würzburg 1835); Der h. Hildegard Subtilitatum . . . . libri IX, die werthvollste Urkunde deutscher Natur- und Heilkunde aus dem Mittelalter (Ann. des Vereins für Nassauische Altertumskunde, vol. 6, 50–106, Wiesbaden 1859). Ludwig Choulant: Handbuch der Bücherkunde (302–309, 1841). E. H. F. Meyer: Geschichte der Botanik (vol. 3, 517–536, 1856). Paul Kaiser: Die naturwissenschaftlichen Schriften der Hildegard (Prog.; Berlin 1901). Ludwig Geisenheyner: Ueber die Physica der Hildegard und die in ihr enthaltene älteste Naturgeschichte des Nahegaues (24 p., Ber. über die Versammlungen des botanischen Vereins für Rheinland-Westfalen, Bonn 1911; Nachträge, ibidem, 15–24, 1916 (1917). Dom Louis Baillet: Les miniatures du Scivias de Sainte Hildegarde conservé à la bibliothèque de Wiesbaden (Monuments et mémoires publiés par l'Académie des inscriptions, vol. 19, 49–149, 8 pl., 32 fig., Paris 1911). This MS. is of considerable importance for it was made most probably between 1160–1180 under Hildegard's direction; the beautiful illuminations complete the text; they are documents of the first order for the history of art and iconography in the twelfth century. Paul Diepgen: Traum und Traumdeutung (p. 6, Hildegard's views on dreams; Berlin 1912). F. Strunz: Die Vergangenheit der Naturforschung (80 sq., 1913). D. Barduzzi: Di Santa Ildegarda e dei suoi libri di medicina (Rev. di storia critica, anno 4, 50–52, 1913). Erich Wasmann: Hildegard als älteste deutsche Naturforscherin (Biologisches Zentralblatt, vol. 33, 278–288, Leipzig 1913); also (Festschrift Georg v. Hertling von der Görres Gesellschaft dargebracht, 459–475, 1913). Francesca Maria Steele: The life and visions of Hildegard (London 1914). Ildefons Herwegen: Guibert von Gembloux und Hildegard (Der Belfried, vol. 1, 118–123, 1916). Guibert was a friend and correspondent of Hildegard, and he acted as her Latin secretary after Volmar von Disibodenberge's death, for Hildegard herself was a poor Latinist. Charles Singer: The scientific views and visions of Hildegard (Studies in the history of science, vol. 1, 1–55, 1917); elaborate study beautifully decorated with the Wiesbaden miniatures published by Baillet in 1911, and with others. F. W. E. Roth: Studien zur Lebensbeschreibung der hl. Hildegard (Studien und Mit. zur Geschichte des Benediktinerorderns, vol. 39, 88–118, Salzburg 1918) based on painstaking investigations of the sources; Heilkräftige Sympathiewirkungen der Edelsteine im 12. Jahrhundert (Archiv für Gesch. d. Medizin, vol. 11, 315–318, 1919). Helene Riesch: Hildegard (2te. Auflage, 168 p., Freiburg i. Br., 1920; popular biography; Isis, 4, 584). Lynn Thorndike: History of magic (vol. 2, 124–154, 1923). Hermann Fischer: Die heilige Hildegard, die erste deutsche Naturforscherin und Ärztin, ihr Leben und Werk (Münchener Beiträge, nos. 7–8, 162 p., München 1927; important; DLZ, 50, 781–784, 1929). C. Singer: From magic to science (199–239, London 1928); revised and abridged reprint of his paper of 1917. According to Singer the chief points of interest in Hildegard's visions are (a) the cosmic theory on which they are based, (b) the extremely involved presentation of that theory, (c) the remarkably close way in which the miniatures of two MSS. illustrate the text and suggest a living tradition arising with the prophetess herself, and (d) the pathological basis of the visions (megrim or migraine). Hermann Fischer: Mittelalterliche Pflanzenkunde (24–34, München 1929; Isis, 15, 367). Hans Liebeschütz: Das allegorische Weltbild der heiligen Hildegard (Studien der Bibliothek Warburg, 16, 190 p., Leipzig 1930; Isis, 15, 209); very elaborate study of Hildegard's symbolism.

HERRAD OF LANDSBERG

Herrad of Landsberg (or Landsperg). German nun and educator. In 1167 she became abbess of the convent of Hohenberg on Mt. St. Odile in Alsace; she died there in 1195. She composed for the instruction of her nuns a sort of popular encyclopaedia called Hortus deliciarum. It is a collection of extracts dealing with astronomy, geography, natural history, philosophy, etc., Biblical history providing the frame. The sources are largely Biblical and patristic. The unique MS., written and illustrated by Herrad herself, or at any rate under her supervision, was destroyed during the bombardment of Strassburg, August 25, 1870. It counted 324 leaves of vellum of very large size, including 636 colored pen drawings. The text and illustrations held closely together, completing one another. The scientific value of the Hortus was small, its artistic interest much greater. It was a real encylopaedia of Christian iconography. Two pages were dated respectively 1159, 1175.

Christian Moritz Engelhardt: Herrad und ihr Werk (with atlas of 12 pl., Stuttgart 1818). A. Straub and A. G. Keller: Hortus deliciarum (Publié aux frais de la société pour la conservation des monuments historiques de l'Alsace, Strasbourg 1879–1899, 1901; facsimile reproduction of the illustrations).

Woltmann: Allgemeine deutsche Biographie (vol. 12, 205, 1880). Robert de Lasteyrie: Miniatures inédites de l'Hortus deliciarum (Gazette archéologique, 1884–1885; 37 p., Paris 1885). Albert Marignan: Etude sur le MS. de l'Hortus deliciarum (Studien zur deutschen Kunstgeschichte, 125, 86 p., 1910).

VI. VERNACULAR

TROUBADOURS AND TROUVÈRES

One of the most interesting symptoms of the literary revival of Christian Europe was the appearance of a number of poets in southern France, Italy and Catalonia. They appeared towards the end of the eleventh or the beginning of the twelfth century and their number steadily increased until the beginning of the thirteenth century. They were called troubadours (Provençal trobaire or trovador, from low Latin, trovare, to find, invent), and they composed lyrical poetry concerned chiefly with love, in various dialects of the langue d'oc. It is probable that this development was not entirely original in Christendom, but was caused or at any rate stimulated by Muslim examples. These poems were sung, and thus the new literary art was intimately connected with the development of European music. If the troubadours received their musical inspiration from Islām, we may assume that they received also some literary inspiration from the same source, bearing in mind however that melodies and harmonical systems are much easier than literature to transmit, as they need neither translation nor explanation.

The earliest known of these troubadours is William IX, count of Poitiers and duke of Aquitaine, who was born in 1071 and ruled in Poitou from 1087 to 1127. It is significant that most of these troubadours were noblemen, some of them of princely rank like the said Guillaume, and like Richard Lionheart, king of England from 1189 to 1199. About 450 of these troubadours are known by name, and we have some personal knowledge of a quarter of them. Their productions were soon discussed and criticized among them; that is, the new art was conscious almost from the beginning. All this is explained by the fact that it was essentially aristocratic. The troubadours were assisted by men of humbler origin, professional merrymakers, the jongleurs (joculatores, jougleurs, joglars). This very vigorous development was stopped about the year 1210 by the wars and persecutions directed against the Albigenses. In 1209 Béziers and Carcassonne were sacked, the castles of Languedoc were ruined one after another, and finally in 1218 Toulouse was besieged. Many of the troubadours had been patronized by the heretic nobility, or else had strong leanings towards individualism which often meant heterodoxy. The activity of the new religious orders and of the Inquisition completed their doom. The last of the French troubadours was Guiraut Riquier of Narbonne (born about 1230, died 1294), who was obliged to go and live until 1279 at the court of the king of Castile, Alfonso X, the Wise; he was then able to return to southern France, and spent the rest of his life at the court of Henry II, count of Rodez in Rouergue, which was the last refuge of the new poetry in southern France.

Fortunately this literary revival had not remained restricted to the south. It had traveled north, and the northern poets, singing in the langue d'oïl,—the trouvères—had a longer lease of life. It has been claimed that the new poetry was as original to the north as to the south. It is more probable that the trouvères received their first stimulation from the troubadours, even as the latter had received it from Muslim singers. In any case, the soil was ready for the seed; the slightest stimulation was sufficient to give a start to the new movement, and poetic expression to the pent up lyricism. The fact that troubadours, trouvères, and, as we shall see presently, goliards and minnesingers, flourished at about the same time, is the best proof that Western Europe had reached its literary maturity.

The new fashion may have been carried north, for example, by Eléonore of Aquitaine who was the queen of Louis VII from 1137 to 1152. The Crusades helped considerably to bring the north and south of France together, and later the Albigensian crusade caused a northward emigration of southern talent. It is a fact that the golden age of the trouvères occurred in the first half of the thirteenth century, that is, a little later than that of the troubadours. It would seem that the trouvères were never as exclusively aristocratic as the troubadours, and partly because of that we know much less about the personalities of the former than of the latter. But after 1230 the love of poetry spread more and more among the wealthy and progressive bourgeoisie of northern France. The last abodes where the trouvères flourished before decadence finally set in at the end of the thirteenth century, were the rich cities of Arras and Rheims.

The activities of troubadours and trouvères increased linguistic consciousness and pride, developed new literatures, improved poetic and musical expression and last but not least helped considerably to refine manners and thoughts.

Text—Troubadours. François Raynouard: Choix des poésies originales des troubadours (6 vols., Paris 1816–1821). K. Bartsch: Chrestomathie provençale (4th ed., Elberfeld 1880). Duc de la Salle de Rochemaure: Les troubadours cantaliens (2 vols., Aurillac 1910). Giulio Bertoni: I trovatori d'Italia (Modena 1915).

Trouvères. Arthur Dinaux: Les trouvères cambrésiens (3d ed., 194 p., Paris 1837); Les trouvères de la Flandre et du Tournaisis (382 p., Paris 1839); Les trouvères artésiens (491 p., Paris 1843); Les trouvères brabançons, hainuyers, liégeois et namurois (757 p., Bruxelles 1863). These volumes form parts I to IV of a general work entitled Trouvères, jongleurs et ménestrels du Nord de la France et du Midi de la Belgique.

Criticism—Troubadours. Friedrich Diez: Leben und Werke der Troubadours (Zwickau 1829; 2d ed. revised by K. Bartsch, Leipzig 1882); Die Poesie der Troubadours (376 p., Zwichau, 1826; 2d ed. revised by K. Bartsch, Leipzig 1883). Manuel Milá y Fontenals: Los trovadores en España (Barcelona 1861; revised edition, 1889). Camille Chabaneau: Les biographies des troubadours (Toulouse 1885). Ida Farnell: The lives of the troubadours, translated from Provençal and with specimens of their poetry translated into English (London 1896). Justin Harvey Smith: The troubadours at home (2 vols., New York 1899). Henry John Chaytor: The troubadours of Dante (278 p., Oxford 1902). Joseph Anglade: Les troubadours; leur vies, leur oeuvres, leur influence (336 p., Paris 1908); Pour étudier les troubadours; notice bibliographique (Bull. de la Soc. archéologique du Midi, 10 p., 1914–1915). Camille Chabaneau: Onomastique des troubadours (Société des langues romanes, Montpellier 1916). Alfred Jeanroy: Les troubadours en Espagne (Annales du Midi, vol. 27, 5–39, Toulouse 1916); Les "biographies" des troubadours et les "razos" (Archivum romanicum, vol. 1, 289–306, 1917); Bibliographie sommaire des chansonniers provençaux (94 p., Paris 1916). Henry John Chaytor: The troubadours and England (Cambridge 1923). Raimon De Loi (R. D. Jameson): Trails of the troubadours (328 p., New York 1926).

Trouvères. Hyacinthe Binet: Le style de la lyrique courtoise en France aux XIIe et XIIIe siècles (106 p., Paris 1891). Gaston Paris: Les origines de la poésie lyrique en France au moyen âge (Paris 1892).

Musical criticism—E. de Coussemaker: Art harmonique aux XIIe et XIIIe siècles (Paris 1865). Johann Baptist Beck: Die Melodien der Troubadours (210 p., Strassburg 1908; French translation, Paris 1910). Pierre Aubry: Trouvères et troubadours (225 p., Paris 1909; Englished by Claude Aveling, 1914). Julián Ribera y Tarragó: La música andaluza medieval en las canciones de trovadores, troveros y minnesinger (3 parts, Madrid 1923–1925; Isis, 11, 497; 12, 163); Historia de la música árabe medieval y su influencia en la Española (355 p., Madrid 1927; Isis, 11, 496). Jean Baptiste Beck: Les chansonniers des troubadours et des trouvères publiés en facsimile et edités, texte et musique (vols. 1 and 2, Philadelphia 1927; Isis, 11, 423). Barbara Smythe: Grove's dictionary of music (vol. 5, 391–394, 1928).

GOLIARDS

Another sign of the literary awakening of Europe is found in the songs of the wandering students, the Goliardi, which originated about the same time, though a few may be even earlier. They became more and more prevalent during the following century, as university life increased. These songs spread all over France, England and Germany, wherever students went. Being composed in Latin, they were truly international. They were full of spontaneity and of genuine lyrical feeling in spite of frequent coarseness and ribaldry; their aim was generally satirical and anticlerical. Various measures were taken by church and university councils during the thirteenth century to stop their diffusion; apparently in vain. The songs of the Goliards give us a new proof, if such were needed, that mediaeval thought was just as complex and as full of life and rebellion as modern thought.

Text—J. A. Schmeller: Carmina burana. Lateinische und deutsche Lieder und Gedichte (290 p., Stuttgart 1847; 3d ed., Breslau 1894). Gaudeamus! Carmina vagorum in usum laetitiae (Ed. repetita, 230 p., Leipzig 1879). Wilhelm Meyer: Fragmenta burana (Festschrift, Ges. der Wiss., Göttingen 1901). Carmina clericorum (128 p., 4th ed., Heilbronn 1878; 7th ed., 1890). Robert Ulich: Vagantenlieder. Aus der lateinischen Dichtung des 12. und 13. Jahrhunderts. Uebertragen und eingeleitet. Den lateinischen Text bearbeitete Max Manitius (182 p., 8 pl., Jena 1927).

Thomas Wright: The Latin poems commonly attributed to Walter Mapes (Camden Society, London 1841). Karl Breul: The Cambridge songs, a goliard's song book of the eleventh century (130 p., Cambridge 1915).

John Addington Symonds: Wine, women and song (186 p., London 1884); translations in English verse.

Criticism—Max Haessner: Die Goliardendichtung und die Satire im 13. Jahrhundert in England (Diss.; Leipzig 1905). Siegfried Jaffe: Die Vaganten und ihre Lieder (Progr., 38 p., Berlin 1908). Nicolaus Spiegel: Die Grundlagen der Vagantenpoesie (Progr., 34 p., Würzburg 1908). Holm Süssmilch: Die lateinische Vagantenpoesie der 12. und 13. Jahrhunderts (114 p., Leipzig 1917). Helen Waddell: The wandering scholars (Boston 1927). E. K. Rand: A note on the Goliards (Speculum, vol. 3, 595, 1928).

MINNESINGERS

While the troubadours and trouvères flourished in southern and northern France, a similar poetical awakening was taking place in Germany. The love-singers (Minnesänger) received their initial stimulation from the Provençal troubadours. The earliest of them appeared in southern Germany and Austria; for example, Der von Kürenberg (about 1160), on the Danube, near Linz; Dietmar von Aist (died 1171); Heinrich von Morungen, who attended the court of Leopold V, duke of Austria (died in 1194), and was the master of the greatest mediaeval poet of Germany: Walther von der Vogelweide (born in Wipthal, Tirol, about 1170; died about 1230). Even as the trouvères, the minnesingers died out by the end of the thirteenth century.

Like their French brethren, the minnesingers had been at first members of the nobility, or at least their early efforts had been fostered by court life. Their tradition was continued from the fourteenth to the sixteenth century by another group of poets, the Meistersänger, recruited from among the burghers and craftsmen. The two movements, however different, can easily be connected, for the Meistersänger recognized as onę of their founders the Bavarian Wolfram von Eschenbach (died after 1216) who had been in touch with Walther von der Vogelweide. The first school of Meistersingers is said to have been established by Heinrich von Meissen (called Frauenlob) at Mainz, in 1311; the same century saw the creation of other schools in Strassburg, Francfort, Würzburg, Zürich, Prague. During the fifteenth century new schools appeared in Augsburg and Nuremberg; in the sixteenth century the latter became the most important of all, as is illustrated by the genius of Hans Sachs.

I give this brief outline in order that the reader may understand more readily the implications of the literary revival of the twelfth century. A new lyrical stream then began to flow, of which the ultimate ramifications may be followed in every European literature of our day.

Text—F. H. von der Hagen: Minnesänger. Deutsche Liederdichter der 12., 13., and 14. Jahrhunderts (5 vols. and atlas, Leipzig 1838–1856). Karl Lachmann and Moritz Haupt: Des Minnesangs Frühling (2d ed., Leipzig 1875; 3d ed., 1882; 4th ed., 1920, by Friedrich Vogt). Karl Bartsch: Deutsche Liederdichter des 12. bis 14. Jahruhunderts, eine Auswahl (Leipzig 1864; 4th ed., 508 p., Berlin 1901); Die schweizer Minnesänger (694 p., Frauenfeld 1886). Fridrich Pfaff: Der Minnesang des 12. bis 14. Jahrhunderts (2 vols. Stuttgart 1891–1894). Alfred Rottauscher and Bernhard Paumgartner: Das Taghorn. Dichtungen und Melodien des bayrisch-österreichischen Minnesangs (3 vols., Wien 1902).

Frank C. Nicholson: Old German love songs (256 p., London 1907); select poems Englished. Jethro Bithell: The minnesingers (vol. 1, Halle 1909); English versions.

Criticism—Fritz Grimme: Die rheinisch-schwäbischen Minnesinger (346 p., Paderborn 1897). Anton E. Schönbach: Die Anfänge des deutschen Minnesanges (Graz 1898). Anna Lüderitz: Die Liebestheorie der Provençalen bei den Minnesingern der Stauferzeit (139 p., Berlin 1904). Arnold Schiller: Der Minnesang als Gesellschaftspoesie (Diss., 58 p., Bonn 1907). Julius Dieffenbacher: Deutsches Leben im 12. und 13. Jahrhunderts (2 vols., Göschen Sammlung, Leipzig 1907). Otto Gottschalk: Das deutsche Minneleich und sein Verhältnis zu lai und descort (Diss., 135 p., Marburg 1908). Konrad Burdach: Ueber den Ursprung des mittelalterlichen Minnesangs, Liebesromans und Frauendienstes (Berlin 1918).

REYNARD THE FOX

One more literary stream deserves to be considered because of its universality and because of the possibility of connecting it with older streams with which we are already familiar. The cycle of animal stories of which Reynard the Fox, Isengrim the Wolf, Bruin the Bear, Baldwin the Ass, etc., are the heroes is indeed of deep interest to the student of cultural continuity. These stories can be traced back to Aesop, to the Physiologos (vol. 1, 300), also to Sanskrit and Persian sources, and re-discovered in some form or other in the folklore of almost every nation. The form with which we are particularly concerned, the beast epic generally called Reynard the Fox, originated probably in northern France or in Flanders, and was already completed in its essential elements, by the second half of the twelfth century. The purpose of that popular epic was not didactic like that of Aesop and of the Physiologos, but was simply to amuse the readers or listeners, and to satirize feudal usages and the manners of the nobility, of the clergy, of the judges, and of the rich.

When were these stories integrated into a single poem? It is impossible to say. It is probable that there were many independent syntheses using substantially the same heterogeneous materials. At any rate poems of this cycle exist in a great number of European languages and exhibit many variations. A Latin poem, Ysengrinus, was compiled by a Flemish clerk by the middle of the twelfth century; a German poem, Reinhart Fuchs, was completed by Heinrich der Glichezare about 1180; an East Flemish version was published by one Willem about the middle of the thirteenth century.

Text—Only a few of the most important texts can be mentioned. Reynardus Vulpes. Poëma ante a. 1280 a quodam Baldwino e lingua teutonica translatum. Ex unico adhuc superstite exemplo, quod, c.a. 1473 Ultrajecti impressum, edited by M. F. A. G. Campbell (68 p., The Hague 1859). Latin translation by Hartmann Schopper (Francfort 1567).

Oldest Dutch printed text, Antwerp 1487. Karl Breul: The Cambridge Reinaert fragments (Culemann fragments, 75 p., Cambridge 1927). Reintje de Vos van Hendrik van Alkmaar, naar den Lubekschen druk van 1498, edited by Jacobus Scheltema (Haarlem 1826); same text reedited by Hoffmann von Fallersleben (Breslau 1834), by F. H. Dethleff (Rostock 1867), etc. Reinaert de Vos, early Flemish text, edited by Jan Frans Willems (Ghent 1836, 1850, etc.). New edition of the earliest Flemish text by J. W. Muller (Ghent 1914).

Heinrichs des Glichezares Reinhart Fuchs, edited by Georg Baesecke (142 p., Halle 1925).

English version printed by Caxton, June 1481; reprinted for the Percy Society (295 p., London 1844, elaborate introduction by William J. Thoms), and by Edward Arber (136 p., London 1878).

Ernest Martin: Le roman de Renart (4 vols., Strasbourg 1882–1887). New edition by Gaston Raynaud and Henri Lemaitre (2 vols., Paris 1914).

Emilio Teza: Rainardo e Lesengrino (77 p., Pisa 1869).

The story has been told in modern language by many authors: Goethe in German; Paulin Paris, Ch. Potvin, and Léopold Chauveau in French; John Masefield in English; Stijn Streuvels in Flemish; etc. This proves that its interest is perennial.

Criticism—August Todt: Die franco-italienischen Renartbranchen (Diss., Giessen; 124 p., Darmstadt 1903). Leonard Ashley Willoughby: Samuel Naylor and Reynard the Fox (42 p., London 1914). Lucien Foulet: Le roman de Renart (578 p., Paris 1914). Jacob Wijbrand Muller: Critische commentaar op Van de vos Reinaerde (Utrecht 1917). Ulrich Leo: Die erste Branche des Roman de Renart nach Stil, Aufbau, Quellen und Einfluss (Greifswald 1918). J. H. Breasted: The tales of Kalila and Dimna (Chicago 1922; Isis, 5, 264). Gunnar Tilander: Remarques sur le Roman de Renart (Göteborg 1923).

THE NIBELUNGENLIED

The Nibelungenlied (or Nibelungennôt), a long poem written in Middle High German, is the most important Teutonic epic. It is probably of Frankish origin, and its earliest elements may be dated back to the time of Attila, King of the Huns from 434 until his death in 453. After its primary elaboration, the original story or cycle of stories traveled in two main directions; one, across the Rhine into Franconia; the other, northwards into Iceland by way of Ireland. Thus arose two traditions: the Icelandic, represented by a number of poems in the Elder Edda, and by a prose version called the Völsungasaga; and the Germanic, represented by the Nibelungenlied proper.

The Icelandic tradition seems to be the more primitive; it is hardly possible to date the fragments of the poetic Edda relative to it, but the Völsungasaga itself dates only from the thirteenth century. The Nibelungenlied in its present form is the final result of successive elaborations or editions. The study of its origin and development is very complicated and full of moot questions which cannot be considered here. According to Theodor Abeling, the poem was put together for the first time in the last third of the tenth century; a new version was composed about 1140 by one Konrad, and revised about 1190 by another poet. The final version was completed at some time after that date, relatively soon, say, towards the end of the twelfth century or the beginning of the thirteenth, by an unknown poet (Heinrich Traun of Ofterdingen? Rudolf of Ems?).

The direct historical value of the Nibelungenlied is extremely small, in fact negligible, as none of the characters involved can be identified with historical persons beyond doubt. But its indirect historical value is considerable; it is a mirror of early mediaeval Germany. One of its distinctive traits, as contrasted for example with the Chanson de Roland, is the spirit of pessimism which pervades it. It is full of cruelty, brutality and deceit, but also of bravery, of a certain kind of loyalty, and of some genuine poetry; it is a gruesome tale. Its influence upon German thought, culminating in the Wagnerian Tetralogy, has been immense.

Text—Edition by Adelbert von Keller (385 p., Tübingen 1879). By Karl Bartsch (6th ed., 446 p., Leipzig 1886). Karl Lachmann: Der Nibelunge Noth und die Klage (14. Abdruck, 297 p., Berlin 1927).

English translation by William Nanson Lettsom (rev. ed., New York 1901); by George Henry Needler in rhymed verse (New York 1904); by Daniel Bussier Shumway (Boston 1909); and by Arthur S. Way (346 p., Cambridge 1911).

General criticism—Karl Lachmann (1793–1851): Ueber die ursprüngliche Gestalt des Gedichts von der Nibelungen Noth (111 p., Berlin 1816). K. Bartsch: Untersuchungen über das Nibelungenlied (Wien 1865). William Morris (1834–1896): The story of Sigurd the Volsung and the fall of the Niblungs (400 p., Boston 1877). Henri Lichtenberger: Le poème et la légende des Nibelungen (442 p., Paris 1891). Julius Dieffenbacher: Deutsches Leben im 12. Jahrhundert; Kulturhistorische Erläuterungen zum Nibelungenlied und zur Kudrun (177 p., Göschen Sammlung, Leipzig 1899). Gaston Paris: Poèmes et légendes du moyen-âge (Paris 1900). R. C. Boer: Untersuchungen über den Ursprung und die Entwicklung der Nibelungensage (3 vols., Halle 1906–1909). Theodor Abeling: Das Nibelungenlied und seine Literatur (363 p., Leipzig 1907; supplement, 75 p., Leipzig 1909); very full bibliography. Joseph Strobl: Die Entstehung der Gedichte von der Nibelunge Not und der Klage (Halle 1911). Max Ortner and Theodor Abeling: Zu den Nibelungen (207 p., Leipzig 1920). Ernest Tonnelat: La chanson des Nibelungen; étude sur la composition et la formation du poème épique (396 p., 1 map, Strasbourg 1926; Isis, 13, 426).

A few more special studies—Francis Edward Sandbach: The Nibelungenlied and Gudrun in England and America (207 p., London 1903). Helmut de Boor: Die färöische Lieder des Nibelungenzyklus (Diss., Leipzig 1918). August Löwis of Menar: Die Brünhildesage in Russland (Palaestra, 142, Leipzig 1923). Bálint Hóman: Geschichtliches im Nibelungenlied (48 p., Berlin 1924); treats partly of Hungarian traditions. Heinrich Hempel: Nibelungenstudien, 1, Nibelungenlied, Thidrikssaga und Balladen (282 p., Heidelberg 1926; Isis, 11, 424). Aloys Schröfl: Der Urdichter des Liedes von der Nibelunge Nôt und die Lösung der Nibelungenfrage (352 p., München 1927; Isis, 11, 425).

For the Poema del Cid and the Tale of Igor, see Chapter XXV, Historiography.

VII. BYZANTINE

EUSTATHIOS

Εὐστάθιος. Byzantine humanist and chronicler, born probably at Constantinople, where he flourished before 1175; archbishop of Thessalonica since 1175; died about 1193. He wrote commentaries (παρεκβολαί) on Pindar, Homer, and on the geographic poem composed by Dionysios Periegetes (second half of the first century). The last named commentary, ὑπομνήματα, is especially important because it incorporates older scholia and lost texts of Arrian (first half of the second century), and Stephanos of Byzantium (first half of the sixth century). He also wrote a history of the conquest of Thessalonica by the Normans in 1185.

Text—The commentary on Dionysios was edited by G. Bernhardy (Leipzig 1828). Also by Carl Müller: Geographi graeci minores (vol. 2, 201–407, 1855).

De Thessalonica a Latinis capta a. 1185: 1st ed. by L. Fr. Tafel (Francfort 1832); 2d ed. by Imm. Bekker, together with the χρονογραφία of Leo Grammaticus (first half of the eleventh century) in the Corpus scriptorum historiae Byzantinae (Bonn 1842); 3d ed. in Migne's Greek patrology (vol. 136, 1865).

Criticism—K. Krumbacher: Byzantinische Litteratur (536–541, 679, 1897). Joseph Groeger: De codicibus Strabonis, Herodoti, Arriani ab Eustathio in commentario ad Dionysii periegesin usurpatis. (Diss. 88 p., Breslau 1911). H. J. Lulofs: Geographie in den spiegel der oudheid (Tijdsk. van het K. Nederlandsch aardrijkskundig Gen., vol. 35, 822–852, c. 1920).

VIII. IRANIAN

IRANIAN COSMOLOGY

The Būndahishn (The Ground-giving) is a Pahlawī treatise completed (that is, the larger or Iranian version) probably about 1178. It is a compilation embodying many earlier elements; the bulk of it may date from the ninth century, or may have been edited then for the first time. It constitutes one of our best sources for the study of Iranian lore. It is indeed an extensive manual of the knowledge available among Zoroastrians about the end of the twelfth century. The subject is well defined in an introductory statement in the Hindu version: "First the original creation by Aūharmazd and the antagonism of the evil spirit, and afterwards the nature of the creatures of the world, from the original creation till the end." The scope is encyclopaedic.

The fuller, Iranian, version is divided into 46 chapters. It was known to Persian Zoroastrians, but remained entirely unknown to Europeans until 1875.

The Hindu version made for the Bombay Parsis is a collection of extracts from the Iranian version. It contains about 13,000 words, while the Iranian text may have contained originally about 30,000 words. The Hindu version was the first to reach western scholars; it was made known to them by Anquetil-Duperron in 1771.

Text—Abraham Hyacinthe Anquetil-Duperron: Boun-dehesch (Paris 1771); French translation of the Hindu version. Ferdinand Justi: Der Bundehesh (Leipzig 1868); lithographed copy of the Pahlawī text, transcript in Persian characters, German translation, and glossary. English translation by E. W. West in Sacred Books of the East (vol. 5, 1–151, 1880). Facsimile of the TD MS. brought from Persia by Dastur Tirandaz; edited by the late Ervad Tahmuras Dinshaji Anklesaria (Pahlavi text series, 3, Bombay 1908); this is the Great, or Iranian, version.

Criticism—E. W. West in Geiger and Kuhn: Grundriss der iranischen Philologie (vol. 2, 98–102, 1896–1904).

IX. HINDU

HEMACANDRA

See Chapter XXVII, Philology.

GAṄGEŚA

Gaṅgeśvara. Hindu logician who flourished in Bengal at the end of the twelfth century. He founded the Navanyāya,[18] that is, the "new school" of Hindu logic, also called the school of Navadvīpa (Nuddea) in Bengal. His principal work is the Tattvacintāmaṇi, a systematic account of the Nyāya system, the main classic on the subject, and as such the source of innumerable commentaries, and of a scholastic tradition which was especially sterile. It is divided into four books treating of the four sources of cognition: perception, deduction, analogy, etymology (Wortzeugnis).

Text—Edition by K. Tarkavāgīśa, with extracts from various commentaries (Bibliotheca Indica, 1888–1901).

Criticism—Hermann Jacobi: Die indische Logik (Nachr. Ges. der Wiss., phil.

[18] Meaning new Nyāya. The Nyāya is one of the six orthodox schools of Hindu philosophy (Darśana); the word nyāya means method, principle, logical argument, logic.

Kl., 460, Goettingen 1901); elaborate account of the Nyāya system essentially based on the Tattvacintāmaṇi. M. Winternitz: Indische Litteratur (vol. 3, 469, 1922).

DURLABHARĀJA

Son of Narasiṃha. Flourished during the rule of King Kumārapāla of Gujarāt (in the Bombay presidency). In 1160 he wrote a treatise on soothsaying, called Sāmudratilaka, which was completed by his son Jagaddeva.

JAGADDEVA

Aside from completing his father's work, he wrote a book on dreams, the Svapnacintāmaṇi[19] (Wishjewel of dreams), which is interesting not only from the cultural and religious point of view but also from the medical.

Text—J. von Negelein: Der Traumschlüssel des Jagaddeva, ein Beitrag zur indischen Mantik (Sanskrit and German; Religionsgeschichtliche Versuche und Vorarbeiten, XI, 4, 452 p., Giessen 1912).
Criticism—M. Winternitz: Indische Litteratur (vol. 3, 572, 1922). Winternitz mentions a third contemporary work of the same kind, the Adbhutasāgara (Ocean of wonders) begun by Ballālasena, king of Gauḍa, in 1168, and completed by his son Lakshmaṇasena, but the date given (1168) does not agree with epigraphic information according to which the son's rule began in 1119 (?). C. Mabel Duff: The chronology of India (303, 1899).

X. CHINESE

CHU HSI

Chu¹ Hsi¹ (2544, 4081). Often called Chu Tzŭ or Chu¹ Fu¹ tzŭ³ (2544, 3612, 12317). Chinese philosopher and historian, born in 1130 at Yu²-ch'i¹ (13413, 1009), Fuhkien, died in 1200. In 1241 his tablet was placed in the Confucian temple; he was the twelfth of the Twelve Sages of Confucianism, eleven of them being the very pupils of K'ung Fu Tzŭ (sixth century B.C.). He was the last and by far the greatest of the Five Philosophers, wu³ tzŭ³ (12698, 12317), i.e., the leaders of the Confucian revival of the Sung dynasty. (See my note on Chou Tun-i, second half of eleventh century). This so-called neo-Confucianism is a cosmological materialism or pantheism, comparable in some respects to stoicism, if anything, less materialistic than the latter. The name neo-Confucianism is very misleading; of course this philosophy includes Confucian elements, but these are mixed witb Taoist and Buddhist ideas. One of its main tenets is the correlativeness of matter and form.

Chu Hsi revised the annals composed by Ssŭ-ma Kuang (second half of eleventh century), or organized their revision. This work was continued by his disciples and completed in 1223, under the title T'ung¹ chien⁴ kang¹ mu⁴* (12294, 1644, 5900, 8080). Later elaborations of this work form the most complete, if not the most scientific, account of Chinese history. (See my note on Kublai Khān, second half of thirteenth century.)

Text—The most important of his writings (for the student of cosmology) has been translated at least 3 times. Confucian cosmogony. A translation of section

[19] Svapna, somnus, sleep and dream; cintāmaṇi is the philosopher's stone.

49 of the Complete Works of Choo-Foo-Tze, with explanatory notes by the Rev. Thos. McClatchie (London 1879). French translation by Mgr. Ch. de Harlez: Philosophie de la nature[20] (Bruxelles 1890); imperfect. More elaborate French translation with the Chinese text, introduction and notes by Father Stanislas Le Gall (S. J.): Le philosophe Tchou Hi. Sa doctrine, son influence (Variétés sinologiques, 6, 134 p., Shanghai 1894). This 49th section is divided into 3 parts: Form and matter, or Li³ ch'i⁴ (6879, 1064); Great extreme, or T'ai⁴ chi²* (10573, 859); Heaven and earth, or T'ien¹ ti⁴ (11208, 10956).

Charles de Harlez: Les principes gouvernementaux en Chine. Extraits de Tchou-hi. (Giornale della Soc. asiatica italiana, vol. 2, 23 p., 1888; extraits traduits du Tchou-tze-tsieh-yao).

J. Percy Bruce: The philosophy of human nature (460 p., London 1922).

The Library of Congress has at least six editions of the T'ung chien kang mu, all with commentary by Ch'ên² Jên²-hsi²* (658, 5627, 4157). No printing dates are available except in the case of one edition of 1808. The preface dates of four of these editions are: 1072, 1473, 1630, 1701. The remaining one has no preface, nor dated title page.

Criticism—Charles de Harlez: Tchu-Hi, his doctrines and influence (26 p., Louvain 1896); chiefly polemical against Le Gall. H. A. Giles: Chinese biographical dictionary (174–176, Shanghai 1898); Chinese literature (228–231, 1901). A. Wylie: Chinese literature (84–85, 1902). Mrs. Couling: Encyclopaedia Sinica (114, 1917). G. F. Moore: History of religions (vol. 1², 45–47, 1920). Léon Wieger: Histoire des croyances religieuses en Chine (2nd ed., 657–671, Shanghai 1922; Isis, 7, 261). J. Percy Bruce: Chu Hsi and his masters (352 p., London 1923). A Forke: World-conception of the Chinese (1925; Isis, 8, 373–375); by comparing ancient and modern (i.e., neo-Confucian) views on many subjects he proves how little originality there is in Chu Hsi's philosophy.

LU CHIU-YÜAN

Lu⁴*Chiu³-yüan² (7432, 2263, 13713) Style Tzŭ³ ching⁴ (12317, 2179), nickname Hsiang⁴ shan¹ (4287, 9663), Chinese philosopher. Born in 1140 at Chin¹-ch'i¹ (2032, 1007), Fuhkien; in 1190 he became governor of Ching¹ mên² (2157, 7751), Hupeh; he died in 1192. He was canonized as Wên² an¹ (12633, 44), and his tablet was placed in the Confucian Temple in 1530. He opposed Chu Hsi's philosophy to some extent, and carried on a controversy with him. Lu did not believe much in education enforced from the outside; he thought that the real intellectual progress was essentially a personal, internal, development. His few writings were collected under the title Hsiang⁴ shan¹ chi²* (4287, 9663, 906).

H. A. Giles: Chinese biographical dictionary (541, 1898).

[20] This title is a bad translation of the phrase Hsing-li. See Chou Tun-i, second half of eleventh century.

CHAPTER XIX

MATHEMATICS AND ASTRONOMY

(Second Half of Twelfth Century)

I. WESTERN MUSLIM

For Ibn Ṭufail and Ibn Rushd, see Chapter XVIII, Philosophic Background.

AL-BIṬRŪJĪ

Abū Isḥāq al-Biṭrūjī al-Ishbīlī, Nūr al-dīn. Hispano-Muslim astronomer. His name al-Biṭrūjī (hence, Alpetragius) is derived from Pedroche, a town north of Cordova; the name al-Ishbīlī suggests that he flourished also in Seville. Casiri believed that Alpetragius was a corrupted form of the Italian name Petrucci, and that this astronomer was a Christian renegade; this curious error was repeated by Jourdain.

Al-Biṭrūjī was pupil of Ibn Ṭufail (who died in 1185–1186). He wrote a book, Kitāb al-hai'a, on the configuration of the heavenly bodies, which is remarkable because it contains an attempt to revive in a modified form the theory of homocentric spheres. According to al-Biṭrūjī, this theory had been suggested to him by Ibn Ṭufail; and it was clearly influenced also by Jābir ibn Aflaḥ—for example, with regard to the lower planets. The gist of it is as follows: Each heavenly body is attached to a sphere and the motive power (primum mobile) is the ninth sphere outside that of the fixed stars. The prime mover produces in every sphere a motion from east to west; this motion is fastest in the eighth sphere, and it decreases as the distance from the prime mover increases; for example, the fixed stars complete a revolution in 24 hours, while the moon, which is carried by the innermost sphere, requires almost 25 hours for the same revolution. The pole of the ecliptic being different from that of the equator, the planetary orbits are not closed; moreover the planets do not remain at an invariable distance from the pole of the ecliptic; each has its own motion in latitude, and a variable velocity in longitude. The eighth sphere has two motions, the one in longitude (precession), and another caused by the rotation of the pole of the ecliptic around a mean position (this is the imaginary trepidation of the equinoxes). The pole of each planet revolves around the pole of the ecliptic, each in its own way. Al-Biṭrūjī's theory was called theory of the spiral motion (ḥarakat lawlabī). It marked the culmination of the Muslim anti-Ptolemaic movement. However, it was hardly better than the Ptolemaic theory, and it was never sufficiently worked out to have any practical value.

I have explained this theory at some length, in spite of its wrongness and lack of elaboration, because it made quite a sensation. The Kitāb al-hai'a was soon translated into Latin and into Hebrew, and was considerably discussed. Al-Biṭrūjī was considered the representative of a "new astronomy," and was aptly surnamed, in Hebrew, ha-mar'ish, he who causes the doctrine (or the heavens) to vacillate. His strange views were elaborately refuted by Levi ben Gershon in 1328.

Al-Biṭrūjī's theory implied the reintroduction of the notion of impetus vaguely formulated by Simplicios (first half of the sixth century), when the latter stated that the stability of celestial bodies is warranted by the excess of their impetus over their gravity.

Text—The Kitāb al-hai'a was translated into Latin in 1217 by Michael Scot. An extract of it was included in the Hebrew encyclopaedia of Judah ben Solomon ha-Kohen (c. 1247); the whole treatise was translated into Hebrew in 1259 by Moses ibn Tibbon. This Hebrew version was translated into Latin in 1528–1529 by Qalonymos ben David. Qalonymos' translation was printed together with Sacrobosco's Sphaera and other works: Alpetragii arabi planetarum theorica physicis rationibus probata nuperrime latinis litteris mandata a Calo Calonymos hebreo neapolitano (Venice 1531).

Criticism—S. Munk: Mélanges de philosophie juive (412, 500, 518–522, 1859). M. Steinschneider: Hebraeische Uebersetzungen (550–552, 1893). Suter: Die Mathematiker und Astronomen der Araber (131, 1900; Nachträge, 174, 1902). J. L. E. Dreyer: Planetary systems (264–267, 1906). L. Gauthier: Une réforme du système astronomique de Ptolémée (Journal asiatique, vol. 14, 483–510, 1909); important. P. Duhem: Système du monde, (vol. 2, 146–156, 1914); a much longer account than Dreyer's but less satisfactory. Carra de Vaux: Penseurs de l'Islam (vol. 2, 230–236, 1921).

IBN AL-YĀSMĪNĪ

Abū Muḥammad 'Abdallāh ibn Muḥammad ibn Ḥajjāj ibn al-Yāsmīn[1] al-Adrīnī al-Ishbīlī. Muslim mathematician of Berber origin. He (or at any rate his family) came from the vicinity of Fās; he flourished in Morocco and in Seville. He was strangled in Morocco about 1204. He wrote a short poem on algebra (Al-arjūza al-Yāsmīnīya) of which there are many manuscripts.

C. Brockelmann: Arabische Litteratur (vol. 1, 471, 1898). H. Suter: Die Mathematiker und Astromen der Araber (130, 1900; 174, 1902).

MUḤAMMAD AL-ḤAṢṢĀR

Abū Zakarīyā (or Abū Bakr) Muḥammad ibn 'Abdallāh al-Ḥaṣṣār (or Ḥāṣir, the calculator, or the maker of mats). Western Muslim mathematician. Flourished in the twelfth or thirteenth century; at any rate before Ibn al-Bannā', whose Talkhīs was derived from his work. He wrote a treatise on arithmetic and algebra, which was translated into Hebrew in 1271 by Moses ibn Tibbon, in Montpellier.

M. Steinschneider: Hebraeische Uebersetzungen (557, 1893). Heinrich Suter: Das Rechenbuch des Abū Zakarīyā al-Ḥaṣṣār (Bibliotheca Mathematica, vol. 2, 12–40, 1901; containing an analysis of the treatise with extracts); Die Mathematiker und Astronomen der Araber (197, 222, 1900).

For Abū-l-Qāsim al-Ḥaufī, see Chapter XXVI, Law and Sociology.

II. EASTERN MUSLIM

'ABD AL-MALIK AL-SHĪRĀZĪ

Abū-l-Ḥusain 'Abd al-Malik ibn Muḥammad al-Shīrāzī. Muslim mathematician and astronomer who flourished in the second half of the twelfth century. He

[1] Or Yāsamīn, Yāsimīn. Yāsmīn is the flower jasmine or jessamine (words derived from the Arabic).

wrote in Arabic a summary of Apollonios' treatise on conics, based on the translation made in the second half of the ninth century by Hilāl al-Ḥimṣī and Thābit ibn Qurra. He also composed an abridgment (mukhtaṣar) of the Almagest, which was translated into Persian by Quṭb al-Dīn al-Shīrāzī (second half of the thirteenth century).

H. Suter: Mathematiker der Araber (125, 1900). C. Schoy: Encyclopaedia of Islām (vol. 4, 377, 1927).

MUḤAMMAD IBN AL-ḤUSAIN

Muḥammad ibn al-Ḥusain ibn Muḥammad ibn al-Ḥusain. Eastern Muslim mathematician who flourished at the end of the twelfth century and the beginning of the thirteenth. Between 1187 and 1193 he composed (with the assistance of Kamāl al-dīn ibn Yūnus, first half of the thirteenth century) a treatise on conics, called Risāla al-birkār al-tāmm (treatise on the perfect compasses) dedicated to Ṣalāḥ al-dīn (died 1193). The "perfect compass" (or compasses) is an instrument by means of which every conic could be drawn.

Text—Francois Woepcke: Trois traités arabes sur le compas parfait (Notices et extraits, vol. 22 (1), 1–175, 1874; Arabic and French; posthumous publication edited by de Slane). The two other treatises included in Woepcke's memoir were composed by al-Kūhī and by al-Sijzī, respectively, both of them of the second half of the tenth century. The editor has added an analytical verification of the Muslim constructions.

Criticism—Jules Mohl: Avant-propos to Woepcke's editon (4 p., 1874). H. Suter: Mathematiker (139, 1900).

For Ibn al-Dahhān, see Chapter XXVI, Law and Sociology.
For Fakhr al-dīn al-Rāzī, see Chapter XVIII, Philosophic Background.

III. WESTERN JEWISH

For Abraham ben David ha-Levi, Maimonides, and Joseph ibn 'Aqnīn, see Chapter XVIII, Philosophic Background.

IV. EASTERN JEWISH

For Hibatallāh ben Malkā, see Chapter XVIII, Philosophic Background.

SAMŪ'ĪL IBN 'ABBĀS

Abū Naṣr Samū'īl ibn Yaḥyā ibn 'Abbās al-Maghribī. His original Hebrew name was Samuel ibn Judah ibn 'Abbās; he was the son of the poet Judah ibn 'Abbās of Fez, who died in Mūṣul in 1163. He traveled in the Muslim East as far as Qūhistān; in 1163, being then in Marāghah, Adharbayjān, he embraced Islām; he died in Marāghah after 1174. Physician, physicist, and mathematician, writing in Arabic. He wrote the following treatises:

1. An arithmetical introduction, Al-tabṣira fī 'ilm al-ḥisāb.
2. Al-kitāb al-Qiwāmī, on Hindu calculation, written in 1172–1173.
3. On the right-angled triangle.
4. A summary of the Kāfī fī-l-ḥisāb of al-Karkhī (first half of the eleventh century).
5. A poem on finger reckoning; etc. (other mathematical treatises).
6. Exposure of the errors of astrologers, etc. Kashf 'awār al-munajjimīn wa-ghalaṭihim fī-akthar al-a'māl wal-aghlāṭ, written in 1165–1166.

7. On specific gravity, entitled Kitāb al manbar (?); manbar is a pulpit or reading desk.

8. On sexual matters and gynaecology, Nuzhat al-aṣḥāb fī mu'āsharat al-aḥbāb (Recreation of companions and conversation of friends); the first half is erotic, the second medical. It is one of the most elaborate Arabic treatises among a good many on the same subject.

9. A refutation of Judaism, Ifhām ṭā'ifat al-Yahūd (Teaching of the Jews); also called Kitāb al-naqḍ wal-ibrām (Book of dissolution and urging). The author is chiefly known by this work, which was translated into Latin in 1339 by Alfonsus Bonihominis (bishop of Morocco, 1346); this translation obtained considerable success.

Text—The Epistola Samuelis Marocani, that is, the Latin translation of the Ifhām al-Yahūd, was first printed in 1475. There are at least eight other editions in Latin, five in German, and one in Italian; there are also versions in Spanish and Russian. English translation, The Blessed Jew of Morocco, or the Black Moor made white (York 1649). The genuineness of another treatise translated into Latin by the same Bonihominis, Disputatio Abutalib Saraceni et Samuelis Judaei, is uncertain.

Criticism—F. Wüstenfeld: Arabische Aerzte (100, 1840). L. Leclerc: Médecine arabe (vol. 2, 12–17, 1876); containing an analysis of the Nuzhat. C. Brockelmann: Arabische Litteratur (vol. 1, 488, 1898). H. Suter: Mathematiker (124, 1900). Hartwig Hirschfeld: Jewish Encyclopaedia (vol. 1, 37, 38, 1901). M. Steinschneider: Arabische Literatur der Juden (186–193, 1902; quoting eleven works); Europäische Uebersetzungen (4, 1904; apropos of frater Alfonsus Bonihominis). I. Markon: Encyclopaedia judaica (vol. 1, 177–179, 1928).

V. SYRIAC

For Simeon Shanqĕlāwī, see Chapter XXV, Historiography.

VI. BYZANTINE

CAMATEROS

Joannes Camateros, Ἰωάννης ὁ Καματηρός. Inkstandkeeper (ὁ ἐπὶ τοῦ κανικλείου) of Manuel I Comnenos (emperor from 1143 to 1180), and later archbishop of Bulgaria. Author of two astrological poems:

1. On the zodiac and all other things in the sky, 1351 iambic trimeters (περὶ ζωδιακοῦ κύκλου καὶ τῶν ἄλλων ἁπάντων τῶν ἐν τῷ οὐρανῷ.

2. Introduction to astronomy (εἰσαγωγὴ ἀστρονομίας), more popular, 4107 fifteen syllabled iambic lines.

Camateros kept closer to the astronomical facts and was more systematic and complete than his older contemporary Prodromos (first half of the twelfth century).

Text and Translations—The first poem was edited by Emmanuel Miller: Notices et extraits (vol. 23, 40–112, 1872). The second by Ludwig Weigl: Ein Kompendium griechischer Astronomie und Astrologie, Meteorologie und Ethnographie in politischen Versen (142 p., Leipzig 1908). This edition was reviewed by J. L. Heiberg: Deutsche Literaturzeitung (vol. 29, 2843–2846, 1908).

Criticism—Karl Krumbacher: Geschichte der byzantinischen Litteratur (760, 1897). L. Weigl: Studien zu dem unedierten astrologischen Lehrgedicht des Kamateros (Progr., 58 p., Würzburg 1902). Weigl's conclusions were briefly reprinted in the preface to his edition of 1908. Silvio Giuseppe Mercati: Nota a Giovanni Camatero, Εἰσαγωγὴ ἀστρονομίας v. 3750 (Byzantinische Zeitschrift, vol. 26, 286–287, 1926).

VII. LATIN

TRANSLATION OF THE ALMAGEST

The greatest astronomical event in Latin Christendom was the translation of Ptolemy's Almagest. Strangely enough, two independent Latin translations appeared within a short time. Both have already been referred to in Chapter XVI, The Translators, but it is worthwhile to repeat the main facts.

A Greek manuscript of the Almagest was brought to the court of Sicily from the library of Manuel Comnenos by Aristippus of Catania. This Greek text was translated by anonymous authors in Sicily about 1160. It is probable that Eugene the Amīr took part in that translation.

A second translation was made from the Arabic by Gerard of Cremona at Toledo in 1175.

Though the first translation, made directly from the Greek original, was probably superior to the second, it remained practically unknown, and for a long time the Almagest was known in the West not exclusively but chiefly through Gerard's version. Thus the date of introduction of the Almagest to the Latin West is 1175. A more complete answer is given by the symbols "1175 (c. 1160)." The Sicilian translation was only discovered in 1909, by Dean Putnam Lockwood (MS. Vat. 2056).

Charles Homer Haskins and Dean Putnam Lockwood: The Sicilian translators of the twelfth century (Harvard Studies in classical philology, vol. 21, 1910). C. H. Haskins: Studies in mediaeval science 155–193, 1924; a few additions in 2d ed., p. xiii, 1927).

Concerning this and other translations, see my notes on Gerard of Cremona, Aristippus of Catania, and Eugene the Amīr, in Chapter XVI, The Translators.

For English arithmetic, see my notes on Richard Fitzneal, in Chapter XXVI, Law and Sociology.

PRACTICA GEOMETRIAE

The Practica geometriae Hugonis is a text dating in all probability from the second half of the twelfth century. The author, Hugh, is unknown. He may possibly be identified with one Hugo Physicus who lived in Paris and died in 1199, but there is no good reason for identifying him with Hugh of Saint Victor (first half of the twelfth century).

This text is interesting from the archaeological point of view, as it illustrates the slowness of the diffusion of Euclidean knowledge in the Latin West. Indeed this Hugh had some knowledge of theoretical geometry, but it was exceedingly vague. There is no trace of Greco-Arabic learning in his work, except what refers to the astrolabe. It represents the pure Latin tradition at the eleventh hour, so to say, before its final submergence under the new wave of Euclidean geometry.

Text—First published from MS. Munich Clm. 13021, by Max. Curtze: Monatshefte für Math. und Physik (vol. 8, 193–224, Wien 1897). Edition of unpublished parts from other MSS. in Paris and in Cambridge, by P. Tannery and Fourier-Bonnard in Tannery's Mémoires (vol. 5, 361–368; Isis, 6, 432).

Criticism—P. Tannery: Practica Geometriae (Bull. des sciences mathématiques, vol. 23, 140–145, 1899; Mémoires, vol. 5, 204–210); Sur la Practica geometriae Hugonis (Bibliotheca Mathematica, vol. 2, 41–44, 1901; Mémoires, vol. 5, 308–313; Isis, 6, 433).

ROGER OF HEREFORD

English astronomer. Flourished about 1176–1178, and was still young then. He composed a number of mathematical, astronomical, and astrological treatises, as follows:

1. Compotus, in five books and twenty-six chapters, dated 1176; it contains a comparison of the Latin with the Hebrew calendar, and criticisms of Gerland and other Latin compotists.
2. Astronomical tables for the meridian of Hereford, 1178, based on the tables of Toledo and Marseilles.
3. Theorica planetarum, explaining in 32 chapters the use of astronomical tables. The ascription to Roger is not certain.
4. Tractatus de ortu et occasione signorum.
5. Liber de quattuor partibus iudiciorum astronomie. Also perhaps other astrological treatises.
6. De rebus metallicis.

Alfred of Sareshel (first half of the thirteenth century) dedicated to Roger his translation from the Arabic of the pseudo-Aristotelian De vegetabilibus.

Criticism—Short article by W. F. Sedgwick: Dictionary of National Biography (vol. 49, 107, 1897). Superseded by C. H. Haskins' account in The reception of Arabic science in England (English historical review, 65–68, Jan. 1915; reprinted in his Studies 124–126, 1924). Lynn Thorndike: History of magic (vol. 2, 181–187, 1923).

GERALD THE WELSHMAN

See Chapter XXII, Geography.

VIII. VERNACULAR

BJARNI BERGÞÓRSSON

Icelandic mathematician and astronomer who died in 1173. He wrote the earliest Icelandic treatise on the compotus (rím), with the possible exception of the one composed by Stjörnu Oddi, the date of the latter being very uncertain. I said *treatise*, because some Icelandic Easter tables are earlier still, some dating back to 1121 and to 1140. A brief account of chronology had also been given by Ari Fróði þorgilsson (first half of the twelfth century) in his Islendingabók, about 1127. An improved chronology had been started in Iceland about 965, and Christian chronology had of course been introduced together with Christianity in 1002. To return to Bjarni's treatise, it deals with such subjects as length of the months, epactae lunares, saltus lunae, the date of Easter, etc., and is largely based on Bede's De temporum ratione.

Text—First edition by Stephanus Björnonis in the collection called Rimbegla (Copenhagen 1780). Better edition by N. Beckman and Kr. Kålund: Alfraeði islenzk, islandsk encyklopaedisk litteratur. II. Rim I (527 p., Copenhagen 1914–1916); with long introduction.

The Alfraeði islenzk is an Icelandic encyclopaedia, the MS. of which was written in 1387. It contains treatises dating back to the twelfth century (as the rím just quoted), and later ones of the same kind as the Harpestraeng literature. The first part was edited by Kr. Kålund in Copenhagen in 1908. See analyses of both parts by W. Golther in Litteraturblatt für germanische und romanische Philologie (vol. 31, 150, 1910; vol. 40, 293–295, 1919).

IX. HINDU

For Hindu mathematics and astronomy, see my note on Bhāskara in chapter V.

X. CHINESE

The only astronomical document of the time, other than the annals, is a map of the stars, of about 1193. This is discussed in Chapter XXII, Geography.

XI. JAPANESE

FUJIWARA MICHINORI

Japanese statesman and mathematician. He became a Buddhist monk in 1140. He died in 1159. His religious name was Shinzei or Shinsai. Hence he is often called Fujiwara Shinzei, or Shinzei. Adviser to Go-Shirakawa, emperor of Japan from 1156 to 1158. He is said to have been a man of profound learning, which means that he knew the Chinese classics by heart and was steeped in Buddhism and astrology. He studied a mathematical subject called keishi-zan (permutations?), of which a remnant may perhaps be found in the famous Jinkō-ki (1627) of Yoshida Kōyū.

E. Papinot: Dictionnaire d'histoire et de géographie du Japon (99, 1906).
D. E. Smith and Y. Mikami: History of Japanese mathematics (17, 84, 1911).
F. Brinkley: History of the Japanese people (291, 1915).

CHAPTER XX

PHYSICS, TECHNOLOGY, AND MUSIC

(Second Half of Twelfth Century)

I. EASTERN MUSLIM

For Abd al-Raḥmān Ibn Naṣr, see Chapter XXVI, Law and Sociology.
For Muḥammad al-Sā'ātī, see my note on Ibn al-Sā'ātī in Book III.

II. EASTERN JEWISH

For Samū'īl ibn 'Abbās, see Chapter XIX, Mathematics and Astronomy.
For Ibn Jamī', see Chapter XXIV, Medicine.
For Joseph ibn 'Aqnīn, see Chapter XVIII, Philosophic Background.

III. LATIN

For Eugene the Amīr, see Chapter XVI, The Translators.
For Alexander Neckam, see Chapter XVIII, Philosophic Background.

PIONEER ENGINEERING WORK IN NORTHERN ITALY

The most remarkable engineering achievement of that time was accomplished in Lombardy. The waters coming down from the Alps and gathering in the Lago Maggiore and the Ticino would often overflow and run in a wasteful way to the sea. A canal, the Naviglio Grande, of about thirty miles length was built, begun in 1179 and completed in 1258, which led these waters to Milano, irrigated her fruitful fields, and brought wealth to her citizens.

At about the same time, about 1276–1283, Genoa built a gigantic mole to protect her harbor, and in 1295 captured the streams of the Ligurian Alps by means of a splendid aqueduct.

J. A. Symonds: Renaissance in Italy (vol. 3, 30, 1897). Giuseppe Cordara: I navigli di Milano (190 p., 22 pl., Milano 1927).

IV. EUROPEAN MUSIC

FRANCO OF COLOGNE

Theorist of music who flourished in Cologne probably towards the end of the twelfth century. His personality is very mysterious, and difficult to differentiate from that of the earlier Franco (of Liége; second half of the eleventh century, vol. I, 757). Two musical treatises are ascribed to him: Ars cantus mensurabilis (or De musica mensurabili); and Compendium discantus.

The author of the Ars cantus mensurabilis is named, in the Milano manuscript, Franco Parisiensis. This may be a mistake, or one or both Francos may actually have sojourned in Paris, or a third Franco may be meant. The second treatise, the Compendium, begins with the words Ego Franco de Colonia. This second work seems to be much younger than the first, and therefore would encourage the ascription of the Ars cantus to Franco of Liége, or the placing of the Compendium in the thirteenth century.

At any rate, these writings are very important, being the earliest accounts of mensural music in Christian Europe. Mensural (or measured) music is "music in which the notes have an exact time-value or ratio among themselves, instead of the fluid time-values of plain-song" (Grove's Dictionary). That invention was probably of Muslim origin (vol. I, 542, 628, 703). Apparently Franco did not invent anything, but he transmitted the invention to the Latin West and organized it. The system of notation which he introduced is often called the Franconian notation; its principles have not been superseded; they still underlie our modern notation. Its diffusion was very slow.

Text—Ars cantus mensurabilis, in Martin Gerbert: Scriptores ecclesiastici de musica (vol. 3, 1784). Also in Edmond Coussemaker: Scriptores de musica medii aevi (vol. 1, 1864). Separate edition of chapter 11. De discantu et ejus speciebus by H. Bellermann (Berlin 1874).

Compendium discantus edited by Coussemaker (op. cit., vol. 1).

Criticism—H. Bellermann: Allgemeine deutsche Biographie (vol. 7, 246–247, 1878). P. and L. Hillemacher: La musique mesurée et polyphonique (in Albert Lavignac: Encyclopédie de la musique, vol. 1, 571, 1913). Henry George Farmer: Clues for the Arabian influence on European musical theory (Journal R. Asiatic Soc., 74, 1925; Isis, 8, 508–511). Sylvia Townsend Warner: Grove's Dictionary of music (vol. 2, 304–306, 1927).

For the music of the troubadours, trouvères, and minnesingers, see the notes concerning them, in Chapter XVIII, Philosophic Background.

CHAPTER XXI

CHEMISTRY

(Second Half of Twelfth Century)

I. MUSLIM

IBN ARFA' RA'SAHU

Abū-l-Ḥasan 'Alī ibn Mūsā ibn Arfa' ra'sahu al-Jaiyānī, Burhān al-dīn. Muslim alchemist who died in Fās, in 1196–1197. He compiled a collection of poems on the philosopher's stone, entitled Dīwān shudhūr al-dhahab fī fann al-salāmāt.

Criticism—C. Brockelmann: Arabische Litteratur (vol. 1, 496, 1898).

II. LATIN

For Roger of Hereford, see Chapter XIX, Mathematics and Astronomy.
For Alan of Lille, see Chapter XVIII, Philosophic Background.

ALCOHOLIC DISTILLATION

H. Diels had claimed in 1913 that the manufacture of alcohol could be traced back to the beginning of our era. The process would have been discovered in Alexandria. A paper by H. Degering in 1917 traced it back to the eighth century. There does not, however, seem to be any proof that alcohol was actually distilled before the middle of the twelfth century. The oldest mention of alcoholic distillation is found in a treatise by the so-called Magister Salernus, who flourished about 1130–1160. It was probably the distillation of rosewater which suggested that of alcohol; at any rate the great Salernitan Manuscript of Breslau, about 1160–1170, speaks of distillation, but not of aqua ardens.

In short, the discovery of alcohol cannot be ascribed with certainty to Hellenistic or Oriental chemists; the evidence hitherto available credits this discovery to the Salernitan school, or to Christian chemists living in south Italy about the middle of the twelfth century.

The discovery of alcohol, and a little later (in the thirteenth century) that of mineral acids, may be said to mark the beginning of a new period in the history of chemistry, the period of transition between ancient and modern chemistry.

H. Diels: Die Entdeckung des Alkohols (Abhd. der preuss. Ak. d. Wiss., phil. Kl., 35 p., 1913); important. Hermann Degering: Ein Alkoholrezept aus dem 8. Jahrhundert (Sitzungsber. d. preuss. Ak. d. Wiss., vol. 36, 503–515, 1917). K. Sudhoff: Ein Alkoholrezept aus dem 8. Jahrh. (Naturwissenschaftliche Wschr., vol. 16, 681–683, 1917). E. O. v. Lippmann: Neue Beiträge zur Geschichte des Alkohols (Chemiker Z., p. 865, 883, 909, 1917); Zur Geschichte des Alkohols (ibidem, nr. 102, 1920; Isis, 3, 322–324; 4, 135). H. Diels: Antike Technik (2te Auflage, 107, 153, 1920; Isis, 3, 433).

See also my Vol. I, p. 339, Alexandrian claims; p. 681, Muslim; p. 723, Chinese.

III. WESTERN TRANSMISSION OF CHINESE PORCELAIN

We call porcelain that kind of ceramics of which the substance is vitrified and more or less translucent. The word comes through the French porcelaine, from the Italian porcellana, meaning a cowrie shell or Venus shell (Cypraea porcellana). Porcelain was invented by the Chinese, but it is impossible to state exactly when. They had been the first to see the advantage of baking their ceramics at very high temperatures; under these circumstances certain ceramic wares—a mixture of kaolin and fusible feldspar—would necessarily be vitrified and remain translucent. The earliest foreign account of Chinese porcelain is that given by Sulaimān the Merchant (first half of the ninth century). Thus porcelain was certainly made in China during the T'ang dynasty; however the earliest examples extant date only from the Sung.

The earliest recorded appearance of porcelain in the Near East was in 1171, or 1188, when Ṣalāḥ al-dīn sent a present of forty pieces of Chinese porcelain to the sulṭān of Damascus. Porcelain was not known in Europe until after the Crusades. It is said that one Maestro Antonio made some with Bolognese earth in 1470 in Venice, and that he had learned the art from the Arabs; a similar claim is made for a Venetian mirror maker, Leonardo Peutinger, in 1518. These claims are unproved. Increasing quantities of Chinese porcelain were imported into Europe, but the secret of its fabrication was not discovered until the very end of the seventeenth century, or the beginning of the eighteenth, by Ehrenfield Walter von Tschirnhaus, or by the latter's assistant Johann Friedrich Böttger, or by both.

F. M. Feldhaus: Die Technik (810–816, 1914). Thomas Francis Carter: Invention of printing in China (89, 93, New York 1925; Isis, 8, 361).

CHAPTER XXII

GEOGRAPHY

(Second Half of Twelfth Century)

I. WESTERN MUSLIM

AL-IDRĪSĪ

Abū 'Abdallāh Muḥammad ibn Muḥammad ibn 'Abdallāh ibn Idrīs, al-Ḥammūdī, al-Ḥasanī, al-Qurṭubī, al-Ṣaqalī (the Sicilian). Often called al-Sharīf al-Idrīsī, because his ancestor Idrīs was a descendant of the Prophet through Fāṭima. The spelling Edrisi is not uncommon.

Muslim geographer; one of the greatest geographers and cartographers of the Middle Ages. He was born in Ceuta in 1099–1100, studied in Cordova, then flourished at the Norman court in Palermo. He died in 1166. He made for King Roger II, shortly before the latter's death in 1154, a planisphere in silver (not a globe), and described the world in Al-kitāb al-Rujārī (Roger's Book), also entitled Nuzhat al-mushtāq fī ikhtirāq al-āfāq (The delight of him who desires to journey through the climates). The Rujārī is the most elaborate description of the world of mediaeval times. In contrast with almost all other Muslim geographies it contains information on many Christian countries as well as on the Islāmic world—a feature undoubtedly due to the fact that al-Idrīsī's patron was a Christian king—and also mentions botanical, zoological, and therapeutical facts.

Later, about 1161, al-Idrīsī compiled for William I, king of the Sicilies from 1154 to 1166, another geographical encyclopaedia, even larger than the former, entitled Rawḍ al-uns wa-nuzhat al-nafs (Pleasure of men and delight of souls) or more prosaically, Kitāb al-mamālik wal-masālik. This second work is entirely lost, unless the Rawḍ al-furaj (Garden of pleasure) composed by an unknown author in 1192 may be considered a summary or a partial copy of it.

A manuscript recently discovered in Constantinople contains the lost treatise on botany and materia medica, ascribed to al-Idrīsī. Its introduction deals with botanical generalities in the Aristotelian vein; however it is different from Theophrastos' work, and also from the De plantis. This is followed by the description of some 360 simples, the first of which is the absinth. The work seems to contain original facts and views relative to botany; but concerning medical matters, al-Idrīsī (who was not a professional physician)[1] contented himself with following other authors whom he names. The synonyms of plant names mentioned by him, according to custom, include many in modern Greek.

Text—A synopsis of the Rujārī, entitled Nuzhat al-mushtāq fī dhikr al-amṣar wal-aqtār wal-buldān wal-jazā'ir wal-madā'in wal-āfāq, was printed in Rome in 1592; and a poor Latin translation of that synopsis, by the Maronites Gabriel Sionita and Joannes Hesronita, was published under the stupidly inaccurate title Geographia Nubensis (332 p., Paris 1619).

[1] He was a mutaṭabbib, not a ṭabīb.

There is no complete edition of the text and maps of the Rujārī; but there is a complete, if inaccurate, translation into French by P. Amédée Jaubert: Géographie d'Edrisi (Recueil de voyages et de mémoires publié par la Société de géographie, vols. 5 and 6; Paris 1836–1840). A critical edition and an English translation of this work are badly needed.

Towards the end of last century, J. Horovitz discovered in the Library of Ḥakīm Oghlū 'Alī Pasha in Stambul, a MS. (no. 688) entitled Rawḍ al-furaj wa nuzhat al-muhaj (Garden of pleasure and delight of souls), said to have been composed by Idrīsī in 1192. This is impossible, for Idrīsī died in 1166, but it may be a copy, or a summary, of a part of the Rawḍ al-uns. The late C. F. Seybold (d. 1921) was preparing an edition of the text. In the Stambul MS. this text is accompanied by 73 small maps, forming a sort of pocket atlas. This atlas has been recently edited by Konrad Miller (see below).

Partial editions of the Rujārī—Description de l'Afrique et de l'Espagne par R. Dozy et M. J. de Goeje (Leiden 1866); Arabic and French.

Africa curavit J. M. Hartmann (654 p., Ed. altera, Göttingen 1796).

Spain, by J. A. Conde (Madrid 1799); Arabic and Spanish. By Antonio Blásquez (Madrid 1901); Spanish only.

Italy, by M. Amari and C. Schiaparelli (Atti del R. Acc. d. Lincei, vol. 8, 1876–1877; Roma 1883); Arabic and Italian.

Syria and Palestine, by Joannes Gildemeister (Bonn 1885); Arabic and German. By R. A. Brandel (Upsala 1894); Arabic and Swedish.

O. J. Tallgren-Tuulio and A. M. Tallgren: La Finlande et les autres pays baltiques orientaux (Géographie, VII, 4). Edition critique du texte arabe avec facsimilés de tous les manuscrits connus, traduction, étude de la toponymie, aperçu historique, cartes et gravures, ainsi qu'un appendice donnant le texte de VII, 3 et de VII, 5 (Studia orientalia, III; Societas orientalis fennica; 157 p., 12 pl., Helsinki 1930; Isis, 15, 404).

Maps—Konrad Miller: Mappae arabicae (Stuttgart 1926–1927; Isis, 9, 458–462); part 2 of vol. 1 discusses the larger map of the world (c. 1154); part 3, the smaller map of 1192; both maps are reproduced schematically and analyzed; vol. 6 contains 336 photographic reproductions of all the Idrīsī maps available in MS. (80 pl., Stuttgart 1927; Isis, 11, 173).

Criticism—J. T. Reinaud: Géographie d'Aboulféda (vol. 1, cxiii–cxxii, Paris 1848). E. H. F. Meyer: Geschichte des Botanik (vol. 3, 285–301, 1856). L. Leclerc: Histoire de la médecine arabe (vol. 2, 65–70, 1876). E. Saavedra: La geografia de España nel Edrisi (Bol. soc. geogr. Madrid, vol. 18, 225–242, 1885). W. Tomaschek: Zur Kunde der Haemus-Halbinsel. II. Die Handelswege im 12. Jahrh. (Sitzungsber. Wiener Akad., phil. Cl., 113, 285–373, 1887). C. Brockelmann: Arabische Litteratur (vol. 1, 477, 1898). F. Pons Boigues: Ensayo bio-bibliográfico (231–240, Madrid 1898). Edgar Blochet: Contribution à l'étude de la cartographie chez les Musulmans (Bone, 1898, Bulletin de l'académie d'Hippone). C. F. Seybold: Edrisiana. 1. Triest (Z. der deut. morgenl. Ges., vol. 63, 591–596, 1909). S. Günther: Der arabische Geograph Edrīsī und seine maronitischen Herausgeber (Archiv für Gesch. d. Naturw., vol. 1, 113–123, 1909). H. von Mžik: Ptolemaeus und die Karten der arabischen Geographen (Mit. der geogr. Ges., vol. 58, 152, Wien 1915). Giuseppe Pardi: Quando fu composta la geografia d'Edrisi (Rivista geografica italiana, vol. 24, 380–382, Firenze 1917; Isis, 3, 455). C. F. Seybold: Encyclopaedia of Islām (vol. 2, 451, 1919). G. Pardi: L'Italia nel XII secolo descritta da un geografo arabo (Supp. alla Rivista geogr. ital., n. 38, 59–171, 1919); description of Italy arranged by states. E. L. Stevenson: Terrestrial and celestial globes (vol. 1, 27, 33, 1921); apropos of Idrīsī's planisphere. Konrad Miller: Einleitung zu den Karten des Idrisi (Mappae arabicae, 1, 2, p. 35–63, 1926; Isis, 9, 458). H. R. Palmer: The central Sahara and Sudan in the twelfth century (Journal of the African society, 28, 368–378, 1929; Isis, 15, 210). Max Meyerhof: Über die Pharmakologie und Botanik des arabischen Geographen Edrisi (Archiv für Geschichte der Mathematik, vol. 12, 45–53, 1929; Isis, 13, 424); Die allgemeine Botanik und Pharmakologie des Edrisi (ibidem, vol. 12, 225–36, 1930; Isis, 15, 210).

AL-MĀZINĪ

Abū 'Abdallāh (or Abū-l-Ḥāmid) Muḥammad ibn 'Abd al-Raḥīm (or ibn 'Abd al-Raḥmān) ibn Sulaimān al-Qaisī al-Māzinī al-Andalusī al-Gharnāṭī. Born in 1080–1081 in Granada; died in 1169–1170 in Damascus. Hispano-Muslim geographer.

In 1114–1115 he was in Egypt, but he must have returned to his country not long afterwards; in 1117 he left Spain, sailing to Egypt via Sardinia and Sicily; in 1122–1126, he was in Baghdād; in 1130 in Abhar, Jibāl; in 1131 at Sakhsīn (or Saqsīn) on the Upper Volga—he spent many years in that region; in 1135–1136 he was in Bulghār (near Kazan, on the Volga); in 1150–1151 in Bashgird, Hungary; in 1160 in Baghdād; after that he resided in various places in Khurāsān and Syria—for example, in 1162 he was in Mūṣul. He died in Damascus in 1169–1170.

He wrote various geographical works: (1) in Baghdād in 1160, Al-mughrib 'an ba'ḍ 'ajā'ib al-Maghrib (Collection of singularities relative to some of the marvels of the Maghrib); (2) in Mūṣul in 1162, Tuḥfat al-albāb wa nukhbat al-a'jāb (Gift to the hearts and choice of wonders); (3) Nukhbat al-adhān fī 'ajā'ib al-buldān; (4) 'Ajā'ib al-makhlūqāt (Wonders of the creatures). It would seem that 3 and 4 are completely or partly identical with 1 and 2.

His accounts of foreign countries are largely anecdotic and include many fables. The Tuḥfat is divided as follows: Introduction; (1) general description of the world and its inhabitants, men and jinn; (2) singularities of various countries; (3) seas and islands, extraordinary animals living in them; (4) caverns, fossils, etc.

During his stay among the Bulgars in 1136 he witnessed the trade in fossil bones (ivory?), which were exported as far as Khwārizm for the making of combs. Al-Māzinī's account of fossil ivory is not by any means the earliest. Theophrastos speaks of it (ἐλέφας ὀρυκτός) in his book on stones (περὶ λίθων, 37), and this is repeated by Pliny. Aelian's story, according to which elephants shed their tusks once in ten years and bury them, may have originated to explain finds of fossil ivory.

Text—Gabriel Ferrand: Le Tuḥfat al-albāb édité d'après les MSS. 2167, 2168, 2170, de la Bibliothèque Nationale, et le MS. d'Alger (Journal Asiatique, vol. 207, 1–148, 193–304, 1925) Arabic text followed by an analysis, partial translation and notes; this is not yet the complete edition which we need, but it brings us much nearer to it (Isis, 11, 424).

Criticism—Ḥājī Khalīfa: Lexicon (vol. 2, 222, no. 2548, 1837; vol. 4, 189, no. 8072, 1845; the author's name is written differently in each note). J. T. Reinaud: Géographie d'Aboulféda (vol. 1, cxi–cxiii, 1848). C. Brockelmann: Arabische Litteratur (vol. 1, 477, 1898). F. Pons Boigues: Ensayo bio-bibliográfico (229–231 Madrid 1898). Bassett Digby: The mammoth (London 1926; Isis, 12, 425; no mention of al-Māzinī). Emilio Bussi: Ricordi d'Italia di un viaggiatore arabo del XII secolo (Rivista geografica italiana, 36, 138–143, 1929; Isis, 15, 209).

IBN JUBAIR

Abū-l-Ḥusain Muḥammad ibn Aḥmad al-Kinānī (that is, from the Kināna tribe). Hispano-Muslim traveler. He was born in Valencia in 1145, studied at

Játiva, made the Pilgrimage and traveled in the Near East in 1183–1185; he returned to the East in 1189–1191, and again in 1217; during the course of this last journey he died at Alexandria in 1217. The account of his first journey, Raḥlat al-Kinānī (Kinānī's journey) is one of the most important works of its kind in Arabic literature. It contains much interesting information: geographical observations, technical notes—for example, on ships; descriptions of hospitals, of pitch deposits, etc.; conditions obtaining in Sicily under William II the Good, king from 1166 to 1189. This account was much used by Ibn Juzai, Ibn Baṭūṭa's editor.

Text—Partial edition and French translation by Michele Amari: Voyage en Sicile sous le règne de Guillaume le Bon (1846). Complete Arabic text published by William Wright (Leiden 1852). New edition revised by M. J. de Goeje: The travels of Ibn Jubayr (416 p., Gibb memorial series, vol. 5, Leiden 1907).

First complete translation (in Italian): Ibn Gubayr, Viaggio in Ispagna, Sicilia, Siria e Palestina, Mesopotamia, Arabia, Egitto, da Celestino Schiaparelli[2] (430 p., Roma 1906, with an introduction and good indexes of proper names, and a glossary).

Criticism—J. T. Reinaud: Géographie d'Aboulféda (vol. 1, p. cxxiv-cxxvi, 1848). R. Röhricht: Bibliotheca geographica Palaestinae (41, 1890). C. Brockelmann: Arabische Litteratur (vol. 1, 478, 1898). Francisco Pons Boigues: Ensayo bio-bibliográfico sobre los historiadores y geógrafos arábigo-españoles (267–272, Madrid 1898). Encyclopaedia of Islām (vol. 2, 373, 1916).

II. EASTERN MUSLIM

MUḤAMMAD IBN MAḤMŪD AL-ṬŪSĪ

Muḥammad ibn Maḥmūd ibn Aḥmad al-Ṭūsī al-Salmānī. Persian cosmographer who flourished under Ṭughril II (last Saljūq ruler of 'Irāq and Kurdistān, 1177–1194). In 1160 al-Ṭūsī wrote a Persian cosmography entitled 'Ajā'ib al-makhlūqāt (The marvels of creatures).

The unique manuscript of the cosmography (Gotha Persicus 35) contains at the beginning six very crude maps representing the Caspian Sea, the Mediterranean Sea, Jibāl, Sind, the Arabian Sea, and Arabia.

Ḥājī Khalīfa: Lexicon (vol. 4, 188, no. 8071, 1845). Wilhelm Pertsch: Die persischen Handschriften der herzogl. Bibl. zu Gotha (58–61, Wien 1859), reproducing the table of contents in Persian. Konrad Miller: Mappae arabicae (Stuttgart 1926 sq.; Isis, 9, 458).

'ALĪ AL-HARAWĪ

'Ali ibn abī Bakr ibn 'Alī al-Harawī. The last word means of Herāt, in Khurāsān. He was born in Mūṣul, but his family hailed from Herāt. Muslim traveler and ṣūfī. He visited Jerusalem in 1173–1174 (Jerusalem being then in Christian hands); witnessed an eruption of Etna,[3] and was in touch with Manuel I Comnenos (emperor from 1143 to 1180), in Constantinople. In 1191 he was caught at sea by the fleet which was taking Richard Coeur-de-lion to the siege of Acre, and he then lost a part of his notes. He died at Aleppo in 1214–1215. He wrote a guide book for pilgrims, Kitāb al-ishārāt fī ma'rifat al-ziyārāt (Indications

[2] Younger brother of the astronomer Giovanni Virginio Schiaparelli.

[3] According to Karl Sapper: Katalog der geschichtlichen Vulkanausbrücke (p. 32, Strassburg 1917; Isis, 4, 196), eruptions of Etna occurred in 1169, 1175(?), 1194, 1197.

for the knowledge of pilgrimages), wherein he deals successively with Syria, Palestine, Egypt, the Byzantine empire, Mesopotamia, India, Arabia, the Maghrib and Abyssinia, and gives brief but first-hand information concerning all of these countries except the two last mentioned. He quotes another work of his, Kitāb al-'ajā'ib (Book of marvels).

J. T. Reinaud: Géographie d'Aboulféda (vol. 1, cxxvii–cxxix, 1848). Charles Schefer: Archives de l'orient latin (vol. 1, 587–609, 1881); French translation of the part treating of Palestine. C. Brockelmann: Arabische Litteratur (vol. 1, 478, 1898).

III. JEWISH

BENJAMIN OF TUDELA

Benjamin ben Jonah of Tudela, in Navarra. Hispano-Jewish traveler who flourished about 1160–1173. He left Saragossa in 1160, visited slowly and carefully the countries of southern Europe, and the Near East, went as far as Baghdād, and came back by way of Egypt and Sicily to Castile in 1173. The greatest part of his time was spent in Constantinople, Jerusalem, Baghdād, Alexandria, and Sicily. The record of his journeys, Massa'ot shel R. Benjamin, is the earliest important work of its kind in Hebrew literature, and it is very important indeed, being one of the most valuable travel accounts of mediaeval times. It contains first-hand and trustworthy information on Jewish communities, commerce, industries, etc.; also some second-hand news about countries further east which he did not visit himself.

Text—First edition, Constantinople 1543; second, Ferrara 1556 (these two editions are exceedingly rare); third, Freiburg i.B., 1583; etc. Itinerarium Beniamini Tudelensis . . . ex hebraico latinum factum Bened. Aria Montano interprete (Antwerp 1575). Another Latin translation, together with the Hebrew text, by Constantin l'Empereur (Leiden 1633). Of the many ulterior editions of the Hebrew text I quote only because of its convenience the one included in J. D. Eisenstein: Ozar massaoth (New York 1926; Isis, 11, 147).

Jean Philippe Baratier: Voyages de R. Benjamin, traduits de l'Hébreu et enrichi de notes et de dissertations (2 vols., Amsterdam 1734). I quote this imperfect French translation for the sake of curiosity. The translator was born in Schwabach, near Nuremberg, 1721; he died in 1740; he was only eleven years old when he completed this work! See Moïse Schwab in Jewish Encyclopaedia (vol. 2, 523, 1902).

Hebrew text with English translations by A. Asher (2 vols., London 1840–1841), and by Marcus Nathan Adler (London 1907). Partial English translation in Thomas Wright: Early travels in Palestine (63–126, 1848).

Dutch translations by J. Bara (Amsterdam 1666) and by S. Keyzer (Leiden 1846).

Hebrew text with German translation by L. Grünhut and M. N. Adler (Francfort 1903–1904).

First Spanish translation by Ignacio González Llubera (Madrid 1918); with apparatus criticus and notes; important edition, even for the study of the Hebrew text.

Russian translation by P. Margolin (Petersburg 1881).

Criticism—Eliakim Carmoly (i.e., David Goschel Behr, 1802–1875): Notice historique sur Benjamin de Tudèle. Nouv. éd. suivie de l'examen géographique de ses voyages par J. Lelewel (77 p., Bruxelles 1852); also, Lelewel's Géographie du

Moyen Age, part 4. Potthast (145, 1896). C. R. Beazley: Dawn of modern geography (vol. 2, 218–274, 1901). W. Bacher: Jewish Encyclopaedia (vol. 3, 34–35, 1902). Paul Borchardt: Die Karawanenstrassen in Arabien nach R. Benjamin (Anthropos, vol. 16–17, 1056–1057, 1921–1922); Die grossen Ost-west Karawanenstrassen durch die Libysche Wüste (Petermanns Mitteilungen, vol. 70, 219–223, map, 1924); L'itinéraire de R. Benjamin en Chine (T'oung Pao, 23, 31–35, 1924); Der Reiseweg des R. Benjamin und des R. Petachia in Mesopotamien und Persien (Jahrbuch der jüdisch-literarischen Gesellschaft, 16, 137–162, Frankfurt 1924; Isis, 8, 539); Benjamin aus Tudela (Encyclopaedia judaica, vol. 4, 130–136, map, 1929).

PETAḤIAH BEN JACOB

Petaḥiah ben Jacob ha-Laban. Often called Petaḥiah of Ratisbon. Jewish traveler. He was born at Prague, flourished about 1175–1190. He traveled from Ratisbon to Palestine via S. Russia, Armenia, Persia, and Babylonia. The account of his journey was edited by his countryman the great mystic Judah ha-Ḥasid (first half of the thirteenth century). This account is very inferior to that, somewhat anterior, of Benjamin's journey. However it contains some interesting information on the Tartars of S. Russia, on Jewish sects and communities, on the Jewish college of Baghdād, on Palestine, etc.

Text—First edition entitled Sibbub (Prague 1595). Second, in Johann Christoph Wagenseil: Exercitationes sex varii argumenti (160–203, Altdorf 1687), Hebrew and Latin. Third, in Blasius Ugolinus: Thesaurus antiquitatum sacrarum (vol. 6, Venice 1744, etc.)

Eliakim Carmoly: Sibbub ha-'olam. Tour du monde (Paris 1831); Hebrew and French.

A. Benish and W. F. Ainsworth: Travels of Rabbi Petachia (London 1856); Hebrew and English.

L. Grünhut: Hebrew text with German translation (Jerusalem 1904).

Hebrew text in J. D. Eisenstein: Ozar massaoth (New York 1926; Isis, 11, 147).

Criticism—R. Röhricht: Bibliotheca geographica Palaestinae (40, 1890). C. R. Beazley: Dawn of modern geography (vol. 2, 264–274, 1901). Schulim Ochser: Jewish Encyclopaedia (vol. 9, 656, 1905). Paul Borchardt: Der Reiseweg des R. Benjamin und des R. Petachia in Mesopotamien und Persien (Jahrbuch der jüdisch. literarischen Gesellschaft, 16, 137–162, Frankfurt 1924; Isis, 8, 539).

JACOB BEN NATHANIEL

Jacob ben Nathaniel ha-Kohen. Jewish pilgrim to the Holy Land who flourished at an unknown time. According to the latest editor, J. D. Eisenstein, whom I follow, he flourished about 1180–1187; but Grünhut places him in the middle of the thirteenth century, and Steinschneider between the thirteenth and fourteenth centuries. He made a pilgrimage to Palestine to visit the tombs of the saints. He wrote a narrative which throws some light upon the relations between the Palestinian aborigines and the Crusaders.

Text—Edited by L. Grünhut as an appendix to his edition of Petaḥiah ben Jacob (Jerusalem 1904), and in the Jerusalem Year Book edited by A. M. Luncz (vol. 7, 1905). J. D. Eisenstein: Ozar massaoth. A collection of itineraries by Jewish travelers to Palestine, Syria, etc. (New York 1927; Isis, 11, 147).

Criticism—R. Röhricht: Bibliotheca geographica Palaestinae (95, Berlin 1890); placing him in the thirteenth-fifteenth century, after Steinschneider.

IBN JAMĪ'

See chapter XXIV, Medicine.

IV. BYZANTINE

PHOCAS

Joannes Phocas, son of Matthew (Ἰωάννης Φωκᾶς). He was born in Crete. A soldier in the army of Manuel Comnenos (emperor 1143–1180); later a monk in the isle of Patmos, where he died. He visited the Holy Land in 1185, and wrote a brief description of the castles and cities from Antioch to Jerusalem, Ἔκφρασις ἐν συνόψει τῶν ἀπ' Ἀντιοχείας μέχρις Ἱεροσολύμων κάστρων καὶ χωρῶν Συρίας, Φοινίκης καὶ τῶν κατὰ Παλαιστίνην ἁγίων τόπων. It is a little more critical and far better written than the Latin accounts of John of Würzburg and Theoderich.

Phocas' description of the Holy Land is the second Byzantine account, in point of time. The earliest which has come down to us is that of a monk named Epiphanios (beginning of the ninth century, before 820).

Text—First edition by F. Morellus, together with Latin translation (Paris 1620). Second edition by Leo Allatius (Cologne 1653). Reedited in Greek and Latin by Emmanuel Miller in the Recueil des historiens des croisades (Historiens grecs, 1, 527–558, 1875). Englished by Aubrey Stewart (Palestine Pilgrims' Text Society, 11, 36 p., London 1889).

Criticism—R. Röhricht: Bibliotheca geographica Palaestinae (41, 1890). Potthast (674, 1896). K. Krumbacher: Byzantinische Litteratur (420, 1897); according to Krumbacher the date of this pilgrimage was 1177 (?). C. R. Beazley: Dawn of modern geography (vol. 2, 199–203, 1901).

EUSTATHIOS

See Chapter XVIII, Philosophic Background.

V. LATIN

"PRESTER JOHN"

Presbyter Joannes. This is the legendary personality of a Christian monarch who combined the characters of king and priest (rex et sacerdos) and ruled over a vast empire somewhere in Asia. A legend has almost always a nucleus of truth. In this case the Nestorian King of some Central Asiatic people may have been the archetype of the legendary John.

However legendary this Prester John, he exerted for centuries a very real influence upon the social and intellectual élite of Christian Europe. The earliest mention of him is found in the chronicle of Otto of Freising (first half of the twelfth century); but his prestige really began about 1165, the date of the letter which he is supposed to have written to the emperor Manuel Comnenos. Many manuscripts of this letter are extant, and it was often published. A third document is the letter (probably a genuine letter) addressed in 1177 to Prester John by Pope Alexander III (1159–1181). Thirteenth century travelers to the East do not fail to speak of him, or of his descendants; for example, Càrpini and the Armenian Sempad in 1248, William of Rubruquis in 1253, Marco Polo, and finally John of Monte Corvino.

After that time the legend takes a very strange turn. In the fourteenth and fifteenth centuries one still believes in the existence of Prester John—the more so because the need of a powerful ally to fight Islām was greater—but his dominions have been mysteriously transferred from India to Abyssinia. It should be noted that in ancient and mediaeval times India and Abyssinia have often been confused. The name India or Indies was (and is still) a very vague one; the name Abyssinia was for most people (and is still) hardly more than a name. The Christian king of Abyssinia or Ethiopia had become, so to say, the heir of the legendary John. At any rate, Prester John provided a powerful stimulus to geographic exploration from the end of the twelfth century to the end of the fifteenth.

Text—The earliest edition of the letter of c. 1165 appeared in the Itinerarius Joannis de Hese presbyteri ad Hierusalem (Deventer 1499); the undated Paris edition may be earlier (?) It is entitled Epistola ad Emanuelem Romae gubernatorem de ritu et moribus Indorum. Fr. Zarncke: Zwei lateinische Redactionen des Briefes des Presbyter Johannes und ihr Verhältniss zum französischen Texte (48 p., Ber. d. phil. Kl. d. Ges. d. Wiss., Leipzig 1877); Nachtrag. Englischer Text (ibidem, 6 p., 1878). For the Hebrew translations, see M. Steinschneider: Hebraeische Uebersetzungen (951–956, 1893).

Of the early books devoted to Prester John, or seeming to be devoted to him, I will mention only the very popular one of Francisco Alvarez (c. 1465–1540): Ho preste Joam das indias. Verdadera informaçam das terras do Preste Joam (Lisbon 1540); new edition identical with the first (207 p., with facsimiles, Lisbon 1889). That book was really devoted not to Prester John but to Abyssinia; it was the first detailed description of it available to Europeans; Alvarez had spent many years in Abyssinia. His "Prester John" was the emperor David (David II, ruled 1508–1540). The Verdadera informaçam was soon translated into Italian, French, Spanish, German, and English. The German translation (1566, 1567, 1573, etc.) contains an introduction concerning the origin of the name Prester John. The anonymous editor of that translation remarks that the name was used indiscriminately to designate various eastern potentates, even as eastern people called the Christians of Europe Franks, irrespective of their nationality.

Criticism—Gustav Oppert: Der Presbyter Johannes in Sage und Geschichte. Ein Beitrag zur Voelker- und Kirchenhistorie und zur Heldendichtung (Berlin 1864; 2te. verbess. Aufl., 236 p., 1870); contains the text of the documents quoted above. Fr. Zarncke: Der Priester Johannes (Abhdl. d. phil. Kl. d. Ges. d. Wiss., vols. 7 and 8, Leipzig 1876–1879); contains also the Latin text of the letter, with a German translation. Potthast (674, 1896). Sir Henry Yule: Article Prester John (Encyclopaedia Britannica, 11th ed., 5½ col., 1910). Constantin Marinesco: Le prêtre Jean; son pays, explication de son nom (Bull. de la section d'histoire de l'Académie roumaine, 40 p., Bucarest 1923; Isis, 11, 425). Lynn Thorndike: History of magic (vol. 2, 236–245, 1923). Ch. V. Langlois: Les merveilles du prêtre Jean (La vie en France an Moyen âge, vol. 3, 44–70, 1927).

GERALD THE WELSHMAN

Gerald of Barri, son of William. Giraldus de Barri, Cambrensis, also called Sylvester, derisively. Welsh historian and topographer; the greatest topographer of his time in Christendom. He was a descendant on his mother's side from the princes of South Wales. He was born about 1147 at Manorbeer castle, Pembrokeshire; studied in Paris; visited Ireland in 1183, 1185–1186; traveled thrice to Rome. He died at St. David's, about 1223. His chief works are: (1) a history of the conquest of Ireland (1166–1185), Expugnatio hibernica, completed about 1188, of great value in spite of his violent bias against the Irish; (2) description of Ireland, Topographia hibernica, completed in 1188; (3) itinerary across Wales,

Itinerarium Cambriae, relating a journey made in 1188, and containing notes on natural history; first published in 1191; third recension about 1214; (4) description of Wales, about 1194; second recension 1215. The following from among his minor works must still be cited: (5) Libri de rebus a se gestis tres, autobiography composed in 1204–1205; (6) an autobibliography, De libris a se scriptis catalogus brevior; (7) a treatise on the education of princes, De instructione principum libri tres.

His topographical works are of special importance from our point of view. For example, the Topographia hibernica contains good observations of tides—their comparative height on various shores of the Irish sea being noted—and an attempt to combine the lunar astrological theory with other mediaeval explanations. Gerald gives good descriptions of rivers, mountains, and other physical features; also of manners and customs; and he discusses the influence of climate upon temperament.

The last mentioned work, De instructione principum, might be usefully compared with a contemporary treatise of the same kind, Oculus pastoralis (Liber erudiens futurum rectorem populorum) composed about 1222, probably by the Florentine Boncompagni.[4]

The fantastic story of the barnacle geese, a story generally believed for many centuries—it was still necessary to refute it at length in the eighteenth century—was fully stated by Gerald in his Topographia of Ireland (cap. XV, De bernacis ex abiete nascentibus earumque natura). A similar statement was made by his contemporary Alexander Neckam, and both were preceded by a briefer one by Pietro Damiani of Ravenna, cardinal bishop of Ostia (1007–1072). This myth has been traced back to Mycenaean times, but one does not know how it was transmitted from, say, the ninth century B.C. to the eleventh century A.D.

Text—Opera omnia edited by J. S. Brewer, J. F. Dimock, and G. F. Warner (Rolls series, 8 vols., London 1861–1891); nos. 1 and 2 of my list above are included in vol. 5; nos. 3 and 4 in vol. 6; nos. 5 and 6 in vol. 1, and no. 7 in vol. 8. First edition of the Itinerary and Description of Wales by David Powel (London 1585). William Cambden: Anglica-Normannica, Hibernica, Cambrica, a veteribus scripta (Francfort 1603); contains p. 692–892, a reprint of Powel's edition, and also the Description and history of Ireland. Sir Richard Colt Hoare: The itinerary of archbishop Baldwin through Wales, 1188. Translated into English with annotations and a life of Giraldus (2 vols., London 1806). The historical works of Giraldus Cambrensis, containing the Topography of Ireland and the History of the Conquest of Ireland translated by Thomas Forester, the Itinerary through Wales and the Description of Wales, translated by Sir Richard Colt Hoare. Rev. ed. with notes by Thomas Wright (544 p., Bohn's Library, London 1881). The Itinerary through Wales and the Description of Wales (Everyman's Library, 233 p., London 1908).

Frère Philippe: Les merveilles de l'Irelande. Texte provençal publié par Jacques Ulrich (86 p., Leipzig 1892); thirteenth century translation of the Libellus de descriptione Hybernie, an abridgment of Gerald's Topography.

Criticism—Potthast (1896, 528–29). H. R. Luard: Dictionary of national biography (vol. 21, 389–393, 1890). A. G. Little: Mediaeval Wales (London 1902). Henry Owen: Gerald the Welshman. New and enlarged edition (206 p., London 1904). John Edward Lloyd: History of Wales (2 vols., London 1911). Charles Gross: Sources of English history (366, 504, 1915). P. Duhem: Système du monde (vol. 3, 119–125, 1915), theory of tides. Cornelia C. Coulter and F. P.

[4] Potthast (163, 873, 1896).

Magoun, Jr.: Giraldus on Indo-Germanic philology (Speculum, 1, 104–109, 1926). Edward Heron-Allen: Barnacles in nature and in myth (Oxford 1928; Isis, 12, 340).

For Godfrey of Viterbo, Roger of Howden, and William of Tyre, see Chapter XXV, Historiography.

ANONYMOUS PILGRIMS TO THE HOLY LAND

The three anonymous pilgrimage accounts of the first half of the twelfth century are of little value (see Chapter VIII). Six more anonymous accounts relate to the second half of the century; more exactly, to the period anterior to 1187 when Jerusalem was taken by Ṣalāḥ al-dīn. I cite them briefly in chronological order:

1. Innominatus VI (Pseudo-Bede), about 1150–1170. "Sumamus inicium a Chebron." The author was an Englishman. This is the most important anonymous account of the twelfth century. Edited by Wilh. Ant. Neumann: Oesterr. Vierteljahrschrift für katholische Theologie (vol. 7, 397–438, 1868).
2. Innominatus II, about 1170. "Per viam superiorem ab Accaron nec intrare nisi post veram penitentiam potuit." Similar in some respects to the Bordeaux-Jerusalem itinerary, A.D. 333 (vol. I, 371), and to Saewulf and Theoderich. Edited by Titus Tobler: Theoderici libellus de locis sanctis (118–127, 1865).
3. Innominatus III, about 1170–1175. "Primo de portu Brandicae quae est civitas petivit de una muliere peccatrice bibere. Item de Samaria." Next in importance to Pseudo-Bede's account, it is the most picturesque of the whole series. It starts from Brindisi. Edited by Tobler (ibidem, 128–134).
4. Innominatus VIII, about 1175–1185. "Omnibus volentibus visitare terram promissionis." De terra ultra maria. Edited by Tobler: Descriptiones Terrae sanctae (193–196, Leipzig 1874).
5. Innominatus IX, about 1175–1185. "Si quis · de Joppe in Ierusalem." Edited by W. A. Neumann: Tübinger theolog. Quartalschrift (534–539, 1874).
6. Innominatus V. Terra Jherosolimitana. Account written in two parts, both after 1187, the pilgrimage itself having taken place shortly before that date. It contains valuable information on the European settlements in Syria, the chief orders of knighthood, and the ecclesiastical divisions of the Latin kingdom. Edited by Thomas: Sitzungsber. der bayer. Ak. (vol. 2, 141–160, 1865). Shorter text edited by W. A. Neumann: Oesterr. Vierteljahrschrift für kathol. Theologie (221–257, 1866).

All of these twelfth century anonymous accounts are apparently derived from an old guidebook which is lost. They are eclipsed by the anonymous French description "La Citez de Iherusalem" which was composed about 1222 (see Book III).

Reinhold Röhricht: Bibliotheca geographica Palaestinae (Berlin 1890). C. R. Beazley: Dawn of modern geography (vol. 2, 203–208, 1901).

JOHN OF WÜRZBURG

German priest who went to Jerusalem as a pilgrim sometime between 1160 and 1170. In spite of John's credulity, the account of his pilgrimage written by himself is valuable because of its genuiness and its fulness. It is written in the form of a letter addressed to one Dietrich (dilecto suo socio et domestico).

Text—First edition in Bern. Pez: Thesaurus anecdotorum (vol. 9); second in Migne: Patrologia latina (vol. 155). Johannis Wirziburgensis descriptio Terrae

Sanctae, edited by Titus Tobler: Descriptiones Terrae Sanctae (108-192, Leipzig 1874). Englished by Aubrey Stewart (Palestine Pilgrims' Text Society, 14, 84 p., London 1890).

Criticism—Brief note by W. Wattenbach: Allgemeine Deutsche Biographie (vol. 14, 484, 1881). R. Röhricht: Bibliotheca geographica Palaestinae (38, 1890). C. R. Beazley: Dawn of modern geography (vol. 2, 190-195, 1901).

THEODORIC THE PILGRIM

Theoderich, Dietrich, etc. A monk of Hirschau, who traveled to the Holy Land about 1169-1173. He may be the Dietrich to whom John of Würzburg addressed the account of his own pilgrimage; his narrative has the same qualities and defects; it is sincere and detailed, but uncritical. It includes a brief description of Judaea.

Text—Titus Tobler: Libellus de locis sanctis editus c. 1172. Cui accedunt breviores aliquot descriptiones Terrae Sanctae (St. Gallen 1865). Englished by Aubrey Stewart: Description of the holy places (Palestine Pilgrims' Text Society, 17, 96 p., London 1891).

Criticism—C. R. Beazley: Dawn of modern geography (vol. 2, 195-199, 1901).

BURCHARD OF STRASSBURG

Burchardus Argentinensis (Not to be confused with Burchardus de Monte Sion, second half of the thirteenth century). German traveler. In 1175 he was sent by the emperor Frederic I Barbarossa on a diplomatic errand to Ṣalāḥ al-dīn; he visited Egypt, Syria, and the Holy Land, and wrote an account of his journey. The text which has come down to us is very corrupt.

Text—First edition under the title Gerardi (sic) Friderici I in Aegyptum et Syriam ad Saldinum legati itinerarium, in H. Bangert's edition of Helmold's Chronica Slavorum (Lübeck 1659). Later editions by J. Moller in his Chronica Slavorum (Lübeck 1702), and by Leibniz: Scriptores rerum Brunsvicensium (vol. 2, Hanover 1710). Baron de St. Genois: Voyages en Terre Sainte par Thetmar en 1217 et par Burchard en 1175, 1189 ou 1225 (Mémoires de l'Académie de Belgique, vol. 26, 58-61, 1851). J. C. M. Laurent in Serapeum (145-154, 1858; 174-176, 1859). German translation by Laurent, together with his translation of Arnold of Lübeck in Geschichtschreiber der deutschen Vorzeit (XIII, 3, Berlin 1853).

Criticism—R. Röhricht: Bibliotheca geographica Palaestinae (39, 1890). Potthast (176, 1895). Ch. Kohler: Grande Encyclopédie (vol. 8, 441).

RICHARD LIONHEART

Richard I Coeur-de-lion, born in 1157, King of England from 1189 until his death in 1199. He hardly belongs to our story, but a life of his, Gesta regis Ricardi, wrongly ascribed to Benedict of Peterborough (died 1193), is of considerable topographical interest. It relates Richard's voyage to the Holy Land in 1190, and gives much information on the routes to be followed, and on the appearance and particularities of the countries traversed. It was probably derived from some manual of navigation. See my note on Howden, Chapter XXV, Historiography. Another Gesta Ricardi (to 1192) was written by Richard of Devizes, a contemporary Benedictine monk in Winchester.

Text—Edited by William Stubbs in The Chronicle of the Reigns of Henry II and Richard I (Rolls Series, 2 vols., London 1867).

Criticism—Charles Gross: Sources of English history (385, 1915). J. K. Wright: Geographical lore (1925). For another history devoted to Richard Coeur-de-Lion see my note on Ambroise the Jongleur, in the Appendix to Book II.

FETELLUS

Also Fretellus. Archdeacon of Antioch about 1200. Author or editor of a pilgrim narrative, the substance of which may be dated back to soon after 1118. (See my note on Anonymous pilgrims to the Holy Land, first half of the twelfth century). It is a typical guide-book, impersonal and arid, continuing the tradition of the Bordeaux-Jerusalem itinerary, A.D. 333 (vol. I, 371). It contains some interesting facts, and a large number of pious or gratuitous absurdities.

Text—Liber locorum sanctorum Terrae Jerusalem. Edited in Etienne Baluze: Miscellanea novo ordine digesta (vol. 1, 434–440, 1761); also in Migne's Patrology (vol. 155, 1039–1054). Account of Jerusalem and the Holy Land about 1130. Translated and annotated by J. R. Macpherson (Palestine Pilgrims' Text Society, 19, 68 p., London 1892).

Criticism—R. Röhricht: Bibliotheca geographica Palaestinae (33–35, 1890); in which other editions are quoted, the earliest dating from 1653. C. A. Beazley: Dawn of modern geography (vol. 2, 186–190, 1901).

VI. VERNACULAR

NIKULÁS SAEMUNDARSON

Nicholas Saemundarson. A monk in the Benedictine abbey of Thingeyrar in Iceland. He visited the Holy Land in 1151. He died in 1158. He wrote in Icelandic an itinerary to Rome and the Holy Land (1151–1154), and a catalogue of the relics kept in Constantinople and Jerusalem. His itinerary is an interesting geographical and topographical document. In opposition to Adam of Bremen (second half of the eleventh century), who regarded the northern countries outside Scandinavia as islands in the ocean surrounding the earth, Nikulás considered Greenland as a part of the mainland, one of his reasons being the existence in Greenland of continental animals. It was first believed that the author's name was Nikulás Bergsson of Thverá.

Text—(1) Itinerary. Ericus Christianus Werlauff: Symbolae ad geographiam medii aevi ex monumentis islandicis (61 p., Copenhagen 1821); Icelandic text with Latin translation and notes. Annotations géographiques dues a l'abbé Nicolas de Thingeyrar (Antiquités russes d'après les monuments historiques des Islandais, vol. 2, 394–415, Copenhagen 1852); reproducing Werlauff's text and translation.

(2) Catalogue of relics. Antiquités russes (vol. 2, 416–425, 1852); Icelandic and Latin, together with similar Icelandic texts. Partially reproduced in Paul Riant: Exuviae sacrae Constantinopolitanae (vol. 2, 213–216, Geneva 1878).

Criticism—Paul Riant: Expéditions et pèlerinages des Scandinaves en Terre Sainte (80–87, Paris 1865); Exuviae (vol. 1, p. ccv, 1877). R. Röhricht: Bibliotheca geographica Palaestinae (36, 1890). Potthast (855, 1896). Fridtjof Nansen: In northern mists (vol. 2, 237, London 1911). J. K. Wright: Geographical lore (115, 405, 1925).

ANTHONY OF NOVGOROD

Archbishop of Novgorod who visited Constantinople in 1200. He wrote in Russian an account of the sanctuaries of that city. This account is of special interest because many of the treasures seen by him were then on the eve of destruction or dispersion (Constantinople was sacked by the Latin Crusaders in 1204).

Text—The old Russian text was edited by Paul Sawaitow, together with a translation in modern Russian and abundant notes (Imperial Academy, St. Petersburg 1872). Partial edition based on a better MS., by Ismail Ivanovich Sreznevskii (Bulletin of the Russian Academy, vol. 12, 340–349, 1875). Partial Latin translation by Jos. Martinov: Liber qui dicitur Peregrinus, seu descriptio ss. locorum Caesareae civitatis, in Paul Riant: Exuviae sacrae Constantinopolitanae (vol. 2, 218–230, Geneva 1878). Mme. B. de Khitrovo: Itinéraires russes en Orient traduits pour la Société de l'Orient latin (87–111, Genève 1889).

Criticism—Paul Riant: Exuviae sacrae Constantinopolitanae (vol. 1, p. ccvii, Geneva 1877).

VII. CHINESE

FAN CH'ÊNG-TA

Fan^{4} Ch'êng^{2}-ta^{4} (3426, 762, 10470). Sung geographer, topographer, botanist, and lexicographer, born in 1126. He was also a poet and official of the Sung dynasty; a magistrate in Chehkiang; then in 1170 an envoy to the Chin Tartars; finally in 1179 a minister of state. He died in 1193. Canonized as Wên^{2} Mu^{4} (12633, 8082). He wrote the following: (1) A topographical account in 50 books of the present Su^{1}-chou^{1} (10320, 2444) region in Chiang^{1}-nan^{2} (1208, 8128), entitled Wu^{2}-chün^{4} chih^{4} (12748, 3273, 1918); this is one of the earliest prefecture gazetteers.[5] (2) A treatise on the geography and natural history of southern China, Kuei^{4} hai^{3} yü^{2} hêng^{2} chih^{4} (6435, 3767, 13608, 3912, 1918). (3) A treatise on the chrysanthemum, Fan^{4} ts'un^{1} chü^{2*} p'u^{3} (3426, 11968, 2964, 9515), wherein he describes thirty-five varieties cultivated by himself. (4) Accounts of his journeys, chiefly that from Ssŭch'uan to Hang^{2} chou^{1} (3856, 2444) in 1177, the Wu^{2} ch'uan^{2} lu^{4*} (12748, 2742, 7386); in this work he speaks of a mission of three hundred monks to India in search of Buddhist relics. (5) A small collection of rhymes, Shih^{2*} hu^{2} tz'ŭ^{2} (9964, 4931, 12401).

The Fan ts'un chü p'u had been preceded by at least two other treatises of the same kind: (1) the Liu^{2}-shih^{4} chü^{2*} p'u^{3} (7270, 9978, 2964, 9515) written by Liu^{2} Mêng^{2} (7270, 7763) early in the twelfth century, containing the description of thirty-five varieties of chrysanthemum indigenous to Honan; and (2) the Shih^{3}-shih^{4} chü^{2*} p'u^{3} (9893, 9978, 2964, 9515), written by Shih^{3} Chêng^{4}-chih^{4} (9893, 687, 1918) independently, a little later, wherein twenty-seven varieties of southern China are described.

Text—The following editions are available in the Library of Congress.

A photolithographic reproduction of the Wu-chün chih printed in 1914, from a Sung edition dated 1229. This work is in 16 vols. and 50 chüan.

Kuei hai yü hêng chih, in volume 18 of the ts'ung shu entitled Pai^{3} ch'uan^{1} hsüeh^{2*} hai^{3} (8560, 2728, 4839, 3767).

Fan ts'un chü p'u in the encyclopaedia T'u^{2} shu^{1} chi^{2*} ch'êng^{2} (12128, 10024, 906, 762), section 20, chüan 87.

Wu ch'uan lu. Undated edition in one volume and two chüan.

Shih hu tz'ŭ in vol. 88 of the Chih^{1} pu^{1*} tsu^{2*} chai^{1} ts'ung^{1} shu^{1} (1783, 9456, 11840, 234, 12039, 10024).

[5] On Chinese gazetteers, or ti^{4}-li^{3}, (10956, 6879), see my vol. 1, 676.

Liu-shih chü p'u and Shih-shih chü p'u in the T'u shu, section 20, chüan 87; also in the Pai ch'uan hsüeh hai, vol. 17.

Criticism—A. Wylie: Chinese literature (35, 46, 56, 151, 250, 1902). H. A. Giles: Biographical dictionary (212, 1898).

For the Wu ch'uan lu, see my note on Chi-yeh (second half of the tenth century, vol. I, 676).

CHINESE CARTOGRAPHY

A map of China was compiled about 1193 for the instruction of a king of Chia[1] (1158), who became emperor in 1194 under the name of Ning[2] Tsung[1] (8328, 11976). This map is oriented with the north at the top; it shows the forests, and gives much importance to the outline of mountains; a long notice is written at the bottom. It is one of four documents engraved in 1247, and now kept in the Confucian temple, Wên[2] miao[4] (12633, 7867) of Su[1]-chou[1] (10320, 2444). The other three, made with the same purpose, are the following: a chronological table of sovereigns; a map of the stars, with a long notice (this is a very important source for the history of Chinese astronomy); a map of the city of Su-chou.

Reproductions of these documents, with elaborate descriptions and commentaries, have been published by Edouard Chavannes: L'instruction d'un futur empereur de Chine en l'an 1193 (Mémoires concernant l'Asie orientale, vol. 1, 19–34, 5 pl. 1913).

For the sake of comparison see my note in Chapter VIII on the two oldest Chinese maps extant (1137).

WANG HSIANG-CHIH

Wang[2] Hsiang[4]-chih[1] (12493, 4287, 1787). Chinese geographer of Tung[1]-yang[2] (12248, 12883) in Chehkiang. He compiled about 1200 a description of southern China entitled Yü[2]-ti[4] chi[4]-shêng[1] (13533, 10956, 922, 9876) which was considered by the authors of the Chinese Imperial Catalogue (suppt., bk. V, 71) as the best geographical treatise of the Sung period. It included 200 books, of which 156 are completely and 16 partially extant. It is different from the official gazetteers[6] in that much more space is devoted to curiosities, natural and archaeological, ching[3]-wu[4]* (2143, 12777) and ku[3]-chi[4]* (6188, 834); its historical interest is thus considerable; the author might be called a Sung Pausanias.

Text—The text was edited by Wu[3] Ch'ung[2]-yao[4] (12699, 2930, 12954) in 1855, with three prefaces: by the author, dated 1200; by Li[3] Chih[2]* (6884, 1846) dated 1220; and by the editor, dated 1851. The Library of Congress has a copy of this edition of 1855, in 200 chüan bound in 24 vols.

Criticism—Erich Hänisch: Ein chinesischer Baedeker aus dem 13. Jahrhundert (Ostasiatische Zeitschrift, vol. 7, 201–220, 1919), analysis with extracts, (Isis, 7, 191).

[6] See vol. I, 676.

CHAPTER XXIII

NATURAL HISTORY

(Second Half of Twelfth Century)

I. WESTERN MUSLIM

For al-Idrīsī and al-Māzinī, see Chapter XXII, Geography.
For Ibn Ṭufail, see Chapter XVIII, Philosophic Background.

AL-GHĀFIQĪ

Abū Ja'far Aḥmad ibn Muḥammad al-Ghāfiqī (not Rāfiqī). Spanish Muslim physician and botanist who originated probably in Ghāfiq near Cordova. He died in 1165. He wrote medical treatises; for example, a Kitāb al-adwiya al-mufrada (on simples). He had gathered plants in Spain and Africa and was the greatest expert of his time on simples. His description of plants was the most precise ever made in Islām; he gave the names of each in Arabic, Latin, and Berber. He is very often quoted by Ibn Baiṭār (first half of the thirteenth century). His work contains information on yellow amber and sal ammoniac. Among his other works we may also mention a treatise on eye-diseases.

Two abridgments of the Kitāb al-adwiya were made, the one by Aḥmad ibn 'Alī al-Jumhurī, otherwise unknown, the other by Abū-l-Faraj (Barhebraeus), between 1264 and 1286. Barhebraeus translated it into Syriac, but the Syriac text is lost. It is not enough to say that Ibn al-Baiṭār quoted al-Ghāfiqī very often; he embodied the whole of the latter's work into his own!

Text—Max Meyerhof and Gorgy Sobhy of Cairo are preparing for the Egyptian University an edition of the Kitāb al-adwiya, together with an English translation, notes and glossary (private communication, July 20, 1930). This edition will enable us to have a more definite idea of the extent of Ibn Baiṭār's borrowings from al-Ghāfiqī.

M. Meyerhof is also preparing a French translation of a great part of al-Ghāfiqī's treatise on ophthalmology (for the International ophthalmological congress scheduled to meet in Madrid in 1933).

Criticism—Ibn abī Uṣaibi'a (vol. 2, 52). Wüstenfeld: Arabische Aerzte (98, 1840). E. H. F. Meyer: Geschichte der Botanik (vol. 3, 210–215, 1856). L. Leclerc: Médecine arabe (vol. 2, 79–80, 1876), under the name Er' r'afequy. Brockelmann: Arabische Litteratur (vol. 1, 488, 1898). Max Meyerhof: Über die Pharmakologie und Botanik des Aḥmad al-Ghāfiqī (Archiv für Geschichte der Mathematik, vol. 13, 65–74, 1930; Isis, 15, 405).

IBN AL-'AWWĀM

Abū Zakarīyā Yaḥyā ibn Muḥammad ibn Aḥmad ibn al-'Awwām al-Ishbīlī. Hispano-Muslim agriculturist who flourished at Seville about the end of the twelfth century. He wrote a treatise on agriculture, Kitāb al-falāḥa, which is the most important Muslim work as well as the most important mediaeval one on the subject; it is divided into thirty-four chapters, of which the first thirty deal with agriculture proper, and the last four with cattle and poultry raising and apiculture. It is based on Greek and Arabic writings, but also on practical knowledge. The main literary source was probably Ibn Waḥshīya (first half of the tenth century); in fact, Ibn Khaldūn[1] speaks of Ibn al-'Awwām's work as if it were only a summary of Al-falāḥa al-nabaṭīya, but this is wrong.

Ibn al-'Awwām's treatise deals with 585 plants, and explains the cultivation of more than fifty different fruit trees. It contains striking observations on the different kinds of soil and manure and their respective properties, on various methods of grafting, on sympathies and antipathies between plants, etc. The symptoms of many diseases of trees and vines are indicated, as are also methods of cure.

Text—The Kitāb al-falāḥa was edited with a Spanish translation by Jos. Ant. Banqueri (2 vols., folio, Madrid 1802). French translation entitled Le livre de l'agriculture, by Clément-Mullet (2 tomes in 3 vols., Paris 1864–1867). This edition and these two translations are very unsatisfactory. In 1889 Carlo Crispo Moncada communicated a part of the text concerning the trimming of grapevines, which had remained unpublished. Sul taglio della vite di Ibn al-'Awwām. Testo arabo inedito con traduzione ed annotazioni (Actes du VIIIe congrès des orientalistes, vol. 2, 215–257, Stockholm 1889; Leide 1891).

Criticism—Ernst Meyer: Geschichte der Botanik (vol. 3, 260–266, 1856). L. Leclerc: Médecine arabe (vol. 2, 109–113, 1876). Léon Moulé: La médecine vétérinaire arabe (26–30, Paris 1896). C. Brockelmann: Arabische Litteratur (vol. 1, 494, 1898). J. Ruska: Encyclopaedia of Islām (vol. 2, 365, 1916). Herbert Hice Whetzel: Outline of the history of phytopathology (20, Philadelphia 1918). F. S. Bodenheimer: Materialien zur Geschichte der Entomologie (vol. 1, 152–156, 1928; Isis, 13, 388).

II. EASTERN MUSLIM

For Ja'far ibn 'Alī and 'Abd al-Raḥmān ibn Naṣr, see Chapter XXVI, Law and Sociology.

For Ibn Munqidh, see Chapter XXV, Historiography.

For al-Niẓāmī-i-'Arūdī, who wrote in Persian, see Chapter XVIII, Philosophic Background.

For Muḥammad ibn Maḥmūd al-Ṭūsī, who also wrote in Persian, see Chapter XXII, Geography.

III. WESTERN JEWISH

For Berakya ha-Naqdan, see Chapter XVI, The Translators.

A Hebrew treatise on falconry is considered next.

IV. MUSLIM AND JEWISH FALCONRY

Three dated Arabic treatises relative to this period have been quoted by Hammer-Purgstall; and after him by Harting, whose titles I copy:

(1) The Book of the Great Khágán, and King of India, by Izzud-Din Muhammed Pelasgúní A.H. 577 = 1181–1182 (I wonder whether the date meant is not 777 = 1375–1376, when one Khāghān was a Khān of the line of Shaibān in the Uzbeg or Kirghiz Kazak steppes).

(2) The Book of Badr ud Din Muhammed Balkhi. A.H. 577 = 1181–1182.

[1] Prolégomènes (vol. 3, 165).

(3) The Book of Nushírván the Wise by Imád ud Din Isfahání. A.H. 590 = 1193–1194. (This author may be identical with 'Imād al-dīn al-Iṣfahānī, the historian, who died in 1201; see Chapter XXV, Historiography).

Jos. von Hammer-Purgstall: Falknerklee (Wien 1840). James Edmund Harting: Bibliotheca accipitraria (203, 1891).

We are on safer ground with the memoirs of Usāmah ibn Munqidh, completed about 1182 in Damascus. The last part of it deals almost exclusively with falconry and the chase, and contains abundant anecdotes on the hunted and hunting animals. In spite of its unsystematic nature—it is mainly a collection of anecdotes—it may be considered the earliest Arabic treatise on falconry composed by a known author.

To these may be added a Hebrew treatise on hunting birds, Sefer ha-'ofot ha-tofesim aḥarim, dating from 1197–1199, the author of which is unknown. It was probably translated from the Arabic. It deals with the diseases of these birds and their cures.

M. Steinschneider: Hebraeische Übersetzungen (969, 1893).

See also my note on Sancho et Sabio, under Vernacular, in this chapter.

V. BYZANTINE

THE PORICOLOGOS

The Poricologos is a curious little text of unknown date, which may be traced back perhaps to the twelfth century. It is entitled *Διήγησις τοῦ πωρικολόγου*, which we might translate, Story of the fruit trees (*πωρικά* = *ὀπωρικά*, dealing with fruit; the ending of the word was probably suggested by the word Physiologos). A number of fruit trees, each of which bears one of the usual Byzantine titles (*λογοθέτης*, chancellor; *πρωτονοτάριος*, first "notarius;" *πρωτοβεστιάριος*, first "vestiarius;" etc.), are sitting in judgment to consider the case of the grapevine accused of conspiracy and high treason. The purpose is to point out the dangers of wine drinking, and incidentally to deride bureaucratic pomposity. This little piece may offer some botanical interest. Its success is also a matter of cultural interest; Serbian-Slovenian and Turkish adaptations have come down to us.

Text—Greek text in Βίος Αἰσώπου τοῦ Φρυγίου (93–96, Venice 1783). Longer text edited by K. Sathas in Κλειώ (1871).

Serbian-Slovenian adaptation edited by V. Jagić: Condemnatio uvae (Archiv für slavische Philologie, 1, 611–617, 1876).

Turkish text edited by O. Blau (Z. d. d. morgenl. Ges., 28, 562–576, 1874). German translation by R. Köhler (Archiv für slavische Philologie, 2, 192–194, 1877).

Criticism—K. Krumbacher: Byzantinische Litteratur (883–884, 1897).

VI. LATIN

ROBERT OF CRICKLADE

Robertus Crikeladensis, Robertus Canutus. English humanist, born in Cricklade-on-the-Thames, Wiltshire. Prior of St. Frideswide (now Christ Church) in Oxford from before 1141 until after 1171. He visited Italy and Sicily about

1158–1159. He was interested in natural science, and had some knowledge of Hebrew. He wrote a life of Thomas Becket, theological commentaries; and a collection of extracts from Pliny's Natural history, the Defloratio naturalis historiae Plinii Secundi, in nine books, dedicated to Henry II (king from 1154 to 1189). Some of these extracts are our only evidence for the true text.

The article by W. H. Hutton in the Dictionary of national biography (vol. 48, 368, 1898) is unsatisfactory. Karl Rück: Das Exzerpt der Naturalis Historia des Plinius von Robert von Cricklade (Sitzungsber. der philos. Classe der Akad. d. Wiss. zu München, 195–285, 1902); elaborate study with long extracts and with reference to Rück's previous work on the mediaeval tradition of Pliny. K. Rück: Die Geographie und Ethnographie der nat. hist. im Auszüge von Robert von Cricklade (Prog., 54 p. München 1903). C. H. Haskins: Further notes on Sicilian translations (Harvard studies in classical philology, vol. 23, 162, 1912; revised in Studies in mediaeval science, 169, 1924). Sandys: History of classical scholarship (vol. 1, 654, 1921).

For Robert of Torigny, and for Falcandus, see Chapter XXV, Historiography.

For Alan of Lille, and for Hildegard, see Chapter XVIII, Philosophic Background.

For Burgundio of Pisa, see Chapter XVI, The Translators.

Some Latin bestiaries of this time are illustrated, and their illustrations would deserve investigation as well as their text. A comparative study of all such illustrations is much to be desired.

Alexandra Konstantinowa: Ein englisches Bestiar des 12. Jahrhunderts in der Staatsbibliothek zu Leningrad (32 p., Berlin 1929; Isis, 14, 477).

VII. VERNACULAR

SANCHO EL SABIO

Sancho VI el Sabio, King of Navarre from 1150 to 1194, deserves mention because of the code of regulations relating to the chase, Los paramientos de la caza, promulgated by him in 1180. This is the oldest as well as the most complete code of its kind in existence, with the exception of the Forest Laws of Canute the Great (king of England from 1017 to 1035). It contains interesting information on hawking; for example, the hawks then used in Navarre were the falcon, the goshawk, and the sparrow-hawk; the method of training them is explained. The original code, a charter written on parchment, is still preserved in the archives of Pamplona.

Text—Edition with introduction and notes by H. Castillon d'Aspet (Paris 1874).

Criticism—James Edmund Harting: Bibliotheca accipitraria (111–112, London 1891).

REYNARD THE FOX

See Chapter XVIII, Philosophic Background.

VIII. HINDU

HEMACANDRA

See Chapter XXVII, Philology.

IX. CHINESE

LOU SHOU

Lou^2 Shou^4 (7343, x[2]), Chinese artist who originated in Yin^2 hsien^4 (13284, 4545) in the prefecture of Ning^2-po^1 (8325, 9336), Chehkiang, and flourished about the middle of the twelfth century. Author of the "Illustrations of husbandry and weaving," Kêng^1 chih^{1*} t'u^2 (6007, 1812, 12128), a collection of forty-five drawings, of which twenty-one deal with the cultivation of rice, and twenty-four with sericulture and silk-industry; with explanatory poems.

Text and translation—The plates were engraved on stone in 1210. Wooden blocks were made in 1237, and the prints published in book form. By command of the emperor K'ang-hsi, a new edition of this album was prepared in 1696 by Chiao^1 Ping^3-chên^1 (1317, 9305, 607), the drawings being changed (under European influence), and new poems by the emperor being added to the original ones. The old edition of 1237, seems to have been faithfully preserved in a Japanese reprint discovered by Berthold Laufer in Tokyo in 1908. This Japanese reprint, which is our closest approximation to the original text, contains a Chinese preface written in 1462, and a postface by the Japanese art historian, Kano Eino, written in 1676.

Both editions were published together with German translation and notes by O. Franke: Kēng tschi t'u. Ackerbau und Seidengewinnung in China. Ein kaiserliches Lehr- und Mahnbuch (200 p., 102 pl., 57 fig.; Abhdl. des hamburgischen Kolonialinstituts, vol. 11, Hamburg 1913). Reviewed by Ed. Chavannes (T'oung Pao, vol. 14, 306–309, 1913).

The Library of Congress has the Kêng chih t'u with preface written by K'ang-hsi in 1696. The Library has two copies of this edition, in one of which the illustrations are colored. What is more interesting, the Library has a set of what seem to be the original illustrations by Chiao Ping-chên. The Library also has two copies of the Kêng^1 chih^{1*} t'u^2 shih^1 (9918) in one chüan. One of these is found in volume 69 of the Chih^1 pu^{1*} tsu^{2*} chai^1 ts'ung^1 shu^1 (1783, 9456, 11840, 234, 12039, 10024); the other in volume 12 of the Lung^2 wei^1 pi^4 shu^1 (7479, 12582, 8932, 10024).

Criticism—A. Wylie: Chinese literature (93, 1902). Berthold Laufer: The discovery of a lost book (T'oung Pao, vol. 13, 97–106, 1 pl., 1912), announcing his discovery of the Japanese edition above mentioned. Paul Pelliot: Apropos du Keng tche t'ou (Mémoires concernant l'Asie Orientale, vol. 1, 65–122, 22 pl., 1913). Otto Franke: Zur Geschichte des Kēng tschi t'u. Ein Beitrag zur chinesischen Kunstgeschichte und Kunstkritik (Ostasiatische Z., vol. 3, 169–208, 19 Abb., 1914). F. S. Bodenheimer: Materialien zur Geschichte der Entomologie (Band 1, 11–26, 1928; Isis, 13, 388). Arthur W. Hummel: Report of the Chinese division of the Library of Congress for 1928–1929 (285–288, 1929).

HAN CH'AN-CHIH

Han^2 Ch'an^3-chih^{2*} (3827, 360, 1846). Governor of Wên^1-chou^1 (12646, 2444), Chehkiang, in 1178. Chinese agriculturist. He wrote a treatise, in three books, on oranges, Chü^{2*} lu^{4*} (3026, 7386), the earliest treatise on citrous fruits in world literature. It contains the description of about twenty-seven varieties of oranges growing in the vicinity of Wên-chou, and explains their cultivation.

Text—Edition princeps, 1178. English translation by Michael J. Hagerty, with introduction by Paul Pelliot (T'oung Pao, vol. 22, 63–96, 1923; Isis, 7, 187).

[2] This character is not included in Giles's Dictionary; it is character 10019 preceded by classifier 96.

Pelliot's introduction contains a French translation of the notice on the Chü lu published in the Imperial Catalogue.

The Library of Congress has a facsimile edition of the Chü lu, and also a reprint in volume 16 of the Pai^3 ch'uan^1 hsüeh^{2*} hai^3 (8560, 2728, 4839, 3767).

Criticism—A. Wylie: Chinese literature (152, 1902). Walter T. Swingle: Report of the Librarian of Congress for 1923 (181–183).

FAN CH'ÊNG-TA

See Chapter XXII, Geography.

X. JAPANESE

HENCHIIN SEIKEN

See Chapter XXIV, Medicine.

INTRODUCTION OF TEA INTO JAPAN

Tea plants were introduced into Japan about 814, during the rule of Saga-tennō (810–823), and were set out in several provinces. However, this attempt must have failed, for the chroniclers speak of a new introduction of the tea shrub from China in 1191. It is said that it was the famous Buddhist reformer Eisai (see Chapter XV, Religious Background) who originated the cultivation of tea in Japan in that year; moreover he wrote a book, the Kissa-yōjō-ki, wherein he explained the virtues of tea.

To complete the early history of tea, it is convenient here to recall that the earliest mention of it is found in a work of Ch'ên^2 Shou^4 (658, 10019) (second half of the third century); that Soṅg-tsen's grandson introduced tea into Tibet in the second half of the seventh century; and that the earliest treatise on tea was written by Lu^{4*} Yü^3 (743? 13617) in the second half of the eighth century.

See vol. I (p. 343, 467, 535). F. Brinkley: History of the Japanese people (280, 374, 1915).

CHAPTER XXIV

MEDICINE

(Second Half of Twelfth Century)

I. WESTERN MUSLIM

"ALCOATIM"

Salome, son of Arit (Sulaimān ibn Ḥārith?), Alcoatim, Alcoati, Alcoatin. Christian physician of Muslim origin who flourished in Toledo. About 1159 he composed a treatise on eye diseases, in five books. It is probable that it was originally written in Arabic. It is entitled Congregatio sive liber de oculis and is divided as follows: 1. De occasionibus propter quas Alcoatin compilavit hunc librum; 2. De anatomia et beneficio oculi; 3. De aegritudinibus oculo accidentibus ut in tunicis et humiditatibus et aliis componentibus ipsum; 4. De medicinis simplicibus valentibus in aegritudinibus oculorum in generali; De medicinis simplicibus in speciali quae operantur in oculis; 5. De medicinis compositis ad oculum. The word congregatio in the Latin title is obviously a translation from the Arabic (majma', majmū', majmū'at). The principal authors quoted are Galen, Ḥunain ibn Isḥāq, Abū-l-Qāsim, and Ibn al-Haitham.

Text—J. L. Pagel: Neue litterarische Beiträge zur mittelälterlichen Medizin (121–194, Berlin 1896) Latin text of the first 3 books; Die Augenheilkunde des Alkoatim (Supplement to Janus, vol. 1, 1896–1897). Partial translations into German by Karl Felsch (1898); Hans Wilm, Friedrich Schlepckow, Karl Schorss, Leo Schwarzweiss, Eduard Allard, Ernst Windmüller (1899); Reinh. Kämpfer (1900); all Berlin theses inspired by Pagel. P. Pansier: Congregatio sive liber de oculis quem compilavit Alcoatin, Christianus Toletanus. Publié d'après les MSS. de Metz et d'Erfurt, avec introduction sur l'histoire des oculistes arabes (Collectio ophtalmologica veterum auctorum, fasc. II, 37–104, Paris 1903).
Criticism—Valentin Rose: Ptolemaeus und die Schule von Toledo (Hermes, vol. 8, 327–349, 337, 1874). Adalbert Block: Beiträge zur Literaturgeschichte der Augenheilkunde im Mittelalter unter besonderer Berücksichtigung der Augenheilkunde des Alkoatim (Diss., Leipzig 1901). M. Steinschneider: Europäische Uebersetzungen (49, 1905).

For al-Ghāfiqī, see Chapter XXIII, Natural History.
For al-Idrīsī, see Chapter XXII, Geography.
For Ibn Tufail, and for Ibn Rushd, see Chapter XVIII, Philosophic Background.

II. EASTERN MUSLIM

IBN HUBAL

Muhadhdhib al-dīn Abū-l-Ḥasan 'Alī ibn Aḥmad ibn 'Alī ibn Hubal al-Baghdādī. Muslim physician, born at Baghdād in 1117. He studied law at the Niẓāmīya college, then medicine; he practised medicine in Mūṣul, later at the court of the Armenian shāh in Akhlāṭ (Khalāṭ), and finally again in Mūṣul, where he died in

1213. He wrote a treatise on logic, but his chief work is a medical one entitled Kitāb al-mukhtār fī-l-ṭibb (The choice treatise on medicine).

Text—Only the part concerning the stone has been edited by P. de Koning, with a French translation, in his Traité sur le calcul dans les reins et dans la vessie (Leyde 1896).
Criticism—Ibn abī Uṣaibi'a (vol. 1, 304, 1884). F. Wüstenfeld: Arabische Aerzte (117, 1840). L. Leclerc: Médecine arabe (vol. 2, 141, 1876). E. Gurlt: Geschichte der Chirurgie (vol. 1, 662, 1898). C. Brockelmann: Arabische Litteratur (vol. 1, 490, 1898).

'ABD AL-RAḤMĀN AL-SHĪRĀZĪ

Abū-l-Faraj 'Abd al-Raḥmān ibn Naṣrallāh ibn 'Abdallāh al-Shīrāzī. Muslim physician who was established in Ḥalab (Aleppo) about 1170. He wrote the following:

1. A book entitled Kitāb al-īḍāḥ fī asrār 'ilm al-nikāḥ (Explanation of the secrets of married life), treating largely of aphrodisiacs, anaphrodisiacs, and other erotic questions of medical interest.
2. Another erotic treatise, Kitāb rauḍat al-qulūb wa nuzhat al-maḥlūb (Garden of hearts and delight of the beloved), which may also contain medical matters.
3. A treatise on the interpretation of dreams, Kitāb khulāṣat al-kalam fī ta'wīl al-aḥlām.

Text—P. Vattier: L'Oneirocrite musulman ou Doctrine de l'interprétation des songes par Gabdorrhachaman fils de Nasar (Paris 1664); French translation of the Khulāṣat.
Criticism—F. Wüstenfeld: Arabische Aerzte (100, 1840). L. Leclerc: Médecine arabe (vol. 2, 49, 1876). C. Brockelmann: Arabische Litteratur (vol. 1, 488, 1898).

For al-Niẓāmī, Ibn al-Jauzī, and Fakhr al-dīn al-Rāzī, see Chapter XVIII, Philosophic Background.

III. WESTERN JEWISH

SHESHET BENVENISTE

Sheshet ben Isaac ben Joseph Benveniste (in Catalan, Benvenist) ha-Nasi (the prince). The Benveniste family was an old Jewish one of Narbonne, distinguished representatives of which were found for centuries in Catalonia, Spain and Provence. Sheshet was a physician and writer who was born probably in Narbonne; he was educated there, but flourished in Barcelona, and later in Saragossa where he died about 1209. He had a great reputation as a physician. He wrote in Arabic a gynaecological treatise which was translated into Hebrew by al-Ḥarizī (first half of the thirteenth century).

Text—David Kaufmann: Lettres de Scheschet b. Isaac b. Joseph Benveniste de Saragosse aux princes Kalonymos et Lévi de Narbonne (Revue des études juives, vol. 39, 62–75, 217–225, 1899).
Criticism—Jewish Encyclopaedia (vol. 3, 41, 1902). This Benveniste is not included in M. Steinschneider: Die arabische Literatur der Juden (Francfort 1902). Joseph Heller: Encyclopaedia judaica (vol. 4, 157, 1929).

For Maimonides, Joseph ibn 'Aqnīn, and Joseph ibn Zabara, see Chapter XVIII, Philosophic Background.

For Samuel ibn Tibbon, see Chapter XXX, The Translators (first half of thirteenth century).

IV. EASTERN JEWISH

For Hibatallāh ibn Malkā, see Chapter XVIII, Philosophic Background.

For Samū'īl ibn 'Abbās, see Chapter XIX Mathematics and Astronomy.

IBN AL-MUDAWWAR

Abū-l-Bayān Ibn al-Muddawar, Sadīd (al-dīn). Egyptian Qaraite, whose Hebrew name is unknown. He died in Cairo in 1184–1185, at the age of eighty-three. He was physician to the last Fāṭimids, then to Ṣalāḥ al-dīn (1169–1193). He published a collection of observations, Risālat al-mujarrabāt fī-l-ṭibb.

Leclerc ascribes to him also the pharmacopoeia entitled Al-dastūr al-māristānī (The hospital's canon). Following Steinschneider, I prefer to credit the Dastūr to a younger contemporary Qaraite, David ben Solomon (first half of the thirteenth century).

Lucien Leclerc: Histoire de la médecine arabe (vol. 2, 55, 1876). M. Steinschneider: Arabische Literatur der Juden (194, 1902). J. N. Simchoni: Encyclopaedia judaica (vol. 1, 615, 1928).

IBN AL-NĀQID

Abū-l-Faḍā'il Ibn al-Nāqid, called al-Muhadhdhab (the pure). Jewish-Egyptian oculist who died in Cairo in 1188–1189. He wrote in Arabic a collection of medical observations, Mujarrabāt.

Ibn abī Uṣaibi'a (Müller ed., vol. 2, 115). L. Leclerc: Médecine arabe (vol. 2, 55, 1876). M. Steinschneider: Arabische Literatur der Juden (193, 1902).

IBN JAMĪ'

Abū-l-Makārim (or Abū-l-'Ashā'ir) Hibatallāh ibn Zain ibn al-Ḥasan, al-Isrā'īlī, Muwaffaq al-dīn, Shams al-riyāsa. Judeo-Egyptian physician, born at Fusṭāṭ. He was physician to Ṣalāḥ al-dīn who died in 1193. He was as famous in his time as 'Alī ibn Riḍwān (first half of the eleventh century) had been more than a century before.

He wrote various medical works in Arabic: A general treatise on medicine, Kitāb al irshād li maṣāliḥ al-anfās wal ajsād (Direction for the improvement of souls and bodies) completed by his son Abū Ṭāhir Ismā'īl, who is sometimes mentioned as the author. A commentary on the fifth book of the Qānūn, Taṣrīḥ al-maknūn fī tanqīḥ al-Qānūn. A description of Alexandria and its climate; etc.

The Irshād is divided into four parts: (1) generalities, fifty chapters; (2) simple medicines and victuals, two chapters, with alphabetic arrangement in the second; (3) hygiene and therapeutics, forty-two chapters; (4) compound medicines and victuals, twenty-two chapters, the twenty-first treating of the explanation of terms in alphabetic order, and the twenty-second of weights and measures. Judging by the number of manuscripts, this work was very much used.

Two treatises of his on lemons and on rhubarb and their uses, were incorporated by Ibn al-Baiṭār in his own work (first half of the thirteenth century).

Criticism—Ibn abī Uṣaibi'a (Müller ed. vol. 2, 112, 1884). F. Wüstenfeld: Arabische Aerzte (101, 1840). L. Leclerc: Médecine arabe (vol. 2, 53–55, 1876). C. Brockelmann: Arabische Literatur (vol. 1, 489, 1898). M. Steinschneider: Arabische Literatur der Juden (178–181, 1902). Max Meyerhof: Notes sur quelques médecins juifs egyptiens (Isis, 12, 113–131).

ABŪ-L-MA'ĀLĪ

Abū-l-Ma'ālī Ibn Hibatallāh al-Yahūdī. Egyptian Jew, physician to Ṣalāḥ al-dīn (1169–1193), and later to al-'Ādil (1199–1218). His children became Muslims. He wrote various medical works in Arabic, one of which was entitled Ta'ālīq wa mujarrabāt fī-l-ṭibb (Medical glosses and experiences).

This Abū-l-Ma'ālī is probably identical with Maimonides' brother-in-law (husband of Maimonides' sister, and brother of Maimonides' wife), who died in 1222. If so, it was his son Yūsuf ibn 'Abdallāh who edited in 1204–1205 the last chapter of Maimonides' Fuṣūl fī-l-ṭibb.

Ibn abī Uṣaibi'a (Müller ed., vol. 2, 117, 1882). David Kaufmann: Un neveu de Maimonide (Revue des études juives, vol. 7, 152, 1883). M. Steinschneider: Arabische Literatur der Juden (197, 1902). I. Broydé: Jewish Encyclopaedia (vol. 8, 233, 1904). M. Zobel: Encyclopaedia judaica (vol. 1, 619, 1928).

V. SALERNITAN

COMPENDIUM SALERNITANUM

Theodor Henschel discovered in 1837 in the library of the Magdalenengymnasium, Breslau, a Compendium Salernitanum dating from about 1160–1170, containing thirty-five treatises (225 folii) which considerably increased our knowledge of Salernitan medicine.

See Th. Henschel in Janus (the first Janus, vol. 1, 40–84, 300–368, Breslau 1846). Karl Sudhoff: Die Salernitaner Handschrift in Breslau (Archiv für Geschichte der Medizin, vol. 12, 101–148, 1920). Many writings of Sudhoff's Institute in Leipzig have been devoted to this Compendium. Some of them are quoted below in the paragraphs concerning Salernitan authors. A useful summary has been published by Friedrich Hartmann: Die Literatur von Früh- und Hochsalerno und der Inhalt des Breslauer Codex Salernitanus (Diss., 70 p., Leipzig 1919; Isis, 4, 621); with a list of the parts already edited and of those awaiting publication.

The twelfth century might be called the golden age of Salernitan medicine. It was indeed an age of great activity, as anyone will realize who reads this book. The premature ending of that golden age was probably hastened by political events. In the course of his war against the kingdom of the two Sicilies, the emperor Henry VI sacked and destroyed Salerno in 1193.

Some writings of this period have remained anonymous, among them the most famous of all, the Regimen sanitatis. A few of these anonymous writings are considered in the following paragraphs:

1. *De aegritudinum curatione*—This is the longest of the treatises contained in the Breslau MS. It is a general compendium of medicine and therapeutics, based chiefly on John Platearius the Younger, also on Copho, Bartholomew, "Trotula," etc. The Breslau text was edited by S. De Renzi: Collectio salernitana (vol. 2, 81–386, 1853). For an analysis of this treatise, see Neuburger: Geschichte der Medizin (vol. 2, 295–299, 1911). Conrad Hiersemann: Die Abschnitte aus der

Practica des Trottus in der Salernitanischen Sammelschrift De aegritudinum curatione (Diss., 37 p., Leipzig 1921; Isis, 5, 213).

2. *Rubrica de pulsibus secundum Romualdum Salernitanum*—(Which Romuald?) Edited by S. De Renzi: Collectio salernitana (vol. 4, 413–414, 1856).

3. *Regimen sanitatis salernitanum*—This is a compendium of Salernitan medicine and hygiene, in rhyming (Leonine) verse, which soon became exceedingly popular, and enjoys some popularity even in our days. It is impossible to date it exactly, for it grew up gradually to its present size. The germ of it was the Epistola Aristotelis ad Alexandrum de conservatione corporis humani, a partial translation of the Sirr al-asrār by John of Seville (first half of the twelfth century). The Regimen sanitatis is sometimes ascribed to John of Milano, who lived at the beginning of the twelfth century. In the time of Arnold of Villanova, the Regimen sanitatis (often credited to him) included only 362 lines. Arnold was probably the earliest editor. Later editions include 2130 verses, and even 3520. To put it briefly, I would call the Regimen sanitatis a thirteenth century poem born in the twelfth century. See my note on Arnold of Villanova (second half of the thirteenth century).

The number of editions and translations in almost every European language is considerable, and new ones appear from time to time. The earliest dated text is that of 1480, but some of the undated ones may be earlier. Lists of editions have been published by Choulant in his Handbuch der Bücherkunde für die ältere Medizin (p. 264–282, Leipzig 1841) quoting 141 editions; and by Baudry de Balzac in S. De Renzi: Collectio salernitana (vol. 5, 145–172, 1859) quoting 246 editions. Of these many editions I will mention only the two included in De Renzi's collection. Flos medicinae. Versi della scuola salernitana, novellamente raccolti da varii codici ed edizioni disposti in nuovo ordine, aumentati di numero e diligentamente confrontati (vol. 1, 417–516, 1852, 2130 verses; vol. 5, 1–104, 1859, 3520 verses). Of the English translations the most popular is that by Sir John Harington (1561–1612): The Englishman's doctor, or the school of Salerne. Or physicall observations for the perfect preserving of the body of man in continuall health (London 1607). Regimen sanitatis. A poem on the preservation of health, in rhyming Latin verse, addressed by the school of Salerno to Robert of Normandy, son of William the Conqueror, with an ancient translation (Harington's), an introduction and notes by Sir Alexander Croke (Oxford 1830). New edition of Harington's version with prefatory notes by Francis R. Packard and Fielding H. Garrrison (215 p., New York 1920).

Paul Tesdorpf and Therese Tesdorpf-Sickenberger: Das medizinische Lehrgedicht der hohen Schule zu Salerno (96 p., Stuttgart 1915). Contains the Latin text as edited by Johann Christian Gottlieb Ackermann (Stendal 1790), and twelve woodcuts taken from an early edition (Francfort 1568). See Isis (15, 406).

Karl Sudhoff: Zum Regimen sanitatis (Archiv für Geschichte der Medizin, vols. 7 to 10, and 12, 1914–1920).

4. *De quattuor humoribus ex quibus constat humanum corpus*—Edited by S. De Renzi: Collectio salernitana (vol. 2, 411–412, 1853), and ascribed by him to a pupil of Constantine; it is more probably a work of the second half of the twelfth century.

5. *De aquis medicinalibus et earum differentiis*—Edited by Hellmuth Reinhardt from the Breslau MS. (Diss., 24 p., Leipzig 1921; Isis, 4, 584).

6. *Other studies on the Breslau Salernitan Manuscript*—Willy Anschütz: Zwei Fieberschriften des Breslauer Codex und die Fieberlehre der Schule von Salerno (Diss., 44 p., Leipzig 1919; Isis, 4, 580). Kurt Kilian: Kur und Diätetik von Nierensteinen (Diss., 16 p., Leipzig 1920; Contra harenulas in renibus . . .). Hermann Heidenreich: Die Abschnitte de clisteribus, de suppositoriis, de siringis, de pessariis, de siropis (Diss, 15 p., Leipzig 1920). Conrad Hiersemann: Die

Abschnitte aus der Practica des Trottus (Diss., 37 p., Lepzig 1921; Isis, 5, 213). Ernst Schlenkermann: Ein Traktat über äusserlich anzuwendende Heilmittel (Diss., 35 p., Leipzig 1922; Isis, 5, 214). A. Hesse: Ein Pulstraktat (Diss., 33 p., Leipzig 1922; Isis, 5, 213).

7. *Other studies on contemporary Latin medicine*—Karl Sudhoff: Schädigungen des Zahnfleisches durch bleihaltige Gesichtsschminken zu Anfang des 12. Jahrh. (Mitt. zur Geschichte der Medizin, vol. 13, 308, 1914); Eine neue Hds. des Liber medicinalis Pseudo-Democriti aus dem 12. Jahrh. (ibidem, vol. 14, 315–322, 1915, Isis, 3, 323); Die medizinischen Schriften, welche Bischof Bruno von Hildesheim 1161, in seiner Bibliothek besass, und die Bedeutung des Konstantin von Afrika im 12. Jahrhundert (Archiv für Geschichte der Medizin, vol. 9, 348–356, 1916); Der Pistoiese Accorso und die Uebersetzung des pseudo-galenischen Liber regiminis vel de virtutibus cibariorum, auch De dissolutione continua genannt (Mitt. zur Geschichte der Medizin, vol. 16, 24–27, 1917).

Erik Maske: Der Münchener Codex latinus 4622 und sein medizinischer Inhalt (Diss., 16 p., Leipzig 1921; Isis, 4, 583).

I might add here, though it refers more particularly to the preceding period, C. Singer: A review of the medical literature of the dark ages, with a new text of c. 1110 (Proc. of the R. Soc. of med., vol. 10, hist. section, 107–160, 1917). This text is extracted from the scientific encyclopaedia contained in MS. 17, St. John's College, Oxford; this MS. was written in England c. 1110, but was based partly on Salernitan knowledge (Isis, 3, 323).

ROGER OF SALERNO

Rogerius filius Frugardi, Ruggiero. (Not Roger of Parma!) Salernitan physician; the greatest Salernitan surgeon. He flourished in Salerno about 1170. The Practica chirurgiae edited by him is the earliest surgical treatise of the Christian West. (It is also called, from its first words, Post mundi fabricam.) It became the surgical textbook of the school of Salerno, and various commentaries were devoted to it. It is based on earlier authorities, chiefly Constantine the African, but also to a considerable extent on Roger's own experience and that of his fellow workers. Among other things it describes a remarkable technique in herniotomy,[1] and the use of mercury salts to fight chronic dermatoses and parasites. (Skin diseases had been traditionally abandoned to the surgeon.)

Text—Editio princeps in the last edition of the Collectio chirurgica veneta (Venice 1546). S. De Renzi: Rogerii medici celeberrimi chirurgia (Collectio salernitana, vol. 2, 426–496, 1853). Karl Sudhoff: Die Chirurgie des Roger Frugardi von Salern (Beiträge zur Geschichte der Chirurgie im Mittelalter, vol. 2, 148–236, 1918). This new edition is followed by various mediaeval commentaries; it is preceded by the edition, p. 103–147, of another surgical text of Salerno which perhaps antedated a little Roger's Practica, the so-called Bamberg surgery. My first statement, however, remains substantially true, for Roger's surgery was the first Christian treatise which incorporated Salernitan experience, and also the first to win recognition.

Previous editions of the Collectio chirurgica veneta (1498, 1519) contain another text entitled Rogerii practica, which may be somewhat anterior to the work we have just considered; it is ascribed to an unknown Roger de Barone (or Varone). Ludwig Choulant mentions the following editions of the Collectio chirurgica veneta: 1490 (?), 1497, 1498, 1499, 1513, 1519, 1546 (Handbuch der Bücherkunde, 416–417, 1841). Another surgical collection (Basel 1541) contains the following tract which

[1] See Isis, 9, 369.

is probably apocryphal: De modis mittendi sanguinem et de cujusque utilitate Rogerii chirurgi peritissimi libellus. This is reprinted in Czarnecki's paper (Leipzig 1919) cited below. The Humani corporis morbis medendi ratio methodica, autore Rolando, printed behind the Methodus medendi Albucasis (Basel 1541), seems to be an edition of Roger's Practica; it begins with the words Post mundi fabricam eiusque decorem.

Criticism—A. Hirsch: Biographisches Lexikon (vol. 5, 60, 1887). M. Steinschneider: Hebraeische Uebersetzungen (825–830, 1893); the Hebrew translations offer difficult problems—e.g., distinction between text and commentaries—which are not yet solved. E. Gurlt: Geschichte der Chirurgie (vol. 1, 701–720, 1898). M. Neuburger: Geschichte der Medizin (vol. 2, 306–307, 1911). R. Czarnecki: Ein Aderlasstraktat angeblich des Roger von Salerno (Diss., 34 p., Leipzig 1919; Isis, 4, 581). Erich Langebartels: Zahnheilkunde und Kieferchirurgie in der chirurgischen Literatur von Salerno und der weiteren Rogerglosse unter Mitherausgabe der zahnheilkundlichen Roger-Marginalien im Codex Amplianus 62a in 8° (Diss., 63 p., Leipzig 1919).

MAURUS

Magister Maurus. Flourished in Salerno after about 1160, and died there in 1214, Anatomist and physician. His principal work is the so-called Anatomia Mauri, one of the earliest Latin texts on anatomy. Like the two earlier texts (see my note on anatomy in the first half of the twelfth century), it is largely of Constantinian origin, though it shows a little more independence; like these texts, it treats of the pig, the description of whose organs is given in the same order; it concludes with a description of the brain, cerebral membranes, and eyes. Maurus composed also a treatise on urine (Regulae urinarum) derived from Theophilos Protospatharios and Isḥāq al-Isrā'īlī, through Constantine; a treatise on venesection (De flebotomia), and a commentary on Hippocrates' Aphorisms. The treatises on urine and venesection were translated into Hebrew.

Text—W. L. H. Ploss: Anatomia Mauri. Eine bisher unbekannte salernitaner Skizze vom Bau des Menschen auf Grundlage einer Zergliederung des Tierkörpers (Diss., 14 p., Leipzig 1921; Isis, 4, 584). Karl Sudhoff: Weitere Texte der Anatomia Mauri (Archiv für Geschichte der Medizin, 14, 56–58, 1922); Codex Fritz Paneth (Archiv für geschichte der Mathematik, vol. 12, 2–32, 1929; critical edition covers p. 27–32; Isis, 13, 498).

Regulae urinarum Magistri Mauri, in S. de Renzi: Collectio salernitana, (vol. 3, 1–51, 1854). Albert Kadner: Ein liber de urinis des Breslauer Codex (Diss., 56 p., Leipzig 1919).

Glosulae aphorismorum (Hippocratis) secundum Magistrum Maurum, in S. de Renzi: Collectio (vol. 4, 513–557, 1856).

Rudolf Buerschaper: Ein bisher unbekannter Aderlasstraktat des Maurus, de flebotomia (Diss., 38 p., Leipzig 1919; Isis, 4, 581).

Criticism—M. Steinschneider: Hebraeische Übersetzungen (810, 1893). F. Hartmann: Die Literatur von Früh- und Hochsalerno (30, 1919). George W. Corner: Anatomical texts of the earlier Middle Ages (29, Washington 1927; Isis, 9, 452). Karl Sudhoff: Die vierte Salernitaner Anatomie (Archiv für Geschichte der Medizin, vol. 20, 33–50, chiefly p. 34, 38, 1928).

RICHARD OF SALERNO, AND (OR) NICHOLAS II OF SALERNO

Salernitan physician who flourished in the second half of the twelfth century. He wrote one of the most important early Latin treatises on anatomy, the so-called

Anatomia Ricardi (Salernitani). A similar text somewhat longer and more complete is entitled Anatomia Nicolai. It is possible that both texts derive from the same original lectures of a Salernitan master called Richard or Nicholas. (These two names could easily be confused in the Beneventan script.) The Anatomia Ricardi is very different from the earlier Latin texts (Anatomia Cophonis, Second Salernitan demonstration, for both of which see my note on anatomy in the first half of the twelfth century, and Maurus' work dealt with above), in that it purports to describe human rather than porcine anatomy, and is far more systematic. Otherwise the sources of these early texts are essentially the same: a few Hippocratic writings, Galen's Tegni, Theophilos Protospatharios, Isḥāq al-Isrā'īlī, and 'Alī ibn 'Abbās, all of these as transmitted by Constantine.

If we place the Anatomia Mauri soon after the middle of the century, the Anatomiae Ricardi et Nicolai ought to be placed toward the end of the same century. If the name of the author of the Anatomia Ricardi was really Nicholas, this Nicholas ought not to be confused with the earlier Nicholas of Salerno who compiled the famous Antidotarium (see first half of the twelfth century). Of course these names are relatively unimportant; what matters is to place all of these writings as nearly as possible in their chronological sequence.

Text—Anatomia Ricardi. Julius Florian: Die Anatomie des Richardus (Diss., Breslau 1875). Victor Tarrasch: Die Anatomie des Richardus (Diss., Berlin 1898), with German translation. Ignaz Schwarz: Die medizinischen Handschriften der Kgl. Universitätsbibliothek in Würzburg (Würzburg 1907; appendix).

Anatomia Magistri Nicolai physici. Franz Rederer: Die Anatomia Nicholai und ihr Verhältnis zur Anatomia Cophonis und Ricardi (Diss., Leipzig 1917); English translation in Corner's study cited below (67–86, 1927).

Criticism—E. Littré: Richard, médecin (Histoire littéraire de la France, vol. 21, 383–393, 1847). Robert von Toeply: Studien zur Geschichte der Anatomie im Mittelalter (Wien 1898). Karl Sudhoff: Ein Beitrag zur Geschichte der Anatomie im Mittelalter, speziell der anatomischen Graphik (Leipzig 1908). George W. Corner: Anatomical texts of the earlier Middle Ages (chiefly p. 30–33, 41, Washington 1927; Isis, 9, 452–456). Karl Sudhoff: Der Micrologus Text der Anatomia Richards des Engländers (Archiv für Geschichte der Medizin, 19, 209–239, 1927; Isis, 11, 174).

URSO OF CALABRIA

Salernitan physician who flourished in Salerno in the second half of the twelfth century. Author of a treatise on uroscopy, and of writings on the philosophy of medicine.

He may be the author of one of the Salernitan anatomical treatises, which begins with the words Morbo ocii meo languente animo. This anatomy is not a manual of dissection, like the earlier Salernitan anatomies; it is more philosophical, and also more concerned with physiology and pathology.

Sudhoff calls this text the fourth Salernitan anatomy, but according to our reckoning it is the fifth or sixth. However, it is impossible to say whether the Anatomia Ricardi was anterior or posterior to this text. The complete list of the early texts considered by me is as follows:

Texts	Tentative Date
1. Anatomia Cophonis.	Beginning of twelfth century.
2. Second Salernitan demonstration.	Before middle of twelfth century.

3. Anatomia Mauri.	After middle of twelfth century.
4. Anatomia Ricardi.	End of twelfth century.
4 bis. Anatomia Nicolai.	End of twelfth century.
5. Anatomia Ursonis (?).	End of twelfth century.
6. Anatomia vivorum.	About 1225.

For no. 6, see my note on Richard of Wendover, Chapter XXXVIII, Medicine (first half of thirteenth century).

Text—Compendium Magistri Ursonis de urinis, edited by Piero Giacosa: Magistri salernitani nondum editi (283–290, 1901).

Curt Matthaes: Urso und seine beiden Schriften De effectibus qualitatum und De effectibus medicinarum (Diss., 74 p., Leipzig 1918; Isis, 4, 583).

Gebhard von Jagow: Die naturphilosophischen, ausführlich kommentierten Aphorismen, des Mag. Urso (Diss., 16 p., Leipzig 1924).

Karl Sudhoff: Die vierte Salernitaner Anatomie (Archiv für Geschichte der Medizin, vol. 20, 33–50, 1928; Isis, 11, 425).

Criticism—F. Hartmann: Die Literatur von Früh- und Hochsalerno (31, 1919). Karl Sudhoff: Die erste Tieranatomie von Salerno und ein neuer salernitanischer Anatomietext (Archiv für Geschichte der Mathematik, vol. 10, 136–154, 1927; Isis, 11, 172).

Fritz Rodewald: Eine Leipziger Anatomie angeblich aus einem Lucidarius Almagesti (Diss., 20 p., Leipzig 1924; Isis, 7, 537). This text of the end of the twelfth century or the beginnning of the thirteenth is cited here for the sake of comparison.

PETRONIUS

Petronus, Petroncellus. Not to be confused with an earlier Salernitan physician, Petrocellus (first half of the eleventh century). Salernitan physician who died at Salerno in 1197. He wrote Curae and a Practica.

Text—S. de Renzi: Fragmenta codicis biblioth. Ambrosianae Mediolanensis cui titulum Incipiunt cure Petroncelli (Collectio salernitana, vol. 4, 292–314, 1856), followed by a note on other works attributed to Petroncellus (315–320). The Breslau MS. 1302, written between c. 1160 and 1170 (see above), contains a long Tractatus de egritudinum curatione, made up by the collection of extracts from Platearius, Copho, Petronius, Bartholomaeus, Joh. Afflatius, Ferrarius, Trotus. From this work and from another treatise of the same MS., De febribus, Karl Bloedner has detached all the fragments bearing Petronius' name and published them in his Petronus (Diss., 59 p., Leipzig 1925; Isis, 8, 539).

PETER OF EBOLI

Petrus de Ebulo (Eboli is a city of Campagna, thus not very far from Salerno). Historian and physician who died in 1221 (?). He studied probably at Salerno. In 1195 he wrote a poem concerning Sicilian events from 1189 to 1195; that is, it celebrates the victories of the emperor Henry VI over the Normans, and his conquest of the kingdom of the two Sicilies. I mention him here rather for another poem on the virtues of the mineral waters of Pozzuoli; this poem has been ascribed to the Salernitan Alcadino of Girgenti, and to Eustazio of Matera, but seems to be Peter's work.

Pozzuoli is the ancient Puteoli (Dicaearchia) near Naples, famous from antiquity as a harbor and spa. A kind of earth found and named after that very locality is equally famous; pozzolana (or pozzuolana) mixed with lime forms an excellent cement especially valuable for submarine construction.

Text—First edition, Carmen de motibus Siculis et rebus inter Henricum VI imp. et Tancredum sec. XII gestis, edited by Samuel Engel (Basel 1746). New editions by Ed. Winkelmann (106 p., Leipzig 1874); by Ettore Rota in Rerum italicarum scriptores (xxxi, pt. 1); by Giov. Bat. Siragusa: Liber ad honorem Augusti (258 p., Roma 1906).

The unique MS. of the Bern Library, which may be the original MS., contains various illustrations, including a portrait of the author.

The De balneolis Puteolis is included in the De balneis omnia quae exstant (Venice 1553). Opusculum de balneis Puteolorum, Bajorum, etc. (Naples 1591). I bagni di Pozzuoli, poemetto napoletano del sec. xiv, edited by Erasmo Pèrcopo (Arch. stor. prov. napol., 11, 597–750, 1887).

Criticism—Potthast (916, 1896). Wilhelm Erben: Beiträge zum Geschützwesen im Mittelalter (Z. f. histor. Waffenkunde, vol. 7, 85–102, 117–129, 6 fig., 1916); apropos of arms illustrated in the Bern MS., see Geschichtsblätter für Technik (vol. 3, 31–33, 1916). J. Avalon: Comment Mathieu d'Agello, chancelier du Royaume des Deux-Siciles, soignait sa goutte (Bull. soc. franç. hist. méd., vol. 18, 99–102, 1924).

According to Giammaria Mazzuchelli (Gli scrittori d'Italia, vol. 1, pt. 1, 350, Brescia 1753), the De balneis puteolanis was composed, at the request of the emperor Frederic, by Alcadino (Alcadino Siciliano). This Alcadino, born probably in Syracuse or Girgenti, lived c. 1191; he was a poet, historian, physician; he studied in Salerno; he was physician to Henry VI (emperor 1190–1197), and later to Frederic II (emperor 1212–1250); he died at the age of 52. Is this Alcadino not identical with Peter of Eboli? If this balneological poem was written at Frederic's request, it must be placed in the first quarter of the thirteenth century.

FERRARIUS

Joannes Ferrarius. He taught in Salerno, and was physician to the last Norman king, William II, who ruled from 1166 to 1189. There may have been more than one Magister Ferrarius in Salerno; one died in 1232, and it is possible that he was the one here discussed. Ferrarius wrote a treatise on fevers, called Curae, and another medical work entitled Summa de purgatione quatuor humorum.

This Ferrarius is not to be confused with a contemporary Frater Ferrarius (Efferarius, Euferarius), alchemist, of Ferrara, who is said to have flourished about 1200; this alchemist is practically unknown.

Text—Curae, edited by Piero Giacosa: Magistri salernitani nondum editi (Torino 1901).

Johannes Franke: Der Salernitaner Magister Ferrarius und seine bisher nicht veröffentliche Summa de purgatione (Diss., 26 p., Leipzig 1925); including list of herbs and drugs.

Criticism—John Ferguson: Bibliotheca chemica (vol. 1, 267, 1906). Friedrich Hartmann: Die Literatur von Früh- und Hochsalerno (Diss., 29 p., Leipzig 1919).

JOHN OF ST. PAUL

Joannes de Sancto Paulo, Joannes Castalius, Jean de St. Paul. Salernitan physician. Possibly a Frenchman; this would not conflict with the title "Salernitan," for a period of study or teaching in Salerno would entitle one to it. At any rate, this John is a very mysterious personality. I place him tentatively in the third quarter of the twelfth century. He wrote various medical works; chiefly the De simplicium medicinarum virtutibus, formerly ascribed to Constantine the African; a Practica or Breviarium; a Flores diaetarum, on diet, wrongly ascribed to Bernard of Gordon; etc.

Text—The Liber de simplicium medicinarum virtutibus was printed for the first time in the Opera Ysaac (Lyon 1515). G. H. Kroemer: Johanns von Sancto Paulo Liber de simplicium medicinarum virtutibus, und ein anderer salernitaner Traktat, Quae medicinae pro quibus morbis donandae sunt, nach dem Breslauer Codex hrg. (Diss., 86 p., Leipzig 1920; Isis, 4, 582).

Extracts of the Practica seu breviarium have been published by Val. Rose in his edition of the Viaticus of Giles of Corbeil (Leipzig 1907).

Flores diaetarum, included in the works of Bernard of Gordon (Lyon 1574). H. J. Ostermuth: Flores diaetarum. Eine salernitanische Nahrungsmitteldiätetik aus dem 12. Jahrh. verfasst vermutlich von Johannes de Sancto Paulo (Diss., 70 p., Leipzig 1919; Isis, 4, 583).

Criticism—Emile Littré: Histoire littéraire de la France (vol. 21, 408–411, 1847); Littré places him after 1250. The best account will be found in Kroemer's introduction (1920).

B. Altaner: Zur Biographie des Kardinals Johannes von St. Paul, gest. 1214–1215 (Historisches Jahrbuch, vol. 49, 304–306, 1929). Identifying this John with a Benedictine who flourished in the St. Paul monastery in Rome (hence his name), studied in Salerno, composed medical works, was appointed cardinal priest of St. Priscia in 1193, cardinal bishop of Sabina in 1205, and died in 1214–1215. Whether he belonged to the Roman Colonna family or not is uncertain.[2]

BERNARD OF PROVENCE

Bernardus Provincialis. A Salernitan physician who flourished in Provence in the third quarter of the twelfth century. He wrote commentaries on the Tabulae of Salernus, and on the Practica of Bartholomew (first half of the twelfth century). He showed a tendency towards a simplified pharmacopoeia. His commentary on the Tabulae was translated into Hebrew.

Text—Commentarium Magistri Bernardi Provincialis super tabulas Salerni edited by S. de Renzi: Collectio salernitana (vol. 5, 269–328, 1859).

Criticism—M. Steinschneider: Hebraeische Uebersetzungen (788, 1893). M. Neuburger: Geschichte der Medizin (vol. 2, 303, 1911). F. Hartmann: Die Literatur von Früh- und Hochsalerno (29, 1919).

GILES OF CORBEIL

Aegidius Corboliensis; Gilles de Corbeil (Ile-de-France). French physician and humanist. He studied in Salerno, one of his teachers being Peter of Musanda (first half of the twelfth century) about the middle of the century; he stayed for a while in Montpellier, then went to Paris where he became canon of Notre Dame and archiater to Philip Augustus (king from 1180 to 1223). He died between 1220 and 1224. He wrote medical poems in Leonine verse, which are very important as being the main channel through which Salernitan lore reached the Parisian doctors. These poems also contain interesting information on the medical customs of his time. His principal works are the following:

1. De urinis (or De urinarum judiciis) (352 lines); this is hardly more than a metrical elaboration of Theophilos Protospatharios (first half of the seventh century). Giles' poem remained the most popular textbook on uroscopy in the Christian West until the sixteenth century, as is witnessed by the number of manuscripts, editions, and commentaries.

[2] He is named Colonna in P. B. Gams: Series episcoporum (p. xii, Ratisbon 1873). According to that work he was appointed bishop of Sabina in 1203, and died in 1216.

2. De pulsibus (380 lines). Also a very popular textbook.

3. De laudibus et virtutibus compositorum medicaminum (4663 lines). This antidotary composed about 1195 was far less known than the two works first mentioned, which were the main basis of Giles' popularity and influence; it was entirely superseded by the two earlier works from which it was largely derived, the Antidotarium Nicolai, and the Circa instans of Matthaeus Platearius.

4. Viaticus (or De signis et sinthomatibus egritudinum) (2358 lines), a treatise on pathology, essentially Galenic.

5. De physiognomiis, a short poem which is often considered the fourth part of the De signis. It continued the physiognomic tradition which can be traced back to the pseudo-Aristotelian Physiognomonica, to Polemon of Laodicea (first half of the second century), to Adamantios (first half of the fourth century), etc.; a tradition which found considerable favor throughout the Middle Ages.

6. Ierapigra ad purgandos prelatos (5929 lines), a virulent satire on the weaknesses and abuses of the clergy. Giles was an orthodox Christian; it was the bad shepherds which he meant to criticize, not the Church.

Text—1. De urinarum judiciis. First edition, Padua 1483. French translation in Vieillard (1903). See below.

2. De pulsibus. First edition, Padua 1484. Both texts (nos. 1 and 2) reprinted in Venice in 1494, Lyon in 1505, 1515; etc.

3. De laudibus. First edition in Ludwig Choulant: Aegidii carmina medica (Leipzig 1826); this contains also nos. 1 and 2.

4. De signis. Fragments edited by Ch. V. Daremberg: Notices et extraits des MSS. médicaux (Paris 1853). First edition by Valentin Rose: Viaticus (155 p., Leipzig 1907).

6. Ierapigra. See Vieillard (1909), below.

Criticism—Amaury Duval: Histoire littéraire de la France (vol. 16, 506–511, 1824). Ludwig Choulant: Handbuch der Bücherkunde (318–326, 1841). C. Vieillard: L'urologie et les médecins urologues dans la médecine ancienne (Paris 1903), contains text and French transl. of de urinis; Essai sur la société médicale et religieuse au XIIe siècle, Gilles de Corbeil, médecin de Philippe-Auguste et chanoine de Notre Dame (475 p., Paris 1909), including long extracts (p. 337–420) notably from the hitherto unpublished anticlerical poem Hierapigra ad purgandos prelatos. M. Neuburger: Geschichte der Medizin (vol. 2, 308–312, 1911). Stephen d'Irsay: The life and works of Gilles de Corbeil (Annals of medical history, 7, 362–378, 1925). Karl Sudhoff: Salerno, Montpellier und Paris um 1200 (Archiv für Geschichte der Medizin, vol. 20, 51–62, 1928); Commentatoren der Harnverse des Gilles de Corbeil (Archeion, vol. 11, 129–135, 1929).

VI. LATIN (NON-SALERNITAN)

For Gerard of Cremona, Marc of Toledo, and Burgundio of Pisa, see Chapter XVI, The Translators.

For Hildegard, see Chapter XVIII, Philosophic Background.

For Peter the Eater, see Chapter XXV, Historiography.

VII. ARMENIAN

MEKHITAR OF HER

Armenian physician. Born at Her, in Persian Armenia (that is, in Adharbāyjān); studied at Baghdād (?); was flourishing about 1184 in Cilician Armenia. He was very learned, and knew Greek, Arabic, and Persian. In 1184 (the year 633 of the great

Armenian era) he wrote in Cilician Armenian a medical treatise entitled Consolation in cases of fever; this title was apparently a pun on his own name, mekhitar meaning consoler, mekhitaruthiun, consolation. The Consolation is divided into forty-six chapters. Its substance is derived from Arabic, Persian, and Armenian sources. Most of the technical terms are in Armenianized Arabic. Mekhitar composed other treatises on medicine and anatomy, but these are known only through sundry extracts preserved in later Armenian writings.

Four anatomical Armenian texts edited by F. C. Conybeare deserve to be considered here, if only for the sake of comparison, as they are in all probability of about the same period. According to the manuscripts, they were edited by one Asar of Sebaste (the Turkish Sīwās in Anatolia). Their Armenian idiom is very much the same as Mekhitar's. The first tract is apparently a translation from an Arabic text by a Syrian, Abū Sa'īd, flourishing in 1037, who may well be Abū Sa'īd 'Ubaidallāh (first half of the eleventh century); the translator was possibly Mekhitar himself, or Nerses the Graceful who died in 1173, or Nerses of Lambron, bishop of Tarsus, who died in 1198.

Text—Edition of the Armenian text by the Mekhitarist Fathers of San Lazzaro (Venice 1832), based on MS. no. 246 of the Bibliothèque Nationale, Paris. Ernst Seidel: Mechithar's des Meisterarztes aus Her, Trost bei Fiebern, zum ersten Male aus dem mittelarmenischen übersetzt und erläutert (308 p., Leipzig, 1908).

F. C. Conybeare: Four Armenian tracts on the structure of the human body (Studies in the history and method of science, vol. 2, 359–384, 1921; Isis, 4, 402).

Criticism—Carl Friedrich Neumann: Versuch einer Geschichte der armenischen Literatur nach den Werken der Mechitaristen (164–166, Leipzig 1836). L. Choulant: Handbuch der Bücherkunde (391–392, Leipzig 1841). Joseph Karst: Historische Grammatik des Kilikisch-armenischen (Strassburg 1901). M. Neuburger: Geschichte der Medizin (vol. 2, 229, 1911); (the date 1148 is a misprint for 1184). V. Torkomian: Les manuscrits médicaux arméniens de la Bibliothèque Nationale de Paris (Bull. de la Soc. franç., d'histoire de la médecine, vol. 19, 166–172, 1925); the author is preparing a French translation.

VIII. HINDU

JAGADDEVA

See Chapter XVIII, Philosophic Background.

IX. CHINESE

CHINESE AND JAPANESE MATERIA MEDICA

An important pên ts'ao, the Shao^{4} hsing^{1} chiao^{4} tung^{1} ching^{1} shih^{3} chêng^{4} lei^{4} pei^{4} chi^{2*} pên^{3} ts'ao^{3} (9775, 4611, 1302, 11248, 2122, 9893, 726, 6853, 8804, 892, 8846, 11634), was printed in 1159. It had been compiled by Wang^{2} Chi^{4}-hsien^{1} (12493, 966, 4440), Chang^{1} Hsiao^{4}-chih^{2*} (416, 4334, 1846), Ch'ai^{2} Yüan,^{2} (258, 13704) and Kao^{1} Shao^{4}-kung^{1} (5927, 9775, 6554). According to the imperial catalogue the complete work contained thirty-three books, but the copy printed in 1159 (date of the preface) or soon thereafter is lost, and we know only manuscript copies, all of which are incomplete, containing only twenty-two, nineteen, or even five books. An important feature of that work was its abundant illustrations largely derived from an earlier work, the T'u^{2} ching^{1} pên^{3} ts'ao^{3} (12128, 2122) published in 1061, but now lost.

A copy of the Shao hsing in the Library of Congress is a facsimile of a Japanese manuscript of the Palace Museum Library in the Forbidden City in Peking. It is incomplete, having only the preface, table of contents, and 404 beautiful plates bound in five volumes, not divided into books. The text covers sixty-four closely written pages.

The Shao hsing deeply influenced Japanese medicine, though much later. It was one of the books brought back by Ukita Hideiye from Korea at the time of Hideyoshi's expedition in 1592. The Japanese call it Shōkō kōtei keishi shōrui bikiū honzō; the T'u ching, they call Rukyo hongo (or Jūkō honzō dsukyō).

The Shao hsing is thus triply important: for the sake of its own text and illustrations; for the sake of the T'u ching which it represents; and finally for the sake of its influence on Japanese medicine.

Mitsutaro Shirai: Scientific Japan (216, Tōkyō 1925; Isis, 10, 83). Report of the Librarian of Congress (255, 1927). Private communication from Arthur W. Hummel (June, 1928).

See my note on Henchiin Seiken, in this chapter.

CH'ÊN YEN

Ch'ên^2 Yen^2 (658, 13025). Style name, Wu^2-tsê^{2*} (12753, 11665). Chinese physician who flourished under the Sung about 1174–1189. His most important work is a large medical treatise in eighteen parts entitled The triple causes of illnesses and their treatment, San^1-yin^1 chi^{2*}-i^{1*} ping^4-chêng^4 fang^1 lun^4 (9552, 13215, 859, 5342, 9306, 726, 3435, 7475). The last two parts deal with women's and children's diseases. He also wrote a treatise in 2 parts on obstetrics, Ch'an^3-yü^{4*} pao^3-ch'ing^4 chi^{2*}-fang^1 (360, 13659, 8720, 2211, 906, 3435).

F. Huebotter: Guide (32, Kumamoto 1924; Isis, 7, 259); Die chinesische Medizin (348, Leipzig 1929; Isis 14, 255–263).

X. JAPANESE

HENCHIIN SEIKEN

Japanese scholar who wrote in 1156 three treatises: Yaku shu shō, on drugs; Kō yō shō, on perfumery; and Kokurui shō, on cereals. They were derived from the Chinese pên ts'ao, and contain illustrations taken from the Ch'ung^4 kuang^3 pên^3 ts'ao^3 t'u^2 ching^1 (2914, 6397, 8846, 11634, 12128, 2122) which appeared in China in 1061 (or 1092?). As this work, which the Japanese call Jūkō honzō dsukyō, is now lost in China, the illustrations in Seiken's work are especially valuable.

Mitsutaro Shirai: Scientific Japan (215, Tōkyō 1926; Isis, 10, 83). See my reference to the T'u ching in the note on Chinese materia medica, in this chapter.

CHAPTER XXV

HISTORIOGRAPHY

(Second Half of Twelfth Century)

I. WESTERN MUSLIM

IBN KHAIR

Abū Bakr Muḥammad ibn Khair ibn 'Umar ibn Khalīfa al-Ishbīlī. Hispano-Muslim scholar. He was born in Seville in 1108–1109, and studied in Seville and Cordova. He died in Cordova in 1179. He compiled a bibliography (Fihrist) containing more than 1400 titles of books composed by Spanish Muslims on every subject. This bibliography is very precious, as other standard bibliographies of Arabic writings, compiled by Easterners (notably that of Ḥājī Khalīfa) do not give sufficient importance to the Spanish writings.

Text—This Fihrist was edited by Francisco Codera y Zaidín and Julián Ribera y Tarragó: Index librorum de diversis scientiarum ordinibus quos a magistris didicit (Biblioteca arabico-hispanica, vols. 9 and 10, Saragossa, 1894–1895); vol. 10 contains the index and a Latin introduction.

Criticism—C. Brockelmann: Arabische Litteratur (vol. 1, 499, 1898). Francisco Pons Boigues: Ensayo bio-bibliográfico (242–244, Madrid 1898).

AL-ḌABBĪ

Abū Ja'far Aḥmad ibn Yaḥyā ibn Aḥmad ibn 'Umaira al Ḍabbī al-Qurṭubī. Hispano-Muslim historian. He flourished in Cordova, Ceuta, Alexandria, and for a considerable time in Murcia, in the second half of the twelfth century. He died after 1195–1196. Author of a collection of Hispano-Muslim biographies, preceded by a history of the conquest of Spain and of the Spanish Ummayads and their successors down to 1195–1196. It is entitled Kitāb bughyat al-mutalammis fī ta'rīkh rijāl ahl al-Andalus (Desire of him who is anxious to know the story of the Andalusians).

Text—The Bughyat al-mutalammis was edited by Francisco Codera and Julián Ribera in the Biblioteca arabico-hispanica (vol. 3, Madrid 1885).

Criticism—Fr. Wüstenfeld: Geschichtschreiber der Araber (nr. 282, 1881). C. Brockelmann: Arabische Litteratur (vol. 1, 340, 1898). Francisco Pons Boigues: Ensayo bio-bibliográfico (257–259, 1898).

II. EASTERN MUSLIM

AL-SAM'ĀNĪ

Abū Sa'd 'Abd al-Karīm ibn Muḥammad ibn Manṣūr al-Tamīmī al-Sam'ānī (that is, of the tribe of Sam'ān, a branch of the tribe of Tamīm), Taj al-Islām. Muslim historian, born in Marv in 1113, traveled extensively in Eastern Islām: died in Mary in 1166. He continued the annals of Baghdād begun by al-Khaṭīb (second half of the eleventh century). In 1155 he undertook an extensive study of

Arabic patronymics (nisba), in eight volumes, which is of great historical and geographical interest, for apropos of the names of prominent persons he supplies biographical and topographical explanations. These had been collected by him in the course of his journeys, during which he had met for that very purpose a large number of learned men. This work called Kitāb al-ansāb is chiefly precious with regard to Persia, Transoxiana, and Central Asia, for which countries it is our principal and often only source of information. The Kitāb al-ansāb is better known through an abridgment of it, the Lubāb, compiled by Ibn al-Athīr; or through a further abridgment, the Lubb al-lubāb, by al-Suyūṭī.

Text—There is no complete edition of the Ansāb. For editions of the abridgments see my notes on Ibn al-Athīr (first half of the thirteenth century), and on al-Suyūṭī (second half of the fifteenth century).

Criticism—Ḥājī Khalīfa (vol. 2, no. 2179, p. 119, 1837). Ibn Khallikān: de Slane's translation (vol. 2, 156–159, 1843). F. Wüstenfeld: Geschichtschreiber der Araber (no. 254, p. 87, 1881). C. Brockelmann: Arabische Litteratur (vol. 1, 329, 1898).

IBN ḤAMDŪN

Abū-l-Ma'ālī Muḥammad al-Baghdādī, al-Kātib, Kāfī-l-kufāt, Bahā al-dīn. Born at Baghdād in 1102. He was in the service of the caliphs al-Muqtafī and al-Mustanjid, but fell into disgrace in 1166 and was thrown into prison in Baghdād, where he died soon afterwards in 1167. He compiled a very large collection of historical and literary anecdotes, entitled Kitāb al-tadhkira (The book of remembrance), or Tadhkira ibn Ḥamdūn, in 12 volumes.

Text—Alfred von Kremer: Beiträge zur Kenntnis der Geschichte und Sitten der Araber vor dem Islam (Sitzungsber. d. Wiener Akad., phil. Cl., April 1851); based on the Tadhkira.

Criticism—Ḥājī Khalīfa: Lexicon (vol. 2, 255, no. 2780, 1837). Ibn Khallikān: de Slane's translation (vol. 3, 90–92, 1848). F. Wüstenfeld: Geschichtschreiber der Araber (no. 255, p. 88, 1881). C. Brockelmann: Arabische Litteratur (vol. 1, 280, 1898).

'ALĪ AL-BAYHAQĪ

Abū-l-Ḥasan 'Alī ibn al-Imâm Abī-l-Qāsim Zaid al-Bayhaqī, Ẓahīr al-dīn. He was born in Bayhaq near Nīshāpūr in 1106. He lived mostly in his native town, and in Marw, in Nīshāpūr, and in Ray. He died in 1169–1170 (or 1174?). Persian scientist and biographer. He wrote (presumably in Arabic) a number of books on medicine, mathematics, astrology, and various other subjects, but is chiefly known because of his biographical collection entitled Ta'rīkh ḥukamā' al-Islām (History of the learned men of Islām). That collection was the continuation of an older one entitled Ṣiwān al-ḥikma (Container of wisdom) compiled about 980 by Muḥammad ibn al-Bahrām al-Sijazī al-Sijistānī. 'Alī also wrote a history of Bayhaq, in Persian, completed in Shashtamad in 1168.

Ḥājī Khalīfa: Lexicon (4, 141, 1845; 6, 243, 436, 1852; 7, 784, 1858). C. Brockelmann: Arabische Litteratur (vol. 1, 324, 1898). E. Wiedemann: Einige Biographien nach al-Baihaqī (Beiträge 20, Sitzungsber. d. physik. med. Soz., vol. 42. 59–77, Erlangen 1910); contains the abbreviated translation of 110 biographies of special interest to us; Biographie von al-Baihaqī nach Jāqūt (Beiträge 28, ibidem, vol. 44, 113–117, 1912).

'UMĀRA AL-YAMANĪ

Abū Muḥammad 'Umāra ibn 'Alī ibn Zaidān al-Yamanī, Najm al-dīn. Born in Yemen in 1121–1122, he studied in Zabīd; he traveled to Mecca and Egypt in 1154–1155; he returned to Egypt in 1157 and remained there; he obtained Ṣalāh al-dīn's favor, but later tried to betray him, and was executed in 1174. Muslim, Shāfi'īte, historian. His principal work is a history of his native country, dedicated to the Qāḍī al-Fāḍil (1135–1199), the Ta'rikh al-Yaman. He also wrote various qaṣa'īd, and an autobiography containing extracts from his poetical correspondence, Kitāb al-nukat al-'aṣrīya fī akhbār al-wuzarā' al-Miṣrīya (Contemporary subtleties concerning the viziers of Egypt).

Text—Henry Cassels Kay: Yaman, its early mediaeval history (Arabic text, English translation and notes; London 1892).

H. Derenbourg: Autobiographie et récits sur les viziers d'Egypte (Paris 1898).

Criticism—Ibn Khallikān: de Slane's translation (vol. 2, 367–372, 1843). F. Wüstenfeld: Geschichtschreiber der Araber (90, 1881). C. Brockelmann: Arabische Litteratur (vol. 1, 333, 1898).

IBN 'ASĀKIR

Abū-l-Qāsim 'Alī ibn abī Muḥammad al-Ḥasan ibn Hibatallāh, Thiqat al-dīn, Ibn 'Asākir al-Shāfi'ī. Born in Damascus in 1105. From 1126 he studied in Baghdād and in Persia, and later he taught in Damascus; he died there in 1176. Muslim historian and traditionist. His principal work is an immense history of Damascus (Ta'rīkh madīnat Dimashq, in 80 vols.) modeled after the Ta'rīkh Baghdād;[1] that is, it is essentially a collection of biographies of the learned men of Damascus.

Ibn Khallikān: de Slane's translation (vol. 2, 252–255, 1843). F. Wüstenfeld: Geschichtschreiber der Araber (Nr. 267, p. 92, 1881). C. Brockelmann: Arabische Litteratur (1, 331, 1898).

IBN MUNQIDH

Abū-l-Muẓaffar Usāmah ibn Murshid Ibn Munqidh. Muslim poet, soldier and sportsman. Born in the castle of Shayzar (Caesarea ad Orontem) in the valley of the Orontes, fifteen miles north of Ḥamāh; ruins of that castle are still extant. He flourished from 1138 to 1144 in Damascus, then in Egypt; then again in Damascus from 1154 to 1164; he took part in the war against the Crusaders in 1150–1153, 1162–1164; from 1164 to 1174 he enjoyed the Urtuqid protection in Ḥiṣn Kayfa on the Tigris; in 1174 he returned to Damascus, where he died in 1188. His chief literary work was probably done during the years 1164–1174, a period of relative rest. He wrote many poems, a treatise on rhetoric, Kitāb al-badī', etc. At the age of ninety lunar years (that is, about 1182), he composed or at any rate completed an autobiography, Kitāb al-i'tibār (Learning by example), which is historically important and is one of the first larger works of its kind. (Ibn al-Jauzī's autobiography is much smaller).

As he was very fond of hunting, this biography contains interesting observations on the habits of hunted and hunting animals. The last part of it treats exclusively of falconry and the chase; it is the earliest Arabic treatise on the subject written

[1] By al-Khaṭīb al-Baghdādī (second half of the eleventh century), continued by al-Sam'ānī (second half of the twelfth century).

by a known author. Usāmah relates his father's and his own hunting experiences; they hunted with various kinds of falcons, with cheetahs, and with dogs. He explains the difference between cheetahs (fahd) and leopards (namir). They hunted lions, wild boars, wild asses, etc. He describes briefly different kinds of fishing.

The Kitāb al-i'tibār also contains many anecdotes on the customs of the Franks, which Usāmah had learned to know pretty well; he criticizes their method of ordeal by water and by dueling, and their inferior medical practice; he notes the differences between the Franks settled in the country, and the rough newcomers. Finally, the Kitāb contains many medical anecdotes concerning unusual wounds and cures. The only known physician quoted is Ibn Buṭlān.

Text—Hartwig Derenbourg: Ousāma ibn Mounḳidh (2 vols., Publications de l'Ecole des langues orientales, Paris 1886–1893); vol. 1, Usāma's life; vol. 2, Arabic text of the Kitāb al-i'tibār. H. Derenbourg: Anthologie de textes arabes inédits par Ousāma et sur Ousāma (149 p., Paris 1893); Souvenirs historiques et récits de chasse (Paris 1895), French version of the Kitāb al-i'tibār.

This French version has been followed by Georg Schumann in his German translation (Innsbruck 1905); and by George R. Porter in his English one: The autobiography of Ousāma ibn Mounqidh (sic) (313 p., London 1929; Isis, 13, 426).

Philip K. Hitti: An Arab-Syrian gentleman and warrior in the period of the Crusades. Memoirs of Usāmah ibn Munqidh (278 p., ill., Columbia University, New York 1929; Isis, 13, 365–368); Excellent translation based upon the unique Escorial MS., with valuable notes. New edition of the Arabic text by Philip K. Hitti (300 p., 1 pl., Princeton, N. J., 1930; Isis, 15, 341–342).

Criticism—Hartwig Derenbourg: Ousāma. Un émir syrien du XIIe siècle. Préface du livre du bâton [Kitāb al-'aṣā] (Paris 1887). C. Brockelmann: Arabische Litteratur (vol. 1, 319, 1898). J. E. Sarkis: Dictionnaire de bibliographie arabe (256, Cairo 1928). The best source of information is Hitti's translation.

'IMĀD AL-DĪN AL-IṢFAHĀNĪ

Muḥammad ibn Muḥammad 'Imād al-dīn (pillar of religion) al-Kātib al-Iṣfahānī (the secretary of Ispahan). Born at Ispahan in 1125. He studied in Baghdād. He was appointed secretary by the Zangid Atābeg of Syria, Nūr al-dīn Maḥmūd (d. 1173), and later by the Ayyūbid Ṣalāḥ al-dīn (Saladin); after Saladin's death in 1193 he devoted himself to literary work. He died at Damascus in 1201. Persian historian and writer; he was equally conversant with Persian and Arabic, but his works were written in Arabic. He wrote a history of Saladin's conquest of Syria and Palestine, Kitāb al-fatḥ al-qussī; a history of the Saljūq rulers and their viziers, Kitāb nuṣrat al-fatra, which is an abbreviated translation of a Persian work by Anūshirwān ibn Khālid (d. 1138); historical memoirs entitled Kitāb al-barq al-Sha'mī, the Syrian lightning, in seven volumes (one extant, concerning the years 1182–1184); etc.

He may be the author of the treatise on falconry called Book of Nūshirwān the Wise, ascribed to one 'Imād al-dīn al Isfahānī, dated A.H. 590 = A.D. 1194.

Text—Kitāb al-fatḥ al qussī fī-l-fatḥ al-qudsī (The Qussian interpretation of the conquest of Jerusalem); edited by C. de Landberg (Leiden 1888).

Kitāb nuṣrat al fatra wa 'uṣrat al-fiṭra (Succour against langour and asylum for the human race); a summary of this work was written by al-Bundārī (first half of the thirteenth century).

Criticism—Ibn Khallikān: de Slane's translation (vol. 3, 300–306, 1848). F. Wüstenfeld: Geschichtschreiber (100–102, 1881). C. Brockelmann: Arabische Litteratur (vol. 1, 314–316, 1898). Encyclopaedia of Islām (vol. 2, 471, 1919).

YŪSUF IBN RĀFI'

Abū-l-Maḥāsin Yūsuf ibn Rafi' ibn Shaddād al-Ḥalabī, Bahā' al-dīn. He was born in Mūṣul in 1145. He studied in Baghdād, and assisted in teaching at the Niẓāmīya; later he was a professor in Mūṣul. He was a judge under Ṣalāḥ al-dīn, and after the latter's death, under his son and grandson, al-Ẓāhir and al-'Azīz, who ruled successively in Aleppo. He died in Aleppo in 1234. Muslim, Shāfi'īte, historian. He wrote a history of Ṣalāh al-dīn (d. 1193); a history of Aleppo; etc.

Text—Kitāb al-nawādir al-sulṭānīya wal-maḥāsin al-Yūsufīya. Victa et res gestae Saladini auctore Bohadino filio Sjeddadi, edited with Latin translation, by Albert Schultens (Leiden 1732, 1755). English translation by Claude Reignier Conder (London 1897).

Ta'rīkh Ḥalab. Still unpublished.

Criticism—Ibn Khallikān: de Slane's translation (vol. 4, 417–435, 1871). F. Wüstenfeld: Geschichtschreiber der Araber (115–117, 1881). C. Brockelmann: Arabische Litteratur (vol. 1, 316–317, 1898).

For Ibn al-Jauzī, and for Fakhr al-dīn al-Rāzī, see Chapter XVIII, Philosophic Background.

III. WESTERN JEWISH

For Benjamin of Tudela, see Chapter XXII, Geography.

For Abraham ben David ha-Levi, see Chapter XVIII, Philosophic Background.

EPHRAIM BEN JACOB

Ephraim of Bonn; Shallum. German Talmudist, liturgical poet, and chronicler. He was born in 1133 and flourished mainly in Worms. He died after 1196. He wrote a chronicle of the persecutions suffered by the Jews in Germany, France, and England, between 1146 and 1196. This is very valuable, being based partly on personal experience.

Text—This chronicle was printed for the first time as an appendix to Meïr Wiener: Emek habacha von R. Joseph (ben Joshua) ha Cohen, Aus dem Hebräischen ins Deutsche übertragen (Leipzig 1858). German translation by S. Baer: Hebräische Berichte über die Judenverfolgungen während der Kreuzzüge (Berlin 1892).

Criticism—Louis Ginzberg: Jewish Encyclopaedia (vol. 5, 190, 1903).

IV. ARMENIAN

For Gregory the Priest, see my note on Matthew of Edessa in Chapter XI, Historiography (first half of twelfth century).

For Nerses the Graceful, see Chapter XV, Religious Background.

SAMUEL OF ĀNĪ

Samuel, the Priest of Ānī (Ānī was the capital of greater Armenia). Armenian historian, who was still living, but probably very old, in 1177. He wrote a universal chronicle down to 1177. The ancient part is almost entirely derived, according to his own testimony, from Eusebios and Moses of Chorene. His book is divided, after Eusebios' example, into two main parts, the second dealing with Christian history, with special reference to Armenia.

Text—The Armenian text was edited by Tēr Mikhelian (Wałarshapat, i.e., Edžmiacin, 1893).

Latin translation edited together with the Armenian text of Eusebios by John Zohrab and Ang. Mai: Samuelis praesbyteri Aniensis temporum usque ad suam aetatem ratio e libris historicorum summatim collecta (Milano 1818).

Translation of the chronological tables of the second part of Samuel's chronicle, by Marie Félicité Brosset, with abundant commentary (Collection d'historiens arméniens, St. Pétersbourg, vol. 2, 339–483, 1876).

Criticism—C. F. Neumann: Geschichte der armenischen Literatur (164, Leipzig 1836). Heinrich Gelzer: Sextus Julius Africanus (vol. 2, 475–482, 1898).

V. SYRIAC

MICHAEL THE ELDER

Michaël I, or the Great. Mar Michael. Syriac theologian and chronicler. Born in 1126. Son of Elias Qindasī of Melitēne. Abbot of the monastery of Barṣaumā, near Melitēne; Jacobite patriarch of Antioch from 1166 to the time of his death in 1199. In 1172 he met Kamāl al-dīn ibn Yūnus at the court of the Saljūq sulṭān of Syria, Qilij Arslān II (1156–1188), and discussed religious questions with him. In the course of his third pilgrimage to Jerusalem in 1178–1179 he was honorably received in Acre by Baldwin IV. His chief work is a chronicle in twenty-one books written in Syriac, covering the period from the creation down to 1196; most of the chapters are written in three parallel columns, the first concerning lay history, the second ecclesiastical history, and the third other contemporary events. Almost until the end of the last century this chronicle was known only through two imperfect Armenian versions of the thirteenth century, and through an unpublished Arabic translation; the Armenian versions were abridged, yet contained additional material relative to Armenian events. Michael's sources, quoted by him, were mainly Eusebios and earlier Syriac chroniclers.

Text—Editio princeps of the Syriac text, with French translation by Jean Baptiste Chabot: Chronique de Michel le Syrien (3 vols., Paris 1899–1910).

The shorter Armenian version was published in Jerusalem in 1870, and again in 1871. The longer Armenian version was translated into French by Victor Langlois: Chronique de Michel le Grand, traduite pour la première fois sur la version du prêtre Ischôk (Venice 1868).

The Arabic translation is represented by a British Museum MS.

Criticism—Wm. Wright: Syriac literature (London 1894). Heinrich Gelzer: Sextus Julius Africanus (vol. 2, 431–458, 1898). R. Duval: Littérature syriaque (3d ed., 1907). Anton Baumstark: Syrische Literatur (298, 1922).

SIMEON SHANQĔLĀWĪ

Simeon Shanqĕlāwī (or Shanqelabhādhī, etc.). Syrian chronologist and educator, of Shanqĕlāwah near Irbil, east of Mūṣul. He flourished about the end of the twelfth century. He wrote in Syriac for his pupil John bar Zō'bī a little treatise on the calendar and chronology (different eras, etc.) in the form of a catechism.

Text—Friedrich Mueller: Die Chronologie des Simeon Sankelāwājā (Leipzig 1889); analysis and partial translation.

Criticism—Wm. Wright: Syriac literature (257, 1894). R. Duval: Littérature syriaque (203, 1907). A. Baumstark: Syrische Literatur (310, 1922).

VI. BYZANTINE

MANASSES

Constantine Manasses. Κωνσταντῖνος ὁ Μανασσῆς. Byzantine writer who flourished during the rule of Manuel I Comnenos (1143–1180). His most important work is a rhymed chronicle, Σύνοψις ἱστορική (6733 political verses) covering the period from the creation to the death of Nicephoros Botaniates (1081). Its importance lies chiefly in its popularity, and in its influence not only upon later Byzantine but also upon Slavonic historiography. Indeed a translation dating from about 1350 is one of the main achievements of the so-called Middle Bulgarian-Slovenian literature. Manasses' chronicle also influenced indirectly Rumanian historiography.

Text—First Latin edition by Joh. Löwenklau (Basel 1573). First Greek edition by Joannes Meursius (Greek and Latin, Leiden 1616). Later editions by L. Allatius and C. A. Fabrotus (Paris 1655); I. Bekker (Bonn 1837); also in Migne's Greek patrology (127, 216–472).

For the Slavonic translation see Krumbacher.

Criticism—Potthast (761, 1896). K. Krumbacher: Byzantinische Litteratur (376–380, 1897).

CINNAMOS

Joannes Cinnamos. Ἰωάννης ὁ Κίνναμος. Byzantine chronicler. Born soon after 1143. Private secretary to the emperor Manuel Comnenos whom he accompanied in the field. He was still living in 1185. About 1180–1183 he wrote a history of the reigns of Joannes and Manuel Comnenos (1118–1180); the history stops at 1176. This contains a first-hand account of the second crusade. His literary models were Herodotos and Xenophon. He was convinced of the superiority of eastern Christendom.

Text—First edition by Cornelius Tollius (Greek and Latin, Utrecht 1652). Edition by August Meineke in the Bonn corpus (vol. 25, 1836); also in Migne's Greek patrology (vol. 133, 299–678, 1864).

Criticism—Carl Neumann: Griechische Geschichtschreiber und Geschichtsquellen im 12. Jahrhundert (110 p., Leipzig 1888). Potthast (320, 1895). K. Krumbacher: Byzantinische Litteratur (279–281, 1897).

EUSTATHIOS

See Chapter XVIII, Philosophic Background.

VII. SPANISH

POEMA DEL CID

This Spanish poem (3744 lines) written towards the end of the twelfth century is the greatest Spanish epic, one that immensely influenced Spanish thought throughout the ages, and contributed powerfully not only to the establishment of the Spanish language but to the consolidation of the national character. Like every true epic, it is based on a nucleus of truth. The Cid of romance is the idealisation of a real person, Rodrigo (or Ruy) Diaz de Vivar, surnamed el Cid (that is, the Arabic al-sayyid, the chief), or Mio Cid (sayyidī) el Campeador (the champion). He was born about 1030–1040 at Vivar in the province of Burgos. He lived at a time of extreme political confusion, when the Muslims and Christians of Spain were divided among themselves, and when political rivalries were far stronger than religious allegiance. Like many other Christian knights of his time and country, he was almost as much a Muslim as a Christian in his behaviour, and he fought with Christian and Muslim allies against Muslim and Christian adversaries as the opportunity occurred. In 1074 he married a granddaughter of Alphonso V. He captured Valencia from the Moors in 1094, but after ruling Valencia and Murcia for only four years he suffered a crushing defeat and died soon afterwards in 1099; he was buried near Burgos. Valencia was reconquered by the Moors in 1102. To the Spaniards the Cid soon became a symbol of all the conventional virtues of chivalry. This legend had already become crystallized in a Latin poem of 1147, but it is the Poema del Cid which established it for ever. Many ballads were devoted to him, and his memory remains to this day one of the fundamental sources of inspiration of Spanish literature.

To show how close the Poema del Cid was to Spanish literary origins, it will suffice to recall that the earliest Spanish (Castilian) texts date only from 1145 (charter of Oviedo) and 1155 (fuero of Avilès). I may add that the earliest Catalan and Portuguese texts date respectively from 1171 (a document from the Roda monastery) and 1192 (a charter).

J. Vendryes in A. Meillet and M. Cohen: Les langues du monde (58, 1924).

Text—First edition, Seville c. 1498. Second edition, with a very elaborate study on the Cid by Juan Lopez de Belorado, abbot of Cardeña (Burgos 1512). Many later editions, of which I cite only a few of the latest.

Edition by Victor Aimé Huber (Marburg 1844). By Damas Hinard, with French translation (Paris 1858). Los cantares de myo Cid, by Ed. Lidforss (172 p., Lund 1895). Text and translation, by Archer M. Huntington (3 vols., New York 1897–1903; vol. 1, text, 1897; vol. 2, English translation, 1901; vol. 3, notes, 1903). Cronı́ca rı́mada. Facsimile edition of the MS. in the Bibliothèque Nationale, by Archer M. Huntington (New York 1904). Cantar de mio Cid; texto, gramática y vocabulario, by R. Menéndez Pidal (3 vols., Madrid 1908–1911). Edición paleográfica del Cantar de mio Cid, by the same (112 p., Madrid 1911). Gestas de Rodrigo el Campeador (Gesta Roderici Campidocti), by Adolfo Bonilla y San Martín (103 p., Madrid 1911).

The lay of the Cid, translated into English verse by R. Selden Rose and Leonard Bacon (144 p., Berkeley, Calif., 1919).

Criticism—R. Dozy: Le Cid d'après de nouveaux documents (Recherches sur l'histoire et la littérature de l'Espagne, vol. 2, 1–253, i-xcix, Leyde 1860). Potthast (229, 1895). Long illustrated article in the Enciclopedia europeo-americana (vol. 18, 897–907, Barcelona 1913), with bibliography. E. Lévi-Provençal: al-Sīd (Encyclopaedia of Islām, vol. 4, 400–402, 1927). Ramón Menéndez Pidal: La España del Cid (1110 p., 2 vols., Madrid 1929; DLZ, vol. 51, 1263–1267, 1930).

VIII. ITALIAN

ROMUALD OF SALERNO

Romoaldus archiepiscopus Salernitanus. Died in 1181. Author of a universal chronicle extending to 1178, of great value for the history of the Sicilies. It is not known whether he was identical with the Romuald who composed the Salernitan treatise on the pulse, already mentioned.

Text—L. A. Muratori: Rerum Italicarum scriptores (vol. 7, 7–244), for the years 926–1178. W. Arndt: Monumenta Germaniae historica (Scriptores, vol. 19, 1866), for the years 893–1178. Various other partial editions.

Criticism—Friedrich Hillger: Das Verhältniss des Hugo Falcandus zu Romuald (Diss., 68 p., Halle 1878). Potthast (983, 1896).

FALCANDUS

Hugo Falcandus. Sicilian historian. Born probably in the Sicilies, and educated there. He became a member of the Sicilian curia, and after 1181 wrote a history of that country under the rules of Bad William and Good William (William I and William II, king of the Sicilies from 1154 to 1166, and from 1166 to 1189, respectively). This work, which is beautifully written, contains valuable information on agriculture (sugar cane and other cultivated plants), and on industries (textiles). In spite of his lack of impartiality, Falcandus was one of the best historians of his age. He is much praised by Gibbon.

The identification of Hugo Falcandus with Hugues Foucault, abbot of St. Denis from 1186 to 1197, is unwarranted.

Text—Historia de rebus gestis in Siciliae regno praecipue ab a. 1154–1169, sive de calamitatibus Siciliae sub Wilhelmo I et II regibus. First edition by Gervais de Tournay (Paris 1550). Thomas Fazelli: Rerum sicularum scriptores (Francfort 1579). L. A. Muratori: Rerum italicarum scriptores (vol. 7, 251–344). G. B. Siragusa: La historia (242 p., Roma 1897); Lezione del cod. vatic. lat. 10690 (30 p., Roma 1904).

Criticism—Hoefer: Nouvelle biographie générale (vol. 17, 27, 1856). Friedrich Hillger: Das Verhältnis des Hugo Falcandus zu Romuald von Salerno (Diss., 68 p., Halle 1878). Potthast (444, 1896). For Gibbon's opinion, see Bury's edition (vol. 6, 546).

GODFREY OF VITERBO

Gioffredo da Viterbo, Gotfried, Godefroy; Godefridus Viterbiensis. He was born about 1120, probably in Saxony. He studied in Bamberg. He became bishop of Viterbo in 1184. He was chaplain to three German emperors, and traveled with them and was sent by them on many errands abroad. Towards the end of his life he spent most of his time in Viterbo, and died in or after 1191. He was a very learned chronicler and topographer, and knew Greek and Hebrew. He wrote (partly in prose, partly in verse) a chronicle covering the period from the Creation down to 1186, entitled Memoria seculorum, of little value but very popular. A geographical poem ascribed to him, entitled Denumeratio regnorum imperio subjectorum, contains interesting observations.

Text—Memoria seculorum (also called Pantheon) published by B. J. Herold (Basel 1559). Partim in Migne's Patrology (vol. 198, col. 875–1044). Also in Monum. Germ. hist., Scriptores (vol. 22, 107–307, 1872).

Denumeratio edited by Léopold Delisle: Littérature latine du moyen-âge (41–50, Paris 1890).

For other works see Potthast (533–534, 1896).

Criticism—W. Wattenbach: Deutschlands Geschichtsquellen (vol. 2, 290–299, 1894). J. K. Wright: Geographical lore (119, 1925).

PETER OF EBOLI

See Chapter XXIV, Medicine.

IX. FRENCH

WACE OF JERSEY

Anglo-Norman chronicler and poet. Born in Jersey about 1100; educated at Caen; attached to the court of Henry II, king from 1154 to 1189; became canon of Bayeux. He died probably at Bayeux in the seventies. He wrote, in old French, religious poems and two rhymed chronicles, the Roman de Brut and Roman de Rou.

The Roman de Brut (Geste des Bretons; 16,000 octosyllabic lines) is essentially derived from the Historia Britonum of Geoffrey of Monmouth (first half of the twelfth century), but contains various other traditions; e.g., the first mention of the Round Table. It was completed in 1155 and dedicated to Eleanor of Aquitaine, who had married Henry II in 1152. It was the basis of a poetical English (semi-Saxon) paraphrase, with the addition of a few Welsh traditions, written at the beginning of the thirteenth century, by Layamon, a priest of Areley in Worcestershire.

The Roman de Rou (Geste des Normans; 17000 lines) stops unfortunately at the year 1107: Wace began to work at it in 1160 and ceased soon after 1172. The most important part is that concerning the Norman invasion of England.

The purely historical interest of the Roman de Brut is small: on the contrary, that of the Roman de Rou is very great. Moreover the Roman de Rou is the earliest important historical work written in an European vernacular. It is a sort of transition between the chansons de gestes and the historical works in French prose. Wace's chief sources were Dudo of St. Quentin, William of Jumièges, and probably William of Malmesbury.

Text—Brut, edited by Le Roux de Lincy (2 vols. Rouen 1836–1838).

Layamon's Brut was edited by Frederic Madden (3 vols., London 1847).

Rou, edited by Frédéric Pluquet (2 vols. and suppl., Rouen 1827–1829); also by Hugo Andresen (2 vols., Heilbronn 1877–1879). Partial English translations by Edgar Taylor (London 1837), Sir Alexander Malet (in rhyme, London 1860), and Eugene Mason (Everyman's Library, 1912).

Criticism—J. W. Hales: Dictionary of national biography (vol. 32, 301–302, 1892; Layamon). Potthast (1101, 1896). A. Molinier: Sources de l'histoire de France (vol. 2, 221, 1902). Kate Norgate: Dictionary of national biography (vol. 58, 404, 1909). Alfred Ulbrich: Ueber des Verhältnis von Wace's Roman de Brut zu zeiner Quelle, des Gottried von Monmouth's Historia (Romanische Forschungen, 26, 181–260, Erlangen 1909). Annette Brown Hopkins: The influence of Wace on the Arthurian romances of Crestien de Troies (thesis, 160 p., Chicago 1913). Leo Waldner: Wace's Brut und seine Quellen (Diss., 138 p., Jena 1914). Charles Gross: Sources of English history (2d ed., 377, 394, 1915). De Vincheles Payen-Payne: Wace and the Roman de Rou (30 p., Jersey Society, London 1916). Joseph Henry Philpot: Maistre Wace, a pioneer in two literatures (115 p., London 1925).

PETER THE EATER

Petrus Comestor.[2] Thus nicknamed because of his insatiable appetite for books. French theologian who, like his older contemporary Peter the Lombard, represents

[2] His epitaph read:
Petrus eram, quem petra tegit, dictusque comestor.
Nunc comedor .

the more conservative attitude against the Platonism and rationalism of the school of Chartres, and against other novelties. He was born in Troyes, Champagne. He became dean of the cathedral of Troyes; was chancellor of Paris from 1164 to 1178. He died in Paris in 1198. After 1164 and before 1176, he wrote a manual of sacred history, Historia scholastica, which enjoyed an immense popularity, especially towards the end of the thirteenth century. Indeed it was one of the most popular schoolbooks of the Middle Ages, its success being comparable to that of the Sentences of Peter the Lombard.

Peter the Eater makes some interesting remarks on the physiological effects of the rarity of the atmosphere at high altitudes (Hist. schol., Gen. 34).

Text—Historica scholastica. Many incunabula editions, the first c. 1471 or 1473; at least eight by 1487. Migne's Patrology (vol. 198). French translation (1291) by Guiard des Moulins: La Bible historiée (Paris, s.a., 1495).

Karl Helm: Das Buch der Maccabäer in mittelhochdeutscher Bearbeitung (528 p., Stuttgart 1904). Hans Vollmer: Eine deutsche Schulbibel des 15. Jahrhunderts. Teil 1, Genesis bis Ruth; Teil 2, I. Regum bis II. Macchabäer (Materialien zur Bibelgeschichte und religiösen Volkskunde des Mittelalters, vol 2, 910 p., Berlin 1925–1927); Peter's original text with early German translation. For Dutch version, see note on Maerlant.

Criticism—Hoefer: Nouvelle biographie générale (vol. 11, 332, 1855). Moses Gaster: Ilchester lectures on Greeko-Slavonic literature and its relation to the folklore of Europe (239 p., London 1887). J. K. Wright: Geographical lore (168, 1925).

WILLIAM OF TYRE

Guillaume de Tyr. Guilelmus Tyrius. French historian. Born in 1130 in the Latin kingdom of Jerusalem; educated in the West; flourished in Tyre (Ṣūr) about 1165; ambassador of the King of Jerusalem to Constantinople and Rome; tutor to the prince Baldwin, who appointed him his chancellor when he became king of Jerusalem in 1174; archbishop of Tyre in 1175; attended the third Lateran council in 1179; died in Rome (?) in or soon after 1186. He was very learned, knew Greek and Arabic, and even had some slight acquaintance with Hebrew and Persian. Between 1169 and 1184 he wrote a masterly history of the Crusades from 1095 to 1184, the Historia hierosolymitana or Historia rerum in partibus transmarinis gestarum, the most elaborate mediaeval account of that subject. It is divided into twenty-three books; books one to sixteen (to 1143) are based on earlier works or on oral traditions; the last seven books are more personal and of considerable value.

William's Historia contains many interesting observations on the appearance of the country, its products, the manners of Saracens, descriptions of the Arabian desert and its terrors (for example, the wind samūm), sugar plantations at Tyre, the camels and their usefulness, the trade of Alexandria, etc. It also offers valuable information on the Latin kingdom in the author's time, his point of view being that of the resident Christians. He had written another history, which is lost, concerning Eastern events from the time of Muḥammad down to 1104; this was based on Arabic sources, chiefly Sa'īd ibn al-Biṭrīq (first half of the tenth century).

Text—Belli sacri historia (608 p., Basel 1549). Historia belli sacri verissima (451 p., Basel 1564).

Guillaume de Tyr et ses continuateurs. Texte français du XIIIe siècle revu et annoté par Paulin Paris (2 vols., 1879–1880).

Godefroy of Boloyne; or, The siege and conqueste of Jerusalem by William, archbishop of Tyre. Translated from the French by William Caxton and printed in 1481. Edited with introduction, notes, vocabulary and indexes by Mary Noyes Colvin (Early English Text Society, 390 p., London 1893). Caxton's first edition was reprinted by William Morris at the Kelmscott Press, Hammersmith, c. 1893.

Histoire de la guerre saincte, dite proprement la Franciade orientale, etc. Faite latine par Guillaume, archevesque de Tyr, et traduite en français par Gabriel Du Préau (792 p., Paris 1573, 1574).

Modern editions in F. P. G. Guizot. Collection des mémoires (vol. 16 à 18, 1823, etc.). In Recueil des historiens des croisades. Historiens occidentaux (vol. 1, Paris 1844). In Migne's Patrology (vol. 201, 209–892).

Italian translation by Giuseppe Horologgi (730 p., Venice 1562).

German translation by E. and R. Kausler (642 p., Stuttgart 1840).

Criticism—Potthast (560–562, 1896). Franz Ost: Die altfranzösische Übersetzung der Geschichte Wilhelms v. Tyrus (Diss., 75 p., Halle 1899). Emil Dreesbach: Der Orient in der altfranzösischen Kreuzzugsliteratur (Diss., Breslau 1901). A. Molinier: Sources de l'histoire de France (vol. 2, 303, 1902). M. Steinschneider: Europäische Übersetzungen (81, 1904). Friedrich Lundgreen: Wilhelm und der Templerorden (197 p., illustr., Berlin 1911). J. K. Wright: Geographical Lore (1925). Hermann Probst: Die geographischen Verhältnisse Syriens und Palästinas nach Wilhelm von Tyrus (2 parts, Abh. d. Deuts. Vereins zur Erforschung Palästinas, parts of vols. 4 and 5, 122 p., Leipzig 1927).

ROBERT OF TORIGNY

Robertus de Torineio, sive Robertus de Monte. French chronicler. Born in Torigny-sur-Vire, near Saint-Lô (Manche); died in 1186. He entered the Bec monastery in 1128 and became its prior in 1142 (1149?); he was elected abbot of Mont-Saint-Michel in 1154. In 1139 he revised and continued the chronicle of the Dukes of Normandy (851–1137) written by William of Jumièges who lived about 1027. From 1150 until his death Robert compiled a continuation of Sigebert's universal chronicle (which stopped at the year 1111); this continuation, down to 1186, is very important, being indeed one of the best twelfth century chronicles. He wrote also a treatise on monastic orders and Norman abbeys (1154), perhaps other chronicles of Bec and Mont-Saint-Michel, and a preface to a collection of extracts from Pliny's Natural History, etc. While he was in Bec in 1139 his English colleague Henry of Huntingdon came to see him.

Text—The text of Robert's continuation follows generally that of Sigebert's Chronographia (first half of the twelfth century). Main edition by Léopold Delisle: Chronique de Robert de Torigni, suivie de divers opuscules historiques de cet auteur (2 vols., Rouen 1872–1873). Also in Richard Howlett: Rerum Britannicarum medii aevi scriptores, no. 82 (vol. 4, 1–315, 1890).

Partial English translation by Jos. Stevenson: The church historians of England (vol. 4, 675–813, 1856).

Criticism—M. Morlais: De vita et scriptis Roberti de Torinneio (92 p., Paris 1881). Potthast (976, 1896). A. Molinier: Sources de l'histoire de France (vol. 2, 317, 1902).

X GERMAN

HELMOLD

German chronicler. Born in Holstein; educated in Lübeck; priest in Bosau on the lake of Plön; died in or after 1177. He wrote a very valuable chronicle (down to 1171) of the Christian missions among the Slavs, in which he had taken part, and of the progress of Germanic colonization east of the Elbe. This is important because the expansion of the Germans eastward against the Slavs is one of the most significant movements which occurred in mediaeval Europe, and Helmold was the first historian to give a good account of its beginnings.

Helmold's chronicle was continued down to 1209 by Arnold of Lübeck who died in 1212.

Text—First edition, incomplete, by Siegmund Schorckel (Francfort 1556, 1573). First complete edition by Heinrich Bangert (Lübeck 1659). G. W. Leibniz: Scriptores rerum Brunsvicensium (vol. 2, 537–653). Monumenta Germaniae historica (vol. 21, 11–99, 1869).

German translation by J. C. M. Laurent (Berlin 1852, 1888).

For Arnold's chronicle, same references; i.e., it generally follows Helmold's chronicle.

Criticism—W. Wattenbach: Allgemeine deutsche Biographie (vol. 11, 702, 1880). Paul Regel: Helmold und seine Quellen (Diss., 56 p., Jena 1883). W. Wattenbach: Deutschlands Geschichtsquellen (vol. 2, 338–341, 1894). Potthast (576, 1896). James Westfall Thompson: Feudal Germany (Chicago 1928).

For the Nibelungenlied, see Chapter XVIII, Philosophic Background.

XI. ENGLISH

HUNTINGDON

Henry of Huntingdon. Henricus Huntendunensis, Huntindoniensis. English chronicler. Born about 1080–1090; archdeacon of Huntingdon from 1109; still living in 1154. On his way to Rome in 1139 he met Robert of Torigny at Bec. His main work, the Historia Anglorum, tells the history of England from the time of Caesar's expedition (55 B.C.) down to 1130 (to 1154, in the fifth recension). Down to 1126 it is based mainly on Bede and the Anglo-Saxon chroniclers; after 1126 it becomes more personal, yet it does not contain much new material.

Text—Edition by Sir Henry Savile in his Scriptores post Bedam (London 1596). Best edition by Thomas Arnold (Rolls series, 424 p., London 1879).

English translation by Thomas Forester (Bohn Library, London 1853).

Criticism—H. R. Luard in Dictionary of national biography (vol. 26, 118–119, 1891). Potthast (582, 1896). Charles Gross: Sources of English history (2nd ed., 374, 1915).

For Richard FitzNeal, and for John of Salisbury, see Chapter XXVI, Law and Sociology.

For Gerald the Welshman, and for the Gesta regis Ricardi (the life of Richard Lionheart), see Chapter XXII, Geography.

NEWBURGH

William of Newburgh. Also called William Little, or Petit. Guilelmus Neubrigensis (de Novoburgo), Parvus. English chronicler, born about 1136. Canon at the Austin priory of St. Mary at Newburgh, in the North Riding of Yorkshire. He died about 1201. He wrote a chronicle of England, Historia rerum anglicarum, in five books, dealing with the period 1066–1198. It does not contain much new material, but is chiefly a judicious recasting of other chronicles, showing much common and even critical sense, also a sense of style. For example, he did not hesitate to reject the fables told by Geoffrey of Monmouth, which was a very remarkable attitude in his time. Newburgh's chronicle is especially valuable for the period 1154–1198. It was continued down to 1298 by a monk of Furness abbey, Lancashire.

Text—First edition by William Silvius (Antwerp 1567). Best edition by Richard Howlett (Rolls series, London 1884–1885); with the continuation. Englished by Joseph Stevenson: Church historians of England (vol. 4, London 1856).

Criticism—Potthast (559, 1896). Kate Norgate: Dictionary of national biography (vol. 61, 360–363, 1900). H. E. Salter: English Historical Review (vol. 22, 510–514, 1907). Rudolf Jahncke: Guilelmus, ein pragmatischer Geschichtschreiber des 12. Jahrhunderts (Diss., 41 p., Jena 1911). Charles Gross: Sources of English history (382, 1915).

HOWDEN

Roger of Howden (or Hoveden). English chronicler and topographer. He was born probably in Howden, in the East Riding of Yorkshire. He was one of the clerks of Henry II; after Henry's death (1189) Roger probably retired from public life; at any rate he had then more time for historical work. He died in or after 1201. About 1192 he began to write a chronicle of England for the period from 732 down to his own day; it ends abruptly in 1201. It is valuable for the period 1192–1201. It contains descriptions of routes and coasts, probably derived from manuals of navigation; the account of coastal Spain is particularly elaborate.

Text—First edition by Sir Henry Savile: Rerum Anglicarum scriptores post Bedam (230–471, 1596). Better edition by William Stubbs (Rolls series, 4 vols., London 1868–1871).

English translation by Henry T. Riley in Bohn's Library (2 vols., London 1853).

Criticism—William Hunt: Dictionary of national biography (vol. 27, 428–429, 1891). Potthast (980, 1896). Charles Gross: Sources of English history (373, 1915). J. K. Wright: Geographical lore (109, 308, 322, 1925).

DICETO

Ralph (or Radulfus) de Diceto. English chronicler. The origin of his strange surname is unknown. He was appointed archdeacon of Middlesex in 1152, and dean of St. Paul in 1180; he studied twice in Paris, the second time about 1157. He died about 1202. He wrote various opuscula, and two important chronicles: (1) the Abbreviationes chronicarum, from the time of Christ down to 1147, composed about 1185, almost entirely second hand; (2) the Ymagines historiarum, from 1149 to 1199 (1202). The second account is very valuable for the thirty years from 1169 to 1199; that is, for the end of Henry II's rule, and the rule of Richard Lionheart (1189–1199).

Text—First edition by Roger Twysden in his Historiae Anglicanae (London 1652). Best edition by William Stubbs (Rolls series, 2 vols., London 1876, together with some smaller writings of Diceto).

Criticism—R. L. Poole: Dictionary of national biography (vol. 15, 12–14, 1888). Potthast (949, 1896). Charles Gross: Sources of English history (359, 1915). G. Gundermann: Trogus und Gellius bei Radulfus de Diceto (posthumous publ. edited by G. Goetz; Ber. der Säch. Ak., Phil. Kl., 78, 2; 33 p., Leipzig 1926).

XII. SCANDINAVIAN

SVEND AAGESÖN

Svend Aggesen. Sueno Aggonis filius. Danish historian who flourished at the end of the twelfth century. He wrote for Absalom, archbishop of Lund (d. 1201), a chronicle of the kings of Denmark from the year 300 down to 1187. He translated into Latin the laws of Canute (or Cnut) the Great, king of the English, Danes, and Norwegians (d. 1035).

Text—Suenonis Aggonis filii, Christierni nepotis, primi Danicae gentis historici, quae extant opera Stephan. Johannis Stephanius illustravit (222 p., Soroe 1642). Jacobus Langebek: Scriptores rerum Danicarum medii aevi (vol. 1, Copenhagen 1772). Both editions contain both works. Martin Clarentius Gertz: New edition of Latin text on the basis of the Codex Arnamagnaeanus, no. 33, (200 p., Copenhagen 1915). Danish translation of this text by Gertz (110 p., Copenhagen 1916-1917).

Criticism—Potthast (3, 1895).

XIII. RUSSIAN

RUSSIAN CHRONICLES

I have already spoken of the Russian chronicles (letopisi) in my note on Nestor and Sylvester of Kiev. Theirs was the first, the so-called Primitive Chronicle (Nachalnaya letopis). It was followed by the Chronicle of Kiev covering the period 1116 to 1199; an excellent narrative, some parts of which (for example, those concerning the events of 1146-1154) are equal to the best mediaeval chronicles. Other continuations carried the account down to 1290 (or 1305); but the early part, that is, the Chronicle of Kiev, was the masterpiece of Russian mediaeval historiography.

The earliest Russian annals (letopisi) extant are represented by the Lavrentievski manuscript of 1377, the Ipatski manuscript of the beginning of the fifteenth century, and the Radziwill manuscript (or Königsberg manuscript) of the fifteenth century.

The Lavrentievski manuscript is also called the Suzdal manuscript; it includes a Suzdal chronicle, and was copied by Lavrenti, a monk of Suzdal (near Kostroma), in 1377.

The Ipatski manuscript or Ipatievskaya letopis was called after the Ipatievski monastery founded about 1330 near Kostroma on the Upper Volga; it is misleadingly called in western languages the Chronicle of Hypatios. It includes the Kiev chronicle, and the Volynian chronicle (Volynia is a district west of Kiev); the Kievskaya letopis ends in 1199; the Volynskaya letopis ends with the beginning of the fourteenth century.

Another work which dates probably from about the same time as the Chronicle of Kiev is the famous epic called The campaign of Igor (Slovo o polku Igoreve; the word, or song, of the campaign of Igor). It is written in rhythmical prose, and is the best known classic of early Russian literature. The language reminds one of the early Slavonic translation of Flavius Josephus. Yet there has been much discussion with regard to its genuineness. The manuscript of it (a sixteenth century one) was discovered only in 1795, and it was destroyed a few years later in the fire of Moscow in 1812. It is now represented by a copy prepared for Catharine II (d. 1796), and by the princeps editio of 1800.

Text—For the Chronicle of Kiev, see Potthast (722, 1896). Eduard Sievers: Die altslawischen Verstexte von Kiew und Freising im Verein mit Georg Gerullis und Max Vasmer herausgegeben (Ber. über die Verhdl. d. Sächs. Ak. der Wiss., 76, 2; 60 p., Leipzig 1925).

Campaign of Igor. Facsimile edition of the princeps of 1800 (Moscow 1920). The Russian editions of it are innumerable, and parts of the text, if not the whole of it, are included in every Russian anthology. Eduard Sievers: Das Igorlied metrisch und sprachlich bearbeitet (Ber. über die Verhdl. der Sächs. Ak. der Wiss., Philol. Kl., 78, 1, 55 p., Leipzig 1926). English translation in Leo Wiener: Anthology of Russian literature (vol. 1, 1902). English adaptation by Helen De Vere Beauclerk (London 1918). Leonard Arthur Magnus: Heroic ballads of Russia (London 1921).

Russian text with German version by August Boltz (60 p., Berlin 1854). German translation by Heinrich von Paucker (64 p., Berlin 1884). Many other translations in many languages.

Criticism—See histories of Russia and histories of Russian literature. K. Bestoujev-Rumin: Brockhaus-Efron's Russian Encyclopaedia (vol. 18, 192–197, 1896). M. Speranski: Granat's Russian Encyclopaedia (7th ed., vol. 27, 500–507; vol. 39, 528–532); the volumes are undated; vol. 39 is posterior to the Revolution.

XIV. CHINESE

LUNG TA-YÜAN

See note on Chinese archaeology in Chapter XI, Historiography.

CHÊNG CH'IAO

Chêng^4 Ch'iao^2 (724, 1405). Literary name, Yü^2 chung^4 (13512, 2876); nickname, Chia^{1*} chi^4 (1132, 936). Born in 1104 at P'u^2-t'ien^2 (9489, 11236), Fuh Kien; died in 1162. Chinese historian and archaeologist. He lived for a time at Chia^{1*}-chi^4-shan^1 (1132, 936, 9663), then set out to travel and to observe and collect curious information of all kinds.

After 1149 he wrote a history of China, T'ung^1 chih^4 (12294, 1918) from the time of Fu Hsi down to the T'ang dynasty, in 200 chüan, which was published in 1161. It is divided into four parts: (1) account of the ruling houses from the earliest times to the Sui dynasty, 20 chüan; (2) genealogy, 4 chüan; (3) "twenty sketches," history of social institutions, of costumes, rites and ceremonies, legal codes, criminology, government, economic conditions, etc.; 52 chüan; (4) biography, 124 chüan. There is also an introductory essay discussing the aims and means of historiography.

He was perhaps the most scientific of the Sung historians. He tried to be as objective as possible. He was one of the first to break away from the traditional arrangement of the dynastic histories (see vol. I, 199), advocating the classification of materials into more natural categories. He discussed the growth and decline of population, the distribution of cities, and similar subjects. His comments on the proper methods of studying astronomy, botany, zoology, phonetics, music, bibliography, etc., sound very modern. He aimed to incorporate into his books the practical observations and experiences of the common people. He was not content merely to assign correct names to natural objects, but took pains to describe them. Next to actual contact with concrete materials, he recommended the use of maps and drawings. His manuscript works abounded in these, but unfortunately none of them has come down to us. In his studies of the Classics Chêng Ch'iao advocated the use of the uncommented texts in order to approach the original writings with freshness and without bias.

In a general way we might say that he was the first to try to continue the tradition initiated by Ssŭ-ma Ch'ien (second half of the second century B.C.) in opposition to that of Pan Ku (second half of the first century) followed by the authors of the dynastic histories. His feeling on the subject is well illustrated by his statement that Ssŭ-ma Ch'ien is to Pan Ku as a dragon to a dog. As a result of this antagonism to orthodox historiography, his work was neglected and almost forgotten.

His scientific methods made it possible for him to reach conclusions far in advance of his time. Thus he was led to doubt the Confucian authorship of the Book of Changes (I ching); he questioned the high antiquity ascribed to the dictionary Êrh^{3} ya^{3} (3354, 12807) (see vol. I, 110); and in the treatise Shih^{2*} ku^{3} wên^{2} (9964, 6241, 12633) he claimed that the inscriptions on the Stone Drums in ta^{4} chuan^{4} (10470, 2724) script, traditionally ascribed to the beginning of the Chou dynasty, date only from the second half of the third century B.C.

This last question has been abundantly discussed by Chinese authors and is still unsettled. The inscriptions are certainly ancient, but it seems impossible to date them with any accuracy. There were originally about 700 characters, of which 462 have been directly or indirectly preserved. After many vicissitudes the weatherbeaten stone drums were placed in 1307 in the gateway of the Confucian temple at Fêng-hsiang fu and have remained there ever since.

Text—The Library of Congress has the following works of his: T'ung chih, Li^{3} ching^{1} ao^{4} chih^{3} (6949, 2122, 109, 1790), Liu^{4*} ching^{1} ao^{4} lun^{4} (7276, 2122, 109, 7475), Chia^{1*} chi^{4} i^{2} kao^{3} (1132, 936, 5440, 5932).

Criticism—H. A. Giles: Chinese biographical dictionary (109, 1898). The dates of birth and death quoted by Giles (1108–1166) are inaccurate. Encyclopaedia sinica (149, 1917). For a full and authoritative account of Chêng Ch'iao and his writings, see Chinese articles by Ku^{4} Chieh^{2}-kang^{1} (6254, 1472, 5895) in the Journal of Sinological studies, Kuo^{2*} hsüeh^{2*} chi^{4} k'an^{1} (6609, 4839, 944, 5862), edited by members of the Faculty of Peking National University (vol. 1, 1923). Chang Hsin-hai: Some types of Chinese historical thought (Journal of the North China branch of the Royal Asiatic Society, vol. 60, 1–19, 1929; p. 13–19 discuss Ch'êng Ch'iao).

HUNG KUA

Hung^{2} Kua^{4*} (5252, 6295) Elder brother of Hung Tsun (first half of the twelfth century). He was born in 1117; died in 1184. Chinese archaeologist (epigraphist). In 1167 he published a collection of Han inscriptions in the "official hand" character, together with facsimiles, Li^{4} shih^{4*} (7005, 9983), in nineteen books. A supplement in twenty-one books, Li^{4} hsü^{4*} (7005, 4773), appeared in parts from 1168 to 1180, and a complete edition in 1181.

Text—The Library of Congress has copies of the Li shih printed in 1871 in 5 volumes and 27 chüan; and of the Li hsü, also printed in 1871, in 2 volumes and 21 chüan.

Criticism—A. Wylie: Chinese literature (76, 1902). H. A. Giles: Biographical dictionary (347, 1898).

For Chu Hsi, see Chapter XVIII, Philosophic Background.
For Wang Hsiang-chih, see Chapter XXII, Geography.

XV. JAPANESE

NAKAYAMA TADACHIKA

Grandson of Fujiwara (Kwazan-in) Ietada (1062–1136). Japanese historian. Born in 1131, died in 1195. Author of the chronicle Mizu-kagami (The water mirror) which treats of Japanese history from the time of the first emperor Jimmu (660 B.C.) down to the death of the fifty-fourth emperor Nimmyō (850). He also left a diary.

For other chronicles or "mirrors" see my note on Fujiwara Tamenari (first half of twelfth century).

E. Papinot: Historical dictionary (396, 430, 540, Tōkyō 1909).

CHAPTER XXVI

LAW AND SOCIOLOGY

(Second Half of Twelfth Century)

I. WESTERN MUSLIM

ABŪ-L-QĀSIM AL-ḤAUFĪ

Abū-l-Qāsim Aḥmad ibn Muḥammad ibn Khalaf al-Ḥaufī, of Seville. Died in 1192–1193. Mālikite theologian. Author of one of the most appreciated treatises on the division of inheritances (Kitāb al-farā'iḍ). Ibn Khaldūn said it was the best Mālikite treatise of its kind. Such a subject (al-farā'iḍ) involves arithmetical problems; indeed Muslims consider it a part of arithmetic.

Ibn Khaldūn: Prolégomènes (de Slane, vol. 3, 23, 140). C. Brockelmann: Arabische Litteratur (vol. 1, 384, 1898).

II. EASTERN MUSLIM

IBN AL-DAHHĀN

Abū Shujā' Muḥammad ibn 'Alī ibn Shu'aib ibn al-Dahhān (son of the oilman), Fakhr al-dīn al-Baghdādī. Born in Baghdād; flourished in Mūṣul, Maiyāfāriqīn, Egypt, and Damascus; he died at al-Ḥilla in 1194 on his way back from Mecca to Damascus. Shāfi'ite legist, arithmetician (calculator of inheritance shares), and astronomer. In 1167–1168 he completed legal tables (Taqwīm al-naẓar), divided into ten columns, giving for each question the views of the four orthodox schools, the principles involved, and additional observations; these tables are preceded by an introduction dealing with grammar and logic.

Text—The Taqwīm al-naẓar fī-l-masā'il al-khilāfīya is still unpublished.
Criticism—Ibn Khallikān: de Slane's translation (vol. 3, 175–176, 1848). F. Wüstenfeld: Geschichtschreiber der Araber (no. 281, p. 98, 1881). C. Brockelmann: Arabische Litteratur (vol. 1, 392, 1898). H. Suter: Mathematiker und Astronomen (126, 1900).

JA'FAR IBN 'ALĪ

Abū-l-Faḍl Ja'far ibn 'Alī al-Dimishqī. Arabic economist who flourished in Damascus and other places in Syria at an unknown time. He composed in or before 1175 the Kitāb al-ishāra ilā maḥāsin al-tijāra wa ma'rifa al-jayyid al-a'rāḍ wa radīhā wa ghushūsh al-mudallisīn fīhā (Book explaining the benefits of commerce and the knowledge of good and bad qualities [of wares] and the falsifications of counterfeiters). One of the two manuscripts of it (both Damascene) was completed April 20, 1175. It is a work of great importance dealing not only with the knowledge of many wares and their falsifications, but also with the theory and practice of commerce, and even with economic subjects. To illustrate, it examines such questions as the true meaning of wealth or ownership (ḥaqīqat al-māl), the various kinds of possessions, the origin and use of money, the means of testing money, how to pack and preserve goods, how to determine their average prices, and how to protect property. The chapters relative to wares contain abundant information on stones and metals, perfumes, textiles, etc., and the connected arts and trades.

The Kitāb al-ishāra is partly derived from the Arabic version of the treatise on domestic economy ('ilm tadbīr al-manzil) ascribed to the Pythagorean Bryson.

Text—The text of the MS. dated 1175, kept in the Khedivial Library, Cairo, was published in Cairo, 1318 H. Many extracts are translated into German in Wiedemann's and Ritter's papers cited below.

Criticism—I found no references to this author in Ḥājī Khalīfa or in Brockelmann. Eilhard Wiedemann: Mineralogisches aus einer arabischen Handels- und Warenlehre (Beiträge 30, Sitzungsber. der physik.-med. Sozietät, vol. 44, 229–235, Erlangen 1912); Kulturgeschichtliches und Klimatologisches aus arabischen Schriftstellern (Archiv für Geschichte der Naturwiss., vol. 5, 60–61, 1913); Aus der arabischen Handels- und Warenlehren von Abū'l Faḍl (Beiträge 32, Erlangen Sitzungsber., vol. 45, 34–54, 1914). Hellmut Ritter: Ein arabisches Handbuch der Handelswissenschaft (Der Islam, vol. 7, 1–91, 1917; elaborate analysis; Isis, 13, 425). Martin Plessner: Der οἰκονομικός des Neupythagoreers Bryson und sein Einfluss auf die islamische Wissenschaft (Heidelberg, 29, 1928; Isis, 13, 529).

'ABD AL-RAHMĀN IBN NAṢR

'Abd al-Raḥmān Ibn Naṣr ibn 'Abdallāh ibn Muḥammad al-Nabarāwī al-Shāfi'ī (al-Adawī al-Shairazī). Egyptian author who flourished probably in the time of Ṣalāḥ al-dīn (1169–1193). He wrote a handbook for the use of police officers in charge of markets (muḥtasib; hence, Spanish almotacén; their function was called ḥisbat), enabling them for instance to verify weights and measures and to test the genuineness of wares. That handbook, divided into forty chapters, is entitled Nihāyat al-rutbat al-ẓarīfat fī ṭalab al-ḥisbat (Summus terminus auctoritatis politae de quaerendo munere honorifico praefecturae annonae). An elaboration of it bearing the same title was edited by one Ibn Bassām in the thirteenth or fourteenth century; it contains 114 chapters dealing with almost as many trades or industries. The interest of such handbooks from the cultural point of view or from the point of view of our own studies needs no emphasis.

My dating of the activity of this 'Abd al-Raḥmān is based upon the assumption that he is identical with the one quoted by Brockelmann (I, 461) author of a treatise called Kitāb al-nahj al-maslūk fī siyāsat al-mulūk (Via aperta et trita de regum administratione salutis publicae). This assumption is uncertain but I was anxious to quote this author to draw attention to the very important class of books which his own work represents.

Text—Walter Behrnauer: Mémoire sur les institutions de police chez les Arabes, les Persans et les Turcs (Journal asiatique, 15, 461–508, 1860; 16, 114–190, 347–392, 1860; 17, 5–76, 1861). This contains a long analysis of the Nihāyat al-rutbat, and of various extracts relative to the same subject, for example, extracts from Ibn Khaldūn and al-Maqrīzī. A complete translation of this work seems very desirable, also a comparative study of it and others of the same kind from our special point of view. This would perhaps help to identify this 'Abd al-Raḥmān and to determine which books may be ascribed to him.

Criticism—Ḥājī Khalīfa: Lexicon (vol. 6, 400, nos. 14082–14083, 410, no. 14120, 1852; see also vol. 1, 507; vol. 3, 166, 510, vol. 7, 927). C. Brockelmann: Arabische Litteratur (vol. 1, 461, 1898). Eilhard Wiedemann: Ueber Verfälschungen von Drogen u.s.w. nach Ibn Bassām und Nabarāwī (Beiträge 40, Sitzungsber., vol. 46, 172–206, Erlangen 1914).

IBN MAMMĀTĪ

Abū-l-Makārim As'ad ibn al-Khatīr ibn Mammātī. Born in an important Christian family of Egypt he embraced Islām soon after the conquest of his country by Ṣalāḥ al-dīn (1169)[1] and became eventually secretary of war. The wazīr's enmity obliged him to fly to Aleppo, where he died in 1209 at the age of 62. Muslim statesman who wrote an account of the Egyptian government under the Ayyūbid sulṭān Ṣalāḥ al-dīn (Saladin, 1169–1193), the Kitāb qawānīn al-dawāwīn (Statutes of the councils of state). He wrote also a satirical work called Kitāb al-fāshūsh fī aḥkām Qarāqūsh (Weakmindedness in the judgments of Qarāqūsh). Whether this referred to Saladin's famous chamberlain Qarāqūsh Bahā' al-dīn (d. 1201) or not, the stupid Qarāqūsh of Ibn Mammātī's story is the ancestor of the oriental Punch (Qaragyüz).

Ibn Khallikān: de Slane's translation (vol. 1, 192–196). F. Wüstenfeld: Geschichtschreiber der Araber (106, 1881). P. Casanova: Qarakouch (Communication faite à l'Institut égyptien, 1892); Karakouch (Mém. de la mission archéologique française au Caire, vol. 7, 1893). C. Brockelmann: Arabische Litteratur (vol. 1, 335, 1898). Eilhard Wiedemann: Ueber Vermessung nach Ibn Mammātī (Beitr. 21, Sitzungsber., vol. 42, 300–302, Erlangen 1910). Sobernheim: Karākūsh (Encyclop. of Islām, 2, 742, 1925).

AL-MARGHĪNĀNĪ

Abū-l-Ḥasan 'Alī ibn abī Bakr ibn 'Abd al-Jalīl al-Farghānī al-Marghīnānī al-Rishtānī. Marghīnān and Rishtān are two towns of Farghāna, south of the river Sayḥūn (Jaxartes). Ḥanīfite jurist who died in 1197. His main work is a treatise on law entitled Kitāb bidāyat al mubtadī (Beginning of the beginner), and a large commentary on it, called Hidāyat (Guidance). The Hidāyat obtained considerable popularity in Islām, as may be judged by the number of commentaries devoted to it.

Text—The text of the Bidāyat is generally included in that of the Hidāyat. Persian version of the Hidāyat by Ghulām Yaḥyā (Calcutta 1807). This version was Englished by Charles Hamilton (London 1791); republished by S. G. Grady (London 1870). Many editions of the Arabic text: Calcutta 1834; Bombay 1863; Cawnpore 1872; Lucknow 1874, 1875, 1876, etc.
Criticism—C. Brockelmann: Arabische Litteratur (vol. 1, 376–378, 1898).

FAKHR AL-DĪN AL-RĀZĪ

See Chapter XVIII, Philosophic Background.

III. JEWISH AND SAMARITAN

ISAAC BEN ABBA MARI

Jewish jurist born in Provence about 1122; died probably in Marseilles, after 1193. He often consulted his older contemporary Jacob ben Meïr Tam (first

[1] This conquest over the Fāṭimid caliph implied that Egypt ceased to be Shī'ite and returned to Sunnite orthodoxy.

half of the twelfth century). His main work is the legal compilation called Sefer ha-'iṭṭur (crown) or 'Iṭṭur soferim (begun in 1178; first part completed in 1193), one of the classics of French rabbinical literature. It is based upon the works of a great many Geonim and Talmudists (chiefly Alfasi), yet is to some extent independent. Its popularity is attested by many commentaries.

Text—First edition of the 'Iṭṭur, first part only, anonymous (Venice 1608). First complete edition by Samuel ben Benjamin Schönblum (2 vols., Lemberg 1860). Isaac's marginal notes to the Halakot were first published in the Vilna edition of Alfasi (1881–1897).

Criticism—E. Renan: Rabbins français (520, 747, 1877). Louis Ginzberg: Jewish Encyclopaedia (vol. 6, 618, 1904).

ABŪ-L-ISḤĀQ IBRĀHĪM

For this Samaritan, see Chapter XXVII, Philology.

IV. ITALIAN

PETER OF PIACENZA

Petrus Placentinus. Born at Piacenza; flourished in Mantua and Bologna, and in Montpellier where he died in 1192. Italian civilian. Some time after 1160 he introduced into France (at Montpellier) the teaching of Roman law. He wrote a legal treatise at the beginning of his career in Mantua but his main work—commentaries on the Code and Institutes—was done in Montpellier.

At the beginning of the following century Roman Law spread from the South to the North of France, thanks to the legists attached to the royal court; and a little later still (about 1230), thanks to the University of Orléans.

Text—Gustav Pescatore: Summa "Cum essem Mantuae" sive de accionum varietatibus (78 p., Greifswald 1897).

Criticism—P. de Tourtoulon: Placentin (Paris 1896). Paul Vinogradoff: Roman law in mediaeval Europe (51, 65, London 1909).

BURGUNDIO OF PISA

See Chapter XVI, The Translators.

V. ENGLISH

VACARIUS

Italian civilian. Born in north Italy in the first quarter of the twelfth century; went to England about 1143; he was still living there in 1198. He was the first teacher of the Civil Law in England; he was already teaching it in 1149, possibly in Oxford (he taught in Oxford, but it cannot be shown that he was teaching there in 1149); he also taught, about 1146, in the household of Theobald, archbishop of Canterbury (1138–1161). He wrote a treatise on the Code and Digest, which was called Summa pauperum de legibus (or Liber pauperum), because it was meant for students who could not afford to buy more elaborate books nor to devote more time to the subject (hence the name pauperistae given to the Oxford law students). His teaching was very popular, but was soon interrupted. Indeed toward the end of his rule, Stephen (king of England from 1135 to 1154) forbade Vacarius to continue it. It is possible that the latter taught Canon Law. English civilians were driven to become canonists, hence their disfavor with the king increased.

Text—Frederic William Maitland: Summa de matrimonio (Law quarterly review, vol. 13, 31 p., London 1897). Reprinted in his Collected papers (vol. 3, 87–105, 1911).

F. de Zulueta: Liber pauperum (Selden Society, London 1927).

Criticism—C. F. C. Wenck: Magister Vacarius (Leipzig 1820); Opuscula academica (1834). Adolf Stölzel: Ueber Vacarius (Z. für Rechtsgeschichte, vol. 6, 234–268, Weimar 1867). Hastings Rashdall: Universities of Europe in the Middle Ages (vol. 2, 335–338, 1895). Felix Liebermann: Vacarius (English historical review, vol. 11, 305–314, 1896; vol. 13, 297, 1898). T. E. Holland: Dictionary of national biography (vol. 58, 80, 1899). Sir Paul Vinogradoff: Roman Law in mediaeval Europe (52–58, 84, London 1909).

JOHN OF SALISBURY

Joannes Sarisburiensis, Parvus. Born at Salisbury between 1115 and 1120; studied in Paris and Chartres; he went to England about 1150, and was secretary to the archbishop of Canterbury; when Thomas à Becket became archbishop in 1162, John was continued as secretary; he shared St. Thomas' exile and witnessed his assassination in 1170. Bishop of Chartres in 1176; he spent the rest of his life at Chartres, dying there in 1180. English philosopher, historian, and humanist. He was one of the best educated men of his time, and one of the most learned, at least as far as Latin letters were concerned; but by his time the range of Latin letters had materially increased; for example, the whole of Aristotle's Organon was already available in Latin. He visited Italy at least six times, and on one of these occasions he remained eight years at the papal court. In philosophy he was a moderate realist.

His main work, completed in 1159, is the Polycratus (sive De nugis curialium et de vestigiis philosophorum libri VIII) or Ruler's Book. This was the first attempt since antiquity to deal with political theory without reference to contemporary conditions, though John's experience of these was considerable; the first attempt in Christendom, with the exception of Manegold's pamphlet (after 1085), to formulate a philosophy of the state.

Another important work of his is the Metalogicon (Apologia quasi pro arte dialectica, 1159), which might be called a vindication of humanistic vs. pedantic knowledge. It includes delightful autobiographical fragments.

He wrote lives of St. Anselm and of St. Thomas à Becket. His Historia pontificalis, composed after 1164, is a continuation of the chronicle of Sigebert of Gembloux (first half of the twelfth century) concerning mainly the years 1148 to 1152; it is a theological as well as a historical work.

Text—Opera omnia edited by J. A. Giles (5 vols., Oxford 1848). Migne's Patrology (vol. 199, 1855).

Polycratus. First edition (s.l., 1475 or 1476). Later editions: Paris 1513, Leiden 1595, etc. Critical edition by Clement Charles Julian Webb (2 vols., Oxford 1909). Partial English translation, with introduction, by John Dickinson (Bks 4 to 6, and extracts from Bks 7–8; 500 p., London 1927).

Historiae pontificalis quae supersunt, edited by Reginald L. Poole (228 p., Oxford 1927).

Metalogicon libri IIII. Edited by Clemens C. J. Webb (264 p., Oxford 1929, Isis, 15, 209).

General criticism—Karl Schaarschmidt: Johannes Sarisberiensis (Leipzig 1862). R. L. Poole: Dictionary of national biography (vol. 29, 439–446, 1892). Potthast

(675, 1896). C. H. Haskins: Renaissance of the twelfth century (Cambridge, Mass., 1927).

Special criticism—Paul Gennrich: Die Staats- und Kirchenlehre Johanns (180 p., Gotha 1894). Ernst Schubert: Die Staatslehre Johanns (Diss., 58 p., Erlangen 1897). August Charles Krey: John's knowledge of the classics (Trans. of the Wisconsin Acad., vol. 16, 948–987, Madison 1910). Hans Hublocher: Helinand von Froidmont (d. 1227) und sein Verhältnis zu Johannes; ein Beitrag zur Geschichte des Plagiates in der mittelalterlichen Literatur (Progr., 63 p., Regensburg 1913). Joseph Breck: A reliquary of St. Thomas Becket made for John of Salisbury (Bull. Metropolitan Museum, vol. 13, 220–224, illus., 1918). Sandys: History of classical scholarship (vol. 1, 536–542, 1921). R. W. and A. J. Carlyle: History of mediaeval political theory (vols. 3 and 4, 1915–1922). Lynn Thorndike: History of magic (vol. 2, 155–170, 1923); John's views on astrology, oneirology, etc. John Dickinson: The mediaeval conceptions of kingship and some of its limitations as developed in the Policratus (Speculum, vol. 1, 308–337, 1926).

FITZNEAL

Richard FitzNeale or Fitz[2] Nigel, Richard of Ely. Ricardus filius Nigelli. Educated in the monastery of Ely. Treasurer to Henry II and Richard I; bishop of London from 1189 to his death in 1198. About 1178 he wrote a treatise on the exchequer, called De necessariis observantiis scaccarii (Dialogus de scaccario), wherein the financial administration of England is explained in detail in the form of dialogue between master and pupil. He also wrote a historical work, the Tricolumnis (lost), so-called because the account was divided into three columns: affairs of the church, affairs of the state, law and miscellanea.

Text—Thomas Madox: The history and antiquities of the Exchequer (Appendix, London 1711; and vol. 2, 329–452, London 1769). William Stubbs: Select charters and other illustrations of English constitutional history (2d ed., 168–248, Oxford 1878). Best edition by Arthur Hughes, C. G. Crump and C. Johnson (258 p., Oxford 1902).

English translation by John Rayner (London 1758). Better translation by E. F. Henderson: Select historical documents (20–134, London 1902).

Criticism—Felix Liebermann: Einleitung in den Dialogus de scaccario (Diss., 112 p., Göttingen 1875). E. Venables: Dictionary of national biography (vol. 19, 186–188, 1889). Charles Gross: Sources of English history (385, 418, 1915). H. G. Richardson: Richard fitz Neal and the Diaologus de scaccario (English historical review, vol. 43, 161–171, 321–340, 1928).

GLANVILLE

Ranulf de Glanville (Glanvil, Glanvill). Ranulphus de Glanvilla. English jurist and soldier. Born in Stratford in Suffolk; from 1180 to 1189 he was chief justiciar of England and main assistant to Henry II (king from 1154 to 1189); he went to Palestine with Richard Lionheart; he died at the siege of Acre in 1190. He wrote or edited, about 1187, the earliest textbook of English law, the Tractatus de legibus et consuetudinibus regni Angliae. The date, about 1187, is certain but his authorship is not; the Tractatus has been ascribed also to his nephew, Hubert Walter, who became primate and chief justiciar of England, and died in 1205.

Whoever its real author, the Tractatus was not only the earliest legal classic of England, but the earliest systematic law treatise that appeared after the dissolution

[2] Fitz means filius, fils. Was often used for illegitimate children of princes, or of persons in high standing, e.g., Fitzroy, Fitzclarence.

of the Roman empire, with the exception of Gratian's Decretum (1139). In spite of a few definitions borrowed from the Corpus juris, there is nothing Roman in it; the treatment is thoroughly English. It helped considerably to standardize English law and thus deeply influenced English thought.

One curious consequence of this development of English common law outside of the frame of Roman law, was its exclusion from the Universities (Oxford and Cambridge) where only Roman and Canon law could be taught. This led to the creation of the Inns of Court at London, a school of law entirely independent of the universities.

A Scotch version of the Tractatus was compiled in the first half of the thirteenth century. It is often called, from its incipit, Regiam majestatem.

Text—First edition of the Tractatus, London 1554. Many later editions: 1557, 1604, 1673, 1780. The complete text is included in George Phillips: Englische Reichs- und Rechtsgeschichte (vol. 2, Berlin 1828).

Englished by John Beames (402 p., London 1812; again, 345 p., Washington 1900).

Regiam majestatem in Acts of the Parliament of Scotland (vol. 1, 135–174, 597–641, 1844).

Criticism—Potthast (952, 1896). See histories of English law, e.g., F. Pollock and F. W. Maitland (2d. ed., Cambridge 1898); and W. H. Holdsworth (London 1922–1926). F. W. Maitland: Dictionary of national biography (vol. 21, 413–415, 1890); Glanvill revised (Harvard law review, vol. 6, 1–7, 1893); Collected papers (vol. 2, 266–289); apropos of a revision written or copied c. 1265 by Robert Carpenter of Haresdale. Charles Gross: Sources of English history (403, 1915). A. J. Carlyle: History of mediaeval political theory (vol. 3, 1915).

VI. SPANISH

SANCHO EL SABIO

See Chapter XXIII, Natural History.

VII. SCANDINAVIAN

SVEND AAGESÖN

See Chapter XXV, Historiography.

VIII. HINDU

HEMACANDRA

See Chapter XXVII, Philology.

CHAPTER XXVII

PHILOLOGY

(Second Half of Twelfth Century)

I. EASTERN MUSLIM

IBN AL-DAHHAN

See Chapter XXVI, Law and Sociology.

IBN AL-ANBĀRĪ

Abū-l-Barakāt 'Abd al-Raḥmān ibn abī-l-Wafā' Muḥammad ibn 'Ubaidallāh ibn abī Sa'īd ibn al-Anbārī, Kamāl al-dīn (al-Anbār was an ancient town on the left bank of the Euphrates, about forty-two miles from Baghdād). Muslim philologist. Born in 1119; studied and taught at the Niẓāmīya college in Baghdād; died there in 1181. His main works are: (1) a history of Arabic literature and philology from the beginning to his own times, Kitāb al-nuzhat al-alibbā' fī ṭabaqāt al-udabā', containing 181 biographies in chronological order, the last being that of Abū-l-Sa'ādāt; (2) an Arabic grammar, Kitāb al-asrār al-'arabīya (Secrets of the Arabic language).

Text—Lithographic edition of the Nuzhat (Cairo 1877–1878).
The grammar was edited by C. F. Seybold (Leiden 1886).
Koshut: Fünf Streitfragen des Baṣrenser und Kūfenser (Wien 1878). Extracts from the Kitāb al-inṣāf fī masā'il al-khilāf bain al-naḥwīyīn al-Baṣrīyīn wal-Kūfīyīn, a treatise written for his pupils at the Niẓāmīya.
Criticism—Ibn Khallikān: de Slane's translation (vol. 2, 95, 1843). F. Wüstenfeld: Geschichtschreiber der Araber (93, 1881). C. Brockelmann: Arabische Litteratur (vol. 1, 281, 1898); Encyclopaedia of Islām (vol. 1, 349, 1910).

II. WESTERN JEWISH

JOSEPH QIMHI

See Chapter XVI, The Translators.

MOSES QIMḤI

Moses ben Joseph Qimḥi. Often called Remaq from the initials of his name. Judeo-Provençal theologian and grammarian. We have already spoken of his father Joseph, one of the foremost translators from Arabic into Hebrew, who died about 1170. His younger brother David will be discussed presently. Moses flourished probably at Narbonne, and died about 1190. He wrote Biblical commentaries and grammatical treatises, his most notable work being the Mahalak shebile ha-da'at (Sefer ha-diqduq), which was the earliest concise textbook of Hebrew grammar. This work was very successful and influenced all of its followers; for example, it was the first to conjugate the verb pāqad (to visit) as a paradigm, and to treat the conjugations in the following order: qal, nif'al, pi'ēl, pu'al, hif'īl, hof'al, hithpa'ēl. It was quite popular among Gentiles at the time of the Reformation.

Text—First edition, with an introduction by Benjamin ben Judah, and a commentary by Elijah ben Asher the Levite (Pesaro 1508). Many other editions; e.g., one revised by J. Böschenstain (Augsburg 1520). Another, with notes by Agostino Giustiniani, bishop of Nebbio in Corsica (Paris 1520). Latin translation by Sebastian Münster (Basle 1536). Hebrew Latin edition with notes by C. L'Empereur (Leiden 1631). Etc.

Criticism—Caspar Levias: Jewish encyclopaedia (vol. 7, 497, 1904).

DAVID QIMḤI

David ben Joseph Qimḥi (or Qamḥi). Often called Redaq; also ha-Sefardi, because of his Spanish origin; and Maistre Petit, perhaps because qemaḥ means fine flour, corn ground small. Judeo-Provençal theologian and grammarian. The most illustrious member of the Qimḥi family. Younger brother of Moses Qimḥi. Born in Narbonne in 1160, died there in 1235. He wrote valuable Biblical commentaries, some of which are included in the rabbinical Bibles and translated into Latin. Indeed their influence can be traced in the Authorized Version (1611). Leaving Maimonides apart, David Qimḥi was the most influential Jewish doctor of his time, being comparable to his predecessor, Abraham ibn Ezra, whom he often quoted. David was a vigorous controversialist, and took an active part in the polemics against the Christians, and against those who attacked Maimonides. Towards the end of his life the communities of Lunel and Narbonne sent him to Spain to try to convert their Spanish brethren to the Maimonidean point of view but his journey was interrupted by ill health. His main publication, the Miklol (perfection) was a grammatical work divided into two parts, a comprehensive Hebrew grammar and a dictionary of Biblical Hebrew. The grammar (often called Miklol like the whole work) is based on the treatises of Ḥayyuj (second half of the tenth century), Ibn Janāḥ (first half of the eleventh century), and of his own father, but it contains many small improvements and is better arranged. The dictionary, Sefer ha-shorashim (Book of roots), is also based on the works of Ibn Janāḥ and others, but it includes many personal additions; for example, translations into Provençal. In short, David Qimḥi was an original grammarian who deeply influenced later Hebrew grammarians, the Gentiles as well as the Jews, through Sante Pagnino, Reuchlin, and Seb. Münster.

Text—Sefer ha-shorashim. Undated Italian edition, before 1480. First dated edition, Naples 1490. Many later editions: Constantinople 1513, Venice 1529 (285 p.), 1546–1548, etc. Modern edition by J. H. R. Biesenthal and F. Lebrecht: Radicum liber (475 p., Berlin 1847).

Sefer miklol. First edition, in Italy, 1525. Later editions: Constantinople 1532, 1534; Venice 1545; Fürth 1793. New edition by I. ben A. Rittenberg (Lyck 1862). Vocalized text of the grammar with Latin translation by Agathius Guidacerius (Paris 1540).

The Institutiones Hebraicae (Lyon 1526) and the Thesaurus linguae sanctae (Lyon 1529) of Sante Pagnino are essentially derived from the Miklol.

Commentary on Genesis edited by A. Ginzburg (Pressburg 1842). M. S. Schiller-Szinessy: First book of Psalms (Cambridge, 1883). Louis Finkelstein: Commentary on Isaiah (critical edition of the commentary on chapters 1–40, 328 p., Columbia University, New York 1926). Harry Cohen: Commentary on Hosea

(172p, Columbia University, New York 1930). For the earlier editions of these commentaries, some of them incunabula, see Hebrew bibliographies.

Criticism—Caspar Levias: Jewish encyclopaedia (vol. 7, 494–495, 1904).

For Judah ibn Tibbon, see Chapter XVI, The Translators.

For Judah's son, Samuel, see Chapter XXX, The Translators (first half of thirteenth century).

III. SAMARITAN

ABU-L-ISḤĀQ IBRĀHĪM

Abū-l-Isḥāq Ibrāhīm abū-l (ibn al-) Faraj Shams al-dīn. Samaritan grammarian who flourished about the middle of the twelfth century, probably in Damascus. (The Samaritans[1] had been driven from their home, Nablus or Shichem, by the Crusaders; they settled in Syria, chiefly in Damascus, and in Egypt; many returned to Shichem about the beginning of the fourteenth century). He wrote in Arabic a grammar of Biblical Hebrew, in fourteen chapters. An abstract of it was made in the fourteenth century by Eleazar son of Pineḥas. Ibrāhīm ibn al-Faraj is possibly also the author of the Tafsir ha-miẓwa (Commentary on the laws), explaining the 613 positive and negative commandments of the Torah.

Moses Gaster: The Samaritan literature (Encyclopaedia of Islām, suppt. to vol. 4, 7, 11, 1925).

IV. ARMENIAN

See Nerses the Graceful, Chapter XV, Religious Background; Mekhitar of Her, Chapter XXIV, Medicine.

For Gregory the Priest, see Chapter XI, Historiography (first half of twelfth century).

For Samuel of Ani, see Chapter XXV, Historiography.

V. BYZANTINE

MANASSES

See Chapter XXV, Historiography.

GREGORIOS OF CORINTH

Gregorios, Metropolitan of Corinth. *Γρηγόριος μητροπολίτης Κορίνθου*. Flourished probably in the second half of the twelfth century and at the beginning of the thirteenth century. Byzantine grammarian who enjoyed some popularity. He wrote a book on Greek dialects, a commentary on Hermogenes'[2] work on the method of eloquence, and a little treatise on syntax.

Text—*Περὶ τῶν ἰδιωμάτων τῶν διαλέκτων.* First edition, Venice 1496. G. H. Schäfer: Gregorii Corinthii et aliorum grammaticorum libri de dialectis linguae graecae (1072 p., Leipzig 1811).

[1] Vol. I, 151.

[2] This Hermogenes (Ἑρμογένης) was a precocious rhetorician who flourished under Marcus Aurelius (second half of the second century), and wrote a number of treatises having that kind of brilliant mediocrity which begets success. See Maurice Croiset: Histoire de la littérature grecque (vol. 5, 631–634, 1899).

Ἀπὸ τῆς ἐξηγήσεως εἰς τὸ περὶ μεθόδου δεινότητος τοῦ Ἑρμογένους βιβλίον. First complete edition by Christian Walz: Rhetores graeci (vol. 7, 1088–1352, 1834).

Περὶ συντάξεως τοῦ λόγου ἤτοι περὶ τοῦ μὴ σολοικίζειν Unpublished.

Criticism—K. Krumbacher: Byzantinische Litteratur (588–589, 1897).

VI. LATIN

HUGUTIO

Hugutio of Pisa, Uguccione Pisano. Professor of canon law in Bologna, bishop of Ferrara from 1191 to 1212. Latin lexicographer. He compiled an etymological dictionary, called Derivationes, which was one of the standard textbooks of the Middle Ages. Petrarch considered him, together with Priscian (first half of the sixth century), the chief of grammarians. Yet Hugutio was ignorant of Greek! He quotes Greek words, but only indirectly from Papias the Lombard (second half of the eleventh century), and from the Englishman Osbern (fl. 1090)—both likewise ignorant of Greek—or from their sources. Nothing could better illustrate the intellectual poverty and secondhandedness of the Latin world.

Criticism—John E. Sandys: History of classical scholarship (vol. 1^3, 557, 1921). C. H. Haskins: Studies in the history of mediaeval science (150, 251, 1924).

For Hildegard, and for Alexander Neckam, see Chapter XVIII, Philosophic Background.

For the revival of the Latin classics, the Latin language, and Latin poetry, a subject outside of my field, see a good summary in C. H. Haskins: The Renaissance of the twelfth century (93–192, Cambridge, Mass., 1927; Isis, 10, 62–65).

VII. VERNACULAR

See the notes on the Troubadours and Trouvères, the Minnesingers, the Nibelungenlied and Reynard the Fox, in Chapter XVIII, Philosophic Background.

See the notes on the Poema del Cid, and the Tale of Igor, in Chapter XXV, Historiography.

VIII. HINDU

AGGAVAMSA

Pāli grammarian who flourished in Arimaddana, Burma, about 1154. He was also called Aggapaṇḍita III; King Narapatisithu (1167–1202) was his pupil. He wrote in 1154 a Pāli grammar entitled Saddanīti, which is based on Kaccāyana, and on Sanskrit grammar, but is probably anterior to Moggallāna. Singhalese monks who visited Arimaddana admitted that they had no work comparable to the Saddanīti. It is interesting to notice the parallel activities of Singhalese and Burmese grammarians.

Text—Helmer Smith: Saddanīti. La grammaire palie d'Aggavaṃsa. 1. Padamālā. Pariccheda I-XIV. (Acta reg. societatis humaniorum litterarum Lundensis, XII, 1, 322 p., Lund 1928). Admirable edition (J. R. A. S., 609–610, 1929; O.L.Z., 61–62, 1930).

Criticism—Wilhelm Geiger: Pāli Literatur und Sprache (37, Strassburg 1916).

MOGGALLĀNA

Moggallāyana. Singhalese grammarian who flourished in Anurādhapura during the rule of Parakkamabāhu I (1153–1186). He founded a new school of Pāli grammar, which derived its inspiration partly from the older Pāli grammarians represented by the Kaccāyanappakaraṇa (Kaccāyana's[3] grammar), and partly from Pāṇini and other Sanskrit grammarians. (The older Pāli grammarians had been far more independent of Sanskrit grammar than had the Prākrit grammarians.) Mogallāna is the author of the first or second datable Pāli grammar, called Saddalakkhaṇa (or Moggallāyanavyākaraṇa), and probably of the earliest Pāli dictionary, the Abhidhānappadīpikā. Like the Sanskrit dictionaries upon which it is modeled (chiefly the Amarakośa), it is written in verse. The learned men of Ceylon were deeply interested in grammar, and an abundant literature is based on the works of Kaccāyana and Moggallāna.

Text—Emile Senart: Grammaire pâlie de Kaccāyana; sūtras et commentaire publiés avec traduction et notes (Journal asiatique, vol. 17, 193, 361, 1871). Moggallāna's grammar was edited by H. Devamitta (Colombo 1890). His dictionary was edited by Waskaḍuwe Subhūti, with English and Singhalese interpretations, notes and appendices (2d ed., 373 p., Colombo 1883). Complete index to this dictionary by the same (562 p., Colombo 1893).

Criticism—Wilhelm Geiger: Pāli Literatur und Sprache (33, 36–38, Strassburg 1916). M. Winternitz: Indische Litteratur (vol. 3, 407, 416, 1922).

HEMACANDRA

Born in 1088, flourished under the Caulukya kings of Aṇhilvāḍ, Jayasiṃha and Kumārapāla; the latter ruled from 1143 until 1169 (or 1172). Jaina historian, Sanskrit and Prākrit grammarian and lexicographer. His historical work, though less important than his grammatical, is noteworthy. He wrote (after 1163) an epic poem called Kumārapālacarita (also Dvyāśrayakāvya), concerning the history of the Caulukya kings of Anhilvāḍ, and chiefly Kumārapāla; it consists of twenty-eight cantos, of which the first twenty are in Sanskrit and the others in Prākrit.

His Sanskrit grammar is essentially a revised edition of that of Śākaṭāyana (middle of ninth century); it is the best mediaeval work of its kind. It was written by order of king Jayasiṃha Siddharāja (who ruled until 1143), hence its name Siddhahemacandra; it is also called Haimavyākaraṇa. Hemacandra wrote also two commentaries on his grammar, and two smaller grammatical treatises.

Hemacandra was the greatest lexicographer of India. He compiled four dictionaries, three in Sanskrit, one in Prākrit:

(1) A dictionary of synonyms, the Abhidhānacintāmaṇināmamālā (often abbreviated to Abhidhānacintāmaṇi); it is divided into an introduction and six sections treating respectively of Jaina gods, Brahmanical gods, men, animals, inhabitants of the underworld, and finally abstractions, adjectives and particles; he wrote a commentary on this work, and various additions to it.

(2) The Nighaṇṭuśesha, a botanical glossary, which may be considered a supplement to (1). The plants are divided into six groups (kāṇḍa): trees, shrubs, creepers, vegetables, grasses, and cereals.

(3) A dictionary of homonyms, the Anekārthasaṃgraha; it contains 3900 words divided into seven groups: words of one, two, ... six syllables, and undeclinable words.

[3] This Kaccāyana (Pāli form of the Sanskrit name Kātyāyana) is unknown. He flourished after Buddhaghosa (first half of the fifth century) and before Moggallāna.

(4) A Prākrit dictionary named Deśīnāmamālā (or Deśīśabdasaṃgraha); it is not restricted to pure Prākrit words (deśī, provincialisms), but contains also Prākrit words borrowed from the Sanskrit or derived from it (tatsama and tadbhava). In the preparation of this dictionary, Hemacandra was able to take advantage of an earlier one, the earliest Prākrit dictionary extant, the Pāiyalacchī nāmamālā, written by Dhanapāla in 972.

Finally Hemacandra wrote a treatise on logic, Pramāṇamīmāṃsā in the form of a sūtra, and, at the request of Kumārapāla, an extensive Prākrit work, Bṛihad-Arhannītiśāstra, of which there has come down to us only a part, the Laghv-Arhannītiśāstra, concerning Jaina law and politics.

Prākrit is a vernacular, or rather a group of vernaculars, standing half-way between Sanskrit and some of the living vernaculars of India. It stands to them in almost the same relation as mediaeval Latin does to the ancient Latin on one hand and to the Romance languages on the other.

Text—Dvyāśrayakāvya in the Bombay Sanskrit Series (no. 60, 1900).

Complete edition of the Sanskrit kośa with extracts from the commentaries, entitled Collection of Sanskrit ancient lexicons (2 vols., Bombay 1889, 1896). A new edition by Theodor Zachariae and Joh. Kirste, entitled Quellenwerke der altindischen Lexicographie, is published by the Academy of Vienna (vol. 1, 1893; vol. 2, 1895; vol. 4, 1901). For editions of separate works see Zachariae.

Good edition of the Prākrit dictionary by Richard Pischel (Bombay Sanskrit series, 1880).

Laghv-Arhannītiśāstra, edited with a commentary in Gujarati (Ahmedabad 1906).

Johannes Hertel: Ausgewählte Erzählungen aus Hemacandra's Pariśiṣṭaparvan (272 p., Leipzig 1908). Is this the same Hemacandra? The author of that collection of stories was a Jaina, and he composed it c. 1159–1173.

The Pramāṇamīmāṃsā, edited by Mōtīlāl Lādhājī, together with Sanskrit notes and introduction (134 p., Jain printing works, Poona 1926). The same paṇḍita edited another work of Hemacandra, the Anya-yōgavyavacchēdikā (76 p., ibidem, 1926), including Jain polemics against other schools, followed by an outline of the orthodox Digambara doctrine (Journal R. Asiatic Soc., 864–865, 1927).

Criticism—Joh. Kirste: Epilegomena zu meiner Ausgabe von Hemachandra's Uṇādigaṇasūtra (Sitz. ber., Vienna Ak. d. Wiss., phil. Kl., 1895). Theodor Zachariae: Die indischen Wörterbücher (30–35, Strassburg 1897). M. Winternitz: Indische Litteratur (vol. 3, 92, 401, 414–416, 469, 530, 1922). A. Berriedale Keith: History of Sanskrit literature (Oxford 1928).

IX. CHINESE

FA YUN

Fa^{2*} Yün^{2} (3366, 13812). Flourished under the Sung, about 1157. Chinese Buddhist. In 1157 he compiled an excellent Sanskrit-Chinese lexicon of Buddhist terms, Fan^{1}-i^{4*} ming^{2}-i^{4} chi^{2*} (3390, 5495, 7940, 5454, 906).

Text—The Library of Congress has a fac-simile of a Sung edition of the Fan-i ming-i chi in the great collection known as the Ssŭ^{4} pu^{4} ts'ung^{1} k'an^{1} (10291, 9484, 12039, 5861) vols. 525–531; the work is in 7 chüan.

The Wade Library in Cambridge has an undated work entitled Fan-i ming-i chi hsüan^{3} (4822), containing Buddhist phrases classified under 45 headings, apparently taken from Fa Yün's lexicon.

E. Denison Ross: The preface to the Fan-i-ming-i, translated into English (T'oung Pao, vol. 11, 405–409; this preface is dated 1157).

Criticism—Bunyiu Nanjio: Catalogue of the Chinese Tripiṭaka (1883, no. 1640). H. A. Giles: Catalogue of the Wade collection (1898, A 425). L. Wieger: La Chine (297, 492, 1920).

FAN CH'ÊNG-TA

See Chapter XXII, Geography.

APPENDIX TO BOOK II

(Second Half of the Twelfth Century)

The following notes were added at the time of my final revision of the manuscript. It would have been too troublesome to insert them in their proper places and to take them into account in the survey forming the first chapter of this book. However if it had been possible to take them into account, my conclusions would not have been essentially different.

What do these notes add to our knowledge of scientific and intellectual life in the second half of the twelfth century?

Abraham ben Isaac of Narbonne compiled the Eshkol which was the earliest code of law produced in France. It was in some respects superior to the Halakot of Alfasi and was held in high honor until superseded a century and a half later by the Arba' ṭurim of Jacob ben Asher.

Isaac ibn Crispin composed an ethical treatise, entitled Sefer ha-musar. I speak of it not because of its intrinsic importance, which is small, but because it affords a good illustration of the exchange of influences between the Jewish and Muslim worlds. Indeed the Musar was derived from Arabic sources, if not actually translated from an Arabic original; a few centuries later it was retranslated into Arabic.

The two Chinese physicians, Liu Wan-su and Chang Tzŭ-ho, would be more important if it were possible to date their activities more accurately. All that we know is that they flourished under the Chin or Nü^3-chên^1 (8419, 589) Tartars, the "Golden Horde," who ruled northern China[1] from 1115 to 1260. The average of these two extreme dates being 1187, we may tentatively place these two physicians in the second half of the twelfth century, but this is a mere guess. Either, or both, may have flourished before the middle of the twelfth century, or in the thirteenth century. On the other hand, their medical theory and practice were more typical of Chinese medicine in general than of any particular period. We may be sure that similar ideas were explained and applied by a great many Chinese physicians who came before them or after them.

I thought it also necessary to speak, however briefly, of two additional historians.

Ambroise the Jongleur wrote a poetic account in Anglo-Norman of the third crusade, of which he had been a witness, being a member of Richard Lionheart's household. For a long time Ambroise's history was known only in the form of a Latin version, the Itinerarium regis Ricardi, composed by a younger contemporary, Richard, prior of Holy Trinity in London.

While Ambroise was singing the gesta of Richard Lionheart, another poet was creating the nucleus of the earliest Rājputāna epic. This was Chandra Bardāī, who sang in old Hindī the heroic deeds of the most popular hero of northern India, Prithīrāj, the last Hindu ruler of Delhi. The omission of Chandra was by far the most serious, and I am thankful to have an opportunity of attenuating my guilt in this appendix. Indeed his rhymed chronicle is not only one of the few historical

[1] The Yangtze separated the Chin territories from the Sung territories.

documents of mediaeval India—it marked the beginning of a new literary language, it was the first monument of the Hindu vernaculars of northern India.

ABRAHAM BEN ISAAC OF NARBONNE

Rabad II. Languedocian Talmudist, born probably in Montpellier about 1110; died in Narbonne in 1178–1179. He was the supreme judge (ab bet din, hence his name Rabad for short) of the Jewish community, and headmaster of the yeshiva of Narbonne, which was one of the oldest and most famous Jewish schools in the West. His best known pupil was Abraham ben David of Posquières (Rabad III), who became his son-in-law.

He wrote Talmudic commentaries which were often quoted by other great rabbis, such as Abraham ben David, Isaac ben Abba Mari, Solomon ben Adret, Moses ben Naḥman, etc. He was also the author of many responsa in which he gave proof of little originality and much wisdom.

His main work was the Eshkol (meaning a cluster or bunch, as of fruits or blossoms), which was a compendium of Jewish law answering the same purpose as the Halakot of Alfasi (vol. I, 751), but in a more convenient way. The Halakot followed the order of the Babylonian Talmud; on the contrary, in the Eshkol the legal information was classified by topics. Abraham made considerable use of the Sefer ha-'ittim (Times) of an older contemporary, Judah ben Barzillai ha-Nasi al-Bargeloni (the Barcelonian),[2] to such an extent that some critics have claimed that the Eshkol was nothing but an anthology of extracts from the 'Ittim. The matter is difficult to decide as the 'Ittim is known only in a fragmentary way, but it would seem that the Eshkol was far more than an anthology. The Eshkol was the first important legal work of the French Jewry; its influence can be traced in sundry compilations of Provençal Talmudists, and it was one of the main preparatory steps which were to lead to the Arba' ṭurim of Jacob ben Asher (first half of the fourteenth century). When the Ṭur finally appeared the Eshkol was superseded and soon forgotten.

Text—Partial edition of the Eshkol by Benjamin Hirsch Auerbach (3 parts, Halberstadt 1867–1869). New partial edition by Shalom ben Ezekiel Albeck (Berlin 1910). These editions have entailed bitter discussions.

Responsa are included in the Temim de'im of Abraham ben David of Posquières (Venice 1622), and in the Sefer ha-terumot of Samuel ben Isaac Sardi (or Sephardi) (Salonica 1596, etc).

Criticism—E. Renan: Les rabbins français (510, 518, 520, 543, 1877). Louis Ginzberg: Jewish encyclopaedia (vol. 1, 111, 1901). S. Bialoblocki: Encyclopaedia judaica (vol. 1, 480–485, 1928).

ISAAC IBN CRISPIN

The name Crispin is spelled in Hebrew Qrispin. Judeo-Spanish poet and moralist who flourished in the twelfth century, probably in the second half. He was much praised by Judah al-Ḥarizī, who calls him ha-sar ha-gadol (the great prince).

He composed, in verse and prose, an ethical work entitled Sefer ha-musar (book of instruction), identical with the Mishle anashim ḥakamin and the Mishle 'arab. It was derived, if not translated, from an Arabic model. Isaaç's work was trans-

[2] About him, see Louis Ginzberg: Jewish Encyclopaedia (vol. 7, 340–341, 1904).

lated into Arabic by Joseph ibn Ḥasan (who flourished probably in Yaman? in the fifteenth century?) under the title Maḥāsin al-adab (Best manners), divided into fifty poems.

Text—The Mishle 'arab was poorly edited in the journal Ha-Lebanon (Year 4, Paris 1867).

Extracts of the Sefer ha-musar in M. Steinschneider: Oẓerot ḥayyim, catalogue of the library of Heimann Michael (Hamburg 1848), etc.

Criticism—M. Steinschneider: Hebraeische Übersetzungen (884–887, 1892), includes analysis of the work; Arabische Literatur der Juden (253, 1902). I. Broydé: Jewish encyclopaedia (vol. 4, 363, 1903). M. Zobel: Encyclopaedia judaica (vol. 5, 712, 1930).

LIU WAN-SU

Liu^{2} Wan^{2}-su^{4} (7270, 12457, 10348). Style name, Shou^{3}-chên^{1} (10012, 589). Chinese physician who flourished during the Chin^{1} (2032) dynasty (1115–1260). A good many medical treatises are ascribed to him, as follows:

Ching^{1} yao^{4} hsüan^{1} ming^{2} lun^{4} (2123, 12889, 4805, 7946, 7475).

Su^{4} wên^{4} ping^{4} chi^{1} (10348, 12650, 9300, 787).

Su^{4} wên^{4} hsüan^{2} chi^{1} yüan^{2} ping^{4} shih^{4*} (10348, 12650, 4790, 787, 13700, 9300, 9984).

Pao^{2} ming^{4} chi^{2*} (8711, 7962, 906).

Shang^{1} han^{2} i^{1} chien^{4} (9742, 3825, 5380, 1645).

Shang^{1} han^{2} chih^{2*} ko^{2*} lun^{4} (9742, 3825, 1846, 6029, 7475).

Shang^{1} han^{2} piao^{1} mu^{4*} hsin^{1} fa^{2*} lei^{4} ts'ui^{4} (9742, 3825, 9097, 8077, 4562, 3366, 6853, 11931).

Shang^{1} han^{2} hsin^{1} yao^{4} lun^{4} (9742, 3825, 4562, 12889, 7475).

San^{1} hsiao^{1} lun^{4} (9552, 4297, 7475).

As the titles immediately show, many of Liu's writings were inspired by the old classics, the Huang^{2} Ti^{4} Nei^{4} ching^{1} su^{4}-wên^{4} (5124, 10942, 8177, 2122, 10348, 12650), and the Shang^{1} han^{2} (9742, 3825).

His medicine was dominated by a theory equivalent to the Western one of the microcosmos and macrocosmos. Everything in man as well as in the larger universe is regulated by the two antagonistic and complementary principles yang^{2} (12883) and yin^{1} (13224), that is, the male and female principles. Each of the five tsang^{4} (11584) or viscera corresponds to one of the five elements; the latter do not cease to circulate, and thus they create the wu^{3} yün^{4} (12698, 13817), that is, the interaction of the five elements. In the meanwhile the six influences (yin, yang, wind, rain, light, darkness) liu^{4*} ch'i^{4} (7276, 1064) are constantly moving from the earth up to heaven and down again. The various diseases are caused by the irregularities in the wu yün and liu ch'i.

Liu Wan-su had great confidence in the old remedies, and specially in the cooling ones. He tried to subdue the fire of the heart and to increase the secretion of the kidneys. On account of this he was considered the founder of the school of cooling (medicines), or han^{2}-liang^{2} (3825, 7025). He distinguished three main therapeutic methods: han^{4} (3784), t'u^{4} (12100), hsia^{4} (4230), that is, to sweat, vomit, bring down (diaphoretics, emetics, laxatives). Etc., etc.

Text—All the treatises above mentioned, except the last, were published together in Shanghai in 1909.

Criticism—Franz Huebotter: Guide (Kumamoto, 33, 1924; Isis, 7, 259); Chinesische Medizin (22, 349, 353, Leipzig 1929; Isis, 14, 255–263).

CHANG TZŬ-HO

Chang^1 Tzŭ^3-ho^2 (416, 12317, 3945). Style name, Ts'ung^2-chêng^4 (12028, 687). Chinese physician who flourished during the Chin^1 (2032) dynasty (1115–1260).

His main work is the Ju^2 mên^2 shih^4 ch'in^1 (5675, 7751, 9990, 2081), a treatise on internal medicine in fifteen chüan^4 (3146). The first three contain introductory generalities, the seven following deal with special pathology and therapeutics, including gynaecology and pediatrics; nos. 12, 13, 15, are devoted to materia medica, and 14 to the prognostic signs taught by the ancient physicians.

He also wrote the Shang^1 han^2 hsin^1 ching^4 (9742, 3825, 4562, 2170), and the Liu^{4*} mên^2 êrh^4 fa^{2*} (7276, 7751, 3363, 3366).

His medical theories were apparently the same as those of Liu Wan-su. In practice he attached relatively more importance to purgation (hsia, as opposed to han and t'u). The main purpose of his therapeutics was to drive out the evil influences, ch'ü^1 hsieh^2 (3091, 4395); when this was done, the equilibrium—that is, health—was reëstablished.

Franz Huebotter: Guide (Kumamoto, 34, 1924; Isis, 7, 259); Die chinesische Medizin (22, 349, Leipzig 1929; Isis, 14, 255–263).

AMBROISE THE JONGLEUR

Anglo-Norman poet who composed a rhymed chronicle of the third crusade, L'estoire de la guerre sainte, in about 12350 verses. He was present at the coronation of Richard Lionheart in London in 1189, followed Richard to the Crusade, and remained with him until the latter's departure from the Holy Land in 1192. He was an eye witness of many of the events told by him. He was neither a knight, nor a clerk, nor a soldier, but simply a jongleur in Richard's service; he originated probably from the pays of Evreux. It is not known how he returned westward, but his poem was written after his return in 1195–1196. If he does not succeed in being impartial, at any rate he tries to be fair.

Ambroise's Estoire was freely translated into Latin by Richard, canon and prior of Holy Trinity in London, about 1222. That version entitled Itinerarium Ricardi was believed until relatively recent times to be an original work (that is, by its editor, Wm. Stubbs, in 1864). The former ascription of it to the contemporary English poet, Geoffrey de Vinsauf (de Vino salvo), was erroneous.

Text—Critical edition by Gaston Paris (Collection de documents inédits sur l'histoire de France, 670 p., 2 pl., Paris 1897): with elaborate introduction, translation into modern French, and glossary.

The Itinerarium regis Ricardi was edited by William Stubbs (Rolls series, London 1864).

Criticism—T. A. Archer: Richard de Templo, fl. 1190–1229 (Dictionary of national biography, vol. 48, 198–200, 1896). Miss A. M. Cooke: Geoffrey Vinsauf, fl. 1200 (ibidem, vol. 58, 372, 1899). Kate Norgate: The Itinerarium peregrinorum and the Song of Ambrose (English historical review, vol. 25, 523–547, 1910).

CHAND BARDĀĪ

Chand (or Cand) Bardāī. Hindu annalist and poet who flourished at the court of Prithīrāj (or Rāi Pithorā), the last Hindu ruler of Delhi. He wrote, in archaic western Hindī,[3] a long epic, the Chand Rāisā (or Prithīrāj rāso), which is the earliest of a long series of rhymed chronicles of Rājputāna. Chand's original poem included some 5000 verses, but it was gradually increased by other poets and reciters until the total epic extended to some 125000 verses.

The popularity and continued elaboration of Chand's epic is not surprising, considering that Prithīrāj is the most popular hero of northern India to this day. He seduced and abducted the daughter of Rājā Jaichand (Jayachchandra), about 1175, defeated the Chandēls in 1182, and led the resistance of the Hindu rājās against Shihāb al-dīn Mu'izz al-dīn Muḥammad al-Ghūrī; he was defeated at the second battle of Tarāin (1192), captured, and executed. (Tarāin is in the Punjab, between Karnāl and Thānēsar, 14 m. from the latter place). This second battle of Tarāin clinched the Muslim conquest of Hindostan; it is as big a landmark in the history of India as is the battle of Nihāvend (642) in the history of Persia, or the battle of Hastings (1066) in the history of England.

Text—It is said that the text of Chandra Bardāī's original poem is still in existence in the custody of the poet's descendant, who lives in the Jodhpur State (?).

John Beames and A. F. R. Hoernlé: The Prithīrāja rāsau of Chand Bardai, edited in the original old Hindi (Bibliotheca indica, new series, nos. 269, 304, 408, 430, 489, 577; Calcutta 1873–1886).

Partial English translation by A. F. R. Hoernlé (Bibliotheca indica, no. 452, Calcutta 1881).

The lay of Ālhā, a saga of Rajput chivalry as sung by minstrels of northern India Partly translated into English ballad metre by William Waterfield, with an introduction and abstracts of the untranslated portions by Sir George Grierson (London 1923).

Criticism—James Tod: Annals and antiquities of Rajast'han, or, the central and western Rajpoot states of India (2 vols., folio, London 1829–1832); includes many extracts in English. Popular reprint, unabridged and of handier size, with a preface by Douglas Sladen (2 vols., London 1914). M. Winternitz: Geschichte der indischen Litteratur (vol. 3, 585, 1922). Vincent A. Smith: Oxford history of India (2d ed., 195–197, 218–220, 1923).

[3] A language derived from Sanskrit, and which has itself developed into various vernaculars, the most important of which is Hindūstānī (written in the Devanāgarī but mostly in the Arabic script).